Probability and Statistics for Business Decisions

Probability and Statistics
for Business Decisions

AN INTRODUCTION TO
MANAGERIAL ECONOMICS UNDER UNCERTAINTY

Robert Schlaifer

PROFESSOR OF BUSINESS ADMINISTRATION
HARVARD UNIVERSITY

McGRAW-HILL BOOK COMPANY

New York   Toronto   London

1959

PROBABILITY AND STATISTICS FOR BUSINESS DECISIONS

14 15 16 – MAMM – 7 5 4 3

55309

Preface

This book is a nonmathematical introduction to the logical analysis of practical business problems in which a decision must be reached under uncertainty. The analysis which it recommends is based on the modern theory of utility and what has come to be known as the "personal" definition of probability; the author believes, in other words, that when the consequences of various possible courses of action depend on some unpredictable event, the *practical* way of choosing the "best" act is to assign values to consequences and probabilities to events and then to select the act with the highest expected value. In the author's experience, thoughtful businessmen intuitively apply exactly this kind of analysis in problems which are simple enough to allow of purely intuitive analysis; and he believes that they will readily accept its formalization once the essential logic of this formalization is presented in a way which *can* be comprehended by an intelligent layman. Excellent books on the pure mathematical theory of decision under uncertainty already exist; the present text is an endeavor to show how formal analysis of practical decision problems can be made to pay its way.

From the point of view taken in this book, there is no real difference between a "statistical" decision problem in which a part of the available evidence happens to come from a "sample" and a problem in which all the evidence is of a less formal nature. Both kinds of problems are analyzed by use of the same basic principles; and one of the resulting advantages is that it becomes possible to avoid having to assert that nothing useful can be said about a sample which contains an unknown amount of bias while at the same time having to admit that in most practical situations it is totally impossible to draw a sample which does not contain an unknown amount of bias. In the same way and for the same reason there is no real difference between a decision problem in which the long-run-average demand for some commodity is known with certainty and one in which it is not; and not the least of the advantages which result from recognizing this fact is that it becomes possible to analyze a problem of inventory control without having to pretend that a finite amount of experience can ever give anyone perfect knowledge of long-run-average demand. The author is quite ready to admit that in some situations it may be difficult for the businessman to assess the numerical probabilities and utilities which are required for the kind of analysis recommended in this book, but he is confident that the businessman who really tries to make a reasoned analysis of a difficult decision problem will find it far easier to do this than to make a *direct* determination of, say, the correct risk premium to add to the pure cost of capital or of the correct level at which to conduct a test of significance.

In sum, the author believes that the modern theories of utility and personal probability have at last made it possible to develop a really complete theory to guide the making of managerial decisions—a theory into which the traditional disciplines of statistics and economics under certainty and the collection of miscellaneous techniques taught under the name of operations research will all enter as constituent parts. He hopes, therefore, that the present book will be of interest and value not only to students and practitioners of inventory control, quality control, marketing research, and other specific business functions but also to students of business and businessmen who are interested in the basic principles of managerial economics and to students of economics who are interested in the theory of the firm. Even the teacher of a course in mathematical decision theory who wishes to include applications as well as complete-class and existence theory may find the book useful as a source of examples of the practical decision problems which do arise in the real world.

Because the purpose of this book is not to teach theory for its own sake but to show how theory can be applied to practical advantage in the real world, each new technique of analysis is applied to a realistic business problem as soon as it is introduced. Many of the most important principles are actually restated and reexplained in the contexts of several different kinds of decision problem, and for this kind of repetitiousness the author makes no apology. Learning ·depends on repetition; and if the rate of learning can be increased by printing up a few more sheets of white paper, the gain is well worth the cost. While some of the exposition could have been greatly condensed by the use of simple algebra and calculus, the author feels that even for students who have some familiarity with these techniques it is better to avoid their use in a statement of first principles. Justification of the steps in an argument by economic rather than purely formal reasoning develops an intuitive understanding of the essential features of a decision problem which is likely to be lost if attention is focused from the very first on problems of technical manipulation. On the other hand students who do have some command of mathematical technique may find it a useful exercise to supply proofs where these have been omitted from the text; and many of the examples and problems in the text can be easily modified to require the use of calculus rather than arithmetic for their solution. An appendix on gamma, beta, and related distributions has been added to the book to facilitate the assignment of problems of this sort.

The organization of the book reflects experience gained in teaching the subject in various ways to five successive classes. The basic concepts of decision theory—probability, expectation, and utility—are explained in three introductory chapters, and in the next five chapters (Part One of the book) these concepts are applied in a variety of situations where the required probability distributions can be easily assessed by direct reference to experience. It is only after the student has thus become reason ably familiar with the way in which probabilities are *used* that he is introduced in Part Two to some more powerful methods for the *computation* of probabilities—to the concepts of joint and conditional probability, the distributions associated with Bernoulli and Poisson processes, and the Normal distribution. After a foundation in *both* economic analysis and elementary probability theory has been laid, the student goes on in Part Three to face the special problem of the evaluation by means of Bayes' theorem of the information derived from a sample and to study some new distributions needed for this purpose. It is only after this subject has been thoroughly covered that the problem of deciding when it is economically advantageous to sample and when to stop sampling is taken up in Part Four. The four chapters which constitute Part Five of the book then explain the classical approach to the problems already analyzed from the Bayesian point of view in Parts Three and Four and show how the explicit introduction of losses into the classical analysis leads from operating characteristics to risk functions and how a reasoned comparison of risk functions over *all* values of the parameter under test then leads in the end to exactly the same results which were previously obtained by the explicit use of Bayes' theorem.

This division of the entire subject matter of the course into five separate major topics which are treated successively rather than simultaneously (as was necessary in earlier versions of this book which introduced sampling problems at the outset) has improved the rate at which the material can be absorbed to the point where the author is currently assigning nearly one chapter per 80-minute class session and teaches about three-fourths of the entire book in a one-semester course. The author's students, however, are the small fraction of second-year students at the Harvard Graduate School of Business Administration who voluntarily elect a course in decision theory which is well known to involve a very heavy work load, and obviously no such rate could be maintained with a less highly self-selected group of students. The author would guess that under ordinary conditions the book will prove to contain about the right amount of material for a full-year course, particularly if it is supplemented by some unstructured case problems or by mathematical lectures and exercises for students with a background of algebra and calculus.

The course can be shortened by omission of certain chapters which constitute excursions into interesting areas or problems of application but are not needed for the comprehension of later chapters; Chapters 15, 19, 20, 24, 32, and 36 are all of this sort.   Even with these chapters omitted the student will have had a more than adequate foundation for a second course in statistics, e.g. in sampling theory or experimental design. A course covering only the basic principles of decision theory as such with an absolute minimum of attention to technicalities of probability theory can be given by using only Chapters 1 to 5, 7, 9, 10, 21, 22, 33, and 38. These 12 chapters explain every important basic principle discussed in the course, including the principles of optimal sample size and optimal sequential sampling, without the use of any mathematically derived probability distribution other than the binomial; they are an adequate preparation for the treatment of classical statistics in Chapters 39 to 42 if the examples and problems involving the use of the Normal distribution are omitted from those chapters.   The other chapters in Parts One through Four of the course are there in part to develop the additional probability theory needed to handle a wider variety of applications and in part to develop special methods for the rapid analysis of a few of the most commonly occurring types of business decision problems—in particular, certain problems with linear losses.   Without these methods which make it possible to obtain numerical answers to a fairly wide variety of examples in a reasonable amount of time, there is a real danger that the student will fail to gain any appreciation of the sensitivity or insensitivity of decisions and their associated losses to the various parameters of a decision problem; and without some appreciation of this sort the *practical* use of decision theory is very severely handicapped.

Exercises are provided at the end of each chapter.   Most of them are intended to develop and test the student's comprehension of the theory expounded in the text, but some lead the student to extend this theory in some small degree.   Completely worked solutions to all exercises of the latter sort and to about half those of the former sort will be found in the "Student's Manual" which accompanies the text.   A slide rule is adequate computing equipment for the exercises with worked solutions, since in those problems the student needs only to verify that he understands how the computations were actually carried out, but the student who works problems on his own will usually find that a desk calculator will very greatly reduce the time required to arrive at a solution.   These latter problems are well suited to work in a statistical laboratory.

The author's debt to his colleague Howard Raiffa and to his former colleague Arthur Schleifer, Jr., is far too great to describe adequately.

Mr. Schleifer assisted the author during the first 3 years of the development of the course represented by the present book. He read and made valuable criticisms of nearly every draft of every successive revision of every chapter, and he executed or directed the execution of all the computations and charting. Mr. Raiffa read the semifinal version of the manuscript with the most painstaking care and spent countless hours in showing an often stubborn author how it could and should be improved at many points by substituting logic for unsupported intuition. In particular, the three chapters of the Introduction were wholly recast as a result of these suggestions.

Mr. Gordon Kaufmann gave great assistance in preparing the Student's and Teacher's Manuals and corrected very many of the author's arithmetical lapses in text. The author was extremely fortunate to have Miss Alice Hynes (later Mrs. Paul O'Brien) as his secretary throughout the $4\frac{1}{2}$ years during which the manuscript was being developed. Without her unusual skill it would have been quite impossible to make several rough drafts of each annual or semiannual revision of the notes and then to prepare stencils so that the latest version could be tested in the classroom.

Finally, the author would like to express his very deep gratitude to the administration of the Harvard Graduate School of Business Administration, both for substantially reducing his normal classroom assignments and for granting his every request for assistance at once and without question.

Robert Schlaifer

Contents

INTRODUCTION

The Problem of Decision under Uncertainty

CHAPTER 1

The Meaning of Probability

1.1   The Problem of Decision under Uncertainty

When all of the facts bearing on a business decision are accurately known—when the decision is made "under certainty"—careless thinking is the only reason why the decision should turn out, after the fact, to have been wrong. But when the relevant facts are not all known—when the decision is made "under uncertainty"—it is impossible to make sure that every decision will turn out to have been right in this same sense.   Under uncertainty, the businessman is forced, in effect, to gamble.   His previous actions have put him in a position where he *must* place bets, hoping that he will win but knowing that he may lose.   Under such circumstances, a right decision consists in the choice of the best possible bet, whether it is won or lost after the fact.   The following examples are typical of situations in which business decisions must be made and judged in this way.

An Inventory Problem.   A retailer is about to place an order for a number of units of a perishable commodity which spoils if it is not sold by the end of the day on which it is stocked.   Each unit costs the retailer $1; the retail price is $5.   The retailer does not know what the demand for the item will be, but he must nevertheless decide on a definite number of units to stock.

A Scrap-allowance Problem.   A manufacturer has contracted to deliver at least 100 good pieces of a nonstandard product at a fixed price for the lot.   He feels virtually sure that there will be some defectives among the first 100 pieces produced; and since setting up for a second production run to fill out a shortage would cost a substantial amount of money, he wishes to schedule some additional pieces on the original run as a scrap allowance.   On the other hand, once 100 good pieces have been produced the direct manufacturing cost of any additional production will be a total loss, and therefore he does not wish to make the scrap allowance excessively large.   If the manufacturer knew exactly how many pieces would have to be produced in order to get exactly 100 good pieces, it would be easy to set the "right" size for the production order; but he must decide on some definite size for the order even though he does not know the "right" size.

2

An Investment Problem. A manufacturer is about to tool up for production of a newly developed product. This product can be manufactured by either of two processes, one of which requires a relatively small capital investment but high labor cost per unit produced while the other will have much lower labor costs but requires a much greater investment. The former process will thus be the better one if sales of the product are low while the latter will be better if sales are high; but the manufacturer must choose between the two processes without knowing what his sales will actually be.

A Marketing Problem. The brand manager for a certain grocery product is considering a change of package design in the hope that the new package will attract more attention on the shelf and thereby increase sales. He has done a certain amount of store testing and has found that during the test weeks sales of the new package were greater than sales of the old in some stores but that the contrary was true in other stores. He still feels uncertain whether adoption of the new package will increase or decrease his total national sales, but he must nevertheless either decide on one package or the other or else decide to spend more money on additional testing; in the latter case he must decide whether he should simply continue the test for a few more weeks in the same stores he has already used or spend still more money to draw new stores into his sample.

1.1.1   The Payoff Table

The essential characteristics of all four of these problems, and of all problems which we shall study in this course, are the following.

1. A choice must be made among several possible *acts*.
2. The chosen act will ultimately lead to some definite profit (possibly negative), but for at least some of the acts the amount of this profit is unknown because it will be determined by some *event* which cannot be predicted with certainty.

The first step in analyzing any such problem is to lay out all the possible acts and all their possible consequences in some systematic fashion, and we shall do this for the inventory problem as an example.

In the inventory problem, an "act" is a decision to stock some particular number of units; the "event" is the number of units which the customers will actually demand. If we suppose that the retailer's space limits the number of units stocked to a maximum of 5, then remembering that each unit stocked costs $1 while each sale brings in $5 of revenue we can describe the whole problem by a table like Table 1.1, where each column corresponds to a particular act while each row corresponds to a particular event. Such a table is known as a *payoff table*.

Table 1.1
Payoff Table for the Inventory Example

Event (number demanded)	Act (number of units stocked)					
	0	1	2	3	4	5
0	$0	−$1	−$2	−$3	−$4	−$5
1	0	+ 4	+ 3	+ 2	+ 1	0
2	0	+ 4	+ 8	+ 7	+ 6	+ 5
3	0	+ 4	+ 8	+12	+11	+10
4	0	+ 4	+ 8	+12	+16	+15
5 or more	0	+ 4	+ 8	+12	+16	+20

1.1.2   Comparison of Acts

If we compare any two acts (columns) in Table 1.1, we see that one of the two will be more profitable if certain events occur while the other will be more profitable if other events occur; but when we actually choose among these acts we are implicitly if not explicitly making a single, unconditional evaluation of each act. We are saying that in some sense one of the acts is "better" than any of the others. One conceivable way of evaluating the six possible acts of Table 1.1 is to look only at the worst possible result of each act and assign the value $0 to the act "stock 0," the value −$1 to the act "stock 1," and so forth, leading to the conclusion that "stock 0" is the best of all possible acts. Another conceivable way is to look only at the best possible result and assign the value $0 to the act "stock 0," the value +$4 to the act "stock 1," and so forth, leading to the conclusion that "stock 5" is the best of all possible acts.

Any sensible businessman will of course immediately reject all such simple but arbitrary procedures and will say that even though the retailer cannot predict demand with certainty he ought to know enough about his business and the product in question to have some convictions about what the demand is likely to be. If after weighing all the available information the retailer decides that there is very little chance that customers will demand less than 3 or more than 4 units, he will conclude that the only reasonable act is to stock either 3 or 4 units. Choice between these two acts will be a little more complex, since the larger stock will be only $12 − $11 = $1 less profitable than the smaller if there is a demand for only 3 units while it will be all of $16 − $12 = $4 more profitable if 4 units are demanded. Consequently the retailer will want to stock 4 units even if he believes that the chance of a demand for 4 is somewhat less than the chance of a demand for 3; it is only if he believes that the chance of a demand for 4 is relatively *very* slight that he will reduce his stock to 3 units.

Now this informal kind of reasoning works very well when the decision problem is relatively simple, but one quickly becomes confused when the problem is even slightly more complex. Even in our very simple example, it will be hard for the retailer to see through to a satisfying conclusion if he thinks that there is a substantial chance that demand may have any of three or four different values, and in larger problems of the same sort he may well consider a hundred or a thousand different values as possible. What we would like to do, therefore, is find some way of *systematizing* the kind of analysis which a reasonable man uses in simple problems so that it can be effectively applied in more complex problems.

If we look back at the reasoning used by our hypothetical retailer, we see that in essence he proceeded in two steps: he first gave a numerical *value* to the consequence of each possible act given each possible event, but he then attached more *weight* to the consequences corresponding to certain events (demand 3 or 4) than he did to the others. This suggests that it may be possible to systematize the reasoning underlying *any* decision under uncertainty by proceeding as follows:

1. Attach a definite numerical *value* to the consequence of every possible act given every possible event.
2. Attach a definite numerical *weight* to every possible event.
3. For each act separately, use these weights to compute a *weighted average* of all the values attached to that act.
4. Select the act whose weighted-average value is highest.

Our hope is that we can find rules for using the businessman's own knowledge and beliefs in carrying out steps 1 and 2 in such a way that he will *want* to choose the act with the highest computed value instead of relying on mere inspection of a mass of numbers and informal reasoning of the kind described above. If we are to have confidence in these rules in complex situations, they must yield values which seem reasonable to us when applied in very simple situations, and for this reason many of the examples which we shall use in developing these rules will be artificial ones which avoid the complexities of practical business decisions in order to present their really essential features in the simplest possible form. Because the heart of the problem is the uncertainty concerning the event, we shall begin by developing the rules for attaching weights to events.

1.2   Events

Before we even start to assign numerical weights to a set of events some one of which will determine the consequence of any act we choose, we obviously must have in mind a clear and complete description of the events which may occur. We usually have considerable latitude in defining the possible events in a given problem, but certain rules must be followed if we are to avoid hopeless confusion.

1.2.1   Collectively Exhaustive Events

If before we started to analyze the inventory problem of Table 1.1 the retailer had told us that he was absolutely convinced that there would be a demand for at least 2 units, we could just as well have simplified Table 1.1 by eliminating the rows describing the consequences of the events "demand 0" and "demand 1." In general, impossible events may be totally disregarded if it is convenient to do so, and it is to be emphasized that there is no need to "prove" that an event is impossible before it is eliminated. Our object is to arrive at results which the businessman *wants to accept,* and therefore an event is impossible for our purposes whenever the businessman wants to treat it as impossible.

It is obvious, on the other hand, that we must keep *all* the *possible* events in mind in analyzing any decision problem, since if we fail to include some of the possible events in the payoff table the corresponding consequences will not be duly considered in evaluating the various acts. The same thing can be stated the other way around: the basic list of events must be complete in the sense that *some one of the events on the list is bound to occur.* The events on such a list are called *collectively exhaustive.*

1.2.2   Mutually Exclusive Events

In the inventory example of Table 1.1, demand for each specific number of units from 0 to 4 inclusive was treated as a separate event but demands for all numbers of units above 4 were treated as constituting the same event "demand for 5 or more." Obviously we *could* have treated a demand for exactly 5 units as a separate event and assigned it a separate line in Table 1.1, and similarly for any larger number of units, but nothing was to be gained by so doing because for every act under consideration the consequences of the event "demand for 5" were identical to the consequences of the event "demand for 6" or the event "demand for 7" and so forth.

Careless grouping of events can easily lead to confusion, however. It is obvious that potentially separate events must not be grouped if their consequences differ for any act under consideration. We cannot treat "demand for 3 or 4" or "demand for 4 or more" as a single event in constructing a payoff table for our inventory example. What is often less obvious is that we must not have events with *overlapping definitions* on our list even if it is possible to give a clear description of the consequences of all acts in terms of such a list.

Suppose, for example, that we are given a choice of one or the other of two tickets in a lottery to be conducted by drawing one ball from an urn containing four kinds of balls: dotted red, striped red, dotted green, and striped green.   The first ticket entitles the holder to a prize of value *V* if the ball drawn from the urn is either red or striped; the second entitles the holder to the same prize if the ball is dotted green.   Table 1.2 gives a perfectly clear description of the conditions under which the prize

Table 1.2

Event	Act (choice of ticket)	
	1	2
Red	*V*	0
Striped	*V*	0
Dotted green	0	*V*

will be awarded, but confusion is bound to arise if we base our analysis of this decision problem on this table because the events "red" and "striped" will *both* occur if a striped red ball is drawn.   To illustrate the difficulty by an extreme case, suppose that we know that *all* the red balls are striped and that all the striped balls are red.   Then the events "red" and "striped" are really the same event counted twice, and any weight which we attach to this event will be counted twice in evaluating the acts under consideration.

This kind of difficulty can be avoided by basing our analysis on any of the three lists of events shown in Table 1.3, since the occurrence of any

Table 1.3

A	B	C
Striped red	Red	Red or striped
Dotted red	Striped green	Dotted green
Striped green	Dotted green	
Dotted green		

one event on any of these lists means that *no other event on the same list can possibly occur.*   The events on any such list are said to be *mutually exclusive.*

1.2.3   Elementary and Compound Events

The importance of mutual exclusiveness is so great that it is worth the trouble to find a way of visualizing it.   The events on list *A* of Table 1.3 are obviously mutually exclusive because they have been defined without any grouping at all—balls which differ in *any* respect have been classified as separate events in this list.   These four events will be called the *elementary events* of this problem.

Any set of *elementary* events can be visualized as a set of *points* in a diagram like Figure 1.1, 1.2, or 1.3, where the points represent the four elementary events of list A in Table 1.3. Events such as "red" or "striped" can then be visualized as corresponding to a *group of points* representing elementary events: the events "red" and "green" are

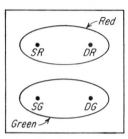 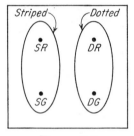 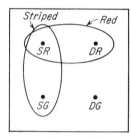

| Figure 1.1 | Figure 1.2 | Figure 1.3 |

depicted in Figure 1.1, the events "striped" and "dotted" in Figure 1.2. Such events will be called *compound events*, and it is obvious that

> Two compound events are mutually exclusive if they contain no elementary events in common.

In Figure 1.3 we illustrate the difficulty with the events used in Table 1.2: the point corresponding to the elementary event "striped red" is included in *both* the compound events "red" and "striped."

1.3   The Basic Rules Governing the Assignment of Weights

We are now ready to develop rules for using a definite number to represent the weight which a decision maker attaches to each of the events in a set of mutually exclusive and collectively exhaustive events. Since we propose to use these numbers in computing weighted averages, our rules must be such that these weighted averages will "make sense"— i.e., they must be such that the decision maker will *want* to choose the act with the highest weighted-average value. On the other hand, this is the *only* way in which we shall use these weights; and if we find that the requirement just stated can be met by more than one set of rules, we are free to choose the one which is most convenient.

To see whether we do have any such choice, let us review the way in which any weighted average is computed. In the first two columns of Table 1.4a we show a set of four values with a weight attached to each value; the meaning of the values and the weights is irrelevant for our present purpose. The weighted average is computed in three steps:

> 1. Each value is multiplied by its weight to form the products shown in the third column of Table 1.4a.

2. Both the weights and the products are added to obtain the sums shown at the bottoms of their respective columns.
3. The sum of the products is divided by the sum of the weights to obtain the weighted average.

Table 1.4a				Table 1.4b		
Value	Weight	Product		Value	Weight	Product
3	2	6		3	.2	.6
2	1	2		2	.1	.2
7	3	21		7	.3	2.1
5	4	20		5	.4	2.0
	10	49			1.0	4.9

Weighted average $= {}^{49}\!/_{10} = 4.9$ Weighted average $= \dfrac{4.9}{1.0} = 4.9$

Observe now that exactly the same weighted average is obtained in Table 1.4b by using weights each of which is one-tenth as large as the corresponding weight in Table 1.4a. It is obvious that this example can be generalized: dividing every weight in a set by the same nonzero number has no effect on any weighted average computed by use of these weights. In other words, *weighted averages are affected by the proportions among the weights attached to the values being averaged but not by the absolute sizes of the weights.*

This means that we are free to specify that the weights assigned to a set of mutually exclusive and collectively exhaustive events shall add up to any amount we choose, and unless we do make such a specification it will be possible to represent the same beliefs by many different sets of weights. If we allow this, confusion is bound to arise, and we shall therefore adopt the following *fundamental convention* as the first of our basic rules for assigning weights to events:

Rule 1. The sum of the weights assigned to any set of mutually exclusive and collectively exhaustive events shall be 1.

The choice of 1 rather than some other number for the specified total is purely a matter of convenience; it eliminates the need to divide by the sum of the weights in order to convert the sum of products into a weighted average.

Having adopted this fundamental convention, we are now ready to develop rules which *must* be observed in assigning weights if the resulting weighted averages are to make sense. In so doing it will be well to have an extremely simple decision problem actually before us, and we may as well use the same problem which we have already used to illustrate the concept of mutually exclusive events. Three lists of collectively exhaustive and mutually exclusive events suitable for analysis of this problem were shown in Table 1.3; payoff tables based on two of these three lists are shown in Tables 1.5a and 1.5b.

Table 1.5a		
Event	Act (choice of ticket)	
	1	2
Striped red	V	0
Dotted red	V	0
Striped green	V	0
Dotted green	0	V

Table 1.5b		
Event	Act (choice of ticket)	
	1	2
Red or striped	V	0
Dotted green	0	V

Let us first consider the problem of evaluating ticket number 2. Since this ticket pays off only if the event "dotted green" occurs, three facts are immediately obvious about the value we will assign to this ticket.

1. If we are absolutely convinced, for whatever reason, that the ball will *not* be dotted green, we will value the ticket at 0.
2. If we are absolutely convinced that the ball *will* be dotted green, we will value the ticket at V—it is just as good as the prize itself.
3. If we are uncertain about the event, we will value the ticket at something between 0 and V.

Now if we assign numerical weights to the events in Table 1.5a or 1.5b and use these to compute a weighted average of the values in the column describing ticket number 2, this weighted average will be simply V times the weight we assign to the event "dotted green"—recall that by Rule 1 the sum of the weights assigned to all the events in either table must be 1 and therefore that as in Table 1.4b the sum of products is left unchanged when it is divided by the sum of the weights.   But if this is so, then our weighted-average valuation will agree with the three direct valuations listed just above only if we assign weight 0 to an event which we believe impossible, weight 1 to an event which we believe certain, and some intermediate number to any doubtful event.   We thus arrive at our second fundamental rule:

Rule 2.   The weight assigned to any event shall be a number between 0 and 1 inclusive, 0 representing complete conviction that the event will not occur and 1 representing complete conviction that it will occur.

We now turn our attention to the valuation of ticket number 1.   If we compute a weighted average of the values in the column describing ticket number 1 in Table 1.5a, we will have the sum of three terms:

$V \times$ weight of "striped red,"
$V \times$ weight of "dotted red,"
$V \times$ weight of "striped green,"

and this sum is equal to V times the sum of the three weights. If on the other hand we compute a weighted average of the values in the corresponding column of Table 1.5b, we will have simply V times the weight of the compound event "red *or* striped." We conclude that the weight assigned to the event "red or striped" must be the sum of the weights assigned to the three mutually exclusive events of which it is composed, and we generalize this example to obtain our last basic rule:

Rule 3. If two or more mutually exclusive events are grouped into a single event, the weight attached to this single event shall be equal to the sum of the weights attached to the original events.

Observe that this rule does *not* hold for events which are not mutually exclusive. Suppose, for example, that for some reason or other we have assigned the weights shown in Table 1.6 to the four mutually exclusive

Table 1.6

Event	Weight
Striped red	.4
Dotted red	.3
Striped green	.2
Dotted green	.1
	1.0

events of Table 1.5a. We can use Rule 3 to show that the weight assigned to "red" must be $.4 + .3 = .7$ or to show that the weight assigned to "striped" must be $.4 + .2 = .6$, but we *cannot* add these two results to obtain $.7 + .6 = 1.3$ for the weight to be assigned to "red or striped"; if we do, we are double-counting the .4 weight originally assigned to the event "striped red."

1.4 The Standard Lottery

Although the three basic rules which we have derived above may seem so broad that they fail to specify exactly what set of numbers should be used as the weights in any given problem of decision under uncertainty, we shall now see that this is not so. In any situation there will exist one and only one set of weights which will both comply with these rules and express the decision maker's attitudes toward a set of collectively exhaustive and mutually exclusive events.

Suppose that we are offered a free chance at a prize of value V under the following conditions. Balls numbered 1 to 100 have been placed in an urn and one of these balls has then been drawn and put in a closed box. We are presented with 100 tickets numbered from 1 to 100 and are allowed to choose one of them. If the number we choose matches the number on the ball which has been drawn from the urn, we will receive the prize; if not, we receive nothing. Suppose further that even though the prize is one which we are extremely anxious to win, we do not feel that it is worth the slightest effort to look for a ticket with any particular number on it and simply take the first one which comes to hand.

In such a situation we shall say that *in our opinion* the 100 possible events are *equally likely*. Notice very carefully that we do not and *cannot* "prove" that the events are "in fact" equally likely: the fact is that the ball which has been drawn has some one particular number and no other. But even though anyone who *knew* which ball has been drawn would not be indifferent among the 100 tickets, *our* decisions must be based on what *we* know or believe about the facts of the world—they *cannot* be based on the unknown truth about these facts. Therefore if *we* are indifferent in the way described, then *for us* the 100 events are equally likely *by definition*.

Now if our state of mind as just described is to be described by numerical weights attached to the 100 possible events 1, 2, . . . , 100, it is clear that *these weights must all be equal*. If the sum of these 100 equal numbers is to be 1, as required by Rule 1, it is also clear that the number attached to each event must be $\frac{1}{100}$. Rule 3 then tells us that events such as "ball number 2 or 7" must have weight $\frac{1}{100} + \frac{1}{100} = \frac{2}{100}$, that events such as "any ball numbered between 1 and 37 inclusive" must have weight $\frac{37}{100}$, and so forth. Thus while Rule 2 specified only that the weight attached to any event must be a number between 0 and 1 inclusive, we have found a way of selecting a specific number within this range to describe our attitude toward any conceivable event in this lottery.

What is more important, a *businessman can find the unique set of weights which describes his attitudes in a more complex situation by using a lottery of this sort as a standard of comparison*. In order to decide what weight to assign to the event "demand 0" in our inventory example, the retailer can imagine that he is given a choice between a certain number of tickets in the standard lottery with a prize of value V as described above and the right to receive *this same prize* in the event of "demand 0." If in his opinion the right to receive this prize in the event of "demand 0" has exactly the same value as 18 tickets in the standard lottery, then *by definition* he considers these two events equally likely and he should assign weight $\frac{18}{100}$ to the event "demand 0." (It goes without saying that if the standard lottery with 100 balls does not offer a fine enough division, the retailer can substitute a similar lottery with more balls. If he feels that the right to receive the prize in case of demand 0 is worth more than 18 tickets but less than 19 in a lottery with 100 equally likely events, he may decide that it is equivalent to 183 tickets in a lottery with 1000 equally likely events.)

Having assigned a weight to the event "demand 0," the retailer can proceed in the same way to assign weights to all the other events in Table 1.1. These weights must of course be such that their total is 1, and therefore what the retailer is really doing is placing the set of collectively exhaustive and mutually exclusive events shown in Table 1.1 into one-to-one correspondence with a set of collectively exhaustive and mutually exclusive events in the standard lottery. When he is through, the event "demand 0" will correspond, say, to the event "ball numbered between 1 and 18 inclusive," the event "demand 1" to balls 19 to 52, and so forth. It is perhaps worth remarking that we are in no sense assuming that a businessman will actually be as ready to gamble on balls drawn from an urn as to make decisions concerning his regular business. We are simply assuming that a rational person can with practice *think abstractly about his feelings of certainty and uncertainty in any given situation*, regardless of any feelings he may have about any other aspects of the situation.

1.5 Logical Consistency and the Mathematical Theory of Probability

In addition to checking to see that the weights assigned to the events of Table 1.1 obey the fundamental convention expressed by Rule 1, the retailer may do well to check whether he is satisfied with some of the logical consequences which result when Rule 3 is applied to these weights. It is easy to assign either too small or too large a weight to an individual event in a long list of events, and after assigning weight .18 to "demand 0" and weight .34 to "demand 1" the retailer may find that the weight .18 + .34 = .52 which he has thus *implicitly* assigned to the compound event "demand less than 2" is not what he would have assigned if he had thought directly about that event. If so, he must reconcile this *logical inconsistency* before proceeding further with the analysis of his problem.

In many problems such checks for logical consistency are of really crucial importance. To cite a very simple but famous example, the mathematician D'Alembert assigned weight $\frac{1}{3}$ to the occurrence of one heads in two tosses of a coin, arguing that the pair of tosses must produce 0, 1, or 2 heads and that in his opinion these three events were equally likely. To see whether we would share this attitude we may reason as follows. An *elementary* event of a pair of tosses of a coin is described by stating the results of each of the two tosses in the order in which they occurred. If we use HT to denote the elementary event "heads on first toss, tails on second toss" and similar notation for all the other possibilities, the four possible elementary events of the double toss are *HH*, *HT*, *TH*, and *TT*.   If we feel that *these* four events are equally likely and therefore assign weight $\frac{1}{4}$ to each of them, we can add the weights assigned to *HT* and *TH* and find that we have implicitly assigned weight $\frac{1}{2}$ rather than $\frac{1}{3}$ to the compound event "one heads."   To state the conclusion the other way around, D'Alembert implicitly assigned the same total weight to the *two* events *HT* and *TH* that he assigned to each of the single events *HH* and *TT*.

Assignments of weights in more complex problems are still more in need of this kind of check.   As a practical business example, consider the scrap-allowance problem which was sketched at the beginning of this chapter.   The actual payoff table for this problem is too complex to discuss at this point, but it is easy to see that because a new setup will be required if less than 100 good pieces are produced on the first run, it will be necessary to assign weights to such events as "more than 80 defectives in a production run of 180 pieces."   An elementary event of a run of 180 pieces can be described by a sequence of 180 g's and d's, g denoting a good piece and d a defective; and in some cases the manufacturer may be able to check any weight he assigns directly to the event "more than 80 defectives" by assigning weights to these elementary events just as we assigned weights to sequences such as *HT* in order to check D'Alembert's probability.   To consider only the simplest possible case, suppose that the manufacturer feels that any one of the 180 pieces is as likely to be defective as it is to be good and assigns *equal* weight to every possible elementary event.   The weight which he has implicitly assigned to the event "more than 80 defectives" can then be computed by simply counting the total number of possible sequences of 180 g's and d's, counting the number of sequences which contain more than 80 d's, and dividing the latter of these two counts by the former.

It is true that this counting would take a very great deal of time, since it can be shown that the total number of sequences is roughly 1 followed by 54 zeros and a substantial fraction of these sequences contains more than 80 d's.   Fortunately, however, actual counting is unnecessary. By the use of simple mathematical short cuts which we shall study later in the course, we can very quickly determine that $922/1000$ of the total number of sequences contain more than 80 d's and therefore that the weight which has implicitly been assigned to the event "more than 80 defectives" is .922.   We shall also see later in the course that these same mathematical short cuts can be used to compute implicit probabilities when the businessman does not think that each piece produced is as likely to be defective as it is to be good, even though the reasoning about the weights to be assigned to the elementary events is more complex in that case.

The whole body of mathematical short cuts used in computations of this kind is known as the *theory of probability*. Like any *mathematical* "theory," the theory of probability is simply a set of logical deductions from certain basic axioms; the axioms of this particular theory are the following:

1. A probability is a number between 0 and 1 assigned to an event.
2. The sum of the probabilities assigned to a set of mutually exclusive and collectively exhaustive events must be 1.
3. The probability of an event which is composed of a group of mutually exclusive events is the sum of their probabilities.

We are justified in using the theory of probability to calculate "weights" in the way in which we have just used it because we have agreed to assign weights in accordance with these three axioms; the axioms are simply our three "basic rules" for assigning weights presented in slightly different language and with the order of the first and second rules reversed. Henceforth we shall use the word *probability* in exactly the same sense that we have hitherto used the word "weight."

1.6   Relative Frequency and the Rational Assessment of Probabilities

Although we have just seen that the theory of probability can be used to show that certain probabilities are mutually inconsistent and although we have said that such inconsistencies must be reconciled before final assignments of probabilities are made, we have as yet said nothing about the way in which a reasonable man will reconcile the inconsistencies he discovers. We have seen that it is inconsistent to assign probability $\frac{1}{3}$ to the event "one heads" and at the same time to assign probability $\frac{1}{4}$ to each of the events HT and TH, but we have given no reason for preferring either one of these assignments to the other. It is to this problem that we now turn our attention.

In our original discussion of the meaning of "weights" or probabilities, we emphasized that any probability is necessarily an expression of a personal judgment and is therefore necessarily *subjective* in the sense that two reasonable men may assign different probabilities to the same event. This by no means implies, however, that a reasonable man will assign probabilities *arbitrarily*.

Reasonable men base the probabilities which they assign to events in the real world on their experience with events in the real world, and when two reasonable men have had roughly the same experience with a certain kind of event they assign it roughly the same probability.

1.6.1   Overwhelming Common Experience

As an extreme example of this principle, consider the assessment of the probability of heads on the toss of a coin which has been very carefully inspected and found to be perfectly symmetric and which is to be tossed in such a way that it will spin an extremely large number of times before it falls. Although we may or may not have had direct experience with this particular coin and this particular tossing procedure, almost everyone has observed that other coins tossed in more or less the same way seem to turn up heads roughly half of the time. We have further observed that although the ratio of heads to tosses is often very far from $\frac{1}{2}$ in short sequences of tosses, it is usually much closer to $\frac{1}{2}$ in long sequences. Still further, we have observed that heads occur about as frequently on tosses which follow heads as on tosses which follow tails, and more generally that heads occur about half the time *whatever* the pattern of heads and tails on previous tosses. Finally, all this experience with coins agrees with our experience with other symmetric objects—all the above statements apply to the event "ace" on the roll of a perfectly symmetric die if $\frac{1}{6}$ is substituted for $\frac{1}{2}$, and so forth.

On the basis of all this experience we proceed to construct a *physical* theory of the behavior of a tossed coin; in other words, we proceed to make *predictions* about the behavior of a tossed coin. This theory asserts that the fraction of tosses resulting in heads is almost certain to be almost exactly $\frac{1}{2}$ if the coin is tossed indefinitely, and it asserts further that in a very long run half the heads will be followed by heads, half the runs of two heads will be followed by a third head, and so forth. We expect, furthermore, that any reasonable man either will adopt this same theory on the basis of his own experience or will adopt it as soon as he is informed of the very great amount of experience which other people have had on the point.

Now such a theory or model of the real world says nothing directly about the *probability* of heads. It predicts what would happen in a very large number of tosses and says nothing whatever about any individual toss. Such a prediction is exactly analogous to a prediction that the average diameter of parts produced by a certain machine will be 1.037 inches, and it is obvious that a predicted average diameter and a probability are not the same thing. On the other hand, a reasonable man will clearly take account of long-run relative frequency in assigning probabilities. If he believes that a certain coin would fall heads half the time when tossed repeatedly under a certain set of conditions, and if he has no way of predicting which particular tosses will be heads, he will assign probability $\frac{1}{2}$ to the event "heads" on any one toss—he will pay neither more nor less for a chance at a prize conditional on heads on a particular toss than he will pay for a chance at the same prize conditional on tails

In general, we shall assume it to be a characteristic of rational behavior that:

> If a person assessing the probability of a given event under a given set of conditions feels absolutely sure that the event would occur with relative frequency p in a very great number of trials made under these same conditions, he will assign probability p to the event.

It is important to make clear the meaning of the words "under these same conditions." In one sense it is tautologically true that if conditions were *really* the same from trial to trial, the same event would always occur. If a coin were tossed several times in *exactly* the same way, it would either always fall heads or always fall tails. What we actually mean when we say that conditions are "the same" is that there is no *observable* difference from one trial to the next which *enables us to predict* the fall of the coin on any particular trial.

We are now able to say something definite about the probability which it is reasonable to assign to "one heads" in D'Alembert's problem. If we have adopted a model of coin behavior in which heads occur in the long run on one-half of all tosses and in which half the heads are followed by heads, and so forth, it is easy to see that in a long run of *pairs* of tosses the events HH, HT, TH, and TT will each occur $\frac{1}{4}$ of the time. Any reasonable man who has adopted this model of the behavior of a given coin will therefore assign the same probability to each of these events and therefore must assign probability $\frac{1}{2}$ rather than $\frac{1}{3}$ to the compound event "one heads." In actual practice, we would not even go through the process of first assigning a probability directly to "one heads" and then checking this against the implications of probabilities assigned to the four elementary events. We know in advance that our assignment of probabilities to the elementary events can be based on experience which is extremely extensive in comparison with the number of times that we have tossed a coin twice and counted the number of heads in the pair of tosses, and therefore we would start by assigning probabilities to the elementary events and stop when we had computed the probability which we had thus implicitly assigned to the event "one heads."

In more complex problems such as the scrap-allowance example we will proceed in the same general way: we will ask the businessman to assign probabilities to those events on which his experience bears most directly and we will then use the theory of probability to compute the probabilities of the events with which he has had less extensive experience. It is for this reason and this reason alone that the theory of probability is of use in making practical business decisions:

> The theory of probability allows the businessman to assign probabilities to those events on which his experience and judgment bear most

directly rather than to the events which will actually determine the profit or cost of his decision but with which he has had little or no direct experience.

1.6.2   Limited Experience

It is only rarely that experience with a given kind of event will be as overwhelming as it is for "heads" on the toss of a coin, but even when experience is limited it is still a guide to the rational assessment of probabilities.   Suppose, for example, that we wish to assess the probability of ace on the roll of a die which has been deformed in such a way that it is no longer symmetric.   In this situation general experience with rolled objects will usually lead a reasonable person to adopt a model of die behavior which is like the coin model except that the fraction of aces is unknown.   Our experience is sufficient to lead us to predict that in the long run the relative frequency of ace will become and remain nearly equal to *some* fraction p, that ace will be followed by ace with this *same* relative frequency, and so forth; but our experience is *not* adequate for a prediction of the exact value of this frequency.

Obviously such a model does *not* tell us exactly what probability to assign to ace.   We can say that *if* we had had enough experience with the die to feel sure that the long-run relative frequency of ace would be .15, *then* we would assign probability .15 to ace on any one roll, and so forth; but our problem is not to make statements of this sort.   If the consequences of a decision depend on the occurrence of ace on the next roll of the die, we must assess the probability of this event in the light of whatever experience we actually have.   Two reasonable people may well disagree concerning the probability to be assigned to ace in a situation like this, since neither of them will have had any great amount of experience with the behavior of a die deformed in exactly the way this one is.   Observe, however, that this does not mean that there is *no* relevant experience: if the deformation of the die is slight, we will *not* consider a person reasonable if he assigns probability .01 or .99 to ace.

1.6.3   Learning from Additional Experience

The case of the perfectly symmetric coin and the case of the deformed die differ not only in the amount of agreement to be expected in the initial assessment of the probabilities of heads or ace but also in the way in which further experience affects any one individual's assessments of these same probabilities on subsequent trials.

In the case of the perfectly symmetric coin, we might still assess the probability of heads on the next toss at $\frac{1}{2}$ even though we had just observed a large number of consecutive heads or tails; our model of the long-run behavior of the coin rests on an extremely great amount of evidence and we may consider this new evidence negligible in comparison.

In the case of the asymmetric die, on the contrary, we will use any experience we gather by rolling the die to modify the probability we originally assigned to ace. Notice, however, that we usually will *not* simply equate the probability of ace to the fraction of aces observed in a limited number of rolls. If we roll the die once and it comes up ace, we will not assign probability 1 to ace; if we roll it six times and get no ace, we will not assign probability 0 to ace.

Our assessment of the probability of ace will continue to be substantially influenced by our observation of the shape of the die, and the relative importance we attach to the observed shape of the die in comparison with the importance we attach to the observed frequencies is necessarily a matter of subjective judgment.

1.6.4 Application to Business Problems

In exceptional circumstances the probabilities involved in a business problem can be simply equated to "known" relative frequencies in the way probability $\frac{1}{2}$ is assigned to heads on the toss of a very symmetric coin. If 50 per cent of the last 100,000 parts produced by some machine have been defective, if we have no reason either in theory or in observation to believe that defectives occur in "streaks," and if a new production run is to be made under the same conditions as all these past runs, we will be strongly tempted to adopt a model of the behavior of the machine which is exactly like the model of coin behavior discussed above. We will be willing to predict that 50 per cent of all future parts will be defective, that 50 per cent of the defectives will be followed by defectives, etc., and we will not change these predictions whatever the pattern of quality in the next few hundred pieces produced. We will then be *justified* in assigning equal probabilities to all possible elementary events in the way we did in Section 1.5 above.

In the majority of cases, however, the problem will not be so simple. If the machine is new or has just been repaired, or if a new operator is employed or a slightly off-standard batch of raw material is received, we will be in the same position that we are when we assess the probability of ace on a slightly deformed die. The probability assigned to defective on the first piece will depend on "judgment" in the sense that two reasonable men may well assign different values. This probability will be revised as more experience is gained, and again judgment will determine the relative weights given to the observed frequencies on the one hand and to other kinds of evidence on the other.

1.6.5 Mental Processes and Relative Frequency

The examples which we have discussed above of the way in which models predicting relative frequencies can be of use in assessing probabilities all involved the relative frequencies of physical phenomena, but the same kind of argument can be of use in connection with mental phenomena. Frequency models of mental processes usually involve uncertainty about the actual value of the long-run frequency in exactly the same way that most frequency models of physical processes do; but in both cases the frequency model is useful even though it is not completely decisive. The value of a large tract of timber is often assessed by having it visually inspected by an experienced timber cruiser whose judgment has previously been calibrated by comparing his estimates of the amount of timber in a number of tracts with accurate measurements made on the same tracts. The probability that his present estimate will be low by 10 per cent, say, is then assessed largely on the basis of the relative frequency of errors of this magnitude on previous occasions.

In the same way a sales manager who bases sales forecasts on his "feel of the market" can very usefully be treated as a "process." If we have extensive records of the errors he has made in his past forecasts, we will assess the probability that his current forecast will be low by 10 per cent almost entirely on the basis of the relative frequency with which this event occurred in past forecasts. If on the other hand we have very little previous experience with his forecasts, or if the nature of the product or the market has been radically changed, we will have to make much larger use of other kinds of experience in assessing this probability, just as we have to depart from exclusive reliance on observed frequencies when we assess probabilities concerning the performance of a new machine or of an old machine under new conditions.

1.7   Relative Frequency and the Mathematical Theory of Probability

If we think back to the three axioms of the mathematical theory of probability as stated in Section 1.5 above, we will see that relative frequencies—either those predicted for the long run or those actually observed in a finite number of trials—are numbers which agree with these axioms. The relative frequency of any event is a number between 0 and 1 inclusive, the sum of the relative frequencies of all possible events is 1, and the relative frequency of a compound event such as "either ace or deuce" is the sum of the relative frequencies of the mutually exclusive events of which it is composed.

This means that the theory of probability can be used to deduce relative frequencies from other relative frequencies in exactly the same way that it can be used to deduce probabilities (i.e. subjective weights) from other probabilities. When we first discussed the scrap-allowance example, in Section 1.5, we assumed that the manufacturer assigned equal *probability* to every possible elementary event, i.e. to every possible sequence of 180 g's and d's, and from these probability assignments we deduced that the probability of the compound event "more than 80 defectives" was .922. We pointed out in Section 1.6.4, however, that the assignment of equal probabilities to the elementary events was warranted only on the basis of a "model" of the production process which implies that these events would occur with equal *relative frequencies* in a very great number of runs of 180 pieces, and this gives us an alternative way of expressing the same calculation. Given that the elementary events occur with equal relative frequencies, the theory of probability can be used to show that the *relative frequency* of the compound event "more than 80 defectives" must be .922; we can then assess the probability of this compound event by equating it to its *own* relative frequency.

A relationship of this kind between probabilities and relative frequencies can be imagined even in a problem where the probabilities of the elementary events have *not* been assessed by reference to any frequency model. In other words, we can *visualize* all the probabilities involved in *any* problem as being equal to relative frequencies in an imaginary sequence of trials whether or not the particular trial with which we are dealing is of such a nature that it could conceivably be repeated. Since relations among actual numbers of events are easier to grasp than relations among abstract numbers called probabilities, we shall often make use of this device to "explain" the results of calculations involving probabilities; but the student must always remember that such "explanations" do not imply either that probabilities *are* relative frequencies or that they are necessarily *equal* to *real* relative frequencies.

PROBLEMS

1. Five different lotteries *i* through *v* are to be conducted according to rules given below. Any one of these lotteries will pay the player either a $100 cash prize or nothing. Answer the following three questions for each of the five lotteries separately.

    a. How much would you personally be willing to pay for the right to play?

    b. What probability would you assign to the event "win" if you played?

    c. Try to imagine what would happen if the lottery were repeated over and over with the same player, not necessarily yourself, and say what you can about the relative frequency with which the player would win in the long run. To what extent does your answer depend on the way in which the person conducting the lottery behaves? On the way in which the player behaves?

Description of the Five Lotteries

    i. Fifty red and fifty black balls will be placed in an urn and stirred thoroughly. The player will then be allowed to draw one ball without looking and will receive the prize if the ball he draws is red.

    ii. Same as *i* except that the person conducting the lottery may place in the urn any mixture of red and black balls that he pleases and the player will *not* be told what the mixture actually is.

    iii. Same as *i* except that the player may call either "red" or "black" just before drawing the ball and will receive the prize if the ball is of the color he calls.

    iv. Same as *ii* except that the player may call his color.

v. Same as *iv* except that the player must toss a coin and call "red" if the coin falls heads, "black" if it falls tails.

2. A lottery is conducted by the use of one *master urn* and a number of *secondary urns* labeled respectively *A, B, C,* and so forth. Every *secondary* urn contains the same number of balls; this number will be denoted by

N_S: total number of balls in any one secondary urn.

The number of balls in the *master* urn may be different; it will be denoted by

N_M: total number of balls in the master urn.

The balls in every individual urn, master and secondary, are serially numbered starting with 1, and every ball bears one other label in addition to its serial number. In the *master* urn, every ball is labeled with a letter corresponding to some one secondary urn; the number of balls labeled with each letter will be denoted by

$A_M, B_M, \ldots$: number of balls in the master urn labeled *A, B,* etc.

Every ball in every *secondary* urn is labeled either "win" or "lose," and we define

$W_A, W_B, \ldots$: number of winning balls in urn *A,* in urn *B,* etc.

A single ball will be drawn from the master urn, the letter on this ball will be read, and a single ball will then be drawn from the secondary urn marked with this same letter. The player wins if this latter ball is marked "win," and we wish to compute the probability which he should assign to the drawing of such a ball.

a. An *elementary event* (cf. Section 1.2.3) of this compound lottery can be described by a symbol of the form $M3\text{-}A2$, meaning that the first ball drawn was serial number 3 in the master urn and that the second ball drawn was serial number 2 in the urn *A.* Show that the total number of different possible elementary events is given by the formula

Total number of possible elementary events $= N_M N_S$.

b. If a ball labeled *A* is drawn from the master urn, the second ball will be drawn from secondary urn *A* and the player will win if this second ball is any one of the W_A balls in that urn which are marked "win." Show that the number of different *winning* elementary events involving urn *A* is $A_M W_A$ and that the *total* number of winning elementary events of the entire lottery is given by the formula

Number of winning elementary events $= A_M W_A + B_M W_B + \cdots$.

c. The *ratio* of the number of *winning* elementary events to the number of *possible* elementary events is thus

$$\frac{A_M W_A + B_M W_B + \cdots}{N_M N_S} = \frac{A_M}{N_M} \frac{W_A}{N_S} + \frac{B_M}{N_M} \frac{W_B}{N_S} + \cdots.$$

Exactly what assumption has to be made about the basic attitudes of the player before we may say that this is the *probability* which he should assign to winning?

d. If we arbitrarily define symbols

$$p_A = \frac{A_M}{N_M}; \qquad p_B = \frac{B_M}{N_M}; \qquad \text{etc.}$$

and symbols

$$\pi_A = \frac{W_A}{N_S}; \qquad \pi_B = \frac{W_B}{N_S}; \qquad \text{etc.}$$

the formula given in part c can be written

$$\text{Probability of winning} = p_A\pi_A + p_B\pi_B + \cdots$$

Exactly what assumptions must we make before we may interpret each term in this formula as the product of the *probability* of drawing a particular secondary urn times the *probability* of winning *if* that secondary urn is drawn?

CHAPTER 2

Expected Value and Utility

At the beginning of Chapter 1 we said that any problem of decision under uncertainty can always be described by a payoff table in which there is a column for every possible *act* and a row for every possible *event;* each cell in the table describes the *consequence* of a particular act given a particular event. We said that we would try to find a way of choosing among the acts in the face of uncertainty concerning the events by

1. Assigning a definite numerical *value* to every consequence (every cell in the table),
2. Assigning a definite numerical *weight* to every event,
3. Evaluating each act by taking a *weighted average* of all the different values which might result from that act.

In the remainder of Chapter 1 we concentrated our attention on the second of these three steps; we now go on to consider how we can carry out the first step in such a way that the result of the third step will in fact be a "correct" guide to action.

2.1   Definitions of Conditional and Expected Value

Conditional Value.   Each of the values which have to be assigned in step 1 of the procedure outlined just above is the value which some particular act will have *on condition* that some particular event occurs, and therefore these values will be called *conditional values.*   We define

Conditional value of an act given a particular event: the value which the person responsible for a choice among acts attaches to the consequence which that particular act will have if that particular event occurs.

Expected Value.   After probabilities have been assigned to events in step 2 of the procedure we propose to use, step 3 consists in obtaining a *single* value for each act by taking a weighted average of all the various conditional values of that act, each conditional value being weighted by the *probability* that the act will in fact have that value.   The standard name for an average in which all possible values are weighted by their probabilities is *expected value;* we define

> *Expected value* of an act: a weighted average of *all* the conditional values of the act, each conditional value being weighted by its probability.

Such a weighted average is also called the *expectation* of the conditional values of the act.

Mistakes are bound to occur unless we adopt some kind of systematic procedure for the actual computation of expected values according to the definition just given. We have already said that the analysis of any decision problem must start by (1) drawing up a *payoff table* showing the *conditional value* of every act given every event and (2) assigning a *probability* to every event in the payoff table. After both these steps have been completed, we shall take the acts of the payoff table *one at a time* and compute the expected value of each one on a work sheet like the one shown in Table 2.1, filling out this work sheet according to the following rules:

Table 2.1
Computation of the Expected Value of an Act

Event	Probability	Value	
		Conditional	Expected
A	.3	+5	+1.50
B	.3	+3	+ .90
C	.4	−4	−1.60
	1.0		+ .80

1. List every possible *event* in column 1.
2. Enter the *probability* of each event in column 2.
3. Enter the *conditional value* of the act given each event in column 3.
4. For each event *multiply* probability times conditional value and enter the product in column 4, *taking care to preserve the algebraic sign.*
5. *Add* the products in column 4 *with due regard to algebraic sign.*

2.2   Expected Monetary Value

The definition of expected value which we have given above applies no matter what *kind* of value is assigned to each consequence in a decision problem. If in an inventory problem like the one discussed in Section 1.1.1 we take the net cash receipts shown in Table 1.1 as representing the value of each consequence, then a computation like the one illustrated in

Table 2.1 will give us the expected net cash receipts of any act. If we value each consequence according to the number of units sold, application of the same rules of computation will give us the expected number of units sold; and so forth. We now turn to our real problem, which is to find out exactly how each consequence must be valued if the businessman is to feel that the act with the highest expected value is really the act he wants to choose.

Our first inclination, of course, is to think that at least in most business problems the value of a consequence can properly be represented by a sum of money, and our first step will be to inquire to what extent this proposition is true. What we shall see is that while expected monetary value is in fact a valid guide to action in the great majority of practical business problems, there are some very important problems in which it would be an extremely misleading guide.

2.2.1   The Importance of the Individual's Attitude toward Risk

Consider two businessmen each of whom believes that if he submits the proper proposal he has a 50-50 chance of being awarded a contract which is sure to yield a $35,000 gross profit, and suppose that preparation of the proposal will cost either of these men $10,000 out of pocket. The expected monetary value of the act "submit the proposal" is shown in Table 2.2 to be a positive $7500 for either of these two men while the

Table 2.2
Expected Monetary Value of Making the Proposal

Event	Probability	Monetary value Conditional	Expected
Get contract	½	+$25,000	+$12,500
Do not get contract	½	− 10,000	− 5,000
	1		+$ 7,500

corresponding figure for not making the proposal is obviously $0, and yet the two men may quite reasonably come to opposite conclusions. If one of them is extremely hard pressed for cash and could easily be bankrupted by the loss of $10,000, he may well decide to let this opportunity go; if the other man has adequate working capital he may with equally good reason decide to make the proposal.

This example obviously implies that there are situations in which expected monetary value is not a valid guide to action if by "valid" we mean a guide which accords with the businessman's own judgment and preferences, but if we look a little more closely we will see that it implies much more than this. What must be decided is simply whether it is

worth risking a loss of $10,000 in order to have an even chance of a
$25,000 profit, and there is *no conceivable* computation or method of
analysis which will be of the least help to anyone in making such a
decision—it *must* turn *entirely* on a direct expression of personal
preference.

The student may well ask at this point how we propose to help a
businessman in any situation whatever if we can be of no help at all in a
situation as simple as the one just described, and the question deserves an
answer before we proceed further.   The answer is this: we propose to
show the businessman how he can make a fully reasoned analysis of
a *very complex* decision problem—one in which there are many possible
acts each of which has many possible consequences—by in effect reducing
this very complex problem to a number of separate problems every one of
which is just as simple as the one we have just discussed.

Suppose, for example, that our two businessmen are given the
opportunity of submitting proposals for another contract and that in this
case they both assign to the act "submit the proposal" the whole set of
possible consequences and associated probabilities shown in Table 2.3

Table 2.3
Description of Act "Submit the Proposal"

Event	Consequence	Probability
A	+$25,000	.1
B	+ 20,000	.1
C	+ 15,000	.1
D	+ 10,000	.1
E	+ 5,000	.1
F	− 10,000	.5
		1.0

Comparison of this table with Table 2.2 shows that the act "submit" is
clearly less desirable in the present example than in the original example,
and consequently the businessman who was hard pressed for cash and
therefore refused to submit the proposal in the original example can
quickly arrive at the same conclusion in the present example; in other
words, he can solve a complex decision problem by referring it to a simple
decision problem in which he can easily see exactly what is at stake.   The
choice is by no means so clear for the other businessman, however, and he
will be substantially aided if we can find some systematic technique of
analysis which in effect reduces his complex problem to a simple problem
in which he can see exactly what is at stake.   We shall now investigate
the conditions under which the computation of expected monetary value
will be a suitable technique.

2.2.2   Conditions under Which Expected Monetary Value Is a Valid Guide to Action

If we think for a moment about what we know about the way in which businessmen in fact make very simple decisions under uncertainty, we will realize that whether or not they formally compute expected monetary value they act in accordance with expected monetary value when the amounts at stake are not too large.   If a businessman believes that there is 1 chance in 1000 that his million-dollar plant will burn down during the next year, he may be willing to pay $1500 as a premium for an insurance policy even though the expected monetary value of his loss if he does not insure is only $1000; but if the same businessman believes that he runs a 1-in-1000 chance of suffering $100 worth of damage to his machinery because of tramp iron in a particular batch of raw material, he is very likely to be unwilling to pay a cent more than the $.10 expected value of this loss for insurance against it.   Remembering that a cash outlay is to be given a minus sign, we see that in the former case he chooses an act with a monetary value of −$1500 even though the alternative act has the greater monetary value −$1000 but that in the latter case he says that he will take the act with expected monetary value −$.10 if the monetary value of the other act is the least amount lower.

This general kind of behavior is not restricted to situations in which the monetary values of all possible consequences are negative or at best zero.   A businessman with net assets of $500,000 who must choose between a deal which is certain to result in a profit of $50 and another which in his eyes is equally likely to result in a profit of $0 or a profit of $110 is likely to choose the latter act in accordance with the fact that its expected monetary value is $55; but if this same businessman is given the happy opportunity to choose between a deal which is certain to net him $5 million and another which has equal chances of yielding $0 and $11 million, he is very likely to take the $5 million.

To sum up: businessmen tend to treat acts which must have one or the other of just two possible consequences as being "really worth" their expected monetary value as long as the worst of the two consequences is not too bad and the best of the consequences is not too good.   This immediately suggests that a businessman who must evaluate an act or acts with a great number of possible consequences can decide whether or not he should use expected monetary value as the basis of his evaluation by looking only at the best and the worst of the consequences and asking himself whether he would act in accordance with expected monetary value if these were the *only* possible consequences.   More specifically, it would seem reasonable for a man faced with a very complex decision problem to decide whether or not he should take expected monetary value as his guide by applying the following very simple

> *Test for the Validity of Expected Monetary Value as a Guide to Action:*
> Expected monetary value should be used as the decision criterion in
> any real decision problem, however complex, if the person responsi-
> ble for the decision would use it as his criterion in choosing between
> (1) an act which is certain to result in receipt or payment of a defi-
> nite amount of cash and (2) an act which will result in either the *best*
> or the *worst* of all the possible consequences of the real decision
> problem.

Later in the chapter we shall see that the correctness of this rule can be
"proved" in the sense that we can show that any person who does not
follow the rule will end up by making choices which in the opinion of
most reasonable people are logically inconsistent.

As an illustration of the application of this rule, let us return to the
businessman who must decide whether or not to submit a proposal for a
contract when the possible consequences of this act are as described in
Table 2.3. The best and worst possible consequences of this act are
+$25,000 and −$10,000; and since the consequence of not submitting
the proposal is certain to be $0, the two consequences previously named
are the best and worst of the entire decision problem. As an initial test,
the businessman can therefore ask himself the following question: "Suppose that I had to choose between (1) receiving a definite amount of cash
and (2) being awarded a contract such that I assigned probability $\frac{1}{2}$ to
the consequence +$25,000 and probability $\frac{1}{2}$ to the consequence
−$10,000, making the expected monetary value of the contract $7500.
Would I (*a*) prefer the contract to the cash if the specified amount of
cash was less than $7500 and (*b*) prefer the cash to the contract if the
specified amount of cash was over $7500?" If the answer to this ques-
tion is yes, expected monetary value will almost certainly be a correct
guide to this businessman's action in his real problem; but in principle he
must go on to ask himself whether he would answer yes to *any* question
of this type *whatever* the probability he assigned to the $25,000 profit.
He should, for example, suppose that he had already signed a contract
with probability .1 assigned to the consequence +$25,000 and probability
.9 assigned to −$10,000, so that the expected monetary value of the con-
tract was −$6500, and then ask himself whether in fact he would (*a*) pre-
fer to pay any amount of cash less than $6500 for a release rather than
perform the contract but (*b*) prefer to perform the contract rather than
pay any sum greater than $6500 for a release.

If the businessman's answer to any of these questions is no, a little
common sense is required. Such an answer implies that expected
monetary value will not give an *exactly accurate evaluation* of any act

which may result in the $25,000 profit or the $10,000 loss, but this does not mean that expected monetary value will necessarily lead to the *wrong choice of act.* In our example, the expected monetary value of the act "submit the proposal" is +$2500, as shown in Table 2.4, and this is very substantially greater than the value $0 of the act "do not submit the proposal." If then the businessman feels that he would value a contract which gave him even chances of +$25,000 and −$10,000 at only slightly less than its expected monetary value of +$7500, he can feel quite sure that the act "submit the proposal" in the real problem is better than an act which is certain to have the value $0 even though he could not be sure that it would be better than an act which was certain to have the value $2400.

Table 2.4

| Event | Probability | Monetary value | |
		Conditional	Expected
A	.1	+$25,000	+$2500
B	.1	+ 20,000	+ 2000
C	.1	+ 15,000	+ 1500
D	.1	+ 10,000	+ 1000
E	.1	+ 5,000	+ 500
F	.5	− 10,000	− 5000
	1.0		+$2500

2.2.3 Delegation of Routine Decision Making

Systematic use of expected monetary value actually simplifies practical business decisions even more than this example suggests, and for two reasons.

1. The person who is ultimately responsible for a certain class of decisions does not have to look at each decision problem individually in order to decide whether expected monetary value is a proper guide to action, as we can easily see by considering the decision which had to be made by the retailer of the example originally discussed in Section 1.1.1. This retailer will presumably have larger numbers of decisions of exactly this same kind to make daily, and he can settle the question of the validity of expected monetary value as a guide to all these decisions once and for all by simply asking himself how large the worst possible loss and the greatest possible profit would have to be before he would *refuse* to use expected monetary value as a guide in a simple two-consequence problem. If he has $10,000 of working capital, he may well decide that he would take expected monetary value as a guide in any inventory-control problem where the worst possible loss did not exceed, say, $100 and where the greatest possible profit did not exceed, say, $500. If his preferences are

of this sort, then a simple statement of policy to this effect will enable his subordinates to solve virtually all of his stock-control problems without having to ask him any further questions about the "value of money," while at the same time he can feel absolutely sure that his preferences are respected.

2. In principle, the person ultimately responsible for a class of risky decisions must himself evaluate the probabilities or weights which he himself attaches to the various possible events in any problem, but this evaluation can also be delegated in the great majority of practical business problems. In most routine problems the executive would follow some systematic procedure for assessing these probabilities if he did assess them himself; and whenever this is true he can delegate the assessment by simply prescribing the assessment procedure or even the general type of assessment procedure to be used. Thus probabilities may be assessed in routine inventory-control problems by examining the record of demand over the past several periods and using this record in some systematic way; probabilities in routine quality-control problems may be assessed by standard statistical procedures which we shall study later in this course, and so forth.

Once the executive has specified the range of problems within which he wants to have expected monetary value taken as a guide to action and the procedures by which probabilities are to be assessed in routine situations, he will be free to make a careful personal analysis of those problems where such an analysis is really worth the effort: problems in which the possible losses and gains are so great that expected monetary value ceases to be a proper guide to action, and problems in which business judgment of a kind not expected of clerks and statisticians is required to assess the probabilities of the events.

2.3 Expected Utility

In the remainder of this chapter we shall study the problem of choice in situations where the amounts at stake are so large that the test described in Section 2.2.2 tells the businessman that he should *not* use expected monetary value as a guide to action, and we shall see that even in these situations the businessman can reach a fully reasoned solution of the most complex problem by deciding how he would want to act in a number of very simple problems. More specifically, we shall see that his decisions in the simple problems can be used as the basis for assigning a *utility value* to each possible consequence in the real problem and that once this has been done the real problem can be solved by the mere mechanical computation of the *expected utility* of every possible act.

This means that the *only* difference between analysis of a problem in which expected monetary value is a valid guide to action and analysis of a problem in which it is not is that in the latter case we must replace the monetary payoff table by a table showing conditional utilities. Once this has been done, probabilities are assigned to the events in the utility table exactly as they would be if the table showed monetary values rather than utilities, and the expected utility of each act is computed from the conditional utilities in exactly the same way that expected monetary value is computed from conditional monetary values. For this reason we shall talk exclusively in terms of the more familiar monetary values in all future chapters, leaving it to the student to remember that in any real problem he must apply the test of Section 2.2.2 and substitute utilities for monetary values if necessary. It follows that the remaining sections of the present chapter can be read just as well at the end of this course as at the present time.

2.3.1   Outline of the Method of Analysis

Suppose that the businessman with limited working capital who refused the contracts described in Tables 2.2 and 2.3 is offered two other contracts to whose possible consequences he assigns the probabilities shown in Table 2.5. It is easy to calculate the expected *monetary* value of contract M as +\$3825 and that of contract N as +\$2025, and the expected monetary value of taking neither contract is obviously \$0; but we assume that the businessman tells us that he would certainly *not* be willing to accept any deal in which there was an even chance of making or losing \$9000, and this by the rule of Section 2.2.2 means that expected monetary value is of no help to him in choosing among the three acts actually open to him.

Table 2.5

Contract M			Contract N		
Event	Probability	Consequence	Event	Probability	Consequence
A	.30	+\$9000	Q	.25	+\$7500
B	.45	+ 7500	R	.60	+ 2000
C	.25	− 9000	S	.15	− 7000
	1.00			1.00	

If the two contracts offered to the businessman had been those described in Table 2.6 rather than those described in Table 2.5, his decision problem would obviously have been much easier. Each of these contracts has only two possible consequences and these consequences are the same for both contracts; the *only* difference between the two contracts is in the probabilities attached to the consequences, and it is obvious that the more desirable contract is the one with the higher probability of obtaining the $10,000 profit. All that the businessman has to do to make a completely reasoned analysis of this problem and

Table 2.6

Contract X		Contract Y	
Consequence	Probability	Consequence	Probability
+$10,000	.8	+$10,000	.7
− 10,000	.2	− 10,000	.3
	1.0		1.0

reach a decision is to make up his mind whether or not he prefers a cer-tainty of $0 to the combination of a .8 chance of +$10,000 and a .2 chance of −$10,000 which he will obtain if he accepts contract X.

We shall now show that the problem of deciding whether to take contract M, contract N, or neither can be reduced to a number of prob-lems every one of which is just as simple as the problem of choosing between contract X and $0 cash certain. To do this we proceed as follows.

1a. We select two *reference consequences* one of which is at least as bad as the worst possible consequence in the real decision problem and one of which is at least as good as the best, invent a number of hypothetical *reference contracts* each of which has a specified probability π of resulting in the better reference consequence and a corresponding probability $(1 - \pi)$ of resulting in the worse, and ask the businessman to tell us how much cash certain is just equivalent in his own opinion to each of these reference contracts.

1b. We take each possible consequence of the real decision problem separately and use the businessman's answers as given in step 1a to find the π which would make a reference contract equivalent in his opinion to this consequence.†

2. We use the results of step 1b to find the π which would make a reference contract equivalent in the businessman's own opinion to the whole real contract M and another π which would make a reference con-tract equivalent to the whole real contract N. Once these two π's have been found, the problem of deciding whether to take contract M, con-tract N, or neither is just as simple as the problem of deciding whether to take contract X, contract Y, or neither.

† In strict logic, we could ask the businessman directly to tell us the probability π which would make a reference contract just equivalent to each possible consequence of the real problem, but it is much easier for the average person to decide how much he would pay for a gamble with specified probabilities than to find the probabilities which would make the gamble have some predetermined value.

2.3.2   Evaluation of Reference Contracts in Terms of Cash

Looking at Table 2.5 we see that $-\$9000$ is the worst of all the possible consequences in the real decision problem and that $+\$9000$ is the best, so that these two consequences could be chosen as reference consequences; but because it is easier to think in terms of round numbers and easier to multiply by 10 than by 9 we choose instead $-\$10,000$ and $+\$10,000$.

We are now ready to take the step which allows the businessman to express his real attitudes toward risk, profit, and loss by considering problems of the simplest possible form.   We ask him a number of questions all of which are of exactly the same form as the following typical question:

Assuming that for some reason or another you have already signed a *regular business contract* which *in your own opinion* has probability $\pi = \frac{3}{4}$ of resulting in a \$10,000 profit and probability $1 - \pi = \frac{1}{4}$ of resulting in a \$10,000 loss,
1. Would you prefer to keep this contract if you had the choice or would you prefer to be released from its terms?
2. If you would prefer to keep it, then for how much cash would you be willing to sell it?
3. If on the other hand you would prefer to be released, then exactly how much cash would you be willing to pay for a release?

The second question will be identical to the first except that we ask the businessman to imagine that in his own opinion the contract which he has already signed involves only a $\frac{1}{2}$ probability of a \$10,000 profit and a $\frac{1}{2}$ probability of a \$10,000 loss; and the third will again be identical except that the probability of the profit is $\frac{1}{4}$ and the probability of the loss is therefore $\frac{3}{4}$.   Observe that each of these questions is equivalent to a number of simple *choices* between (1) a *specified* amount of cash certain and (2) a reference contract with *specified* probabilities π and $(1 - \pi)$ for the two consequences.   We assume that if we did ask for a sequence of such choices keeping the probabilities in (2) constant but gradually raising the amount of cash in (1), the businessman would always *prefer* (2) when the cash was below some critical amount and would always *prefer* (1) when the cash was greater than this critical amount.   Equivalently, we assume that if we held the cash constant in (1) and gradually raised the probability π of the \$10,000 profit in (2), the businessman would *prefer* (1) when π was below some critical value and would always *prefer* (2) when π was above this value.

In Table 2.7 we show the answers which might be given to these three questions by three different reasonable men, together with the answers which we assume that *any* reasonable man would give if he were asked to name the cash equivalent of a contract which was *certain* to result in a $10,000 loss or *certain* to result in a $10,000 profit. A minus sign before the cash value indicates that this is what the person in question would pay to be released from the contract; a plus sign indicates that this is the price he would demand before he would sell it.

Table 2.7
Cash Values of Hypothetical Contracts According to
Three Different Businessmen

Probability of $10,000 profit π	Cash equivalent for Mr.		
	A	B	C
1	+$10,000	+$10,000	+$10,000
¾	− 3,000	+ 9,000	+ 5,000
½	− 7,000	+ 7,000	0
¼	− 9,000	+ 3,000	− 5,000
0	− 10,000	− 10,000	− 10,000

Mr. A in this table represents the hard-pressed businessman whose problem of choice between contracts M and N we are trying to solve. Because a $10,000 loss would put his business in an extremely critical position, he feels that he would rather pay $3000 out of pocket than run the risk of the $10,000 loss even though he thinks that there is only one chance in four that this loss will actually occur against three chances in four that there will be a $10,000 profit. As the chance of the loss becomes larger and the chance of the profit smaller, Mr. A naturally becomes willing to pay even more to avoid the risk: he will pay $7000 for a release when the probability of the loss is ½, and when it is ¾ he will even pay $9000 certain rather than run the risk of losing the extra $1000 which might put him in bankruptcy.

Mr. B has attitudes diametrically opposed to those of the very cautious and conservative Mr. A; he represents the player of long shots, the man who feels that even a large loss could not make things much worse than they are now whereas a large profit would very substantially improve his whole situation. This attitude is more commonly found among players of numbers pools and the like than it is among business executives, but it is perhaps worth pointing out that even the extremely conservative Mr. A might take this attitude if his misfortunes continued to the point where he would not be able to meet his next payroll unless something extremely fortunate happened between now and Friday. Whatever his motives, Mr. B wants an additional $10,000 so badly that he would consider a $\pi = $ ¼ chance of making it to be worth as much to him as $3000 cash certain even though this chance was accompanied by a ¾ chance of taking a $10,000 loss; by the time $\pi = ¾$ and $(1 - \pi)$ is only ¼, he would not sell his chance at $10,000 for less than $9000.

The answers given by Mr. C will serve as a kind of standard of comparison. Mr. C represents a businessman well supplied with working capital who believes in self-insurance against moderate risks, considers

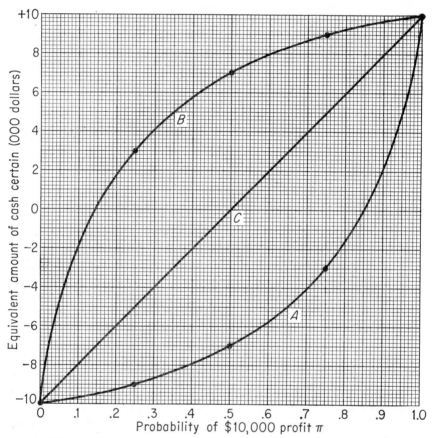

Figure 2.1. Cash values of various reference contracts.

$10,000 to be in fact a very moderate risk, and is therefore willing to use expected monetary value as his guide to action in any problem where the stakes do not exceed plus or minus $10,000. When the chances of a $10,000 profit and a $10,000 loss are equal, Mr. C does not care whether he keeps the contract or gives it away; when the probability π of the more favorable outcome is ¾, he would be willing but not eager to sell the contract for its expected monetary value of $5000; and he would be willing but not eager to pay $5000 for a release if these chances were reversed.

We now try to relieve our businessmen of answering more questions than absolutely necessary by proceeding in the way shown in Figure 2.1.

The curve labeled A is constructed by plotting the five cash values shown in column A of Table 2.7 above the five corresponding values of the probability π and then fairing a smooth curve through the five plotted points; curves B and C are similarly constructed using the cash values in columns B and C respectively. If we were really acting as consultants to Mr. A, we would certainly go on to read from his faired curve some pairs of values which are *not* shown in Table 2.7 and check these values with our client. Curve A asserts, for example, that Mr. A attaches a cash value of only $2000 to a reference contract with $\pi = .9$, and we would do well to ask Mr. A whether this surprisingly low cash value represents his true attitude toward a contract with so high a probability of yielding a $10,000 profit.

2.3.3 Evaluation of Cash in Terms of Reference Contracts

Obviously we can use a curve like any of the three in Figure 2.1 in reverse, i.e. to determine the π which would make a reference contract just equivalent in the businessman's opinion to any specified amount of cash certain rather than to determine the cash equivalent of a reference contract with a specified π. In Table 2.8 we show the π which *in the opinion of Mr. A* would make a reference contract just equivalent to each of the three possible cash consequences of contract M; the student should make sure that he understands what is going on by preparing similar tables for contract N as evaluated from Mr. A's point of view and for both contracts as evaluated from Mr. B's point of view.

Table 2.8
Description of Contract M

Event	Probability	Consequence	π of equivalent reference contract
A	.30	+$9000	.99
B	.45	+ 7500	.98
C	.25	− 9000	.25
	1.00		

2.3.4 Reduction of a Complex Contract to a Reference Contract

It is now that we bring in the really crucial assumption on which our method of analysis rests: we assume that since Mr. A has said that he would be indifferent between receiving any amount of cash shown in the third column of Table 2.8 and being awarded a reference contract with the corresponding π in the last column, *he would not feel that he had gained or lost a thing if the terms of the real contract were modified so that in case of event A he would actually receive a reference contract with $\pi = .99$ instead of receiving $9000 cash, in case of event B he would actually receive a reference* contract with $\pi = .98$ instead of receiving $7,500 cash, and in case of event C he would be obliged to sign a contract with $\pi = .25$ instead of paying out $9000 cash.

The ultimate result of this *modified contract* which we shall call M' can only be a $10,000 profit or a $10,000 loss, despite the fact that its outcome will actually be determined in two stages, the first of which decides which reference contract is awarded to Mr. A while the second decides the final consequence of whatever reference contract is awarded. The desirability of the modified contract therefore depends entirely on the "over-all" probability that it will result in the $10,000 profit, and this probability is very easy to compute. Let us represent the real event A by the drawing of a ball marked A from a *master urn* in which the proportion of balls so marked is p_A, and let us represent the reference contract which will be awarded *if* event A occurs by the right to draw a ball from a *secondary urn* in which the proportion of balls marked "win $10,000" is π_A; and similarly for events B and C and the corresponding reference contracts. Then making use of the formula obtained in answer to Chapter 1, Problem 2, we have for the over-all probability of obtaining the $10,000 profit under the modified contract M':

$$\pi_{M'} = p_A\pi_A + p_B\pi_B + p_C\pi_C;$$

or substituting the numerical values as read from Table 2.8:

$$
\begin{array}{r}
.30 \times .99 \\
+.45 \times .98 \\
+.25 \times .25 \\
\hline
= .80
\end{array}
$$

It is left to the student to show that the corresponding over-all probability of obtaining the $10,000 profit under a modified contract N' equivalent in Mr. A's opinion to real contract N is $\pi_{N'} = .86$.

Since contract M' has only probability .80 of yielding the $10,000 profit while contract N' has probability .86, and since the businessman thinks that M' would be equivalent to the real contract M and N' to N, he should clearly prefer real contract N to real contract M. Roughly speaking, a $9000 loss is so serious in the eyes of Mr. A that a 1-in-4 chance of such a loss outweighs the fact that the profit potential of M is much better than that of N. Mr. A could now reach a final decision by using his judgment to compare contract N with "do nothing," but he has already given us his judgment in curve A: the curve shows that in his opinion the consequence $0 is equivalent to a reference contract with $\pi = .85$ and therefore is slightly inferior to contract N.

Our conclusions can also be expressed in terms of the "real" cash value of each alternative *for Mr. A—not* its "expected" cash value. Curve A shows that a reference contract with $\pi = .86$ is equivalent in

Mr. A's opinion to about +$200 cash certain; and since .86 is the prob-ability of earning the $10,000 profit under contract N', +$200 is the cash equivalent of contract N despite the fact that its "expected" monetary value is +$2025. In the same way we find that contract M is worth −$1700 to Mr. A despite the fact that its expected monetary value is +$3825.

2.3.5   Utility

At the beginning of this section we said that when expected monetary value was not a valid guide to action the person responsible for a decision could always find a valid guide by assigning utility values to the various possible consequences of his acts and then choosing the act with the highest expected utility. We shall now see that this is simply another way of describing the calculation of the π's of modified contracts such as M' and N'.

To analyze any decision problem in terms of utility, we must start by choosing two numbers to represent the utility values of the two reference consequences. The number assigned to the better consequence must be larger than the number assigned to the worse, but otherwise we are free to choose as we please. To show why this is so, we shall work with two different scales simultaneously:

1. We define scale I by saying that the utility of a $10,000 loss is 0 utiles and that the utility of a $10,000 profit is +1 utile;

2. We define scale II by saying that the utility of a $10,000 loss is −10,000 utiles and that the utility of a $10,000 profit is +10,000 utiles.

Once we have defined a utility scale by defining its end points, it is easy to compute the *expected* utility of a *reference contract* with any speci-fied π. As shown in Table 2.9, the utility of such a contract is π utiles on

Table 2.9
Expected Utility of a Reference Contract

Conse-sequence	Proba-bility	Utility on scale I		Utility on scale II	
		Conditional	Expected	Conditional	Expected
+$10,000	π	+1	$+1\pi$	+10,000	$+10,000\pi$
−$10,000	$(1-\pi)$	0	$0(1-\pi)$	−10,000	$-10,000(1-\pi)$
	1		π		$-10,000+20,000\pi$

scale I or $(-10,000 + 20,000\pi)$ utiles on scale II.

The next step is to assign a utility value to every possible conse-quence of the real decision problem by saying that *if a man is indifferent between a specified consequence and a reference contract with some particular π, then the utility of that consequence is equal to the utility of that reference* *contract.* In Table 2.10 we show the utilities which *Mr. A* should assign to the possible consequences of contract M, reading the value of π for each consequence from Table 2.8.

Table 2.10
Conditional Utilities to Mr. A

Event	Consequence	Conditional utility	
		Scale I	Scale II
A	$+\$9000$	.99	$-10,000 + 20,000(.99)$
B	$+7500$	.98	$-10,000 + 20,000(.98)$
C	-9000	.25	$-10,000 + 20,000(.25)$

Finally, in Table 2.11 we compute the *expected utility* of contract M to Mr. A by applying the standard rule for taking the expectation of a set of conditional values (Section 2.1): multiply each conditional value (as read from Table 2.10) by its probability and add the products.

Table 2.11
Expected Utility of Contract M to Mr. A

Event	Probability	Expected utility on scale I	Expected utility on scale II
A	.30	$.30 \times .99$	$-10,000(.30) + 20,000(.30 \times .99)$
B	.45	$.45 \times .98$	$-10,000(.45) + 20,000(.45 \times .98)$
C	.25	$.25 \times .25$	$-10,000(.25) + 20,000(.25 \times .25)$
	1.00	.80	$-10,000(1) \quad + 20,000(.80)$

Observe now that *the .80 which appears in the expected utility on either scale is exactly the same sum of products which gave us the probability* $\pi_{M'}$ *that the modified contract M' would result in the* $10,000 *profit*. If we computed the expected utility of contract N, it would come out in a *form* identical to that of the expression for the utility of M; the only difference would be that the number .80 would be replaced by $\pi_{N'} = .86$. Observe next that *the higher this probability number which appears in the expression for the expected utility, the greater the numerical value of the expected utility.* Since we have already seen that a reasonable man should choose the real act or contract whose corresponding modified contract has the highest probability of resulting in the better reference consequence, it follows immediately that

A reasonable man should always choose the act with the greatest expected utility.

2.3.6   The Interpretation of Utility

In a certain sense analysis of a problem in terms of conditional and expected utilities rather than in terms of modified contracts enables us to gain a better feeling for the reasons behind a given person's preferences, but unless we are very careful this feeling will do our real understanding more harm than good.

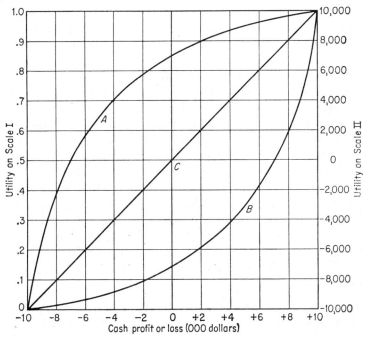

Figure 2.2. Utilities of various cash consequences.

Let us look first at the advantages to be gained from the use of the concept of utility.   In Figure 2.2 we show the utilities of all possible consequences between −$10,000 and +$10,000 for Messrs. A, B, and C as computed by reading from Figure 2.1 the π of the reference contract which is equivalent to each consequence and then applying the formulas

$$U = \pi \qquad\qquad \text{Scale I}$$
$$U = -10,000 + 20,000\pi \qquad \text{Scale II}$$

Looking at curve A we can "explain" Mr. A's extremely cautious attitude toward all risky contracts by observing that moving any given distance to the right of 0 on the horizontal axis increases his utility by much less than moving a corresponding distance to the left decreases it—a profit of any specified amount increases his utility by less than a loss of the same

amount decreases it. For Mr. B, on the contrary, the situation is just
the reverse: a profit of any given amount increases his utility by more
than a loss of the same amount decreases it; while for Mr. C a dollar lost is
worth neither more nor less than a dollar gained.

Now it is true that most people will actually think in terms much
like these when they are deciding how to evaluate risky acts. A person is
likely to say that he would prefer $1 million certain to a 50-50 chance of
$2 million or nothing because he would be almost as well off with $1
million as with $2 million and "therefore" the chance at the extra million
is not worth the risk of losing the first one. Similarly a person who buys
life insurance despite the fact that the premium is always larger than the
expected monetary value of the benefits by the amount of the insurance
company's costs and profits will explain his action by saying that the
dollars he now uses to pay the premium are worth much less to his family
than the dollars which would be paid as benefits in case of his death.

We must be very careful, however, not to lose sight of the fact that
all utilities are and must be evaluated by looking at *particular types* of
risky acts or reference contracts and that a person may well have one
attitude toward risk in one situation and a quite different attitude in a
different situation. The businessman who decided to submit the proposal under the conditions described in Table 2.2 is in effect betting
$10,000 against $25,000 in a situation where he thinks that he has an even
chance of winning his bet; but the same businessman might flatly refuse
to make the same bet on the toss of a coin even though he was absolutely
convinced that the coin was fair and therefore that he had an even chance
of winning the bet.

> Curves like those shown in Figure 2.2 do *not* purport to represent the
> "value of money" as such; they reflect an indecomposable mixture
> of attitude toward risk, profit, and loss in a particular kind of
> situation.

Finally, we warn the student emphatically against two common
interpretations of the meaning of utility which are totally false.

First, the utilities of two separate consequences cannot be added to
obtain the utility of both consequences together—the utility of an apple
plus an orange is usually *not* equal to the utility of an apple plus the
utility of an orange. All that is required to understand this assertion is
to look at curve *A* or *B* in Figure 2.2, observe that the utility of a $10,000
profit is not equal to twice the utility of a $5000 profit, and remember the
reason why.

Second, we cannot use curves like those in Figure 2.2 as the basis for
an assertion that any given consequence is worth less or more to one man
than to another if by this we mean that one of the two men "really
needs" the money more than the other or that the money will do more

"real good" to one man than to another; nor can we say for example that because a loss of $10,000 would reduce Mr. C's utility by only .5 utile on scale I while a profit of $10,000 would increase Mr. B's utility by .85 utile on this same scale, therefore there would be a net social gain if Mr. C were taxed $10,000 and the proceeds handed over to Mr. B. *All* that we can say on the basis of curves like those of Figure 2.2 is that one man will *want to behave* differently from another when faced with choices under uncertainty. Ethical and social issues cannot be handled by the methods we shall use in this course.

2.3.7   *Proof of the Rule for Use of Expected Monetary Value*

One interesting by-product of our study of utility is the fact that it permits us very easily to prove the correctness of the rule which we gave in Section 2.2.2 for testing whether expected *monetary* value would be a correct guide to action in a given complex decision problem. What we shall show is that a person who chooses the act with the highest expected monetary value when this rule tells him to do so will necessarily choose the act with the highest expected utility; the student will follow the argument more easily if he first observes that the utility which Mr. C assigns to any consequence on scale II is numerically equal to the monetary value of the consequence and therefore that the expected monetary value of any act involving these consequences will be numerically equal to its expected utility on scale II.

Letting \$$W$ denote the monetary value of the worst possible consequence of any complex decision problem and \$$B$ that of the best, the rule given in Section 2.2.2 said in effect that expected monetary value would be a valid guide to action if and only if the person responsible for the decision would use this guide in simple problems involving a choice between (1) a specified amount of cash certain and (2) a reference contract which would result with probability π in \$$B$ and with probability $(1 - \pi)$ in \$$W$. Such a person is saying that for him the cash equivalent of the reference contract is given by the formula

$$\$W(1 - \pi) + \$B \pi.$$

Since the choice of the end points of a utility scale is always arbitrary, this person can always choose a scale in which the number W without the dollar sign represents the *utility* of the consequence whose monetary value is \$$W$ and in which the number B represents the utility of the consequence whose monetary value is \$$B$. On this scale the utility of the reference contract and therefore of its cash equivalent is *by definition*

$$W(1 - \pi) + B\pi,$$

and we conclude that *a person who values all reference contracts at their expected monetary value* can always find a utility scale such that the utility of every consequence between the reference consequences is numerically equal to the monetary value of the consequence and therefore such that *the expected utility of any act involving consequences within this range is numerically equal to the expected monetary value of the act.* By choosing the act with the highest expected monetary value, such a person automatically chooses the act with the highest expected utility.

2.4 Profits in the Long and the Short Run

2.4.1 The Desirability of Looking Ahead

There is one very serious deficiency in our discussion of the problem of decision under uncertainty which must at least be pointed out before we close this chapter. We have discussed every decision problem which we encountered as if it existed *in vacuo* and could be rationally analyzed without giving any thought whatever to any other problem which the businessman was facing concurrently or which he would have to face later on. That analysis of this sort can easily lead to completely unsound results will now be illustrated by a simple example.

Suppose that Mr. C of Section 2.3 has total assets of exactly $25,000 cash and that it is completely impossible for him to raise any additional capital during the next month. Suppose further (1) that Mr. C is offered the opportunity of participating immediately in a deal which in his opinion is equally likely to result in a profit of $8000 or a loss of $7000, and (2) that at the same time he is definitely informed that one month hence he will be given the opportunity of investing $20,000 in another deal which in his opinion is equally likely to result in a net profit of $9000 or a net loss of $2000 regardless of the outcome of deal I.

Since Mr. C acts in accordance with expected monetary value, he will accept deal I if he looks at this deal by itself. It is obvious, however, that Mr. C should *not* look at deal I by itself, since taking this deal involves a risk that he will end up with only $25,000 − $7,000 = $18,000 cash and thus be unable to participate in the very attractive deal II. The two deals *must* be considered as parts of a *single* decision problem and we must look at the *ultimate* rather than the *immediate* consequences of the two possible immediate acts "accept deal I" and "refuse deal I."

The first step in analyzing this two-stage decision problem is to ask what Mr. C will do at the time the *second* deal becomes available—the reason for settling this question first, before looking at deal I, is that when Mr. C gets to the point where he will actually have to make up his mind about deal II he will have only a *single deal* left to analyze. The expected monetary value of this deal will be ½$9000 − ½$2000 = +$3500, and since Mr. C is guided by expected monetary value it follows that *he will participate in deal II if his assets at the time the deal becomes available are sufficient to permit him to do so.* With this definite result available, we can now go on to make a really correct analysis of the possible consequences of the two possible acts which Mr. C may take in regard to the *first* deal.

Refuse Deal I. If Mr. C refuses deal I, the *immediate* consequence of this act is certain to be $0; but it is also certain that Mr. C will have sufficient assets to participate in deal II when the time comes, and we have already seen that this means that he *will* participate. The act "refuse I" thus has *two* possible *ultimate* consequences, the +$9000 and −$2000 which may result from deal II.

Accept Deal I. If Mr. C accepts deal I, there are obviously two possible *immediate* consequences, +$8000 and −$7000; but to find the *ultimate* consequences of this act we must again look ahead. (1) If Mr. C loses $7000 on deal I, he will not have sufficient assets to participate in deal II and therefore he will be left with his $7000 loss unaltered. In this case the *ultimate* consequence of the immediate act is the same as its immediate consequence. (2) If Mr. C makes $8000 on deal I, he will be able to participate in deal II and we already know that this means that he will in fact participate. If then deal II results in a loss of $2000, the *ultimate* consequence of having participated in deal I will have been +$8000 − $2000 = +$6000; if deal II results in a profit of $9000, the ultimate consequence of having participated in deal I will have been +$8000 + $9000 = +$17,000. The act "accept I" thus has altogether *three* possible *ultimate* consequences: −$7000, +$6000, and +$17,000.

Having listed the possible *ultimate consequences* of the two acts between which Mr. C must choose immediately ("refuse I" and "accept I"), we are ready to compute the expected *ultimate monetary value* of each of these two acts.

Refuse I. Since the ultimate consequences of this act depend only on the event of deal II, their probabilities are simply the probabilities already assigned by Mr. C to the two possible events of deal II. In other words, the expected *ultimate* monetary value of the act "refuse I" is the same as the expected *immediate* monetary value of "accept II," or

$$\tfrac{1}{2}(+\$9000) + \tfrac{1}{2}(-\$2000) = +\$3500.$$

Accept I. To find the expected ultimate monetary value of the immediate act "accept I," we must compute the probabilities which Mr. C should assign to these three possible ultimate consequences. That the probability of −$7000 is $\tfrac{1}{2}$ follows directly from Mr. C's assignment of this probability to the immediate loss of $7000 on deal I. The other two consequences correspond to "winning" on deal I *and then* either "losing" or "winning" on deal II, and their probabilities can be computed as $\tfrac{1}{4}$ each in the same way that in Sections 1.5 and 1.6.1 we showed that the events "heads followed by heads" and "heads followed by tails" on two successive tosses of a coin each had probability $\frac{1}{4}$. Using these probabilities we can then compute the expected ultimate monetary value of the act "accept I" to be +$2250 as shown in Table 2.12.

Although the expected *immediate* monetary value of "refuse I" is $0 against $\frac{1}{2}$8000 − $\frac{1}{2}$7000 = $500 for "accept I," the expected *ultimate* monetary value of "refuse I" is $3500 against $2250 for "accept I," and Mr. C should clearly refuse deal I.

Table 2.12
Expected Ultimate Monetary Value of "Accept I"

Event	Probability	Ultimate monetary value	
		Conditional	Expected
−$7000 on I	$\frac{1}{2}$	−$ 7,000	−$3500
+$8000 on I, −$2000 on II	$\frac{1}{4}$	+ 6,000	+ 1500
+$8000 on I, +$9000 on II	$\frac{1}{4}$	+ 17,000	+ 4250
	1		+$2250

Our understanding of this two-stage decision problem can be aided by stating it graphically in the form of Figure 2.3. Any path traced

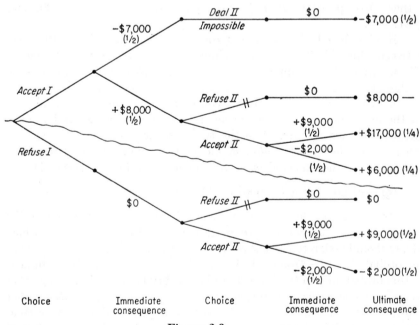

Figure 2.3

from the extreme left of this chart to the extreme right represents a *possible* sequence of choices and events or consequences. Two paths are barred off at the point "refuse II" because we have shown that Mr. C would not want to refuse deal II if he had the choice. The probabilities shown in parentheses next to the branches representing events or *immediate* consequences are those assigned directly by Mr. C; the probabilities shown next to the *ultimate* consequences are computed from those assigned directly by Mr. C.

2.4.2   Utility and the Limitations of Human Capacity

It thus appears that to make a *really complete* analysis of even the smallest and simplest decision problem, the businessman would have to start by laying out on a chart like Figure 2.3 every possible choice and every possible immediate consequence of every possible act in every decision problem he has or ever will have to face, and he would have to assign a *probability* to every immediate consequence on this chart. The next step would be to assign a *utility* to every possible *ultimate* consequence, and here the businessman would run into a problem which we did *not* encounter in our simple example. In that example we tacitly assumed that Mr. C would have no need of money for his personal use or for that of his stockholders before the time at which deal II would be completed, and therefore the ultimate consequences could be described very simply in terms of the total assets which Mr. C would have as of the time of completion of deal II. In real business problems, the ultimate consequences are the stream of dividends and distributions of capital which the company pays to its owners over its whole life; and since a dividend of $10 ten years hence is not in general equivalent to ten annual dividends of $1 each, the utility assigned to each ultimate consequence would have to depend on its date as well as its amount.

Quite obviously no one proposes or ever will propose an analysis of this sort, but it is only by seeing what *would* be involved in such an analysis that we can really understand either the objectives which we should have before us in making any analysis or the real meaning of the utilities which are assigned as part of these analyses.

1. While there is usually something to be gained by extending the scope of an analysis, such an extension always adds appreciably to the cost of the analysis and at some point a balance must be struck. The judgment required to strike a reasonable balance can be acquired only by some actual experience with the benefits to be gained from multistage analysis and some actual knowledge of the costs likely to be involved, and it is probably true that the average businessman both underestimates the gains and overestimates the costs. Although we must learn to walk before we run and therefore must devote most of our time in this introductory course to the analysis of single-stage problems, we shall pay some

attention to multistage problems and at least suggest the remarkable results obtainable with modern computing equipment.

2. The assignment of utilities to "immediate" rather than "ultimate" consequences is actually an expression of the businessman's best guess at what would be shown by the missing part of the analysis. When the businessman says that he is willing to use expected monetary value as a guide to action in a particular problem, he is usually saying that the amounts at stake are so small that in his judgment no possible outcome of the decision can noticeably affect his ability to make profits in the future and therefore he will choose the act with the greatest immediate expected profit. When on the contrary he assigns utilities like those of Mr. A, he is really saying that in his judgment his *long-run* expected profit is increased by playing it safe until he has built up greater financial strength and therefore he will choose an act whose immediate expected profit is less than that of some other, riskier act.

PROBLEMS

A. Problems on Expected Monetary Value

1. Assuming that the retailer of the example discussed in Section 1.1.1 has decided to use expected monetary value as his criterion of choice in any problem where the greatest possible loss does not exceed $50 and the greatest possible profit does not exceed $100, and assuming that he assigns to the events of Table 1.1 the probabilities shown in Table 2.13, how many units should he stock and what is his expected gross profit?

Table 2.13

Event (number demanded)	Probability
0	$\frac{1}{20}$
1	$\frac{3}{20}$
2	$\frac{6}{20}$
3	$\frac{5}{20}$
4	$\frac{3}{20}$
5 or more	$\frac{2}{20}$
	1

2. *a.* A roulette wheel of the kind used at Monte Carlo has 37 numbered positions on which one may bet. Those who bet on the winning number get back their bets and 35 times as much in addition. What is the value to the house of a 1000-franc bet on number 17?

b. Of the 37 positions, 18 are red, 18 black, and 1 green. A player can bet on red or black but not green. Those who bet on a winning color get back their bets and an equal amount in addition. What is the value to the house of a 1000-franc bet on red?

c. "There is little possibility of the exercise of skill in roulette, though a certain judgment is advisable in betting; it would, for example, be unwise to place a bet on red and also on the number 17, which is black, for if one bet wins the other must lose." (*Encyclopedia Britannica,* edition of 1953, s.v. "Roulette.") Discuss.

3. A company has $100,000 available to invest in a new plant. If business

conditions continue as they are, the investment will return 10 per cent, but if there is a mild recession, it will return only 2 per cent. Alternatively the money can be invested in government bonds for a sure return of 3 per cent. What probability must management assign to a recession to make the two investments have the same expected monetary value?

B. Problems on Utility

4. Verify the assertion in Section 2.3.4 that .86 is the probability of obtaining the $10,000 profit under the modified contract N' which is equivalent *in Mr. A's opinion* to the real contract N.

5. Show that in the contracts M'' and N'' which *in Mr. B's opinion* are equivalent to M and N the probabilities of obtaining the $10,000 profit are respectively .48 and .27. Explain in nontechnical language why the probability is greater under M'' than under N'' when the probability under Mr. A's M' was smaller than under N'.

6. *a.* What are the true cash equivalents of contracts M and N for Mr. B?

b. What are their expected utilities for Mr. B on scales I and II?

7. By subtracting an appropriate constant amount from every one of Mr. A's scale-II utilities it is possible to define a third scale such that the utility of $0 is 0 utiles.

a. Make a rough graph showing the utility of every consequence from −$10,000 to +$10,000 on this new scale.

b. Compute the expected utility of contracts M and N for Mr. A on this new scale.

c. Show that the *relative* ratings of the acts "take M," "take N," "take neither" are exactly the same on this new scale as they were on scale II.

8. Mr. A is presented with a deal which in his opinion has probability ⅔ of resulting in a $10,000 profit but probability ⅓ of resulting in a $10,000 loss.

a. Show that Mr. A should refuse the deal.

b. Suppose that five people with utility curves exactly like Mr. A's all assign the same probabilities to the possible consequences of this deal. Show that if they agree to share the profit or loss equally, the deal becomes attractive for all of them.

CHAPTER 3

Random Variables and Probability Distributions

3.1 Random Variables

In Chapter 1 we saw that the first step in the analysis of a problem of decision under uncertainty is always to draw up a list of mutually exclusive and collectively exhaustive events. In this chapter we shall introduce the important concept of a *random variable* which assigns a "value" to an event and is often more convenient to work with than the event itself, and we shall then see how the probabilities assigned to the possible values of a random variable may be laid out systematically in a *probability distribution.*

Suppose that a manufacturer is about to manufacture a cylindrical shaft, that he intends to use go and no-go gauges to check both the diameter and the length of the finished piece, and that we wish to use every bit of information supplied by the gauging to describe the outcome of this "trial." If we let g, u, and o respectively denote that the *diameter* is good, undersize, or oversize, and if we let G, U, and O convey the same information for the *length*, we can say that the possible events of this trial are the nine which are listed in the first column of Table 3.1. In the

Table 3.1

Event	Probability
gG	.55
gU	.07
gO	.03
uG	.10
uU	.08
uO	.02
oG	.05
oU	.04
oO	.06
	1.00

second column of the table probabilities have been assigned to each of these events for use in our further discussion; these probabilities are completely arbitrary except that they add to 1 as all good probabilities must—how they were assessed is irrelevant for our present purpose.

Suppose now that it will cost the manufacturer $1 to rework either

50

an oversize diameter or an oversize length and that it will cost $4 to
replace a piece which is undersize and must therefore be scrapped. Since
we are looking only at costs incurred *after* the original piece has been produced and inspected, we can say that the cost due to a good piece will
be $0.

These statements suffice to assign a *value* to every elementary event
in Table 3.1. The value $0 is assigned to the event gG, the value $1 to
the events oG and gO, the value $2 to the event oO, and the value $4 to all
other events. The probability of each of these four *values* is obtained in
exactly the same way that we obtained the probabilities of *compound
events* in Chapter 1, by adding the probabilities of the corresponding elementary events; the results are shown in Table 3.2.

Table 3.2

Value	Elementary events	Probability
$0	gG	.55
1	oG, gO	.08
2	oO	.06
4	All others	.31
		1.00

Monetary values are not the only interesting values which may be
attached to events. In our example, the manufacturer may be interested
not only in costs but in the amount of raw material which will be used in
manufacturing replacements for pieces which cannot be reworked and
must be scrapped. Suppose that it takes .3 pound of bar stock to manufacture one piece: if we recall that a piece which is undersize in either
dimension must be scrapped, we see that a "value" of .3 pound is attached
to the events gU, uG, uU, uO, and oU of the list in Table 3.1 while the
value 0 pound is attached to all the other elementary events. Adding
the probabilities of these two groups of elementary events we obtain the
probabilities for the two possible values of the quantity "amount of raw
material" shown in Table 3.3.

Table 3.3

Value	Probability
0 pound	.69
.3 pound	.31
	1.00

Quantities such as cost and amount of material in these two examples
are known as random variables; in general, we define

Random variable: any quantity which has a definite value corresponding to every possible event.

A list of the possible values of a random variable can be regarded as being simply a list of elementary and/or compound events defined in a special way; but it is important to realize that while a particular value of a random variable can always be regarded as an event, it is *not* true that all events can be regarded as values of random variables.   First, the values of a random variable have a *meaningful order* whereas events like those of Table 3.1 do not.   "More than $1" makes sense but "more than gU" does not.   Second and much more important, the concepts of average value and *expected value* have meaning when applied to a random variable but not when applied to events in general.   We have already applied these concepts to monetary random variables in Chapter 2, and in Chapter 5 we shall see that they apply to all random variables without exception.

Observe on the other hand that the existence of a meaningful order and a meaningful average or expected value are the *only* properties which we require of the "values" of a random variable.   If the manufacturer of our example is interested in the quality of the work done in his shop as measured by the number of individual defects produced, we may consider "number of defects" a random variable describing the outcome of each trial (each piece produced) even though we have attached no economic worth to a defect and even though the economic worth of one defect may be quite different from that of another.   The probability distribution of this variable is shown in Table 3.4.

Table 3.4

Value of the random variable	Elementary events	Probability
0	gG	.55
1	gU, gO, uG, oG	.25
2	All others	.20
		1.00

Observe also that in many cases the *value* of a random variable may be identical to the natural *description* of an event.   If the manufacturer had measured his pieces instead of using gauges, an "event" would have been described by a pair of numbers—e.g., diameter 1.23 inches, length 2.07 inches.   These two numbers can equally well be regarded as "values" of two random variables "diameter" and "length," and we shall ordinarily so regard them.   In just the same way we can regard the various possible events in the inventory problem described in Table 1.1 as values of the random variable "demand."

3.2   Probability Distributions and Frequency Distributions

A table like Tables 3.2 through 3.4 which assigns a probability to every possible value of a random variable is called a *probability distribution* of that random variable. Since by the definition of a random variable every possible elementary event corresponds to *some* value of the variable, the sum of the probabilities in any probability distribution must be 1.

3.2.1   Assessment of Probability Distributions

Although a random variable is *defined* in terms of values attached to the elementary events of a trial, it is not to be assumed that the probability distribution of a random variable must necessarily be *assessed* by first assigning probabilities to elementary events and then adding the probabilities of a number of elementary events to obtain the probability of each value of the variable as we did in the examples of the previous section.   It has already been pointed out that in some cases a random variable will attach a different value to each elementary event (e.g., the random variable "demand" in the inventory example), so that there is only a verbal difference between assigning probabilities to elementary events and assigning probabilities directly to the possible values of the random variable.   Later in the course we shall see that even when each value of a random variable does correspond to a large number of elementary events, it is often better to proceed by using our experience to make a direct assessment of the distribution of two or more random variables and then to use these distributions to compute the probabilities of the elementary events if they are needed in the problem at hand.

Whenever probabilities are assigned *directly* to the values of some random variable, we shall refer to this variable as a *basic random variable* in order to distinguish it from other random variables which may be involved in the same problem.   Suppose, for example, that a can of coffee is to be filled by an automatic machine and that a loss will be incurred if either more or less than 1 pound of coffee is put into the can.   What we really want in such a problem is a probability distribution for the random variable "loss," but the most effective way of using our experience may well be to start by assessing the distribution of the random variable "weight."   If we do proceed in this way, "weight" is the basic random variable of the problem.

3.2.2   Frequency Distributions

The *probabilities* which a reasonable man assigns to the values of a basic random variable will often (though by no means always) be largely if not wholly determined by consideration of the *relative frequencies* with which these values have occurred in past trials.   To continue with the example of the coffee, suppose that the net weight of the coffee in each of the last 50 cans filled by the machine has been determined to the nearest $\frac{1}{100}$ pound with the results shown in the first two columns of Table 3.5. By dividing the *number of occurrences* of each value by the *total number of trials* we obtain the *relative frequencies* of each value as shown in the last column of the table.

Table 3.5

Value of the random variable	Number of occurrences	Relative frequency
.98	2	.04
.99	6	.12
1.00	7	.14
1.01	10	.20
1.02	9	.18
1.03	8	.16
1.04	5	.10
1.05	3	.06
	50	1.00

The first and last columns of Table 3.5 together constitute a *frequency distribution* of the random variable "weight," and in general any complete list of the relative frequencies of all the values of any random variable will be called a frequency distribution.   Since it is only in relative frequencies that we are interested, the word "relative" will often be omitted in future discussions: "frequency" will *always* mean relative frequency.   Observe that the total of the frequencies in a frequency distribution must always be 1, just as the total of the probabilities in a probability distribution must always be 1.

Now a frequency distribution like the one shown in Table 3.5 is most definitely *not* in itself a probability distribution for the random variable "weight" on the next trial.   If, however, we have *no other information about the can-filling process which we consider to be of any real importance,* we *may* decide to assign probabilities which are *numerically equal* to the relative frequencies shown in Table 3.5.   In other words, we *may* decide on the basis of the evidence summarized in Table 3.5 that we would be indifferent between the right to receive a certain prize if the next can weighs .98 pound and the right to receive the same prize if a particular ball is drawn in a "standard lottery" with 25 balls in the urn.   In Chapter 6 we shall return to this subject and look at some of the questions we should ask before actually proceeding in this way, particularly when the available frequency distribution is based on only a few trials.

3.3   Graphic Representation of Distributions

Our thinking about a probability or frequency distribution can often be considerably clarified if we represent the distribution graphically, and in Chapter 6 we shall also see that graphical representation is often of considerable help when we try to assess a probability distribution rationally. Frequency distributions and probability distributions can both be represented by exactly the same devices; we shall use the frequency distribution of Table 3.5 as an example.

One form of graphic representation is shown in Figure 3.1.   The

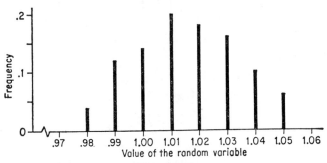

Figure 3.1

horizontal axis shows the various *values* of the random variable; the height of the vertical line at any particular value represents the *frequency* with which that value occurs.

Another form of representation is shown in Figure 3.2, where the

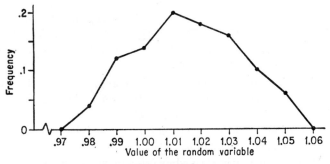

Figure 3.2

frequency of each value of the variable is shown by the height of a point and the points are then joined by straight lines.   Since values of this variable other than .97, .98, .99, etc., are meaningless—the measurements were made to the nearest $\frac{1}{100}$ pound—the lines have no meaning except at those points; in between, they serve simply as guides to the eye.

Histograms. Frequencies or probabilities can be represented by areas as well as by heights, and the histogram of Figure 3.3 is such a representation for the data of Table 3.5: the frequency of each value of the random variable is represented by the *area* of the bar centered on that value. A great many problems which we shall encounter later in the

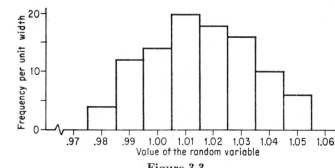

Figure 3.3

course will be far easier to understand if we visualize probability distributions in terms of histograms than if we visualize them in any other way, and we therefore advise the student to pay close attention to the rules which we shall now give for the construction and interpretation of graphs of this sort even though these rules may seem needlessly complex at the moment.

Observe first that the edges of the bar for any value of the variable in Figure 3.3 are halfway between the location of that value and the adjacent values of the variable. Thus the edges of the bar for the value 1.02 are located at 1.015 and 1.025. This means that the width of this bar can be taken as $1.025 - 1.015 = .01$, and in general *the width of any bar in any histogram can be taken as equal to the difference between two successive possible values of the variable.*

Now since it is the *area* of a bar which represents the frequency or probability of the corresponding value of the variable, and since the area of a bar is equal to its width times its height, we must interpret the *height* of a bar as showing *frequency or probability per unit width.* In Figure 3.3 the height of the bar for the value 1.02 of the variable can be read as 18 on the vertical axis; the width of this bar is .01 as we have already seen; and therefore

$$\text{Area} = \text{frequency} = 18 \times .01 = .18$$

in agreement with Table 3.5. *It is exactly this trick of interpretation which will make the use of histograms so useful a little later on, and we urge the student to fix it firmly in his mind.*

3.3.1   Grouped Distributions

When a random variable has a very large number of possible values, it becomes bothersome to tabulate or graph all the small individual frequencies occurring in a historical frequency distribution, and often we find ourselves forced to deal with historical data in which some of this detail has been suppressed. We may be presented, for example, with a historical record of daily sales in which the possible values of the variable have been grouped into "brackets" and the frequencies of all values within each bracket have been added together as in Table 3.6. We shall also see later on that even when the full detail of a frequency or

Table 3.6

Sales	Relative frequency
55–59	.05
60–64	.09
65–69	.18
70–74	.27
75–79	.21
80–84	.14
85–89	.06
	1.00

probability distribution is given to us, the labor involved in many calculations can be materially reduced with little or no loss of accuracy by grouping the distribution in this way before performing the calculations.

By far the best graphical representation for a grouped distribution is a histogram, since the grouping into brackets can be directly represented by the widths of the bars. A histogram for the data of Table 3.6 is shown in Figure 3.4. The bar representing the frequency of sales from 55 to 59 units inclusive is represented by a bar with its left edge at 54.5 and its right edge at 59.5—*the bar covers exactly the same interval on the horizontal axis which would have been covered by the individual bars for the values in question.* The *width* of this bar is thus $59.5 - 54.5 = 5$ units, and since its *area* is .05 by Table 3.6 it has been drawn with a *height* of $.05/5 = .01$. Similarly the frequency of values from 60 to 64 units inclusive can be read from the graph as

$$\text{Area} = \text{frequency} = \text{height} \times \text{width} = .018 \times 5 = .09.$$

3.4   Cumulative Distributions

We are often interested, not in the frequency or probability of an *individual* value of a random variable, but in the frequency or probability of *all values less than* some specified value or of *all values greater than* some

specified value.   In the example of the cans of coffee which were supposed to contain exactly 1 pound, we may want to know the probability
that the next can will contain less than 1 pound or the probability that it
will contain more than 1 pound.   For other purposes we may want to
know the probability that a variable will be *equal to or less than* some
specified value or that it will be *equal to or greater than* the specified value.

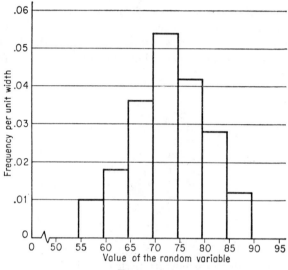

Figure 3.4

Cumulative frequencies or probabilities of this sort are computed
from individual frequencies or probabilities in a way which is perfectly
obvious.   In the example of Table 3.5, the frequency of values equal to
or less than .98 is simply the frequency of .98 itself, or .04.   The frequency of values equal to or less than .99 is the frequency of .98 plus the
frequency of .99 or .04 + .12 = .16.   Proceeding systematically in this
way we can compute the complete *cumulative distribution* of this random
variable with the results shown in Table 3.7, where the individual frequencies are repeated from Table 3.5 for the student's convenience.

3.4.1   "Tail Areas"

Graphically, the frequency or probability of a *specified value* or less is
represented by the total area of all bars of a histogram starting from the
extreme left and continuing *up to and including* the bar representing the
specified value.   This area will frequently be called the area of the *left
tail* of the distribution; the corresponding *right-tail* area represents the
frequency of values *greater than* the specified value.   We are not com-
pelled, however, to include the area of the bar representing the specified
value itself in the left tail of the distribution.   We can equally well

Table 3.7

Value of the random variable	Relative frequency	Cumulative frequency of that value or less
.98	.04	.04
.99	.12	.16
1.00	.14	.30
1.01	.20	.50
1.02	.18	.68
1.03	.16	.84
1.04	.10	.94
1.05	.06	1.00
	1.00	

define the right tail as including this bar, in which case the area of the left tail represents the frequency or probability of values *less than* the specified value. The proper definition of a tail area—the proper specification of a cumulative probability or frequency—depends on the way in which the probability or frequency is to be used in a particular problem, and care must be taken both in deciding on the proper specification and in computing the probability or frequency so that it actually corresponds to the specification.

3.4.2   Direct Graphic Representation of Cumulative Distributions

It is often convenient to have a graph from which cumulative probabilities or frequencies can be read directly rather than as the sum of the areas of a number of bars of a histogram. Figure 3.5 is such a graph for the data of Table 3.7: for every value of the random variable, Figure 3.5 shows the relative frequency of *that value or less* and thus conveys exactly the same information which is conveyed by the last column of Table 3.7. Three points need special attention in constructing or reading a graph of this sort.

First, the graph of any *cumulative* distribution has meaning for *every* value of the variable and not just for those values which the variable did or could actually take on. Even though the value 1.003 itself neither occurred nor could occur when the weighing was done only to the nearest $\frac{1}{100}$ pound, it is perfectly sensible to say that the frequency with which the random variable had values of 1.003 pounds or less was .30. Similarly we can read from Figure 3.5 the meaningful information that values of .97 or less occurred with frequency 0 and that values of 1.06 or less occurred with frequency 1.

Second, a special convention is needed to draw and read a graph like Figure 3.5 at those values of the variable which actually did occur or to which a nonzero probability is assigned, since at each such value the graph necessarily makes an abrupt vertical jump of an amount equal to the individual probability or frequency of the value in question. Thus the cumulative frequency of all values up to and including 1.00999 · · · is .30, no matter how many 9's we write down; but as soon as we reach 1.01 itself, the cumulative frequency jumps to .50. For this reason a heavy dot is used in Figure 3.5 to indicate which of the two horizontal lines should be read at each point of this sort.

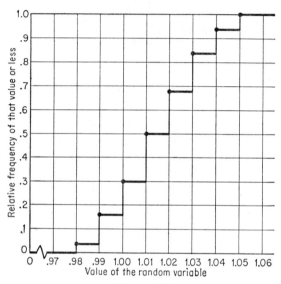

Figure 3.5

Finally, observe that a graph showing the frequency of all values *less than* a given value would look exactly like Figure 3.5 except that the heavy dot would be on the lower of the two lines at each jump rather than on the higher of the two lines. The frequency of all values *less than* an impossible value like 1.003 is exactly the same as the frequency of all values *equal to or less than* such a value; but whereas the frequency of all values *less than* 1.01 is .30, the frequency of 1.01 *or less* is .50, the difference being the frequency of this value itself.

3.5 Notation

Finally, let us introduce some shorthand notation which will be very convenient in writing about probabilities and random variables. Any *probability* will be denoted by a capital P followed by parentheses showing the *event* whose probability is in question. Thus P(red) will denote the probability that a ball is red, P(defective) will denote the probability that a manufactured part is defective, and so forth.

A *random variable* will be denoted by a letter with a "tilde" above it; thus we may use $\tilde{z}$ to denote the random variable "tomorrow's demand" or $\tilde{r}$ to denote the random variable "number of defectives in the next lot received." We have already seen in Section 3.1 that any value of a random variable is an event, and therefore we may write

$P(\tilde{z} = 4)$ or $P(4)$: the probability that the random variable $\tilde{z}$ has the value 4.

The symbol $<$ means "less than," $>$ means "greater than," $\leq$ means "less than or equal to," and $\geq$ means "greater than or equal to."

$P(\tilde{z} < 4)$: the probability that the random variable $\tilde{z}$ has a value less than 4.

The following relations between the tails of a distribution will give an example of the use of this notation.

$$P(\tilde{z} \leq 4) = 1 - P(\tilde{z} > 4).$$
$$P(\tilde{z} < 4) = 1 - P(\tilde{z} \geq 4).$$
$$P(\tilde{z} < 4) + P(\tilde{z} = 4) + P(\tilde{z} > 4) = 1.$$

In many cases we shall need a symbol which denotes *any* value of a random variable, and for this purpose we shall use the same letter we use to denote the random variable itself but without the tilde. Thus the horizontal axis of a cumulative probability distribution may be labeled z while the vertical axis is labeled $P(\tilde{z} < z)$. We can write

$$P(\tilde{z} \leq z) = 1 - P(\tilde{z} > z)$$

because this relation between the tails of the distribution holds for *any* specified value z and not just for the value 4 used in our previous illustration.

When the probability distribution of a random variable is represented by a histogram, the heights of the bars represent probability *per unit width*, and to denote this quantity we shall use the symbol P' (P prime):

$P'(z)$: probability per unit width (height of the histogram) *at the point z* on the horizontal axis.

For any *possible* value z of the random variable $\tilde{z}$,

$$P(z) = P'(z) \times \text{(width of bar corresponding to the value } z\text{)}.$$

For impossible values this equation is of course meaningless.

PROBLEMS

1. The number of units sold by the XYZ Company on 20 successive days was 4, 3, 1, 3, 2, 0, 4, 5, 3, 1, 2, 3, 6, 2, 4, 5, 3, 1, 4, and 3 units.

a. Make a (relative) frequency distribution of this data in the form of a table, a graph like Figure 3.2, and a histogram.

b. Make a table showing both the left-tail and the right-tail cumulative frequencies of the data, defining the left tail as "specified value or less" and the right tail as "specified value or more."

c. Make a graph like Figure 3.5 of the left-tail cumulative frequencies, defining the left tail as in part *b* of this question.

2. An automobile dealer sold 21 cars on Monday, 9 on Tuesday, 13 on Wednesday, 7 on Thursday, and 9 on Friday.

a. Graph the cumulative daily sales as they occurred chronologically.

b. Graph the left-tail cumulative distribution of the same data considered as a frequency distribution, defining the tail as in Problem 1*b*.

3. A company which has been basing its production scheduling on demand forecasts made by the sales department decides to investigate the accuracy of these forecasts. The record for the past 10 months turns out as follows:

Forecast demand	Actual demand	Discrepancy
22	23	+1
20	18	−2
17	19	etc.
20	15	
19	19	
19	22	
23	28	
25	21	
23	18	
20	19	

Graph the frequency distribution and left-tail cumulative distribution (defined as in Problem 1*b*) of the *discrepancies* between actual demand and forecast demand. In so doing define the discrepancy as *actual minus forecast*, and *do not neglect or reverse the algebraic signs*.

4. Figure 3.6 is a histogram showing the number of cars sold daily by an automobile salesman.

a. What fraction of the time did he sell between 7 and 9 (inclusive) cars?

b. What fraction of the time did he sell more than 9 cars?

c. What fraction of the time did he sell more than 2 cars?

5. Figure 3.7 is a cumulative frequency distribution of per cents defective in samples of 100 drawn from lots of a product manufactured on an automatic screw machine.

a. What fraction of samples was 5 per cent or less defective?

b. What fraction was more than 12 per cent defective?

c. What fraction was 7 per cent defective?

d. What fraction had per cents defective between 3.5 and 10.8 per cent inclusive?

6. Figure 3.8 is a frequency distribution of daily sales volume for a certain product.

a. On what fraction of all days were sales below 15 units?

b. On what fraction of days were sales between 15 and 24 units inclusive?

c. On what fraction of days were sales at least as high as 20 units?

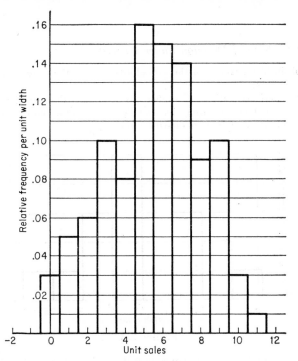

Figure 3.6

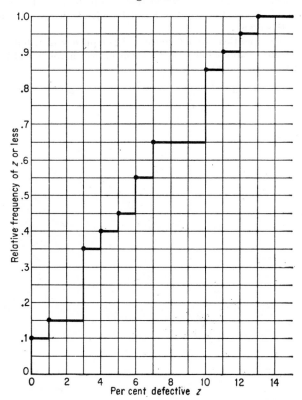

Figure 3.7

7. Graph in histogram form the probability distributions corresponding to the following statements.

a. "Our experience with this supplier has been such that I believe that only a quarter of the relays we buy from him next year will contain no defective contacts, half will contain one, and another quarter will contain two."

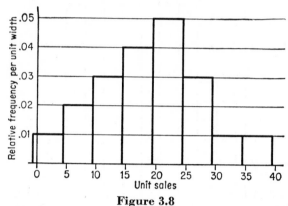

Figure 3.8

b. "I believe that there is 1 chance in 5 that sales next month will be between 0 and 3 units inclusive, 2 chances in 5 that they will be between 4 and 7 units, and 2 chances in 5 that they will be between 8 and 11 units." (Be careful in labeling the vertical scale of this graph.)

8. Under what conditions would you use the frequency distributions given in Problems 1 through 6 as probability distributions on which you would be willing to base a decision?

PART ONE

The Use of Probabilities
Based Directly on Experience

CHAPTER 4

The Simplest Problems of Inventory Control; Incremental Analysis

4.1 Construction of Payoff Tables

In Chapter 1 we defined a payoff table as a table showing the consequence of every possible *act* given every possible *event*. The fact that the decision is being made under uncertainty has no bearing whatever on the *construction* of the payoff table, since *the entries in the row describing any particular event are exactly the same as they would be if that event were certain to occur,* and consequently we shall pause only briefly to remind the student of the basic principle which must be observed in making *any* economic comparison of two or more possible acts.

This basic principle states simply that before choosing among two or more acts we must take into account *all present and future flows of cash which are affected by the decision* and that these cash flows are the *only* elements of profit or cost which we should take into account. If a certain act involves the consumption of materials already in inventory, then according to circumstances these materials should be considered as the *equivalent* either of the cash for which they could otherwise have been sold or of the cash which will ultimately be spent in order to replace them, but their value as thus determined should not be inflated by allocations of fixed costs or expenses whose total amount will actually remain the same whether these materials are used or not.

The one rule to follow in drawing up a payoff table is therefore the following:

For each act-event combination, list every item of cash or the equivalent which will flow out of the business and every item of cash or the equivalent which will flow into the business; the net of all these amounts is the amount to enter in the table.

If the payoff table is being drawn up in terms of *profit*, the outflows are subtracted from the inflows; if the table is being drawn up to show *costs*, the reverse procedure is followed. In either case, some of the entries in the table may be negative; and if they are, *the minus signs must not be neglected:* they must be entered in the table and observed in all subsequent computations.

An Example. As an example, let us take a slightly more complex version of the kind of inventory problem which we discussed in Chapter 1. Once a week a retailer stocks a perishable commodity which deteriorates on the shelf so that stock which remains unsold at the end of the week must be salvaged at a fraction of its full value. The commodity is bought by the retailer for $2.50 per unit and is offered for sale at a price of $3.70 per unit during the week in which it is stocked; leftover stock has a salvage value of $.50 per unit. The retailer's rent, insurance, etc., average $.12 per dollar of total sales of all commodities; clerks' wages, delivery expenses, etc., average $.41 per dollar of total sales. The retailer assigns the probability distribution shown in Table 4.1 to the basic random variable "next week's demand" and consults us to determine how many units he should stock.

Table 4.1

Demand z	Probability $P(z)$
0	.05
1	.10
2	.25
3	.30
4	.20
5	.10
6+	0
	1.00

Our first step in analyzing this problem is to draw up the payoff table, and in so doing we should recognize immediately that the fact that overhead and selling expense have *averaged* $.12 + $.41 = $.53 per dollar of sales in no way implies that these expenses are *variable* with sales. On the other hand we *do* have to inquire whether there are any costs or expenses which are directly attributable to sales of this commodity, and we shall suppose that our inquiries lead to the information that special materials costing $.20 are used to package each unit sold at full price.

We are now ready to construct the payoff table. If Q is the number stocked and z is the number of fresh units demanded, the *net* cash *inflow* or "gross profit" will be:

For $z \leq Q$ (demand no greater than stock on hand)

Sale of fresh units:	$+ \$3.70\, z$
Wrapping fresh units:	$- \quad .20\, z$
Salvage of leftovers:	$+ \quad .50\, (Q - z)$
Purchase cost of stock:	$- \quad 2.50\, Q$
Net inflow:	$\$3.00\, z - \$2.00\, Q$

For z > Q (demand exceeds stock)

Sale of fresh units:	+$3.70 Q
Wrapping fresh units:	− .20 Q
Salvage of leftovers:	0
Purchase cost of stock:	−$2.50 Q
Net inflow:	+$1.00 Q

The entries in Table 4.2 are obtained by applying the appropriate one oi these two formulas to every Q, z combination in the table.   For example:

$$Q = 4, z = 2: (\$3 \times 2) - (\$2 \times 4) = -\$2,$$
$$Q = 2, z = 4: \$1 \times 2 = +\$2.$$

Values of Q above 5 are excluded from the table because by Table 4.1 the retailer is certain that no more than 5 units can be sold fresh and ne loses $2.50 − $.50 = $2.00 on every unit salvaged.

Table 4.2
Payoff Table

Demand z	Stock Q					
	0	1	2	3	4	5
0	$0	−$2	−$4	−$6	−$8	−$10
1	0	+ 1	− 1	− 3	− 5	− 7
2	0	+ 1	+ 2	0	− 2	− 4
3	0	+ 1	+ 2	+ 3	+ 1	− 1
4	0	+ 1	+ 2	+ 3	+ 4	+ 2
5	0	+ 1	+ 2	+ 3	+ 4	+ 5
6+	0	+ 1	+ 2	+ 3	+ 4	+ 5

The *expected* profit of any act (any value of Q) can now be computed by taking a weighted average of the corresponding column in Table 4.2,

Table 4.3
Expected Profit with Stock of 3

Demand z	P(z)	Conditional profit	Expected value
0	.05	−$6	−$ .30
1	.10	− 3	− .30
2	.25	0	+ 0
3	.30	+ 3	+ .90
4	.20	+ 3	+ .60
5	.10	+ 3	+ .30
6+	0	+ 3	0
	1.00		+$1.20

the probabilities of Table 4.1 being used as the weights.   The expected profit for a stock of 3 is computed in Table 4.3 by way of review; it is left to the student to verify the expected profits for the other stocks shown in Table 4.4.

Table 4.4
Expected Profits of All Acts

Act Q	Expected profit
0	$0
1	+ .85
2	+ 1.40
3	+ 1.20
4	+ .10
5	− 1.60

4.2   Incremental Analysis

Provided that expected monetary value is a valid guide to action in a given decision problem, the best act can always be found by the method used just above, i.e. by computing and comparing the expected profits or costs of all possible acts, but when the number of possible acts is large this method becomes extremely tedious.   In many practical inventory problems the random variable "demand" will have hundreds or even thousands of possible values and consequently it will be necessary to choose among hundreds or thousands of acts (stock levels) none of which is *obviously* unreasonable.   We would therefore like very much to find some way of selecting the best act without having to compute the expected profit of *every* act, and in some kinds of problems this can be done very easily by the use of *incremental analysis*.

A decision on a stock level in an inventory problem of the kind we have been discussing can be analyzed incrementally by thinking of the decision as being the result, not of a direct choice among the acts $Q = 0$, 1, 2, and so forth, but as the result of *a whole sequence of decisions* each of which *increases* the stock level *by one unit*.   In principle, we first decide whether a *first* unit should be stocked; if the answer is yes, we then decide whether a *second* unit should be stocked; and we continue in this way until we come to a point where we decide to increase the stock no further. In general, any decision which consists of selecting a *quantity* can be analyzed in this way, whether the quantity is a number stocked, a scrap allowance, or anything else:

Instead of looking at the problem as one of making a *single* decision on a particular *number* of units, we can look at it as one of making a whole *sequence* of decisions, each one involving *one more* unit.

The great advantage of the incremental method over the "direct" method which we have used previously lies in the fact that we can usually identify the *last* unit which should be added without actually making any computations whatever concerning the earlier units in the sequence, but before showing how this can be done we shall explain the basic logic of the incremental method by analyzing a complete sequence of incremental decisions. We take the inventory problem discussed in the previous section of this chapter as an example, and we start with the question whether or not to stock a *first* unit.

The First Unit. For this restricted problem of the first unit, there are just two possible *acts:* "stock" and "do not stock"; and there are just two *events* of interest: "no demand for a first unit" and "demand for a first unit." If the first unit is *not* stocked, the retailer's profit will obviously be 0 regardless of the event. If the first unit *is* stocked, the profit depends on the event: if the unit is demanded, the retailer's profit will be $3.70 − $.20 − $2.50 = $1.00; if it is not demanded, he will have a negative profit of −$2.50 + $.50 = −$2.00. The payoff table for the decision concerning the first unit is shown as Table 4.5.

Table 4.5
Payoff Table for the First Unit

Event	Act	
	Do not stock	Stock
No demand for a first unit	$0	−$2
Demand for a first unit	0	+ 1

By merely looking at Table 4.5 we see that the *expected* profit of *not* stocking a first unit is 0; but to find the expected profit of stocking, probabilities must be assigned to the events "no demand for a first unit" and "demand for a first unit." Now there will be *no* demand for a first unit if and only if the *total* quantity demanded is *less than one* unit, i.e. if $\tilde{z} = 0$, and the probability which the retailer has assigned to this event is .05 by Table 4.1. Similarly the probability that there *will* be a demand for a *first* unit is the same thing as the probability that the *total* quantity demanded will be *one or more* units, and

$$P(\tilde{z} \geq 1) = 1 - P(\tilde{z} < 1) = 1 - .05 = .95.$$

Given these two probabilities, the expected profit of stocking the first unit is +$.85, as shown in Table 4.6; and since this is greater than the 0 profit of not stocking, we conclude that the first unit should be stocked.

The Second Unit. We now proceed to consider stocking a *second* unit. The possible acts are again "stock" and "do not stock"; the relevant events are "no demand for a *second* unit" and "demand for a

Table 4.6
Expected Profit of Stocking First Unit

Event	Probability	Conditional profit	Expected value
$z < 1$; no demand for a first unit	.05	−$2	−$.10
$z \geq 1$; demand for a first unit	.95	+ 1	+ .95
	1.00		+$.85

second unit." In making the entries in the payoff table we must remember that *a final decision has already been made concerning the first unit*, so that we are interested only in the consequences of a decision to stock or not to stock a *second* unit and not in the consequences of a decision to stock *two* units. If the retailer chooses not to stock the second unit, the *incremental* profit of *this* decision will be 0 regardless of the event, i.e. whether or not there is a demand for a second unit; *all the cash flows which occur will be due to the previous decision to stock the first unit.* If the retailer does decide to stock the second unit, his profit will be *increased* by $3.70 − $.20 − $2.50 = $1.00 if the second unit is demanded and can be sold at full price; it will be *decreased* by $2.50 − $.50 = $2.00 if the second unit is not demanded and has to be salvaged. Accordingly the payoff table for the second unit has the entries shown in Table 4.7.

Table 4.7
Payoff Table for the Second Unit

Event	Act	
	Do not stock	Stock
No demand for second unit	0	−$2
Demand for second unit	0	+ 1

As in the case of the first unit, the *expected* profit of *not* stocking is obviously 0 but probabilities must be assigned to the events of Table 4.7 before we can compute the expected profit of stocking. These probabilities can again be obtained from Table 4.1 by a very simple argument. If the *total* quantity demanded is *less than two* units, there will be *no* demand for a *second* unit; if the total quantity demanded is *two or more* units, there *will* be a demand for a *second* unit. From Table 4.1 we can compute

$$P(z < 2) = P(z = 0) + P(z = 1) = .05 + .10 = .15,$$
$$P(z \geq 2) = 1 - P(z < 2) = 1 - .15 = .85,$$

and we can then find that the expected profit of stocking the second item

Table 4.8

Expected Profit of Stocking Second Unit

Event	Probability	Conditional profit	Expected value
$\tilde{z} < 2$; no demand for a second unit	.15	$-\$2$	$-\$.30$
$\tilde{z} \geq 2$; demand for a second unit	.85	$+\$1$	$+\$.85$
	1.00		$+\$.55$

is $+\$.55$ as shown in Table 4.8.   Since this is greater than the 0 profit of not stocking, we conclude that the second unit should be stocked; the *total* stock should be *at least* 2 units.

The jth Unit.   The general pattern of the analysis should now be clear.   Every successive incremental decision has *exactly the same payoff table* with 0's in the column describing the act "do not stock" and with a $-\$2$ and a $+\$1$ in the column describing the act "stock."   The only difference from one of these decisions to the next is in the probabilities assigned to the events "demand for a jth unit" and "no demand for a jth unit," where j is the "serial number" of the unit in question.   The argument by which we obtain these probabilities from the distribution of the basic random variable is always the same, however:

If the *total* quantity demanded is *less than j*, there is *no demand* for the jth unit; if the total quantity demanded is *j or more*, there *is* a demand for the jth unit.

Consequently the *expected* incremental profit of not stocking the jth unit is always 0, while the expected profit of stocking the jth unit is always

$$\$1\ P(\tilde{z} \geq j) - \$2\ P(\tilde{z} < j).$$

In Table 4.9 this formula is used to compute the expected incremental profit of stocking every successive unit from the first through the fifth; the student will recall that the retailer is sure that no more than 5 units can possibly be sold at full price.   The "serial number" of each successive

Table 4.9

Complete Incremental Analysis

Serial j	$P(\tilde{z} < j)$	$P(\tilde{z} \geq j)$	Incremental profit	Cumulated profit
1	.05	.95	$-\$ .10 + \$.95 = +\$ .85$	$+\$ .85$
2	.15	.85	$- .30 + .85 = + .55$	$+ 1.40$
3	.40	.60	$- .80 + .60 = - .20$	$+ 1.20$
4	.70	.30	$- 1.40 + .30 = - 1.10$	$+ .10$
5	.90	.10	$- 1.80 + .10 = - 1.70$	$- 1.60$

item stocked is shown in the first column; the cumulative probabilities in the second and third columns are computed from Table 4.1. The incremental profits due to each successive decision to stock *one more* unit are computed in the next to the last column; the first two of these entries have already been discussed in detail. Notice that the incremental profit of the third and all following units is *negative*—the better act is *not* to stock any of these units.

In the last column of Table 4.9 the incremental profits are cumulated to give the *total* expected profit which results from a decision to stock *j units*. If a single unit is stocked, the retailer's total expected profit is simply the profit due to the first unit. If 2 units are stocked, his total expected profit is the sum of the expected profit from the first unit and the expected profit from the second unit or \$.85 + \$.55 = \$1.40. Since the incremental expected profit which results from stocking a third unit is a *negative* \$.20, the total expected profit with a stock of 3 is \$.20 *less* than with a stock of 2 or \$1.40 − \$.20 = \$1.20. Each subsequent addition to the stock reduces the total expected profit by still more until with a stock of 5 the total expected profit itself becomes negative. *Notice that the total profits as calculated by the incremental method in Table 4.9 agree exactly with the results obtained by the direct method as shown in Table 4.4.*

4.2.1 *Practical Selection of the Best Decision*

Behavior of Incremental Profit with Increasing j. If we look at the incremental profits in the next to the last column of Table 4.9, we see that each successive entry is less favorable than the one before it; and this suggests that if all we were looking for had been the best number to stock, we could have stopped computing and settled on a stock of 2 as soon as we found that the incremental profit of a third unit was negative. It is easy to prove that this guess is correct. As we already know, the incremental profit of stocking the *j*th item is

$$\$1 \; P(\tilde{z} \geq j) - \$2 \; P(\tilde{z} < j).$$

Since $P(\tilde{z} \geq j)$ is the right tail of the distribution of $\tilde{z}$, the first term in this expression must either remain the same or become smaller as j increases, i.e. as we move farther out into the tail. On the other hand $P(\tilde{z} < j)$ is the left tail of the distribution, and therefore the second or negative term in the expression for expected profit must either remain the same or become larger as j increases. The whole expression therefore either remains the same or decreases with each increase in j, and therefore we can be sure that:

1. If the incremental profit is *positive* for any particular value of j, it is positive for all *lower* values.
2. If the incremental profit is *negative* for any particular value of j it is negative for all *higher* values.

Since these conclusions do not depend in any way on the particular costs or the particular probability distribution used in our example, we may conclude that:

All that we need to do to find the best stock level in any problem of this sort is to find the highest value of j for which the incremental expected profit of stocking is positive.

Location of the Last Profitable Unit.   Let us now see how we can find the highest value of j which gives a positive incremental profit without actually computing *any* expected profits.   In order to express our results in a way which will be useful in *any* problem of the present type we define two new symbols:

k_p: the *positive* incremental profit which results from stocking the jth unit if it is *sold.*

k_n: the *negative* incremental profit which results from stocking the jth unit if it is *not* sold.

In our example, $k_p = \$1$ and $k_n = \$2$.   The incremental *expected* profit of stocking the jth item in any problem of this sort can then be written

$$k_p\, P(\tilde{z} \geq j) - k_n\, P(\tilde{z} < j)$$

and it will pay to stock the jth item if this quantity is *positive*, i.e. if

$$k_n\, P(\tilde{z} < j) < k_p\, P(\tilde{z} \geq j).$$

We wish to find the *highest* value of j for which this condition is met, and it will be easier to do this if we have only one cumulative probability to deal with instead of two.   Therefore we replace $P(\tilde{z} \geq j)$ by $1 - P(\tilde{z} < j)$ and write the condition in the form

$$k_n\, P(\tilde{z} < j) < k_p[1 - P(\tilde{z} < j)].$$

By the use of a little elementary algebra this can be rewritten as

$$P(\tilde{z} < j) < \frac{k_p}{k_p + k_n} \qquad \textit{Condition for stocking the jth unit}$$

The best act in any problem of this sort can now be found by the following steps:

1. Determine the values of k_p and k_n by analyzing the *incremental* cash flows which result from stocking and either selling or failing to sell *one more* unit.

2. Compute the "*critical ratio*" $k_p/(k_p + k_n)$.

3. From the values already assigned to $P(z)$, compute $P(\tilde{z} < j)$ for $j = 1, 2, 3$, etc., until the last value of j has been found for which $P(\tilde{z} < j)$ is less than the critical ratio.

In our example, the critical ratio is

$$\frac{k_p}{k_p + k_n} = \frac{\$1}{\$1 + \$2} = .33.$$

Looking at the list of values of $P(\tilde{z} < j)$ in Table 4.9 we see at once that 2 is the highest value of j for which this probability is less than .33; the best stock level is therefore $Q = 2$.

4.2.2   Applicability of the Short-cut Incremental Method

Although incremental analysis can be used to compute the total expected profit of any act which consists in the choice of a quantity (e.g., to stock or to allow for scrap), the short-cut method which we have just applied to find the last unit which it is profitable to include in this quantity can be used only in special circumstances. In *any* situation it is true *by definition* that total profit with a stock of 3 units is the sum of the incremental profits due to the first, second, and third units, but this fact alone does not ensure the validity of the short-cut method. *The validity of the short-cut method depends on the assumption that if the incremental profit of any given unit in the sequence is positive, the incremental profits of all earlier units are also positive.* It is this assumption which is true only under special circumstances, and in problems where the assumption is false it may well be that it will pay to stock 4 units even though the incremental profit of the third unit is negative.

As an example of a type of problem in which this can happen, suppose that the retailer of our example is offered a quantity discount on the units he purchases: if he buys 3 units or less, he pays $2.50 per unit as we assumed originally, but if he buys 4 units or more he pays only $2.10 per unit. To find the incremental expected profit of stocking the fourth unit we must now reason as follows. Because buying a fourth unit reduces the price the retailer pays for the first three units, stocking the fourth unit does not actually cost the retailer $2.10; it costs $(4 \times \$2.10) - (3 \times \$2.50) = \$.90$. Therefore if the fourth unit is sold, the incremental profit will be $\$3.70 - \$.20 - \$.90 = \$2.60$; if it is not sold the profit will be $\$.50 - \$.90 = -\$.40$. The *expected* incremental profit of stocking a fourth unit is therefore

$$\$2.60\, P(\tilde{z} \geq 4) - \$.40\, P(\tilde{z} < 4) = (\$2.60 \times .30) - (\$.40 \times .70)$$
$$= +\$.50$$

and is thus *greater* than the expected incremental profit of the third unit, which is still $-\$.20$ as before. The really important point to notice is the following: the total incremental profit of the *fourth and third units together* is now $\$.50 - \$.20 = +\$.30$, and therefore *stocking 4 units is $.30 better than stocking 2 even though stocking 3 units is $.20 worse than stocking 2.* In general,

The short-cut incremental method for locating the last unit to add to the decision quantity is applicable only when the conditional profits k_p and k_n are the same for every unit which might be added.

PROBLEMS

1. A manufacturer must decide whether to manufacture and market a new seasonal novelty which has just been developed to sell at $1.50 per unit. If he decides to manufacture it, he will have to purchase special machinery which will be scrapped after the season is over. If a machine costing $1000 is bought, the variable cost of manufacturing will be $1 per unit; if a machine costing $5000 is bought, the variable manufacturing cost will be $.50 per unit. In either case it will be possible to manufacture in small batches as sales actually occur and there will be no danger of having unsold merchandise left over at the end of the season. The manufacturer's probability distribution for sales volume is shown in the table below.

Sales volume	Probability
1,000	½
5,000	¼
10,000	¼
	1

a. Draw up a payoff table, remembering that there are *three* possible acts.
b. Compute the expected profits of the three possible acts.
2. Draw up a complete payoff table for the modified example discussed in Section 4.2.2, where stock costs the retailer $2.50 per unit in quantities of 3 or less but costs only $2.10 per unit in quantities of 4 or more. Use the direct method of Table 4.3 to compute total expected profit with stocks of 2, 3, and 4 units and thus verify that total profit is $.20 less with a stock of 3 than with a stock of 2 but is $.30 greater with a stock of 4 than with a stock of 2.
3. A newsstand operator buys the *Daily Racing Form* for 30 cents per copy and sells it for 50 cents. Any copies remaining unsold after the races are valueless. The operator believes that it is very important to avoid running short, since he is afraid that he will lose customers permanently if they find him an unreliable source of supply, and in order to minimize this risk he has adopted the policy of ordering 30 copies a day. The distribution of daily requests for the journal over the last 100 days has been as follows:

Number requested	Relative frequency	Number requested	Relative frequency
Less than 20	0	27	.12
20	.01	28	.10
21	.04	29	.08
22	.07	30	.05
23	.10	31	02
24	.12	32	.01
25	.14	Over 32	0
26	.14		

   a. By the use of incremental analysis compute the expected profit of every stock level from 20 to 32 inclusive.

   b. Check your work in part *a* by using the direct method of analysis to compute expected profit with a stock of 30 copies.

   c. If running short would actually have no effect on any customer's tendency to return, how much is the operator losing by his decision to stock 30 copies?

   d. If the cost of the journal to the operator were reduced from 30 to 25 cents, by how much could he increase his expected profit over the best he can do with a 30-cent cost?

   4. The Beacon Catering Corporation operated a cafeteria in a medium-sized industrial firm, serving about 50 of the firm's employees at lunchtime. The ordinary check amounted to about 50 cents, and the gross margin was about 40 per cent. After several years' operation, the management decided to offer its customers a special $1 hot lunch. Gross margin on this item would also be about 40 per cent.

   A question arose as to how much food to prepare for the special $1 lunch. Any remaining at the end of the day would have to be thrown out; if the cafeteria ran short, on the other hand, the extra gross margin would be lost. Any food remaining at the end of the day from the other items on the menu could be saved until the next day. The manager decided to experiment by preparing enough special lunches on each of the first 20 days to run a negligible risk of running short on any day. Sales of the special lunch on these 20 days were as follows:

Day	Unit sales = demand	Day	Unit sales = demand
1	20	11	20
2	19	12	17
3	20	13	20
4	16	14	17
5	24	15	17
6	21	16	23
7	20	17	18
8	22	18	15
9	19	19	21
10	22	20	19

   Assuming that all buyers of hot lunches would buy a cold lunch if the hot lunches were not available, how many hot lunches should be prepared in the future and what is the expected profit of this decision?

   5. A wholesaler has a fleet of 10 trucks with which he makes deliveries from two warehouses. Trucks are dispatched at 10 A.M., a trip takes an entire day, and the truck returns to the warehouse about 5 P.M. If the orders on hand at either warehouse at 10 A.M. are too many to be handled by the trucks available at the warehouse, extra trucks are hired for the day; the *excess cost* amounts to about $50 more than the out-of-pocket cost of operating one of the wholesaler's own trucks for a day. The table on page 78 shows the total number of trucks *required* at each warehouse on each of the past 300 days.

   a. If 3 of the 10 trucks are assigned to Warehouse A and 7 to B, what is the expected *excess cost* at each warehouse?

   b. What is the probability that a 4th truck will be required at A? That the 7th truck will be required at B?

Number of trucks	Number of days	
	Warehouse A	Warehouse B
0	15	0
1	45	3
2	66	12
3	69	27
4	51	39
5	30	48
6	15	48
7	6	42
8	3	30
9	0	24
10	0	15
11	0	9
12	0	3
13+	0	0
	300	300

c. What is the *net* effect on total excess cost if the wholesaler assigns 4 trucks to A and 6 to B instead of 3 to A and 7 to B?

d. What is the optimum assignment for this problem?

e. Derive a general rule for optimum assignment in problems of this sort by first considering what the wholesaler should do if he owns only one truck, then what he should do if he acquires a second truck, and so forth.

f. Generalize your rule to situations where there are more than 2 warehouses.

CHAPTER 5

Measures of Location:
Fractiles and Expectations;
Linear Profits and Costs

In many situations we do not really need all the detailed information contained in a probability distribution or frequency distribution. In order to compute the total number of defectives in 100 lots of parts, we do not need to know the frequency with which each possible number of defectives occurred. All we need to know is a single number: the average or mean number of defectives per lot. Similarly we have seen in the previous chapter that in one kind of inventory problem we do not need the entire probability distribution for tomorrow's demand in order to decide on the best number of units to stock. All we need to know is a single number: the greatest number Q for which $P(\tilde{z} < Q)$ is less than a certain "critical ratio."

Numbers such as these are known as *measures of location* of a frequency or probability distribution. If we think of the distribution as represented by a histogram, we can think of such a number as specifying the *location* of the histogram on the horizontal axis without specifying anything about the *shape* of the histogram. We shall study two quite different kinds of measures of location in this chapter. The first kind consists of *fractiles*, of which the median is the best known example; the second consists of *expectations*, of which the ordinary arithmetic mean is the best-known example.

Our interest in measures of location is due only in small part to the fact that the amount of arithmetic required to solve a problem is often reduced by their use. Their real importance lies in the fact that when correctly used a measure of location *focuses our attention on the particular aspect of the probability distribution which is really critical for the problem at hand* and keeps us from being distracted by those aspects of the distribution which are irrelevant for that particular problem. On the other hand, the use of measures of location is attended by considerable danger. To cite a single example, one of the most common errors made by both students and businessmen is to assume that the best quantity to stock can be determined by looking only at average demand in situations where in fact the best decision *cannot* be found in this way. *In studying this chapter the student must therefore pay as close attention to what* cannot *be done with a given measure of location as he pays to what* can *be done with it.*

5.1   Fractiles

5.1.1   The Median

Before defining fractiles in general, let us consider the best known of the fractiles, the median.   Given a set of values (which may or may not be values of a random variable)

Any value which is *both* (a) equal to or greater than half the values in the set *and* (b) equal to or less than half the values in the set is a *median* of the set.

In order to apply this definition to a given set of values we must:
1. List the values *in order of increasing size;*
2. Split the arrayed set in half.

To find the median of the values 5, 3, 2, 4, we first array them in the order 2, 3, 4, 5.   We then observe that since there are four values in the whole set, there must be two in each half.   The largest value in the lower half is therefore 3, the smallest value in the upper half is 4, and any value from 3 to 4 inclusive is a median of the set.   Notice that a value such as 3.2 is a median of this set even though the value 3.2 is not itself a *member* of the set.

Table 5.1

Serial number of lot	Number of defectives
1	2
2	4
3	0
4	2
5	4
6	3
7	3
8	1
9	3
10	5
	27

In many cases a set can be divided in half only by assigning some of the members with a certain value to the lower half and other members with this same value to the upper half.   Thus in order to divide the set 2, 3, 3, 4 in half, we must assign one of the 3's to the lower half and one to the upper half.   The only median of this set is 3.   In other cases— whenever the number of members in the set is odd—one of the individual members must be "split" in order to divide the set into halves.   The only median of the values 2, 3, 4 is 3: we may think of the member with value 3 as going half in the lower half of the set, half in the upper half.

Suppose now that 10 successive lots of purchased parts have been 100 per cent inspected, that the number of defectives found in each lot is as shown in Table 5.1, and that we wish to find the median or medians of these 10 values of the random variable "number of defectives." We first array the values in order of size: 0, 1, 2, 2, 3, 3, 3, 4, 4, 5. Since there are 10 values in the set, 5 must go in the lower half and 5 in the upper. The fifth value from the bottom is 3 and so is the sixth, so that the median is 3.

5.1.2 Fractiles in General

As we have said, the median is simply a special case of a *fractile*. The median of a set of values is known as the .5 fractile (read: point 5 fractile) and will be denoted by $F_{.5}$ because it is equal to or greater than *half* the values in the set. We now generalize this idea to define the "point f" fractile, where $.f$ is *any* fraction between 0 and 1. Given any set of values,

Any value which is *both* (a) equal to or greater than a fraction $.f$ of the values in the set *and* (b) equal to or less than a fraction $(1 - .f)$ of the values in the set is a $.f$ *fractile* of the set.

To find the .25 fractile or $F_{.25}$ of the values 5, 3, 2, 4, we first array them in the order 2, 3, 4, 5 and then split this set of four values into two parts, a lower part containing $.25 \times 4 = 1$ value and an upper part containing the remaining three values. The largest value in the lower part of the set is 2, the smallest value in the upper part is 3, and therefore any value from 2 to 3 inclusive is a .25 fractile of this set. Similarly any value from 4 to 5 inclusive is a .75 fractile of the set.

In many cases a set can be divided into a lower part containing $.f$ of the members and an upper part containing the remainder only by assigning some of the members with a certain value to the lower part and other members with this same value to the upper part. The only .2 fractile of the values 2, 2, 3, 4, 5 is 2: one of the 2's in the set is assigned to the lower .2 of the set and the other to the upper .8. In other cases one of the individual members must be "split" in order to divide the set in the specified manner. The only .3 fractile of the values 1, 2, 3, 4 is 2: we need 1.2 members to make up the lower .3 of this set of four values, and we may think of the value 2 as going partly in this lower .3 of the set and partly in the upper .7.

5.1.3 Computation of Fractiles from Relative Frequencies or Probabilities

Now that we have seen how to compute fractiles from a *complete list* of the values taken on by a random variable we are ready to learn how to compute them when the values taken on by the variable have been put into the form of a frequency distribution. As an example we show in Table 5.2 a frequency distribution of the values of the random variable "number of defectives" which are listed in Table 5.1 in their historical order, and in Figure 5.1 we show a graph of the cumulative frequencies of Table 5.2.

Table 5.2

Value z of the random variable	Relative frequency of z	Cumulative frequency of z or less
0	.1	.1
1	.1	.2
2	.2	.4
3	.3	.7
4	.2	.9
5	.1	1.0
	1.0	

Suppose now that we wish to find the .5 fractile of the distribution of Table 5.2.   Recalling the rules for reading graphs of cumulative distributions as given in Section 3.4.2, we can see from Figure 5.1 that .4 of the frequency belongs to values of the variable *less than* 3 while .7 of the frequency belongs to values of 3 *or less*.   In order to divide the whole set of values into a lower .5 and an upper .5, we must split the 3's and assign some of them to the lower group and some to the upper.   Accordingly the .5 fractile or median of this distribution is 3.

The horizontal dotted line in Figure 5.1 shows how any fractile can be located immediately by use of a graph of a cumulative distribution.   If we are looking for the .5 fractile, the line is drawn at height .5 on the *vertical* axis; the .5 fractile is then the value on the *horizontal* axis directly below the point where the dashed line cuts the graph of the distribution.   In general,

To find the $.f$ fractile of any frequency distribution, plot the cumulative distribution, read across from the value $.f$ on the vertical axis to the curve, and read down from this point on the curve to the horizontal axis.

Thus we can immediately read from Figure 5.1 that $F_{.3} = 2$, that $F_{.8} = 4$, and so forth.

We have already seen that in some cases a fractile has a range of values rather a single, unique value.   In terms of a graph of the cumulative distribution, these are the fractiles whose broken lines coincide with a "flat" in the graph rather than cutting a "riser."   If we look for the .4 fractile of the distribution of Figure 5.1, the fact that a line drawn at height .4 would coincide with the top of the jump above the value 2 on the horizontal axis shows that *all* the 2's in the set must go in the lower .4; the fact that the same dashed line would coincide with the bottom of the jump above the value 3 shows that *all* the 3's must go in the upper .6; accordingly any value in the interval 2 to 3 inclusive is a .4 fractile of this distribution.   Similarly any value from 1 to 2 is a .2 fractile, any value from 3 to 4 is a .7 fractile, and so forth.

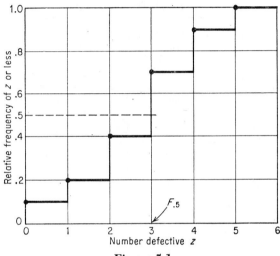

Figure 5.1

No new problems arise when we wish to compute the fractiles of a *probability* distribution:

The fractiles of a probability distribution are computed by using the probabilities in exactly the same way that relative frequencies are used in computing the fractiles of a frequency distribution.

5.1.4 *An Example of the Use of Fractiles*

In Chapter 4 we saw that in a certain class of inventory problems the best stock level was the highest number Q for which

$$P(\tilde{z} < Q) < \frac{k_p}{k_p + k_n},$$

and we discussed in detail an example in which the "critical ratio" $k_p/(k_p + k_n)$ had the value .33.   The probability distribution assigned to "demand" in that example is reproduced in Table 5.3 and the cumulative

Table 5.3

Demand z	Probability $P(z)$	Cumulative $P(\tilde{z} \le z)$
0	.05	.05
1	.10	.15
2	.25	.40
3	.30	.70
4	.20	.90
5	.10	1.00
	1.00	

probabilities are graphed in Figure 5.2. If now we draw in a dashed line

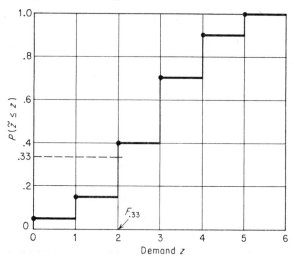

Figure 5.2

to locate the .33 fractile of this distribution, we can make the following observations:

1. $F_{.33} = 2$.
2. $P(\tilde{z} < 2) < .33$ but $P(\tilde{z} < 3) > .33$.

In other words:

> The optimum stock level in problems of this sort is simply the $k_p/(k_p + k_n)$ fractile of the distribution of the random variable "demand."

Henceforth we shall refer to this fractile as the "critical fractile" in problems of this kind.†

† It is left to the student to show that when the critical fractile has a range of values rather than a single value, total expected profit is the same whichever one of

5.2   Expectations

5.2.1   *The Arithmetic Mean*

The arithmetic mean of a set of values is simply their everyday "average," defined as follows:

Arithmetic mean: the sum of a set of values divided by the number of values in the set.

The mean of the values in Table 5.1 is

$$\tfrac{1}{10}(2 + 4 + 0 + 2 + 4 + 3 + 3 + 1 + 3 + 5) = {}^{27}\!/_{10} = 2.7.$$

5.2.2   *Computation of the Arithmetic Mean from Relative Frequencies or Probabilities*

When we computed fractiles from original data, all we did was arrange the individual values in order of size and then count off from the left; when we computed them from relative frequencies, all we did was arrange the values in this same way and then cumulate their relative frequencies. There was no need for arithmetical operations. The mean, on the contrary, rests on an *averaging* operation; and if we replace the original data by a frequency distribution *we must use the frequencies as weights in this averaging.*

Table 5.4

Value of the random variable
0
1
2
2
3
3
3
4
4
5
27

Table 5.5

Value of the random variable	Number of occurrences	Product
0	1	0
1	1	1
2	2	4
3	3	9
4	2	8
5	1	5
	10	27

Let us reexamine the computation of the mean of the distribution of Table 5.1 as we carried it out above. If we rearrange the data in order of increasing value of the variable we have Table 5.4; the mean is still the total divided by the number of items, or ${}^{27}\!/_{10} = 2.7$. Now instead of writing down two identical rows for the value 2, three rows for 3, and two rows for 4, we can get the same total, 27, by writing each value of the

---

these values is selected for the stock level.   If the critical fractile had been .40 instead of .32 in our example, then total expected profit would have been the same with a stock of 3 units as with a stock of 2 units.

variable once and multiplying it by the number of times that the value occurs. This is done in Table 5.5. To get the mean we *divide the sum of the products by the sum of the weights;* this divisor, of course, is simply the total number of occurrences as before.

Again we will get exactly the same result if, instead of adding the products and then dividing their sum by 10, we divide each of the individual products by 10 before adding; and instead of doing that, we can divide each of the numbers of occurrences by 10 before computing the products. The last two columns of Table 5.5 would then be as shown in Table 5.6. *Since the sum of the weights is now* 1, *the mean is simply the total in the last column.*

Table 5.6

Value of the random variable	Number of occurrences divided by 10	Product
0	.1	0
1	.1	.1
2	.2	.4
3	.3	.9
4	.2	.8
5	.1	.5
	1.0	2.7

The weights of this last table are actually relative frequencies, and in general:

The mean of a frequency distribution is a *weighted average* of the values of the variable, each value being weighted by its relative frequency. Since relative frequencies always add to 1, the sum of the weights is 1 and there is no need to divide by it to get the average.

No new problems arise when we wish to compute the mean of a *probability* distribution:

The mean of a probability distribution is computed by using the probabilities in exactly the same way that relative frequencies are used in computing the mean of a frequency distribution.

5.2.3   The Expected Value of a Random Variable

Recall now that to compute the *expected value* of the various profits which might result from a given act, we multiplied each possible profit by the probability that it would be made and added these products. But "*profit*" *in such a computation is just a special case of a random variable, i.e. a variable which has a definite "conditional" value for every possible event;* and when we compute the mean of the probability distribution of *any* random variable we are computing the expected value of that variable. In general, we define for any random variable:

> *Expected value or expectation:* the quantity obtained by multiplying each possible value of a random variable by the probability of that value and adding the products.

We shall uniformly denote the expected value of a random variable by the symbol E (for expectation) followed by the "name" of the variable in parentheses. Thus if the random variable is called $\tilde{z}$, the expected value of $\tilde{z}$ or mean of the distribution of $\tilde{z}$ will be denoted by $E(\tilde{z})$.

5.2.4   Partial Expectations

In many practical decision problems we shall be interested, not in the number which results from multiplying *all* the values of a random variable by their probabilities and adding these products, but in a number which results from multiplying *some* of the values by their probabilities and adding these products. Such a number will be called a *partial* expectation.

As an example of the computation of partial expectations, consider Table 5.7 below, where the first two columns again give the probability distribution of the random variable "demand" for the inventory problem discussed in Chapter 4. The expectation of this variable is computed in the third column of the table in exactly the same way that the mean number defective was computed in Table 5.6 except that two subtotals have been brought out: one showing the sum of products for values of $\tilde{z}$ less than or equal to 2 and one for values of $\tilde{z}$ greater than 2. The grand total 2.80 is the "complete" or *ordinary* expectation of $\tilde{z}$; the first subtotal .60 is the *partial expectation of $\tilde{z}$ over the interval 0 to 2 inclusive,* and the second subtotal 2.20 is the *partial expectation of $\tilde{z}$ over the interval from 3 to "infinity."* Partial expectations will be denoted by the expecta-

Table 5.7

z	$P(z)$	$z\,P(z)$	
0	.05	0	
1	.10	.10	
2	.25	.50	
			.60
3	.30	.90	
4	.20	.80	
5	.10	.50	
6 to infinity	0	0	
			2.20
			2.80

tion symbol E with a subscript and a superscript to indicate the ends of the interval over which the partial expectation is computed. The expectations computed in Table 5.7 above will be written

$$E_0^2(\tilde{z}) = .60, \qquad E_3^\infty(\tilde{z}) = 2.20,$$

and in general *the subscript on the symbol* E *shows the lowest value of the random variable which is included in the partial expectation while the superscript shows the highest included value.*

5.3 Straight-line Conditional Profits; Applications of Expectations

The great majority of the decision problems which we shall study in this course will involve conditional profits or costs which are *linear functions* of some basic random variable, and in all such problems the burden of analysis can be lessened and clarity increased by the use of expectations of the basic random variable.

5.3.1 *Completely Linear Conditional Profit*

Let us start by considering a simple artificial problem which will illustrate the meaning and importance of linear or straight-line conditional profits. Suppose that a lottery is to be conducted by rolling an irregular die with faces serially numbered from 0 to 5 rather than 1 to 6, that we are given a ticket which entitles us to receive $2 times the number which comes up plus an additional $5 regardless of the result of the roll, and that after inspection of the die we assign the probability distribution shown in Table 5.8 to the basic random variable "number which comes up." If we use z to denote the value actually taken on by this basic random variable, the conditional profit of holding the ticket can be written

Conditional profit = $5 + $2 z.

In Table 5.8 our usual method of computation is used to show that the *expected* profit of holding this ticket is $10.40, but we shall now see

Table 5.8

z	$P(z)$	Conditional profit	Expected profit
0	.1	$5 + 0 \times $2 = $ 5	$ .50
1	.1	$5 + 1 \times $2 = 7	.70
2	.2	$5 + 2 \times $2 = 9	1.80
3	.3	$5 + 3 \times $2 = 11	3.30
4	.2	$5 + 4 \times $2 = 13	2.60
5	.1	$5 + 5 \times $2 = 15	1.50
	1.0		$10.40

that *this expected profit can be calculated from the expected value of the basic random variable $\bar{z}$ without the use of any other information concerning the distribution of $\bar{z}$.*　Instead of computing the net conditional profit for each value of the basic random variable and then multiplying this net by the probability of that value as we did in Table 5.8, we could have made each entry as the sum of two parts, as we shall show by taking the entries for $\bar{z} = 3$ as an example.　The \$11 conditional profit for $\bar{z} = 3$ is made up of the two parts,

$$\$5 + (3 \times \$2),$$

and instead of entering $.3 \times \$11 = \$3.30$ in the last column of Table 5.8 we could have multiplied .3 into each of the two parts separately and entered

$$(.3)\$5 + .3(3 \times \$2).$$

Furthermore it is obviously legitimate to regroup the term $.3(3 \times \$2)$ and write it as $(.3 \times 3)\$2$, so that for $\bar{z} = 3$ the complete entry in the last column could have been written as

$$(.3)\$5 + (.3 \times 3)\$2.$$

Table 5.9 is identical to Table 5.8 except that all the entries in the last column have been made in this new form; to obtain the total of

Table 5.9

z	P(z)	Conditional profit	Expected profit
0	.1	$\$5 + 0 \times \$2$	$(.1)\$5 + (.1 \times 0)\$2$
1	.1	$5 + 1 \times \$2$	$(.1)\$5 + (.1 \times 1)\$2$
2	.2	$5 + 2 \times \$2$	$(.2)\$5 + (.2 \times 2)\$2$
3	.3	$5 + 3 \times \$2$	$(.3)\$5 + (.3 \times 3)\$2$
4	.2	$5 + 4 \times \$2$	$(.2)\$5 + (.2 \times 4)\$2$
5	.1	$5 + 5 \times \$2$	$(.1)\$5 + (.1 \times 5)\$2$
	1.0		$(1.0)\$5 + (2.7)\$2$

this column, which will give us the expected profit, we now make two observations.

　1. The first term in each line consists of P(z) multiplied by the constant factor \$5.　Instead of multiplying out each of these terms and then adding, we can add the values of P(z) and then multiply by the constant \$5.　But since the total probability of all possible values of any random variable is 1, the result of this calculation is simply 1 times the constant \$5.

　2. The second term in each line consists of the product z P(z) (in parentheses) multiplied by the constant factor \$2.　Instead of multiplying out each of these terms and then adding, we can multiply out only the portion z P(z) within the parentheses, add *these* products to get the

total 2.7, and then multiply this total by the constant \$2.   This 2.7, however, is simply the expected value of the basic random variable $\tilde{z}$, since it is computed by multiplying every possible value of $\tilde{z}$ by its probability and adding the products, and therefore in this example

Expected profit = \$5 + \$2 E($\tilde{z}$).

The important thing to notice is that *this formula for the* expected *profit is identical to the formula given previously for the* conditional *profit except that z is replaced by* E($\tilde{z}$).   This result can be generalized as follows:

Whenever the conditional profits for *all possible values* of the basic random variable are given by a formula of the type

Conditional profit = $K + kz$,

where K and k are *constants*, the expected profit is given by the formula

Expected profit = $K + k$ E($\tilde{z}$).

The student must pay particular attention to the words "all possible values" in this rule: *it is only because we summed the products z* P(z) *for all possible values of $\tilde{z}$ in Table 5.9 that the quantity* E($\tilde{z}$) *appeared in our result.*

Graphic Representation of Linear Conditional Profits.   Conditional profits given by formulas of the type $K + kz$ are called straight-line or *linear* because when the conditional profit is plotted against the value of the basic random variable the graph is a straight line.   The principle is illustrated in Figure 5.3 for the example just discussed.

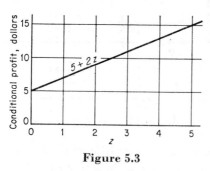
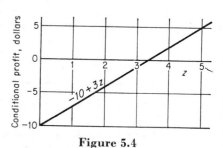

Figure 5.3   Figure 5.4

Application to an Inventory Problem.   Let us now reconsider the computation of expected profit with a stock $Q = 5$ in the inventory problem discussed at length in Chapter 4.   In Section 4.1 we saw that when the demand z was no greater than the stock Q, the conditional profit was given by the formula

Conditional profit = $-\$2\,Q + \$3\,z = -\$10 + \$3\,z.$

Since values of $\tilde{z}$ greater than 5 are impossible by Table 4.1, this formula applies to *all possible* values of $\tilde{z}$ when $Q = 5$; the conditional profit for this case has the graph shown in Figure 5.4.

The fact that this graph of conditional profit is a straight line over the whole range of possible values of $\tilde{z}$ entitles us to apply the formula

Expected profit $= K + k \, \mathrm{E}(\tilde{z})$.

It was shown in Table 5.7 that $\mathrm{E}(\tilde{z}) = 2.8$ for the probability distribution assigned by the retailer; noticing that in our present problem K has a *negative* value,

$$K = -\$10,$$

we obtain

Expected profit $= -\$10 + \$3 \, \mathrm{E}(\tilde{z}) = -\$10 + \$8.40 = -\$1.60$

in agreement with Tables 4.4 and 4.9.

5.3.2 Broken-line Conditional Profit

Suppose now that we wish to use expectations of $\tilde{z}$ to compute expected profit in this same inventory problem but with a stock of 2

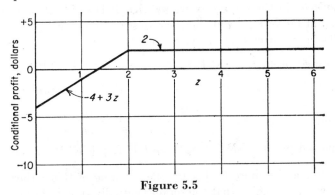

Figure 5.5

rather than with a stock of 5. In this case, as shown in Section 4.1, we have two different formulas for the conditional profit, one of which applies when $z \le 2$, the other when $z > 2$:

$$\text{Conditional profit} = \begin{cases} -\$4 + \$3\,z & \text{if } z \le 2, \\ +\$2 & \text{if } z > 2. \end{cases}$$

This conditional profit is graphed in Figure 5.5, where it appears as a *broken* straight line.

The expected profit for this case is computed in Table 5.10 by a method similar to the one used in Table 5.9 except that two *subtotals* are brought out, one for the values of $\check{z}$ to which the first formula for conditional profit applies and one for the values to which the second formula applies. If now we analyze the *first subtotal* in the last column of Table

Table 5.10

z	P(z)	Conditional profit	Expected profit
0	.05	$-\$4 + 0 \times \$3 = -\ \$4$	$.05(-\$4) + (.05 \times 0)\,\$3 = -\$.20$
1	.10	$-\$4 + 1 \times \$3 = -\ 1$	$.10(-\$4) + (.10 \times 1)\,\$3 = -\ .10$
2	.25	$-\$4 + 2 \times \$3 = +\ 2$	$.25(-\$4) + (.25 \times 2)\,\$3 = +\ .50$
Subtotal	.40		$.40(-\$4) + .60 \times \$3 \quad = +\$.20$
3	.30	$\$2$	$.30 \times \$2 \qquad = +\ .60$
4	.20	$\$2$	$.20 \times \$2 \qquad = +\ .40$
5	.10	$\$2$	$.10 \times \$2 \qquad = +\ .20$
Subtotal	.60		$.60 \times \$2 \qquad = +\$1.20$
Total	1.00		$+\$1.40$

5.10 in the same way that we analyzed the total in Table 5.9, we see that the term $.40(-\$4)$ is $P(\check{z} \le 2)$ multiplied by the constant factor $-\$4$; comparing Table 5.7 we also see that the term $.60 \times \$3$ is the *partial expectation* $E_0^2(\check{z})$ multiplied by the constant factor $\$3$. Analyzing the *second subtotal* in the same way we see that it is $P(\check{z} > 2)$ multiplied by the constant factor $\$2$. Putting these observations together we obtain a "formula" for expected profit with stock $Q = 2$:

Expected profit $= [-\$4\ P(\check{z} \le 2) + \$3\ E_0^2(\check{z})] + \$2\ P(\check{z} > 2)$.

Generalizing this example we conclude that in *any* problem where

$$\text{Conditional profit} = \begin{cases} K + kz & \textit{if } z \le Q, \\ K' & \textit{if } z > Q, \end{cases}$$

Expected profit $= [K\ P(\check{z} \le Q) + k\ E_0^Q(\check{z})] + K'\ P(\check{z} > Q)$.

In order to acquire more feeling for the meaning of this rather complex formula, we can imagine that the retailer actually stocks Q items on each of a number of occasions and that the *relative frequencies* with which the values of $\check{z}$ actually occur on these occasions are numerically equal to the probabilities of Table 5.10. In this imaginary situation the term in brackets gives the ratio

$$\frac{\text{Total profit on all days when } z \le Q}{\text{Total number of days}}$$

while the other term gives the ratio

$$\frac{\text{Total profit on all days when } z > Q}{\text{Total number of days}}.$$

5.4   The Choice and Use of a Measure of Location

The student is not expected to memorize formulas like those which we have just derived for expected profit or methods like the one derived in Section 5.1.4 for finding the best stock level by the use of fractiles.   What the student *is* expected to remember is this:

> When probability distributions are to be used as the basis for a business decision, the question whether the full distribution can be replaced by a measure of location, and if so which one, is not to be answered by some kind of vague discussion concerning the "representativeness" of various possible measures.   A measure of location may be used in place of a full probability distribution if and only if it can be *proved* that *in the particular problem at hand* the expected costs can be correctly calculated or the best decision can be correctly identified by use of the particular measure under consideration.

One of the commonest errors in dealing with problems involving uncertainty is to assume incorrectly that the full distribution can be replaced by some "measure of central tendency" such as the mean or median.   When the full distribution can be replaced by some measure of location, the correct measure is usually *not* a "measure of central tendency."   In inventory problems of the kind we have been studying, the best decision can be found by use of the median only when the critical ratio $k_p/(k_p + k_n)$ has the value .5; the cost of a decision can be evaluated by use of the mean only when the decision is to carry so much stock that there is absolutely no chance that it will fail to meet the demand.

Even more important, it is not to be assumed that *every* problem can be solved by the use of *some* measure of location and that the only problem is choosing the correct measure.   *Most problems require the full distribution; it is only exceptionally that we can replace it by a measure of location or by any other single number.*

PROBLEMS

1. Considering the distribution given in Chapter 4, Problem 3, as a probability distribution rather than a frequency distribution:

a. Graph $P(\tilde{z} \leq z)$ against z.

b. Show that $F_{.1} = 22$, $F_{.2} = 23$, $F_{.5} = 26$, and that $F_{.74}$ is any value from 27 to 28 inclusive.

c. Using $\tilde{z}$ to denote the random variable "number requested," show that $E(\tilde{z}) = 25.70$, $E_0^{23}(\tilde{z}) = 4.88$, $E_{24}^\infty(\tilde{z}) = 20.82$.

d. Compute the critical ratio from the cost data in the original problem, use your answer to (*a*) to find the optimum stock by the method of Section 5.1.4, and check against your answer to the original problem.

e. Use the formula derived in Section 5.3.2 to compute expected profit with optimum stock and check against your answer to the original problem.

2. Considering the distribution given in Chapter 4, Problem 4, as a probability distribution and using $\tilde{z}$ to denote the random variable "demand":

  a. Graph $P(\tilde{z} \le z)$ against z.

  b. Compute the critical ratio from the data of the original problem, use your answer to (*a*) to find the optimum stock by the method of Section 5.1.4, and check against your answer to the original problem.

  c. Use the formula derived in Section 5.3.2 to compute the expected profit with optimum stock and check against your answer to the original problem.

3. A store sells for $4 an item costing $3. Selling expenses amount to 10 per cent of sales. If the item is out of stock, customers demanding it will simply go next door, where it is displayed in the window. At the end of one day, the manager notices that there are only 5 units left in stock. Under the following assumptions what is the expected loss due to the manager's failure to reorder earlier?

  a. It always takes exactly 1 day to place an order with the supplier and to get delivery. Demand for the item over the past 1000 days has been as follows:

Number demanded	Number of occurrences	Number demanded	Number of occurrences
5	3	12	148
6	21	13	59
7	45	14	34
8	75	15	22
9	130	16	12
10	186	17	2
11	263		

  b. Sales of the item have been regularly 10 units every day, but the time to place an order and get delivery is irregular: it usually takes 3 business days, but 25 per cent of the time it takes 4 days and 10 per cent of the time it takes 5.

  c. Daily sales are distributed as in part *a* and delivery time is distributed as in part *b*. [HINT: Take "lead time" as the basic random variable and use your answer to (*a*) to get the conditional losses.]

CHAPTER 6

Assessment of Probabilities
by Smoothing Historical Frequencies

Our object in the last two chapters has been to learn how to use probabilities once they have been assessed rather than to learn how to assess them, and accordingly we have simply equated probabilities to historical relative frequencies in various exercises without stopping to worry about the arguments given in Section 1.6 to show that when *all* the available information is considered such a procedure will often appear to be clearly unreasonable, particularly when the historical frequencies rest on only a small number of trials. In this chapter we shall study one group of methods by which observed relative frequencies may be modified or adjusted in order to make more reasonable assessments of probabilities.

6.1 The Historical Record Considered as a Sample

Consider the historical frequency distribution of daily demand shown in Table 6.1 and graphed in Figure 6.1a. There is a "dip" in the relative

Table 6.1

Demand z	Number of occurrences	Relative frequency
2	1	.063
3	3	.187
4	2	.125
5	4	.250
6	3	.187
7	2	.125
8	0	.000
9	1	.063
10+	0	.000
	16	1.000

frequencies between demand for 3 units and demand for 5 units and another between 7 and 9 units. Before adopting a probability distribution for tomorrow's demand which is a mere copy of this frequency dis-

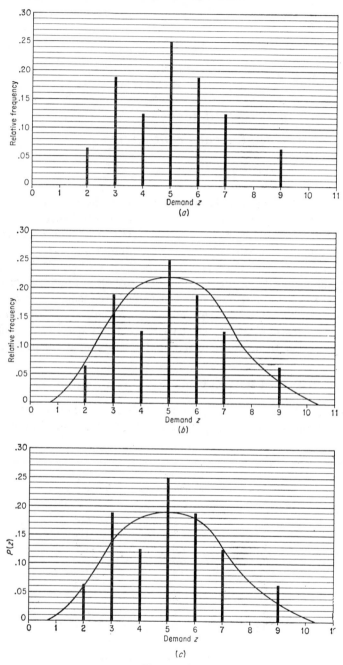

Figure 6.1

tribution, we should ask ourselves whether such a distribution is reasonable in the light of whatever general knowledge we have of the factors affecting demand; and in the light of the discussion in Section 1.6 this means that we must ask ourselves whether we would expect demand on a large number of days "like" tomorrow to have a frequency distribution like that of Figure 6.1*a*.

Under most circumstances almost any sensible person would answer immediately that it is *not* reasonable to expect demands for 7 and 9 units to occur with relative frequencies .125 and .063 while demands for 8 units never occur at all. Unless some definite, *assignable cause* can be found which *prevents* demands for 8 units, it is reasonable to believe that a long run of days like tomorrow would produce demands for 8 units with a relative frequency somewhere *between* the frequencies of 7 and 9 units.

Similarly for the dip in relative frequency between 3 and 5 units: unless a specific cause can be found to explain the dip, a reasonable person would be willing to bet that in a hypothetical long run the relative frequency of demands for 4 units would be *between* the frequencies for 3 and 5 units and would assign probabilities to tomorrow's demand accordingly.

Finally, the fact that no demand for less than 2 or more than 9 units has occurred in the 16 days in the record is not in itself a proof that such demands are impossible; and a reasonable person might well want to assign them some small probability.

This intuitive feeling that it is not logical to assign probabilities in this problem by simply equating them to the historical frequencies can be rationalized as follows. Certain factors affecting demand on any given day can be identified and their effects can be isolated and measured. Thus we may know that Saturday demand tends to be greater than Friday demand by a certain amount. But after we have identified all the factors we can identify and thus explained a part of the variation in historical demand, we are usually left with a certain amount of unexplained variation. It is because we are unable to *explain* all the variation in *past* demand that we are *uncertain* about *tomorrow's* demand.

It is usually reasonable to think of this unexplained variation as being the joint effect of a large number of factors each of which individually has only a small effect, since any individual factor which has a large effect can and should be identified. Furthermore we may usually think of these small, residual factors as acting independently of each other—if several small factors tend to act together, the group as a whole will produce large effects and therefore can and should be identified. Consequently *it is reasonable under most circumstances to think of demand on any one day as being equal to some "basic" amount determined by the identified factors plus or minus a "deviation" which is really the sum of a large number of small, independent deviations due to the unidentified factors.* Let us now simplify the problem for a moment by imagining that although some deviations will be positive while others will be negative, all the deviations are of equal absolute size.   If this were true, the variation in demand would be something like the variation in the number of heads turning up when 100 coins are tossed repeatedly.   Even though some or all of these coins may be badly bent, so that the probability of heads for any one coin may be far from $\frac{1}{2}$, intuition tells us immediately that in the long run:

1. There will be some one most common number of heads;
2. The relative frequencies of other numbers of heads will be smaller the farther the numbers are from this most common number.

If, therefore, a very short series of tosses showed, say, that 54 heads had occurred twice, 56 heads once, and 55 heads not at all, we would nevertheless insist that *in the long run* 55 heads would occur with a relative frequency somewhere between the frequency of 54 heads and the frequency of 56.   In other words, irregularities in the long-run frequency distribution of number of heads would seem inconsistent with our intuitive ideas concerning the nature of the chance mechanism or random process generating this number.   We would say that the irregularities in the record are due to the fact that these tosses are only a "sample" of the behavior of the random process and that the absence of 55 heads from the record reflected "sampling error" rather than the true long-run behavior of the process.

We do not, of course, really think that the total deviation of demand from its most common value is the sum of deviations which are exactly of equal size, but this part of the analogy is not essential.   A closer analogy would be a sequence of rolls of 1000 deformed dice, all different, and here again intuition tells us (and it can be proved) that in any really long sequence of rolls of the 1000 dice:

1. There will be some one most common total number of spots showing,
2. The relative frequencies of other numbers will be smaller the farther the numbers are from this most common number.

This analogy is close enough to our notions of the mechanism generating demand to justify the proposition that the *long-run frequency distribution and therefore the probability distribution of demand should fall away* smoothly *on either side of a* single *most probable value.*

6.2   Smoothing a Frequency Distribution

In a great many situations the *only* available evidence on the behavior of the random process generating values of some random variable is (1) a frequency distribution of values actually generated by the process in the

past and (2) the knowledge that we have eliminated from this distribution the effect of every assignable cause which we are able to identify.   In
such cases the only reasonable way of estimating the long-run behavior of
the process and thus assessing a probability distribution for the next
value which will be generated by the process is to smooth this historical
frequency distribution.

This has been done for the data of Table 6.1 in Figure 6.1*c* (not *b*).
A smooth curve has been drawn in such a way that the *total amount added
to the frequencies of certain demands equals the total amount subtracted from
the frequencies of all other demands*.   Like the type of graph shown in
Figure 3.2, the curve has no meaning except at the points corresponding
to integral values of the sales volume.

Fitting the Curve.   It is difficult in a single operation to fit a smooth
curve to an irregular graph like Figure 6.1*a* and make it come out in such
a way that it both has the right shape and leads to probabilities which
add up exactly to 1.   In practice it is easier to break the fitting procedure
down into two steps.

1. Fit by eye a smooth curve which has the right general *shape*.
2. Adjust the curve so that the probabilities will add to 1 by reading
   the curve at each possible value of the variable, adding the readings, and then increasing or decreasing every point on the curve
   by the same proportional amount.

The curve shown in Figure 6.1*c* was actually derived from the curve in
Figure 6.1*b*.   This latter curve was fitted by eye and the ordinates listed
in column 2 of Table 6.2 were read from it.   Each figure in column 2 was
then divided by the total of the column (1.16) to obtain a set of *probabilities* which would add to 1.   Once these probabilities were listed in column

Table 6.2

Demand	Ordinate of Figure 6.1*b*	Probability
0	0	0
1	.01	.009
2	.07	.060
3	.16	.138
4	.21	.181
5	.22	.190
6	.21	.181
7	.15	.129
8	.08	.069
9	.04	.034
10	.01	.009
11+	0	0
	1.16	1.000

3 of the table, the smoothing was really complete; the only reason for plotting the probabilities in Figure 6.1c and drawing a smooth curve through the plotted points was to obtain a visual check on the reasonableness of the final results.

6.2.1 Assignable Causes

Now that the student has learned how to smooth out all the irregularities in a frequency distribution, let him beware of doing this indiscriminately. *Assignable causes for irregularities often exist:* if we make the effort, we *are* often able to find reasons for dips in a historical frequency distribution. In the case of daily demand, this means that we can often explain why the frequencies bunch in two or more ranges by looking for factors which were present on the days (or months or other periods) showing high demand and which were absent on the days showing low demand or vice versa.

It has already been pointed out that if the data in the record apply to all days in the week, we may find that demand was usually higher on Saturday than on other days. Unless our general knowledge of consumer behavior leads us to a strong belief that there is no real reason for this phenomenon, we should *not* reject it as an accident of chance, which is what we are doing implicitly if we assess a probability distribution by smoothing a frequency distribution containing data on both Saturdays and other days. Rather, we should use only Saturday data to arrive at a probability distribution for next Saturday's demand, and so forth. If demand in summer was higher than demand in winter and it is reasonable to believe that there is a real cause for this phenomenon, summer and winter data should not be lumped in arriving at a probability distribution.

The help which even a professional statistician can derive from probability theory in deciding whether irregularities in a historical frequency distribution are to be attributed to an assignable cause or to chance is usually very slight. *Basically, the problem is one to be decided by the use of judgment, and judgment must be based more on a general understanding of the real phenomena under study than on statistical theory.*

6.3   Smoothing Grouped Distributions

We saw in Section 3.3.1 that in some situations the available data will be insufficient to compute the relative frequency with which each individual value of some random variable has occurred in the past and that we may then be forced to work with a grouped frequency distribution. Furthermore it is often better to work with a grouped distribution even when the available data *do* give us the historical relative frequencies of the individual values of the random variable. We have just seen that "sampling error" means that individual relative frequencies are poor guides to probabilities unless these relative frequencies are based on fairly large absolute numbers of occurrences.   If the values of the variable are grouped into brackets, the number of occurrences in each bracket may be large enough to make the observed relative frequency of each bracket a very good indication of its true long-run frequency; and we can then use a smoothing technique to obtain good estimates of long-run individual frequencies.

Suppose then that we have either been given the grouped distribution of sales volumes shown in the first two columns of Table 6.3 or have con-

Table 6.3

Demand z	Relative frequency	Frequency per unit width
0–4	.051	.0102
5–9	.256	.0512
10–14	.325	.0650
15–19	.222	.0444
20–24	.094	.0188
25–29	.043	.0086
30–34	.009	.0018
	1.000	

structed it by deliberately grouping the frequencies in a more detailed record.   This distribution is graphed in Figure 6.2, where a histogram is

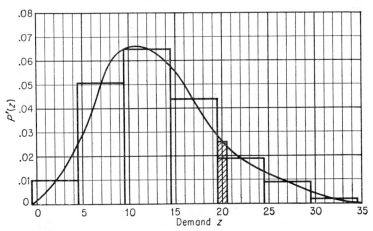

Figure 6.2

used rather than a graph like Figure 6.1 because the frequencies do not pertain to a single value of the variable.   As we saw in Section 3.3, it is the *areas* of the bars of the histogram which represent the relative frequencies; the heights of the bars represent frequency *per unit width.* Since the width of each bar in Figure 6.2 is 5 units, the height of each bar as shown in column 3 of Table 6.3 and on the vertical axis of Figure 6.2 is one-fifth of the frequency.

Fitting and Reading the Curve. After the histogram of the grouped frequency distribution has been drawn, a probability distribution can be assessed by fitting a smooth curve in such a way that for each bracket the area under the *curve* is approximately equal to the area of the corresponding *bar*. This curve approximates the outline of a histogram giving the probability of each individual value z of the demand.

The detailed probability histogram itself could then be constructed in the way indicated by the shaded bar for the individual $z = 20$, but it is easy to find the probability of any individual value without actually drawing its bar. The width of the bar for any individual value is 1, its height can be obtained by reading the height of the curve at the mid-point of the interval which *would* be occupied by the bar, and its area can then be computed by multiplying height times width. Thus from the curve in Figure 6.2 we can quickly find

$$P(\tilde{z} = 20) = 1 \times P'(20) = 1 \times .026 = .026,$$
$$P(\tilde{z} = 21) = 1 \times P'(21) = 1 \times .022 = .022,$$

and so forth.

The total area under a curve fitted in this way will, of course, usually differ slightly from 1. We could adjust for this by reading the height of the curve at each possible value of the variable and then adding and adjusting these readings in the manner of Table 6.2, but usually the practical gain will not be worth the effort.

6.4 Smoothing of Extremely Sparse Data

Consider next the historical frequency distribution of demand shown in Table 6.4 and graphed in Figure 6.3. As can be seen in the figure, the

Table 6.4

Demand z	Number of occurrences	Relative frequency
9	1	.1
11	1	.1
15	1	.1
16	1	.1
17	1	.1
20	1	.1
22	1	.1
24	1	.1
29	1	.1
35	1	.1
	10	1.0

demands "bunch" in the range 15 to 24 and suggest that the probability distribution should be of the same general shape as the curves in Figures 6.1c and 6.2; but because all the individual bars in the figure are of the same height it is impossible to fit a smooth curve by the method used to produce Figure 6.1c, and because the total number of occurrences is so small grouping would help very little. When the historical data are as sparse as those of Table 6.4, it is much more effective to make a smoothed assessment of the *cumulative* probability distribution than it is to use either of the methods previously described.

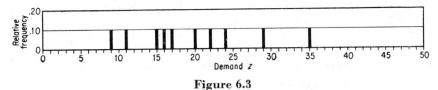

Figure 6.3

When we smoothed the frequency distribution of Figure 6.1a, what we did in effect was:

1. Take the historical relative frequency of each recorded demand as a *preliminary estimate* of the long-run relative frequency of that demand;

2. *Adjust* these preliminary estimates so that the whole distribution would be smooth and of reasonable shape.

In our present problem we shall use an analogous procedure:

1. Make a *preliminary estimate* of the long-run *cumulative* relative frequency corresponding to each recorded demand;

2. *Adjust* these preliminary estimates so that the whole distribution will be smooth and of reasonable shape.

6.4.1 Estimates of Fractiles

The first point to observe when we set out to estimate a long-run *cumulative* frequency is this: *when the record contains only a very few observations, it is contrary to common sense to use the historical cumulative frequency of any value of a random variable as an estimate of the long-run cumulative frequency of that value.* The truth of this assertion can easily be seen by considering the values 35 and 9 of the random variable "demand" in our example.

As can be seen from Table 6.4, the historical cumulative frequency of 35 or less is 1. We know, however, that it is extremely unlikely that a "sample" of only 10 demands includes the *highest possible* demand; and therefore 1 is not a sensible estimate of the long-run cumulative frequency of 35 or less. Similarly, the historical cumulative frequency of less than 9 is 0; but it is not at all likely that 9 is the *lowest possible* demand and therefore 0 is not a sensible estimate of the long-run cumulative frequency of less than 9.

In order to find a way of making more reasonable preliminary estimates of long-run cumulative frequencies, let us think of what would happen if the random process generating tomorrow's demand were to operate on each of a very large number of days "like" tomorrow, and to make the discussion concrete let us think of 11,000 days. Further, let us think of these 11,000 days as having been arrayed in order of quantity demanded and then given a *rank number*. The day with the smallest demand will have rank 1; the day with the largest demand will have rank 11,000; days with identical demands are ranked arbitrarily among themselves. Then it can be proved that if a sample of 10 days is drawn from these 11,000 days, the expected rank number of the lowest-ranking day in the sample is 1000, the rank number of the $\frac{1}{11}$, *not* the $\frac{1}{10}$, fractile of the 11,000 demands. The expected rank of the second-lowest day in the sample is 2000, the rank of the $\frac{2}{11}$ fractile of the 11,000 demands; and so forth. The expected rank of the highest-ranking day in the sample is 10,000, *not* 11,000, and this is the rank of the $\frac{10}{11}$ fractile of the 11,000 demands.

Consequently the smallest demand in a sample of 10 demands is a reasonable estimate of the $\frac{1}{11}$ fractile of the distribution of demands from which the sample is drawn; the largest demand in the sample is a reasonable estimate of the $\frac{10}{11}$ fractile of the distribution; and so forth. More generally,

> If a sample of n observations is drawn from some distribution and arrayed in order of size, the kth observation is a reasonable estimate of the $k/(n + 1)$ fractile of the distribution.

If there are 25 observations in the sample, the third smallest is a reasonable estimate of the $\frac{3}{26} = .115$ fractile of the distribution from which the sample is drawn, and so forth.

6.4.2   *Fitting and Reading the Cumulative Probability Distribution*

Let us now proceed to assess a probability distribution for tomorrow's demand by using the 10 demands in the record of Table 6.4 as estimates of the fractiles of the long-run frequency distribution of demand. In Figure 6.4 we plot the smallest of the 10 demands at a cumulative probability of $\frac{1}{11}$ rather than $\frac{1}{10}$, the second smallest at a cumulative probability of $\frac{2}{11}$, and so forth, and we then adjust these preliminary estimates and assess the complete cumulative probability distribution by fitting a smooth curve to the 10 plotted points.

When we come to read a cumulative probability from the fitted curve, a new problem turns up. We saw in Section 3.4.2 that when a cumulative probability distribution is graphed exactly, the graph takes the form of a "step function" and $P(\tilde{z} < z)$ is read at the bottom of each jump in the curve while $P(\tilde{z} \leq z)$ is read at the top.   Since the fitted curve in Figure 6.4 has no jumps, this rule cannot be applied; and in order to decide how to read the curve we must again think of the historical data as a sample of 10 demands drawn from an extremely large number of "possible" demands.

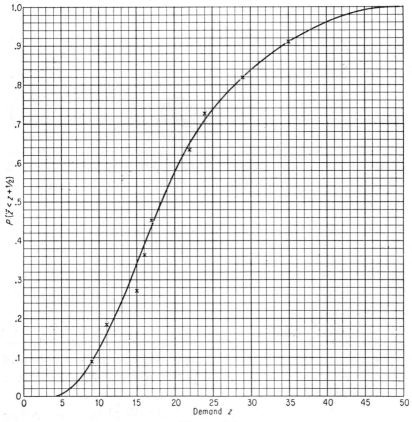

Figure 6.4

Suppose first that we actually knew the true long-run distribution of demand, that this distribution had been accurately graphed as a step function, and that we had used the method of Figure 5.1 or 5.2 to locate the *true* $\frac{1}{11}$, $\frac{2}{11}$, . . . , $\frac{10}{11}$ fractiles of this distribution.   The dashed lines locating some of these fractiles would cut the graph at or near the top of a jump, others would cut at or near the bottom, and still others would cut near the middle.   If then a smooth curve were put through the intersections between the dashed lines and the graph, its height at any z would in general give us *neither* $P(\tilde{z} < z)$ *nor* $P(\tilde{z} \leq z)$ but something in

between. $P(\tilde{z} < z)$ would be given by the height of the curve somewhat
to the *left* of z, and $P(\tilde{z} \leq z)$ would be given by the height of the curve
somewhat to the *right* of z.

It is such a curve which is estimated by the curve of Figure 6.4, and
therefore the height of that graph at any z gives neither $P(\tilde{z} < z)$ nor
$P(\tilde{z} \leq z)$ but something in between.   The best we can do in this situation
is to adopt the following very rough and ready rule:

> $P(\tilde{z} < z)$ will be read above the point $z - \frac{1}{2}$ on the horizontal axis.
> $P(\tilde{z} \leq z)$ will be read above the point $z + \frac{1}{2}$ on the horizontal axis.

The vertical scale of Figure 6.4 is labeled $P(\tilde{z} < z + \frac{1}{2})$ to remind us
that what we read above the point 10.5 on the horizontal axis is $P(\tilde{z} < 11)$,
and so forth; it could equally well have been labeled $P(\tilde{z} \leq z - \frac{1}{2})$ to
remind us that this same reading can be interpreted as $P(\tilde{z} \leq 10)$.   The
rough-and-ready character of this rule need worry us very little, since the
difference between $P(\tilde{z} < z)$ and $P(\tilde{z} \leq z)$ will be very small when the
number of possible values of the variable is at all large; and it is only when
this number *is* large that we will want to smooth the cumulative form of
the historical frequency distribution by the use of fractile estimates.

6.4.3   *Individual Probabilities*

Suppose now that we wish to obtain probabilities for individual
values of $\tilde{z}$ from the cumulative distribution of $\tilde{z}$ given by Figure 6.4.   In
principle these values of $P(z)$ can be obtained from the curve by using the
relation $P(\tilde{z} = z) = P(\tilde{z} < z + 1) - P(\tilde{z} < z)$, but the accuracy will be
so poor that the results are worthless.   Because the difference $P(z)$
between any two adjacent cumulative probabilities in Figure 6.4 is so
small, very small relative errors in reading the two cumulative probabilities will produce an error which is enormous relative to their difference.

The only way the accuracy can be improved is to increase the size of
the difference we are trying to read, and we can do this by proceeding in
two steps rather than one:

1. We first obtain a *grouped* probability distribution by reading
   Figure 6.4.
2. We then obtain *individual* probabilities by smoothing this grouped
   distribution.

To obtain a grouped distribution from Figure 6.4, we must first decide on
the width of the brackets we are going to use, i.e. on the number of values
of $\tilde{z}$ to include in each; and in doing this we must keep in mind that:

1. Very narrow brackets reduce the relative accuracy with which we
   can read the total probability of each bracket from Figure 6.4.
2. Very wide brackets increase the errors which we will make in
   smoothing the grouped distribution.

Without trying to prove that this choice is correct, let us obtain a grouped distribution from Figure 6.4 using brackets 5 units wide. The first bracket will include $\tilde{z} = 0$ to 4 inclusive, the second will include $\tilde{z} = 5$ to 9, and so forth. The probability that $\tilde{z}$ is between 0 and 4 units inclusive can be obtained simply by reading $P(\tilde{z} < 5)$ from the chart; recalling that this cumulative probability is read above the point 4.5 on the horizontal axis, we see that its value is 0. The probability that $\tilde{z}$ is between 5 and 9 inclusive is computed as .108 by subtracting $P(\tilde{z} < 5) = 0$ from $P(\tilde{z} < 10) = .108$, the latter value being read above 9.5 on the horizontal axis. The probability that $\tilde{z}$ is between 10 and 14 inclusive is computed as .212 by subtracting $P(\tilde{z} < 10) = .108$ from $P(\tilde{z} < 15) = .320$, and so forth. In general:

The probability of any bracket is obtained by subtracting the cumulative probability at the left edge of the bracket from the cumulative probability at the left edge of the next higher bracket, the left edge of any bracket being located $\frac{1}{2}$ unit to the left of the lowest value in the bracket.

In Table 6.5 this procedure is applied to obtain a complete grouped distribution from the cumulative distribution of Figure 6.4. The remainder

Table 6.5

Demand z	Cumulative probability at left edge of bracket	Total probability of bracket	Probability per unit width
0–4	0	0	0
5–9	0	.108	.0216
10–14	.108	.212	.0424
15–19	.320	.234	.0468
20–24	.554	.170	.0340
25–29	.724	.104	.0208
30–34	.828	.074	.0148
35–39	.902	.054	.0108
40–44	.956	.034	.0068
45–49	.990	.010	.0020
50–54	1.000	0	0
		1.000	

of the procedure for determining individual probabilities is identical to the procedure used in dealing with Table 6.3. We first compute the probabilities per unit width shown in the last column of Table 6.5 by dividing the total probability of each bracket by its width, which is 5 units. We then graph the histogram of the grouped distribution and fit a smooth curve in such a way as to leave the area in each bracket essentially unchanged. The work is done for our example in Figure 6.5.

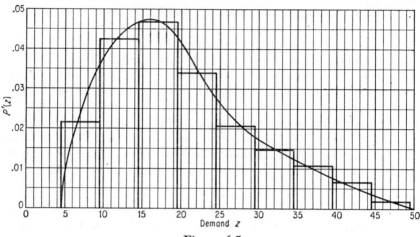

Figure 6.5

6.4.4   The Relation between the Shape of Noncumulative and Cumulative Distributions

Because it is easier to visualize the shape of the frequency distribution which would tend to be generated by a given random process than it is to visualize the shape of the corresponding cumulative distribution, we shall point out some simple relations between the two. These relations should be kept clearly in mind when assessing a probability distribution by smoothing fractile estimates.

The basic relation is simply this: when a cumulative distribution is accurately represented by a stepped graph, each *jump* in the cumulative distribution is equal to the area and therefore proportional to the *height* of the corresponding bar in the frequency distribution. This means that when both distributions are smoothed, the *slope* of the cumulative distribution at any value of the variable is proportional to the *height* of the frequency distribution at that value.

Consequently a *one-humped frequency distribution* corresponds to an *S-shaped cumulative distribution* like the curve in Figure 6.4. Comparing Figure 6.4 with Figure 6.5, which was derived from it, we see that as the value of the variable increases, the *height* of the frequency distribution at first increases and therefore the *slope* of the cumulative distribution increases. Beyond the point corresponding to the peak of the frequency distribution, the height of that distribution decreases and with it the slope of the cumulative distribution.

A *two-humped* frequency distribution would correspond to a cumulative distribution in which the slope at first increased, then decreased, then increased again, and then decreased again. If the dip in the frequency distribution went down to 0, the cumulative distribution would become absolutely flat at the corresponding value of the variable. It is such irregularities which we will ordinarily want to smooth out in assessing a probability distribution; but as we have already said, this must be done only after we have asked ourselves whether the observed flattening may represent a genuine *assignable cause*.

Normal-probability Paper. Even when we are aware of these relations between the shapes of noncumulative distributions and cumulative distributions it is usually very difficult to say whether a graph of cumulative probabilities like Figure 6.4 is reasonable—i.e., expresses our considered judgment about the workings of the underlying mechanism or process. For the reasons explained in Section 6.1 we will usually be of the opinion that our noncumulative probability distribution should be smooth and single-humped; and when this is true it will usually be easier to sketch the corresponding cumulative distribution on graph paper with a special grid known as "Normal-probability paper."

The statistical theory underlying this special grid will not be discussed until later in the course; for the moment we shall justify its use solely by example. The lines labeled I, II, and III in Figure 6.6a represent three hypothetical cumulative distributions; the corresponding noncumulative distributions are shown as Figure 6.6b. The points to notice are the following:

1. A perfectly straight line on Normal-probability paper corresponds to a symmetrical, one-humped probability distribution, the tails of which never quite fall to zero. It is impossible to plot the cumulative probabilities 0 or 1 on this paper, although we can plot .0001 and .9999.

2. Most reasonable one-humped probability distributions will correspond to *nearly* straight lines on this paper *except at the two tails;* if the "ends" of the distribution are to be represented, this must be done by turning the ends of the graph parallel to the vertical axis. The point at which the ends turn vertical will necessarily be largely arbitrary, but fortunately this is rarely of any practical importance whatever. *The small probabilities in the extreme tails will have little effect on expected costs and even less or none at all on the actual decision.*

6.5 Computation of Expectations from Grouped Distributions

Suppose now that we are faced with an inventory problem of the kind studied in Chapter 4 and that Figure 6.4 represents our assessment of the probability distribution of demand. After computing the critical ratio $k_p/(k_p + k_n)$ we can determine the value of the critical fractile directly from Figure 6.4 and thus determine the best number to stock, but we will have much more trouble when we try to compute the expected profit of stocking this or any other number of units. If we use the basic method of computation which we used in Chapter 4, we must know $P(z)$ for every

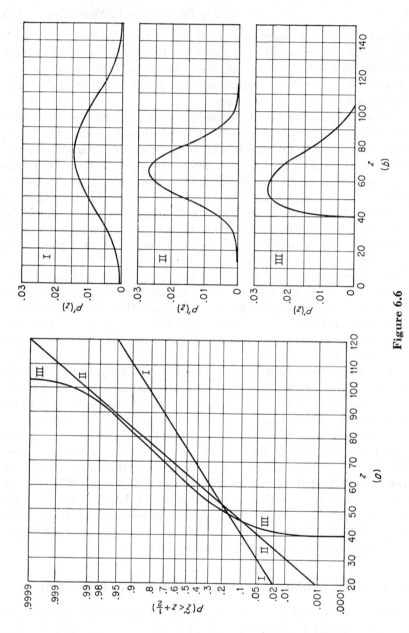

Figure 6.6

110

possible z, and this means not only that we must go through the entire process of deriving the smooth curve of Figure 6.5 from the original assessment in Figure 6.4 but also that we must then read $P(z)$ from this curve for *every* z and multiply each probability into the corresponding conditional profit. Even if we short-cut the computations by using a partial expectation in the way described in Section 5.3.2, we shall still have to produce the smooth curve of Figure 6.5 and read $P(z)$ from it for every z up to and including the number of units stocked. Although the actual computations could be mechanized, this kind of chart reading would clearly become totally impractical in a problem in which demand had a really large number of possible values.

Fortunately this kind of detailed chart reading is not really necessary, since expectations can be computed directly from an unsmoothed grouped distribution like that of Table 6.5 with an accuracy which is more than adequate for all practical purposes. We shall first explain the logical basis of this approximate method of computation by means of an artificially simple example and we shall then go on to apply it to the distribution of Table 6.5 and Figure 6.4.

Suppose that the probabilities assigned to the six lowest possible values of a random variable $\tilde{v}$ are those shown in Table 6.6a. The partial expectation $E_0^5(\tilde{v})$ can then be computed to be .42 as shown in the last column of the table. In Table 6.6b the same value is obtained for $E_0^5(\tilde{v})$ by grouping three values per bracket and *multiplying the value of the variable at the mid-point of the bracket by the total probability of the bracket.* Notice carefully that the partial expectation .42 computed in Table 6.6b applies to the whole interval $\tilde{v} = 0$ to 5 inclusive, i.e. to *the whole interval from the left edge of the first bracket to the right edge of the last bracket included in the computation.*

Table 6.6a

v	$P(v)$	$v\,P(v)$
0	.02	0
1	.02	.02
2	.02	.04
3	.03	.09
4	.03	.12
5	.03	.15
		.42

Table 6.6b

v	Mid-point	Grouped probability	Product
0–2	1	.06	.06
3–5	4	.09	.36
			.42

Grouped computation gave the *exact* value of the partial expectation in this example because all values of the variable within any one bracket had exactly the same probability. Grouped computation will give reasonably good results even when the individual probabilities within each bracket are not exactly equal provided that they do not vary too widely, and we shall now apply the method to the distribution of Table 6.5.   The basic computations are carried out in Table 6.7, where columns 1 and 3 are simply copied from Table 6.5 and column 4 is computed in the same way as column 4 of Table 6.6*b*.   The last column of Table 6.7 gives the cumulative or progressive sum of column 4 and thus shows a whole series of partial expectations of $\bar{z}$, each one covering the interval from 0

Table 6.7

z	Mid-point	Grouped probability	Product	Cumulative sum
0–4	2	0	0	0
5–9	7	.108	.756	.756
10–14	12	.212	2.544	3.300
15–19	17	.234	3.978	7.278
20–24	22	.170	3.740	11.018
25–29	27	.104	2.808	13.826
30–34	32	.074	2.368	16.194
35–39	37	.054	1.998	18.192
40–44	42	.034	1.428	19.620
45–49	47	.010	.470	20.090
50–54	52	0	0	20.090
		1.000	20.090	

to the *right edge* of the last bracket included in its computation.   Thus we read, for example,

$$E_0^9(\bar{z}) = .756; \qquad E_0^{24}(\bar{z}) = 11.018.$$

The "complete" or ordinary expectation of $\bar{z}$—the mean of the distribution of $\bar{z}$—is

$$E_0^\infty(\bar{z}) = E_0^{49}(\bar{z}) = 20.090.$$

Partial expectations over intervals whose right edges do not coincide with the right edges of the brackets in Table 6.7 can be obtained by plotting the partial expectations given in the table and fitting a smooth curve through the plotted points.   This is done in Figure 6.7, where we can read, for example,

$$E_0^{32}(\bar{z}) = 15.3; \qquad E_0^{36}(\bar{z}) = 17.0.$$

In problems where only a single partial expectation is required—e.g., because we have determined the optimum stock by use of the cumulative distribution and wish to know expected profit with this stock only—the chart reading and computation represented by Tables 6.5 and 6.7 can be still further reduced. Suppose, for example, that the only partial expectation we require from Figure 6.4 is $E_0^{26}(\check{z})$. Since it is easier to read Figure 6.4 if we choose bracket edges terminating in 0 and 5 than it is if we use any other numbers, we will start by using the first five brackets of Table 6.5 exactly as they are in that table; the cumulative probabilities

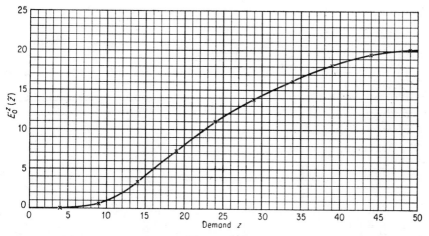

Figure 6.7

and grouped probabilities in the first five lines of Table 6.8 are identical to those of Table 6.5. The last entry in Table 6.8 is then an "off-size" bracket chosen to end with the value $z = 26$ in which we are interested. The probability of this bracket is obtained in exactly the same way as the probabilities of the other brackets, by subtracting $P(\check{z} < 27) - P(\check{z} < 25)$, but we must be careful to notice that because the only values in this bracket are 25 and 26 its mid-point is 25.5.

Table 6.8

Demand z	Cumulative probability at left edge	Total probability of bracket	Mid-point	Product
0–4	0	0	2	0
5–9	0	.108	7	.756
10–14	.108	.212	12	2.544
15–19	.320	.234	17	3.978
20–24	.554	.170	22	3.740
25–26	.724	.048	25.5	1.224
27–	.772			
				12.242

PROBLEMS

1. The fractile estimates shown as X's in Figure 6.4 have been replotted on Normal-probability paper as Figure 6.8.

a. Fit a smooth curve to these points, turning the left end vertical $\frac{1}{2}$ unit to the left of what you believe to be the lowest possible demand and turning the right end vertical $\frac{1}{2}$ unit to the right of what you believe to be the highest possible demand.

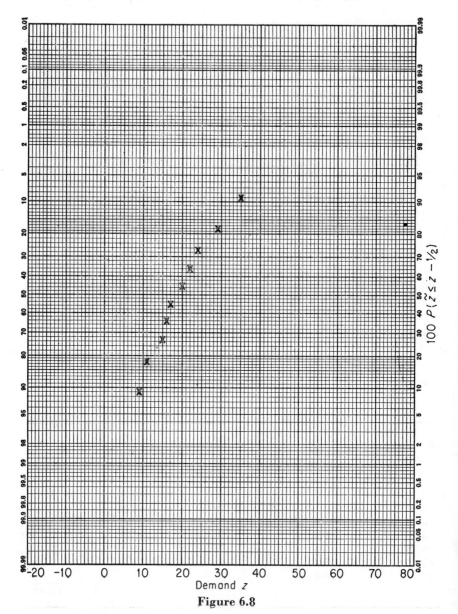

Demand z

Figure 6.8

b. Assuming that the item in question costs $.60, sells for $2, and is a total loss if it is not sold by the end of the day on which it is stocked, decide how many units to stock.

c. From (*a*) obtain a grouped probability distribution like the one in Table 6.5, using brackets 5 units wide.

d. From this grouped distribution compute partial expectations as in Table 6.7 and make a graph like Figure 6.7.

e. Use (*a*) and (*d*) to compute expected profit under your answer to (*b*).

f. Use incremental analysis to determine how much expected profit would be lost by stocking 1 or 2 units more or less than your answer to (*b*).

g. Assume now that some misguided person, unaware of the "correct" probability distribution which you have assessed in (*a*), acts on the assumption that Figure 6.4 is the correct distribution. Use Figure 6.4 to learn how many units he will decide to stock, and use your answer to (*f*) to determine how much (in your opinion) his mistake is costing him.

2. A certain product is stocked daily and spoils if it is not sold by the end of the day. The retailer pays $1.37 per unit for the product; he prices it at $6.50 on the day it is stocked; leftover stock is worthless. The retailer believes that he knows at least approximately the effect which a variety of factors such as season, weather, advertising, etc., exert on demand for this product; and because no one combination of "values" of these factors is ever repeated exactly, he believes that it is impossible to build up a historical frequency distribution of demand on a number of "identical" days. Instead, therefore, of looking at such a distribution before deciding how many units to order, he has based each order on a forecast of the next day's demand. The table below shows the record for the past 19 days of his forecast of demand and the demand which actually occurred; his forecast of tomorrow's demand is 100 units.

Day	Forecast	Demand	Day	Forecast	Demand
1	75	92	11	110	101
2	100	107	12	95	100
3	120	98	13	100	107
4	85	78	14	125	118
5	110	104	15	70	61
6	130	140	16	100	105
7	90	90	17	105	91
8	80	85	18	80	86
9	75	93	19	120	108
10	120	127			

a. Compute the discrepancies between actual demand and forecast demand, defining the discrepancy as *actual minus forecast*, and array them in order from the most negative to the most positive.

b. Assess a probability distribution for tomorrow's *discrepancy* by treating the recorded discrepancies as fractile estimates. Use Normal-probability paper and choose the horizontal scale such that the extreme left of the axis represents $- 50$, the extreme right $+50$. In plotting the estimates, observe that a discrepancy of -9 is the estimate of *two successive* fractiles and that therefore you must plot *two X's* above -9.

c. Making use of the fact that

Demand = forecast + discrepancy,

convert your answer to (*b*) into a probability distribution for tomorrow's *demand* by simply relabeling the horizontal axis.

d. Determine the best number of units to stock and compute expected profit with this stock.

3. In the situation of Problem 2:

a. Compute the *ratio* of actual demand to forecast demand on the 19 days in the historical record, *dividing actual by forecast.*

b. Assess a probability distribution for tomorrow's *ratio* by treating the recorded ratios as fractile estimates. Use Normal-probability paper and choose the horizontal scale such that the extreme left of the axis represents .50, the extreme right 1.50.

c. Making use of the fact that

Demand = forecast × ratio,

convert your answer to (*b*) into a probability distribution for tomorrow's *demand* by simply relabeling the horizontal axis.

d. Determine the best number of units to stock and compute expected profit with this stock.

4. Discuss the merits of the alternative procedures used in Problems 2 and 3. Considering the retailer as a forecasting mechanism or process, what implicit assumptions were made about the behavior of this process in Problem 2? in Problem 3? How in practice would you try to determine which assumptions were closer to the truth?

5. A retailer with costs and prices identical to those of Problem 2 also bases his orders on forecasts of demand but has kept no record of the accuracy of previous forecasts. After reviewing the reports he has received on the state of the market for his product he decides that he would be willing to bet at the following odds on tomorrow's demand:

1 to 99 (1 chance in 100) that $\tilde{z} < 100$.
1 to 9 that $\tilde{z} < 115$.
1 to 1 that $\tilde{z} < 130$.
1 to 9 that $\tilde{z} > 145$.
1 to 99 that $\tilde{z} > 160$.

How many units should he stock?

CHAPTER 7

Opportunity Loss and the Cost of Uncertainty

Even though we choose the best possible decision in the light of the information available *before the fact*, this decision will often turn out "wrong" *after the fact*. To use the example discussed in Chapter 4: the best decision we can make before the fact is to stock 2 units, but after the fact we may wish we had stocked some other number of units. This, of course, is no criticism of the rationality of the original decision: such things are bound to happen when a decision has to be made on the basis of less than perfect information. It does mean, however, that there is a particular interest attached to the *losses which may be incurred because of the imperfection of our information*, and such losses are the subject of the present chapter.

7.1 Definition of Opportunity Loss

Losses of the kind we are now studying will be called *opportunity losses* because they represent the difference between the profit we actually realize and the greater profit we had the opportunity of realizing; or if we measure the consequences of our chosen act in terms of cost, they represent the difference between the cost we actually incur and the lesser cost we had the opportunity of incurring. Formally, we define

Opportunity loss of a decision: the *difference* between the cost or profit *actually* realized under that decision and the cost or profit which *would have been* realized if the decision had been the best one possible for the event which actually occurred.

Observe that an "opportunity loss" may be suffered even when the decision results in a profit rather than a loss in the ordinary sense of the word. Henceforth the word "loss" will be used only in the sense of "opportunity loss" as we have just defined this term, whether or not we repeat the word "opportunity" on every occasion. If a decision results in costs which exceed revenues, we shall call the difference a "negative profit"; we shall no longer call it a "loss."

7.1.1 Expected Opportunity Loss

The opportunity loss which is actually suffered as the result of some decision may be a subject of curiosity and regret, but the businessman

117

will gain little practical advantage from its calculation.   What is really useful to the businessman is to look at the risk of loss *before* he makes his final decision, i.e. to compute the *expected* loss of the act which he is contemplating, since if this expected loss is great he may be able to reduce it either by postponing the final choice of an act until more information has been acquired or by finding some way of hedging the risk.   The real subject of the present chapter is therefore the computation of expected opportunity loss, and this computation can be performed in two different ways:

1. We can look at the various losses which may result from a given act according to the event which actually occurs and compute the expected value of these potential losses.
2. We can compare the profit or cost which can be expected to result from choosing an act on the basis of the information currently available with the profit or cost which could be expected to result from choosing an act on the basis of perfect information.

We shall study both of these methods of computation and shall see that they must necessarily and always lead to exactly the same figure for the expected opportunity loss.

7.2   Computation of Expected Loss from Conditional Losses

7.2.1   The Loss Table

If we wish to compute the expected losses of all the possible acts in any decision problem by the first of the two methods described above, our first step is very similar to the first step we take when we wish to compute the expected profits or costs of all possible acts: we lay out a table which shows the *conditional* loss which will be incurred as the result of each act given every possible event.   Such a table will be called a *loss table*. Since the conditional opportunity loss of any act given a particular event is simply the difference between the resulting profit or cost and the profit or cost which would have resulted from the best possible act for that event, the most systematic way of computing a loss table for any problem is to start with the payoff table which shows all the profits or costs for that problem.

Although the very definition of opportunity loss makes it virtually obvious how the loss table is to be derived from the payoff table, it is well to follow a systematic procedure in carrying out the calculations and we shall explain this procedure by applying it to the inventory problem discussed at length in Chapter 4.   Table 7.1 is the payoff table for that problem and is identical to Table 4.2 except that the "impossible" event $\tilde{z} = 6+$ has been omitted.   Table 7.2 is the corresponding loss table derived from Table 7.1 in the following two steps:

1. The greatest possible profit for each *event* is identified by starring the greatest profit in each *row* of Table 7.1.
2. Table 7.2 is then constructed row by row, each entry in Table 7.2 being obtained by subtracting the corresponding entry in Table 7.1 from the starred entry *in the same row* of Table 7.1.

Table 7.1
Payoff Table

z	Q					
	0	1	2	3	4	5
0	$0*	−$2	−$4	−$6	−$8	−$10
1	0	+ 1*	− 1	− 3	− 5	− 7
2	0	+ 1	+ 2*	0	− 2	− 4
3	0	+ 1	+ 2	+ 3*	+ 1	− 1
4	0	+ 1	+ 2	+ 3	+ 4*	+ 2
5	0	+ 1	+ 2	+ 3	+ 4	+ 5*

Table 7.2
Loss Table

z	Q					
	0	1	2	3	4	5
0	$0	$2	$4	$6	$8	$10
1	1	0	2	4	6	8
2	2	1	0	2	4	6
3	3	2	1	0	2	4
4	4	3	2	1	0	2
5	5	4	3	2	1	0

Thus the $1 *opportunity* loss attached to the event "demand for 4" under the act "stock 3" represents the fact that the corresponding profit is only $3 whereas with a stock of 4 (the best decision for a demand of 4) the profit would be $4—this is the starred entry in the row for $z = 4$ in Table 7.1. The $6 *opportunity* loss attached to "demand 2" under "stock 5" represents the fact that the corresponding profit is a *negative* $4 whereas with a stock of 2 (the best decision) the profit would be a *positive* $2.

The student should pay very careful attention to the following points concerning algebraic signs:

1. Care must be paid to algebraic signs in subtracting the profit for a given act-event combination from the greatest possible profit for that event, since one or both of these quantities may be negative.

2. Opportunity loss itself can never be negative. The loss of the best possible act for any event is 0, and all other acts necessarily involve positive losses.

Payoff Tables Showing Costs. With two obvious exceptions, the procedure for deriving a loss table from a payoff table which shows costs rather than profits is identical to the procedure described above:

1. The *lowest* cost in each row is starred.
2. The starred entry is *subtracted from* all the entries in the same row.

7.2.2 Expected Loss

The *expected* opportunity loss of any act is computed from the conditional losses in exactly the same way that its expected profit or cost is computed from conditional profits or costs. Thus in our example the expected opportunity loss of a decision to stock 3 units is computed as $1.60 in Table 7.3, where the conditional losses are taken from the proper column in Table 7.2 and the probabilities are taken from Table 4.1.

Table 7.3
Expected Loss with Stock of 3

z	$P(z)$	Conditional loss	Expected loss
0	.05	$6	$ .30
1	.10	4	.40
2	.25	2	.50
3	.30	0	0
4	.20	1	.20
5	.10	2	.20
	1.00		$1.60

In order to get a more intuitive feeling for the meaning of this result, let us imagine that the retailer has actually stocked 3 units in each of the past 100 weeks and that the various values of demand have actually occurred with relative frequencies equal to the probabilities of Table 7.3—there was no demand in 5 of the 100 weeks, demand for 1 unit in each of 10 weeks, and so forth. Then we can say that in this imaginary situation *the retailer's average weekly profit was $1.60 less than it would have been if he had known each week's demand in advance and stocked accordingly.*

7.3 Expected Profit or Cost of Action under Certainty

We now turn to the second method of computing expected loss which we mentioned in Section 7.1.1: comparison of the expected profit or cost of an act chosen in the light of the information actually available with the expected profit or cost of an act chosen in the light of perfect information. To give an intuitive idea of the meaning of such a comparison before we enter into its details, let us reexamine the way in which we visualized expected loss in terms of losses actually realized over a period of 100 weeks. We imagined a situation in which relative frequencies were actually equal to the assigned probabilities and said that the retailer's average profit with a stock of 3 was $1.60 less than it would have been if he had known each week's demand in advance and had stocked accordingly. In terms of such a visualization, what we are now about to do amounts to obtaining this $1.60 figure by actually computing the average profit which the retailer could have made if he had known each week's demand in advance and then subtracting from this the average profit which resulted from stocking 3 units every week.

7.3.1   Computation of Expected Profit under Certainty

The method by which we can calculate the expected profit of acting with perfect information or "under certainty" can easily be made clear by studying Table 7.4, where this profit is computed for the inventory example we have been considering. Since we are now assuming that the retailer will be told the exact demand before he places his order, his *conditional* profit for each event is the *greatest possible* profit for that

Table 7.4
Expected Profit under Certainty

z	$P(z)$	Conditional profit	Expected profit
0	.05	$0	$0
1	.10	1	.10
2	.25	2	.50
3	.30	3	.90
4	.20	4	.80
5	.10	5	.50
	1.00		$2.80

event, i.e. the starred entry in the row describing that event in the payoff table, Table 7.1. The expected value of this random variable "profit under certainty" is then computed as $2.80 in absolutely standard fashion. In terms of the frequency visualization, this is the average profit which the retailer would have made over the 100-week period if he had stocked exactly the right amount each week. Notice very carefully, however, that when we deal with our real problem, i.e. with probabilities and expectations rather than with historical frequencies and averages, the *retailer's expected profit under certainty depends on the probability distribu-*

tion which the retailer assigns to the random variable "demand." Although $2.80 is the retailer's "expected profit under certainty," it is not the profit which the retailer would be certain to make if he had perfect information. This latter figure is known by God alone and is irrelevant to the problem of decision under uncertainty. Observe, however, that the point just made corresponds exactly to the fact that the retailer's *expected loss* due to imperfect information is not a loss which he is *certain* to suffer because of his imperfect information.

Relation of Expected Profit under Certainty to Expected Demand. If we look at the *conditional* profits under certainty in Table 7.4 we see immediately that they are given by the formula

Conditional profit under certainty $= \$1\ z$,

and in *any problem where the same profit k_p is made on every unit sold* we will have a formula of this same type:

Conditional profit under certainty $= k_p z$.

The conditional profit given by a formula of this type is a *linear* function of demand—if we graph $k_p z$ against z the graph is a straight line—and therefore by Section 5.3.1

Expected profit under certainty $= k_p\ \mathrm{E}(\tilde{z})$.

In terms of frequencies rather than probabilities, the retailer's stock *under certainty* would match demand on every day, and therefore his average profit would be simply average demand times profit per unit.

7.3.2   Use of Expected Profit under Certainty to Compute Expected Loss

In Table 4.3 we computed the retailer's expected profit with a stock of 3 as $1.20. Subtracting this figure from the $2.80 profit he could "expect" with perfect information, we obtain $1.60 as his expected loss due to imperfect information. The result is identical to the result we obtained in Table 7.3 by using conditional losses.

To make the relation between these two methods of computing expected loss still clearer, we combine in Table 7.5 the computation of expected profit with a stock of 3 units and expected profit under certainty. The conditional profits with a stock of 3 are taken from the corresponding column in Table 7.1; the conditional profits under certainty are, we repeat, the starred entries in Table 7.1. The expectations of these two random variables are computed in the usual manner in the last two columns of Table 7.5, and the expected loss with a stock of 3 is the difference between the totals of these last two columns.

Table 7.5

	Conditional profit		$P(z)$	Expected profit	
z	With stock of 3	Greatest possible		With stock of 3	Greatest possible
0	$-\$6$	$+\$0$	.05	$-\$ \ .30$	$+\$0$
1	$-\ 3$	$+\ 1$	.10	$-\ \ .30$	$+\ \ .10$
2	0	$+\ 2$	.25	0	$+\ \ .50$
3	$+\ 3$	$+\ 3$	.30	$+\ \ .90$	$+\ \ .90$
4	$+\ 3$	$+\ 4$	.20	$+\ \ .60$	$+\ \ .80$
5	$+\ 3$	$+\ 5$	.10	$+\ \ .30$	$+\ \ .50$
			$\overline{1.00}$	$\overline{+\$1.20}$	$\overline{+\$2.80}$

Observe now that our previous method of finding the expected loss (Table 7.3) consisted in:

1. Taking the differences between individual pairs of entries in columns 2 and 3, i.e. the *conditional losses;*
2. Taking the expectation of these conditional losses, i.e. multiplying each by its probability and adding.

The new method consists in

1. Taking the expectations of columns 2 and 3;
2. Taking the differences between these expectations.

It is obvious that in any problem whatever we will obtain the same results by either of these two methods.

7.4   Interpretations of Expected Loss

7.4.1   *Comparison of Acts in Terms of Expected Loss*

The fact that the expected loss of any act is the difference between its expected profit and the expected profit of action under certainty means that once we have computed the expected profits of all possible acts in any decision problem it is easy to compute the expected losses of all the acts or vice versa. The expected profits for all acts in our inventory example were computed in Chapter 4 and are reproduced in the second column of Table 7.6; the expected losses shown in the last column of the table are computed by simply subtracting the profit of each act from the $2.80 profit of action under certainty.

Notice that this relation among profit, loss, and profit under certainty immediately implies that *in any decision problem whatever:*

The difference between the expected profits of any two acts is equal in magnitude but opposite in sign to the difference between their expected losses.

Table 7.6
Expected Profits and Losses of All Acts

Q	Expected profit	Expected loss
0	$0	$2.80
1	+ .85	1.95
2	+ 1.40	1.40
3	+ 1.20	1.60
4	+ .10	2.70
5	− 1.60	4.40

Thus in our example *profit* with a stock of 3 is *higher* than profit with a stock of 4 by $1.20 − $.10 = $1.10; *loss* with a stock of 3 is *lower* than loss with a stock of 4 by $2.70 − $1.60 = $1.10. The student can easily convince himself that when payoff tables are expressed in terms of cost rather than profit

The difference between the expected costs of any two acts is equal in magnitude and identical in sign to the difference between their expected losses.

7.4.2 *The Cost of Uncertainty and the Cost of Irrationality*

By Table 7.6, the best possible decision which the retailer can make under uncertainty has an expected opportunity loss of $1.40. This $1.40 can be considered to be the *inherent cost of uncertainty itself*, since it is the difference between the *best* that the decision maker can expect to do with the information he has available and what he could expect to do with perfect information. We can also look at this $1.40 loss as being the *greatest price which it would be reasonable for the decision maker to pay for a perfect forecast*, and this way of regarding the cost will be very instructive when we come to consider the expenditure of money on sampling in order to improve our "forecasts" of certain kinds of events. It is thus apparent that the expected opportunity loss of the best possible decision will be a quantity of considerable interest in the analysis of any problem of decision under uncertainty, and we shall therefore give it a name. We define

Cost of uncertainty: the expected opportunity loss of the *best possible* decision under a given probability distribution.

The cost of uncertainty in our example is the loss associated with a stock of 2 units. If instead of stocking 2 units the retailer stocks any other number, his expected loss will be greater than the $1.40 cost of uncertainty. Such an additional expected loss is completely unnecessary, and we define

Cost of irrationality: the amount by which the expected opportunity loss of the chosen decision exceeds the cost of uncertainty under a given probability distribution.

7.5 Expected Loss When the Conditional Losses Are "Proportional"

We saw in Section 5.3.2 that when conditional profit with a given stock Q has a broken-line graph of the form shown in Figure 5.5, we can compute expected profit from a formula which involves only cumulative probabilities and a partial expectation of the basic random variable demand; and we saw in Section 7.3.1 above that when conditional profit under certainty is linear, expected profit under certainty can be computed from a formula involving only the ordinary expectation of demand. This means that we could obtain a formula for expected loss in problems of the type we have been studying by simply subtracting the formula for profit with a stock of Q from the formula for profit under certainty, but we can get results which are applicable to a much wider class of problems by proceeding as follows. We shall first show that the conditional losses in problems of the type we have been studying are *proportional* to the difference between the act Q and the random variable $\tilde{z}$; and we shall then derive formulas for expected loss in *any* problem where the losses are proportional to a difference of this kind, whether or not it is an inventory problem of the kind we have been studying as an example.

7.5.1 Direct Computation of Proportional Conditional Losses

While the conditional losses in *any* problem can always be computed by first constructing a payoff table and then deriving the loss table from it as we did in Section 7.2.1 above, the conditional losses in many problems can be easily computed by a more direct line of reasoning which we shall now explain by using our inventory problem as an example. It is obvious in this problem that if the stock Q chosen by the retailer proves to be exactly *equal* to the quantity actually demanded, the resulting loss is 0; we shall now consider separately the losses which a stock Q entails if it turns out to be *over* or *under* the quantity actually demanded.

Loss Due to Overage. If the retailer's stock is *over* the quantity actually demanded, he will have to salvage the excess units and each unit salvaged will entail a loss amounting to the $2.00 difference between the $2.50 cost of the unit and its $.50 salvage value. Consequently

Conditional loss of overage = $2(Q - z)$.

Loss Due to Underage. The retailer makes a profit ot

$3.70 - $.20 - $2.50 = $1.00

on every unit stocked and sold. If, therefore, his stock is *under* the quantity actually demanded, he has an opportunity loss amounting to $1 for every unit of unsatisfied demand. Consequently

Conditional loss of underage = $1(z - Q)$.

The implications of these two formulas are illustrated graphically in Figure 7.1, which shows the conditional losses for stocks of $Q = 2$ and $Q = 3$. Notice that in both cases the graph forms an asymmetric V whose point shows that loss is 0 when $z = Q$; for all other z, *the height of*

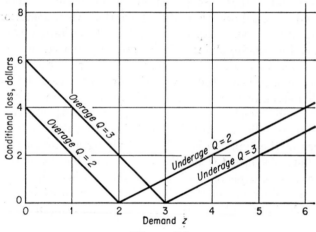

Figure 7.1

either arm of the V is proportional to the difference $(Q - z)$ or $(z - Q)$ as the case may be. Notice carefully that because we have defined an overage as an excess of *stock over demand*, it is the *left-hand* branch of each V which gives the conditional loss of overage while the right-hand branch gives the cost of underage. If $Q = 3$ and $z = 1$, the retailer will have 2 units left *over* and will suffer a loss of $2 \times $2 = 4; if $Q = 2$ and $z = 5$, he will be *under* or short by 3 units and will suffer a loss of $3 \times $1 = 3.

7.5.2   Computation of Expected Loss

We now proceed in Table 7.7 to compute expected loss with a stock of $Q = 3$. The computation is really identical to the one shown in Table 7.3; the only differences are differences of form which will now be explained.

1. Instead of giving the net conditional loss for each z, the loss is written out according to the appropriate one of the two formulas derived above. Thus where Table 7.3 shows a conditional loss of $4 for $z = 1$, Table 7.7 shows that this 2-unit overage has a loss of $(3 - 1)$2$.

2. Instead of multiplying $P(z)$ into the *net* conditional loss for each z, Table 7.7 multiplies $P(z)$ into each part of the conditional loss separately. Thus where Table 7.3 has the entry $.10 \times \$4 = \$.40$ as the last entry in the row for $z = 1$, Table 7.7 has the equivalent $(.10 \times 3 - .10 \times 1)2.

Table 7.7

Expected Loss with Stock of 3

z	$P(z)$	Conditional loss	Expected loss
0	.05	$(3 - 0)$2$	$(.05 \times 3 - .05 \times 0)2
1	.10	$(3 - 1)$2$	$(.10 \times 3 - .10 \times 1)2
2	.25	$(3 - 2)$2$	$(.25 \times 3 - .25 \times 2)2
3	.30	$(3 - 3)$2$	$(.30 \times 3 - .30 \times 3)2
	.70	Expected loss due to overage:	$(.70 \times 3 - 1.50)$2$
4	.20	$(4 - 3)$1$	$(.20 \times 4 - .20 \times 3)1
5	.10	$(5 - 3)$1$	$(.10 \times 5 - .10 \times 3)1
	.30	Expected loss due to underage:	$(1.30 - .30 \times 3)$1$

3. Instead of adding all the entries in the last column to obtain a single figure for expected loss, Table 7.7 brings out two subtotals, one for the values of z which correspond to an *overage* (i.e. to the case $Q > z$) and one for those which correspond to an *underage* (the case $Q < z$). Since there is no loss in the case $z = Q = 3$ exactly, the line for $z = 3$ could have been included in the second half of the table rather than the first or could even have been omitted entirely without changing the numerical value of either of the subtotals; it was put in the first half of the table merely because this makes the resulting formulas a little easier to use when the partial expectations are computed graphically.

If now we examine the *first subtotal* in Table 7.7, we see that the .70 inside the parentheses is the sum of $P(z)$ for all $z \leq 3$ and is therefore $P(\tilde{z} \leq 3)$ while the 1.50 in these same parentheses is the sum of $z \, P(z)$ for all $z \leq 3$ and is therefore $E_0^3(\tilde{z})$. Thus

$$\text{Expected loss due to overage} = \$2[3 \, P(\tilde{z} \leq 3) - E_0^3(\tilde{z})].$$

Examining the *second subtotal*, we see that the 1.30 inside the parentheses is the sum of $z \, P(z)$ for all $z > 3$ and is therefore $E_4^\infty(\tilde{z})$ while the .30 in these same parentheses is the sum of $P(z)$ for all $z > 3$ and is therefore $P(\tilde{z} > 3)$. Thus

$$\text{Expected loss due to underage} = \$1[E_4^\infty(\tilde{z}) - 3 \, P(\tilde{z} > 3)].$$

To generalize this example, let us now define for any problem with *proportional conditional losses:*

k_o: loss per unit of *overage*, i.e. the loss per unit by which the stock Q exceeds demand;

k_u: loss per unit of *underage*, i.e. the loss per unit by which the stock Q is insufficient to satisfy demand.†

In our example, we had $k_o = \$2$, $k_u = \$1$, and $Q = 3$. Substituting the general symbols for their numerical values in the formulas given just above we obtain

$$\text{Expected loss due to overage} = k_o[Q\,\mathrm{P}(\tilde{z} \leq Q) - \mathrm{E}_0^Q(\tilde{z})]$$
$$\text{Expected loss due to underage} = k_u[\mathrm{E}_{Q+1}^\infty(\tilde{z}) - Q\,\mathrm{P}(\tilde{z} > Q)]$$

7.6   Incremental Opportunity Loss

In Chapter 4 we saw that the expected profit of a decision to stock Q units can be regarded as the sum of the incremental expected profits of decisions to stock a 1st, 2d, . . . , Qth unit and not to stock any additional units; and this way of looking at the decision problem has proved useful in two respects: it makes it much easier to identify the best number of units to stock, and it makes it much easier to compute the effect on expected profit of changes in the total number of units stocked.   We shall now see that incremental analysis can be applied just as well when we are working in terms of loss as when we are working in terms of profit.

7.6.1   *Conditional Incremental Loss*

The conditional losses of any incremental decision can always be found by starting from the payoff table for the decision in question.   In Section 4.2 we saw that the payoff table for a decision concerning the jth unit in our inventory example had the form shown in Table 7.8, and in Table 7.9 we proceed to derive the corresponding loss table in exactly the same way that we derived Table 7.2 from Table 7.1.   We star the highest profit in each row of the payoff table, and we then subtract each entry in the payoff table from the starred entry in the same row.

In many problems conditional incremental losses can also be derived

---

† It is easy to see that in the particular kind of inventory problem we are using as an example the quantity k_o defined here must have the same *value* as the quantity k_n of Section 4.2.1 and that k_u must have the same value as k_p.   The *definitions* are entirely different, however, and we shall see in later chapters that the concepts of loss per unit of overage and underage are applicable in many problems in which the quantities k_n and k_p as defined in Section 4.2.1 would have no meaning.

Table 7.8
Payoff Table for the *j*th Unit

Event	Act	
	Do not stock	Stock
$\tilde{z} < j$	$0*	−$2
$\tilde{z} \geq j$	0	+ 1*

Table 7.9
Loss Table for the *j*th Unit

Event	Act	
	Do not stock	Stock
$\tilde{z} < j$	$0	$2
$\tilde{z} \geq j$	1	0

by direct reasoning, without drawing up a payoff table.   We observe first of all that the loss table for *any* incremental decision must have 0's in the two positions where they are shown in Table 7.9 and 7.10, since not stocking the *j*th unit is obviously the best possible decision when less than *j* units are demanded and stocking the *j*th unit is obviously the best decision when *j* or more units are demanded.   In problems where the conditional *total* losses are proportional in the sense of Section 7.5.1 above we can then derive the other two entries in Table 7.9 or 7.10 by the following reasoning.

Table 7.10
Loss Table for the *j*th Unit

Event	Act	
	Do not stock	Stock
$\tilde{z} < j$	0	k_o
$\tilde{z} \geq j$	k_u	0

1. If the *j*th unit *is* demanded, i.e. if $\tilde{z} \geq j$, then *not* stocking this unit either creates a 1-unit underage or increases the underage due to previous incremental decisions by 1 unit; in either case an incremental loss of amount k_u is incurred.   In the particular example we are studying, this incremental loss is simply the profit which could have been made by stocking and selling the *j*th unit.

2. If the *j*th unit is *not* demanded, i.e. if $\tilde{z} < j$, then *stocking* this unit either creates a 1-unit overage or increases the overage due to previous incremental decisions by 1 unit; in either case an incremental loss of amount k_o is incurred.   In the particular example we are studying, this incremental loss is simply the difference between the cost of the unsold unit and its salvage value.

7.6.2   *Expected Incremental Loss*

In Table 7.11 the expected losses of the two possible decisions whose conditional losses are shown in Table 7.10 are computed by our standard

Table 7.11
Computation of Incremental Expected Loss

Event	Probability	Loss of not stocking		Loss of stocking	
		Conditional	Expected	Conditional	Expected
$\tilde{z} < j$	$P(\tilde{z} < j)$	0	0	k_o	$k_o\,P(\tilde{z} < j)$
$\tilde{z} \geq j$	$P(\tilde{z} \geq j)$	k_u	$k_u\,P(\tilde{z} \geq j)$	0	0
	1		$k_u\,P(\tilde{z} \geq j)$		$k_o\,P(\tilde{z} < j)$

procedure. This computation shows that the incremental expected losses in any problem of this kind are given by the formulas

Expected loss of not stocking the jth unit $= k_u\,P(\tilde{z} \geq j)$
Expected loss of stocking the jth unit $= k_o\,P(\tilde{z} < j)$

Let us now apply these two formulas to the *first unit* in the example we have been studying. In that example $k_o = \$2$, $k_u = \$1$, $P(\tilde{z} \geq 1) = .95$, and $P(\tilde{z} < 1) = .05$, so that

Expected loss of not stocking the first unit $= \$1 \times .95 = \$.95$,
Expected loss of stocking the first unit $= \$2 \times .05 = \$.10$.

Thus it is $\$.85$ better to stock this first unit than not to stock it. The $\$.10$ loss attached to the *better* act is the unavoidable *cost of uncertainty* attached to the decision concerning the first unit. The $\$.85$ difference between this unavoidable loss and the loss of the *worse* act is the *incremental profit* of making the correct decision, i.e. of stocking the first unit—recall that the expected profit of *not* stocking is obviously 0 and that the difference between the expected profits of *any* two decisions is equal in magnitude to the difference between their expected losses.

Table 7.12
Complete Incremental Analysis

Serial j	$P(\tilde{z} < j)$	Loss of stocking	$P(\tilde{z} \geq j)$	Loss of not stocking
1	.05	$ .10	.95	$.95
2	.15	.30	.85	.85
3	.40	.80	.60	.60
4	.70	1.40	.30	.30
5	.90	1.80	.10	.10

In Table 7.12 these two formulas are used to compute the expected incremental losses of both possible decisions for every successive unit in our example from the first through the fifth; the student will recall that no more than 5 units can possibly be sold at full price. The *total* expected loss of stocking any particular *number of units* Q can be found from this table by adding (1) the incremental losses of *stocking* all units up to and including Q plus (2) the incremental losses of *not* stocking all units with serial numbers higher than Q. Thus expected loss with a stock of 3 is $.10 + $.30 + $.80 + $.30 + $.10 = $1.60, in agreement with Table 7.3.

Notice that while a decision not to stock a particular unit always has 0 expected profit, it does not in general have 0 expected loss. It is only when we are *certain* that a particular unit will or will not be sold that we can make a decision concerning that unit without expected loss.

7.6.3   Practical Selection of the Best Decision

Behavior of Incremental Loss with Increasing j. Looking at Table 7.12 we see that the expected incremental loss of *stocking* becomes *higher* for each successive unit stocked while the expected loss of *not* stocking becomes *lower* for each successive unit stocked. Furthermore the expected incremental losses *must* behave in this way in any problem in which the conditional losses k_o and k_u are the same for every successive unit stocked, since when this is true the only factors in the expected losses which change from one unit to the next are the tail probabilities $P(\tilde{z} < j)$ and $P(\tilde{z} \geq j)$, and the former of these can never decrease with an increase in j while the latter can never increase with an increase in j. It follows that in any problem of this sort the expected loss of stocking will be less than the expected loss of not stocking for *every* successive unit up to a certain value of j while the reverse will be true for *every* unit above this value of j, and therefore:

> In any problem where the *conditional* incremental losses are the *same for every successive unit,* all that we need to do to find the best stock level is to find the highest serial number j for which the expected incremental loss of stocking is less than the expected incremental loss of not stocking.

Location of the Last Profitable Unit. The greatest j for which the loss of stocking is less than the loss of not stocking can easily be found without actually computing *any* expected losses. Using the formulas for the expected losses of stocking and not stocking derived in Section 7.6.2 above, we see that the jth unit should be stocked if

$$k_o \, P(\tilde{z} < j) < k_u \, P(\tilde{z} \geq j).$$

Replacing $P(\tilde{z} \geq j)$ by $1 - P(\tilde{z} < j)$ and doing a little elementary algebra we put this condition in the more convenient form

●━━●━━●

$$P(\tilde{z} < j) < \frac{k_u}{k_u + k_o}$$ *Condition for stocking the jth unit*

●━━●━━●

We remind the student that *this formula holds only when the per-unit losses k_u and k_o are the same for every unit which might be added to the decision quantity Q.* When this is *not* true, it may well be that the incremental loss of stocking *both* a third and fourth unit is less than the loss of not stocking these 2 units even though the loss of stocking the third unit alone is greater than the loss of not stocking this unit. An example of such a situation was discussed at the end of Chapter 4.

PROBLEMS

1. Table 7.6 shows an expected loss of $1.95 for the act $Q = 1$ in the example discussed in the text. Verify this loss by taking the expectation of the conditional losses for $Q = 1$ (the method of Table 7.3).

2. In the situation of Chapter 4, Problem 1:

a. Draw up a loss table.

b. Compute the expected losses of the three possible acts by taking the expectations of the conditional losses.

c. Compute expected profit under certainty.

d. Verify your answers to (*b*) by using your answers to (*c*) above and to (*b*) of the original problem.

3. In the situation of Chapter 4, Problem 3, and Chapter 5, Problem 1:

a. Compute expected profit under certainty using the mean of the distribution of demand.

b. Using your answers to (*a*) above and to (*a*) of the original problem, compute the cost of uncertainty on the assumption that failure to meet a demand has no effect on future demand.

c. What are the per-unit losses of underage and overage k_u and k_o if the operator believes that failure to satisfy any one customer's request for a journal will lead to *future* lost profits amounting to $1 *in addition* to the lost profit on the immediate sale? This is an example of good-will cost, which we define as follows:

> Good-will cost: the loss *over and above* immediate loss of profit which is incurred for *each unit* of unsatisfied demand.

d. How many units should the operator stock under the condition of (*c*) and what is the cost of uncertainty?

e. What is the smallest good-will cost which would justify a stock of 30 copies?

4. In the situation of Chapter 4, Problem 4, and Chapter 5, Problem 2, compute the cost of uncertainty:

a. By use of expected profit under certainty.

b. By use of the formula derived in Section 7.5.2.

5. In the situation of Chapter 6, Problem 2, compute the cost of uncertainty using the formula derived in Section 7.5.2.

CHAPTER 8

Lump-sum Losses; Scrap Allowances

In the last chapter we saw that in inventory problems of the kind we have been studying hitherto the conditional losses of overage and underage are *proportional* to the difference between the decision quantity Q and the value of the basic random variable. Another type of conditional loss frequently encountered in practical business problems is one which is incurred if there is *any* underage but whose amount is *independent of the size of the underage*. In the present chapter we shall use a certain class of scrap-allowance problems as an example of situations in which a "lump-sum" loss of this kind is present, but we shall see in the exercises at the end of the chapter that it can occur equally well in problems of inventory control.

8.1 The Economics of Scrap Allowances in Production to Order

When a production run is scheduled to fill a requirement for a specified number of pieces rather than to produce for stock, uncertainty concerning the number of defectives which will be produced in a run of any given size usually creates a risk of loss. On the one hand the number of good pieces resulting from the run may fall short of the requirement—an *underage* may occur. If this happens, it may be necessary to set up the process again in order to fill out the requirements, or at the very least the underage will result in a reduction of the profit realized on the sale of the good pieces. On the other hand, the extra material scheduled into production in order to reduce the risk of a shortage may prove excessive—an *overage* may occur. If this happens, the product of the excess material may have to be treated as scrap whether or not it is actually defective, and even at best the value of the good pieces produced from the excess material is never enough to cover the cost of the material and the labor put into it—if it were, the excess pieces would have been scheduled for profit rather than as a scrap allowance.

8.1.1 Conditional Loss Due to Overage

In some situations the loss *per unit of excess production* will vary with the number of excess units produced—a few can be disposed of at a good

133

price but a larger quantity cannot, and so forth. In many situations, however, the loss per excess piece will be the same regardless of the number of excess pieces, and this is the only case which we shall study in this chapter. In this case the *total* loss due to overage will be *proportional* to the size of the overage and is thus identical in form to the loss due to overage in the inventory problems studied in earlier chapters; accordingly we shall use the same symbol for the per-unit loss which we used there:

k_o: loss incurred by scheduling one unneeded piece into production.

Considerable care must be taken in determining the value of k_o. The simplest situation is the one in which the excess pieces will have to be sold as scrap whether they come out good or defective, so that k_o is simply variable manufacturing cost less scrap value. This is the only situation which will be studied in this chapter, but it is far from being the only one occurring in practice. In many situations, excess good pieces can be inventoried for later sale; in this case k_o is the expected cost of carrying a piece in inventory until it is needed.† In other situations, excess good pieces can be sold at a reduced price; in this case k_o is the variable manufacturing cost less the expected value of the product.‡

8.1.2 Conditional Loss Due to Underage

As regards the loss due to underage, the scrap-allowance problem will again be very similar to the inventory problem of Chapter 7 if the purchaser accepts the short lot at a reduction in price proportional to the size of the shortage. If, however, the manufacturer is obliged to supply exactly or at least the specified number of good pieces, there is a very material difference between the two problems. An underage of *any* size will make it necessary to schedule a second run to fill out the requirement, and it is obvious that the resulting loss will *not* be proportional to the size of the underage. It will on the contrary be almost completely independent of the size of shortage, and we therefore define

K_u: total amount of the loss resulting from an underage,

using a capital rather than a small letter to remind the student that this is a *total* rather than a *per-unit* loss.

If idle time is available on all the machines used in the production process, K_u includes the variable labor cost of setting up the machines, doing the paper work involved in scheduling a second lot, and expediting this second lot through the shop. If some or all of the required machines

---

† The probability that the scheduled piece will be good times the cost of carrying it if it *is* good.

‡ (Probability good) × (value good) + (probability defective) × (value defective).

are being used to capacity, we must also include the loss of profits which could have been made on other work during the time the machines are down for the resetup and the "disruption cost" of the general confusion which results from having short lots going through a heavily loaded shop. This last kind of loss, which rarely appears in the accounts, is often a very substantial part of the total real loss entailed by an underrun.

Second-order Losses Due to Underage. In addition to these losses which will *certainly* be incurred if a rerun has to be made, a need for a rerun means that there is a *risk* of incurring still further losses because the rerun may itself result in an overage or an underage. Under certain conditions, however, the expected value of these "second-order" losses is negligible in comparison with the "direct" loss described in the previous paragraph, and it is only this simpler problem which we shall study in this chapter. Rather than try to define these conditions in advance, we shall first study how to solve scrap-allowance problems on the *assumption* that the second-order losses are *strictly zero*. This is equivalent to assuming that *if a rerun is in fact required, the number of pieces scheduled will be just enough to yield the required number of good pieces.* After we have understood the logic of this simpler problem, we shall be able to examine the conditions under which second-order losses may be treated as *practically* zero in reaching a practical decision.

8.1.3   Events and Acts

The random variable whose value will determine the manufacturer's loss in scrap-allowance problems of the kind we are considering in this chapter can best be understood if we visualize the production process as turning out pieces serially rather than simultaneously—whether the pieces are in fact so produced is irrelevant. The *potential* output of the process is then an unending sequence of good and defective pieces in some unknown but "predestined" order such as *ggdgggddg* . . . , and we visualize every piece in this potentially infinite sequence as bearing a *serial number* which shows its position in the sequence. If then we define

G: the required number of good pieces,
n: the serial number of the Gth *good* piece,

we may consider n as being the unknown value of a *random variable $\tilde{n}$.*†
The *events* in the payoff or loss table will be the set of all possible values of this random variable.

The *acts* in a scrap-allowance problem can be described more conveniently by the *total number of pieces produced* than by the size of the scrap allowance as such, and we therefore define

† In terms of the discussion in Section 3.1, every conceivable infinite sequence of *g*'s and *d*'s is an *elementary event*. The random variable $\tilde{n}$ assigns to each elementary event a *value n* equal to the serial number of the Gth good piece in the sequence.

Q: the total number of pieces produced on the initial run; the size of the production order.

Using this notation we can now make our previous discussion of the conditional losses more explicit.

1. If the value n of the random variable $\tilde{n}$ is *equal* to Q, this means that the *last* piece produced on the initial run turned out to be the Gth good piece. The initial run was *just* long enough to produce the required number of good pieces and neither an underage nor an overage has occurred. The act Q was optimal after the fact, and the manufacturer's loss is 0.

2. If n is *less* than Q, the Gth good piece occurred *before* the end of the initial run and all succeeding pieces were excess. An *overage* has occurred of size $(Q - n)$, and the manufacturer's loss is $k_o(Q - n)$.

3. If n is *greater* than Q, the Gth good piece will occur *after* the end of the initial run—the initial run has resulted in an *underage* of size $(n - Q)$. Notice that $(n - Q)$ is *not* the known difference between number of good pieces required and the number actually produced on the initial run; it is the still *unknown* difference between the total number of pieces produced on the initial run and the total number of pieces which must be produced in order to get the required G good pieces. The variable cost $k_o(n - Q)$ which will be incurred in manufacturing these pieces does *not* represent a loss, since this cost would have been incurred even if the pieces had been manufactured on the initial run. The actual loss—i.e., the costs which *could* have been avoided by manufacturing all n pieces on the initial run— will be the sum of (a) the costs of scheduling and setting up for the rerun or reruns which are made before G good pieces emerge and (b) the variable manufacturing cost of all pieces produced *after* the Gth good piece on the last rerun.

If after making the initial run the manufacturer knew the value n, he would of course schedule *exactly* $(n - Q)$ pieces on the first rerun and his loss would be simply the setup cost K_u of this one rerun. When we make our simplifying assumption that exactly the required number of pieces *will* be scheduled on the first rerun and that the loss of underage *will* be exactly K_u, *we are in effect assuming that the manufacturer will know the exact value of n as soon as the initial run has been completed.* We shall see later on that *under certain conditions* the manufacturer's knowledge of n after the initial run will in fact be accurate enough to be treated as exact for all practical purposes.

8.1.4 *Payoff and Loss Tables*

As a first and much oversimplified example intended solely to bring out the implications of the discussion above, suppose that a manufacturer has contracted to deliver exactly $G = 10$ good pieces at a fixed price, that it costs K_u = \$1000 to schedule and set up for one production run, and that each piece produced has a variable manufacturing cost of k_o = \$3. Assume further that the manufacturer is *sure* that he will not have to produce more than 16 pieces in all in order to obtain the required 10 good pieces.

Table 8.1
Payoff Table

Event	Act Q						
n	10	11	12	13	14	15	16
10	\$1030*	\$1033	\$1036	\$1039	\$1042	\$1045	\$1048
11	2033	1033*	1036	1039	1042	1045	1048
12	2036	2036	1036*	1039	1042	1045	1048
13	2039	2039	2039	1039*	1042	1045	1048
14	2042	2042	2042	2042	1042*	1045	1048
15	2045	2045	2045	2045	2045	1045*	1048
16	2048	2048	2048	2048	2048	2048	1048*

On the assumption that n will be known exactly after the initial run has been completed, the *payoff table* for this example will be as shown in Table 8.1. Taking the case where the thirteenth piece produced will be the tenth good piece ($\tilde{n}$ = 13) as an example, we see that if the manufacturer schedules exactly 13 pieces on the initial run (Q = 13) his total cost will be the sum of the \$1000 setup cost of the initial run plus the \$39 variable cost of the 13 pieces produced. If he schedules *more* than 13 pieces ($Q > 13$), he adds \$3 to his costs for every additional piece. If he schedules *less* than 13 pieces ($Q < 13$), he incurs an additional \$1000 setup cost but by our simplifying assumption will produce exactly the required 13 pieces on the two runs together and therefore will incur only the minimum variable cost of \$39.

Table 8.2
Loss Table

Event	Act Q						
n	10	11	12	13	14	15	16
10	\$ 0	\$ 3	\$ 6	\$ 9	\$ 12	\$ 15	\$18
11	1000	0	3	6	9	12	15
12	1000	1000	0	3	6	9	12
13	1000	1000	1000	0	3	6	9
14	1000	1000	1000	1000	0	3	6
15	1000	1000	1000	1000	1000	0	3
16	1000	1000	1000	1000	1000	1000	0

The *loss table* for this same example is shown as Table 8.2.   Again taking $\tilde{n} = 13$ as an example, we see that loss is 0 if $Q = 13$, that loss is $\$3(Q - 13)$ if $Q > 13$, and that loss is $\$1000$ if $Q < 13$.

8.1.5   Computation of Expected Loss

Assume now that the manufacturer of this example assigns to $\tilde{n}$ the probability distribution shown in the first two columns of Table 8.3 and that he wishes to know the expected loss of a decision to schedule $Q = 13$ pieces.   In the remainder of Table 8.3 this loss is shown to be $\$15.85$; the computation is carried out by our "standard" method except that sub-totals are brought out separately for the expected loss of overage ($\$5.85$) and underage ($\$10$).   The separation of the total expected loss into two

Table 8.3

n	$P(n)$	Conditional loss	Expected loss
10	.300	$(13 - 10)\$3$	$\$2.70$
11	.400	$(13 - 11)\$3$	2.40
12	.250	$(13 - 12)\$3$	.75
13	.040	$(13 - 13)\$3$	0
	.990	Expected loss of overage:	$\$ 5.85$
14	.007	$\$1000$	7.00
15	.002	$\$1000$	2.00
16	.001	$\$1000$	1.00
	.010	Expected loss of underage:	10.00
	1.000	Total expected loss:	$\$15.85$

parts serves exactly the same purpose which it served in Section 7.5.2—it makes it easy to derive formulas from which total expected loss can easily be computed in problems where the possible values of $\tilde{n}$ are very numerous and computation by the standard method would be prohibitive.

It has already been emphasized that the conditional loss due to *overage* in our present problem is of the same *proportional* type which we studied in Section 7.5.2, and the student can readily see that the first half of Table 8.1 is identical in form to the first half of Table 7.7.   Accordingly the formula for *expected* loss of overage which was derived in Section 7.5.2 can be applied to our present problem by simply changing the name of the basic random variable from $\tilde{z}$ to $\tilde{n}$:

$$\text{Expected loss due to overage} = k_o[Q \, \mathrm{P}(\tilde{n} \leq Q) - \mathrm{E}_0^Q(\tilde{n})]$$

We *cannot* use the formula for expected loss of *underage* which was derived in Section 7.5.2 because the conditional loss of underage in our present problem is not of the proportional type, but it is easy enough to derive the proper formula by mere inspection of Table 8.1. The $10 expected loss there shown is obviously equal to the $1000 conditional loss of underage multiplied by the probability that there will be an underage, i.e. by $P(\tilde{n} > 13) = .10$, and in general

$$\text{Expected loss due to underage} = K_u \, P(\tilde{n} > Q)$$

8.1.6 Conditional Incremental Loss

As in any problem where an act consists in the selection of a quantity, we may look at the choice of any given Q in our present problem as being the result of a sequence of incremental decisions to schedule a 1st, 2d, . . . , Qth unit, and not to schedule any additional units. The general ideas involved in the application of this kind of analysis to problems of the type we are now studying are the same as in earlier chapters, but there are two very important differences of detail to which the student should pay close attention.

The first of these differences is apparent as soon as we look at the *loss table* for a decision concerning the *jth unit* in problems of the present type. Such a table is shown as Table 8.4; it is derived by the following reasoning.

Table 8.4
Loss Table for the *j*th Unit

Event	Act	
	Do not schedule	Schedule
$\tilde{n} < j$	0	k_o
$\tilde{n} = j$	K_u	0
$\tilde{n} > j$	0	0

Loss of Scheduling. If *j or more* pieces must be produced in order to get G good pieces, i.e. if $\tilde{n} \geq j$, then scheduling the *j*th unit is obviously a good decision after the fact and its loss is 0; this accounts for the two 0's in the column describing the act "schedule." If *less than j* pieces need be produced in order to obtain G good pieces, $\tilde{n} < j$, then scheduling the *j*th piece is simply a waste of the variable manufacturing cost k_o and leads to a loss of this amount. The conditional losses of scheduling the *j*th piece in our present problem thus correspond exactly to the conditional losses of stocking the *j*th unit in Chapter 7.

Loss of Not Scheduling. If *less than j* pieces need be produced in order to get G good pieces, $\tilde{n} < j$, then not scheduling the *j*th piece is obviously the better decision and entails 0 loss. If *exactly j* pieces must be produced, $\tilde{n} = j$, then not scheduling the *j*th piece means that an

underage will occur and a rerun will be required. Since this rerun would
have been unnecessary if the *j*th piece *had* been scheduled, the loss of *not*
scheduling is clearly K_u. If, however, *more than j* pieces must be produced in order to obtain G good pieces, $\tilde{n} > j$, then *scheduling the jth piece
as such would* not *prevent an underage and therefore not scheduling the jth
does* not *create any loss.* In this case the effect of not scheduling the *j*th
piece is simply to subtract k_o from the cost of the initial run and add k_o to
the cost of the rerun; it has no *net* effect on cost whatever.

The conditional losses of not scheduling the *j*th piece in our present
problem are thus quite different from the conditional losses of not stocking the *j*th unit in inventory problems of the kind studied in Chapter 7.
In the problem of Chapter 7, a profit is made on the *j*th unit if *that unit*
can be sold, whether the *total* demand is satisfied or not; k_u is the loss *per
unit* short. In our present problem, the *j*th unit prevents a shortage and
the loss K_u only if the "demand" is for *exactly j* units, neither more nor
less. The student must not think, however, that this difference is a
difference between scrap-allowance problems as such and inventory problems as such. It is a difference between problems with a *lump-sum* loss of
underage and problems with a *proportional* loss of underage. Many
inventory problems involve lump-sum losses, and many scrap-allowance
problems involve proportional losses.

8.1.7   *Expected Incremental Loss; Selection of the Best Decision*

By inspection of the conditional losses shown in Table 8.4, the
student can easily see that

Expected loss of not scheduling the *j*th unit $= K_u \, \mathrm{P}(\tilde{n} = j)$,
Expected loss of scheduling the *j*th unit $= k_o \, \mathrm{P}(\tilde{n} < j)$.

Looked at by itself, a decision to schedule the *j*th unit will be profitable if
and only if the loss of not scheduling is greater than the loss of scheduling,
i.e. if and only if

$$K_u \, \mathrm{P}(\tilde{n} = j) > k_o \, \mathrm{P}(\tilde{n} < j).$$

This condition is more convenient to use in the form

$$\frac{\mathrm{P}(\tilde{n} = j)}{\mathrm{P}(\tilde{n} < j)} > \frac{k_o}{K_u} \qquad \textit{Condition for profitability of jth unit by itself}$$

In our example $k_o/K_u = \$3/\$1000 = .003$. In Table 8.5 we show
the probabilities $\mathrm{P}(\tilde{n} = j)$ copied from Table 8.3, the cumulative prob-
abilities $\mathrm{P}(\tilde{n} < j)$ derived from these, and the ratios $\mathrm{P}(\tilde{n} = j)/\mathrm{P}(\tilde{n} < j)$.
The ratio $\mathrm{P}(=)/\mathrm{P}(<)$ is greater than $k_o/K_u = .003$ for *all* units from the

tenth through the fourteenth and less than .003 for *all* remaining units, so that the best decision is obviously to schedule 14 units into production. It is left to the student as an exercise to find the corresponding total expected loss, which is the *cost of uncertainty* in this situation.

Table 8.5

j	$P(\tilde{n} = j)$	$P(\tilde{n} < j)$	$P(=)/P(<)$
10	.300	0	∞
11	.400	.300	1.333
12	.250	.700	.357
13	.040	.950	.042
14	.007	.990	.007
15	.002	.997	.002
16	.001	.999	.001
17	0	1.000	0
	1.000		

When we used incremental analysis to find the best act Q in inventory problems with proportional losses, we proved (Sections 4.2.1 and 7.6.3) that the incremental profit of adding the jth unit could not increase with j. This meant that up to a certain j *all* incremental units were profitable while beyond this j *all* incremental units were unprofitable, so that the best decision could be found by simply finding the highest j for which incremental profit was positive. In terms of practical computations, all that we had to do was to cumulate left-tail probabilities until we came to a j for which $P(\tilde{z} < j)$ was greater than the critical ratio $k_p/(k_p + k_n)$ or $k_u/(k_u + k_o)$ and then drop back 1 unit to find the best value of Q; there was no need to cumulate any further because we knew in advance that $P(\tilde{z} < j)$ would remain above the critical ratio as j increased.

The student must observe very carefully that no corresponding propositions have been proved or can be proved for problems of the kind we are now studying. It *happens* to be true for the probability distribution of Table 8.5 that the ratio $P(=)/P(<)$ and therefore the incremental profit of scheduling a jth unit decrease steadily as j increases, and this will *usually* be true when the probability distribution is *reasonably smooth* and *single-humped*. It is perfectly possible, however, to have a probability distribution such that $P(=)/P(<)$ first decreases until it is below the critical ratio k_o/K_u, then rises above this ratio, then falls below again, and so forth; an example of such a distribution is shown in Table 8.6. We shall not give rules for finding the best decision in such cases, but the student should observe that with $k_o = \$3$ and $K_u = \$1000$ it would pay to schedule a fourteenth *and* a fifteenth unit under the distribution of Table 8.6 even though it would not pay to schedule a fourteenth unit alone. $Q = 15$ is better than $Q = 13$ even though $Q = 14$ is worse.

Table 8.6

n	$P(n)$	$P(\tilde{n} < n)$	$P(=)/P(<)$
10	.300	0	∞
11	.400	.300	1.333
12	.250	.700	.357
13	.040	.950	.042
14	.002	.990	.002
15	.007	.992	.007
16	.001	.999	.001
17	0	1.000	0
	1.000		

8.2   Assessment of the Distribution of $\tilde{n}$ When All Runs Are Long

In Section 8.1 we simply assumed a probability distribution for the random variable $\tilde{n}$ so that we could make clear the nature and use of this random variable without becoming confused by the problems involved in actually assessing its distribution in a practical situation. We shall now see how this distribution can be rationally assessed in one particular kind of situation, taking the following problem as an example.

Table 8.7

Run number	Total number of pieces	Number good	Number defective	Fraction defective	Ratio total-to-good
1	8100	6496	1604	.198	1.247
2	7500	5597	1903	.254	1.340
3	6300	5097	1203	.191	1.236
4	7800	5595	2205	.283	1.394
5	6700	5107	1593	.238	1.312
6	8200	6805	1395	.170	1.205
7	7100	5028	2072	.292	1.412

A manufacturer wishes to produce 5000 good parts of a new design. Production will involve a rather long sequence of operations—forging, milling, turning, drilling, etc.—in each of which a certain amount of shrinkage will occur, and the manufacturer wishes to assess a probability distribution for the number of pieces he must schedule into the first of these operations in order to have $G = 5000$ good pieces emerge from the last. The only available evidence which he considers relevant is the record shown in Table 8.7 of seven previous production runs on which similar parts were manufactured. Although the parts produced on each of these runs differed slightly in design from the parts produced on every other run and from the parts about to be manufactured, they all involved

the same sequence of operations as the present parts and presented the
same general kinds of production difficulties.

8.2.1   The Random Variable $\tilde{\rho} = \tilde{n}/G$

None of the production runs recorded in Table 8.7 resulted in exactly
$G = 5000$ good pieces, the number which the manufacturer wishes to
produce on his new run, and therefore the record gives no direct evidence
on the number of pieces n which will have to be produced in order to get
exactly $G = 5000$ good pieces on the new run.   It is obvious, however,
that indirect evidence on this question is provided by the last column of
the table, which shows the ratio of the total number of pieces produced to
the number of good pieces emerging on each of these seven runs.   If we
knew what value the ratio $\tilde{n}/G$ would have on the new run, we could get
the value of $\tilde{n}$ for that run by simply multiplying the value of the ratio by
$G = 5000$; and if we assume that the last piece produced on each of the
past runs was good, then the ratio of total to good on each of these runs
gives the ratio n/G for that run.

It is true that the last good piece on each of these runs may not have
been the last piece produced and therefore that the ratio of total to good
may be slightly larger than the true value of n/G, but when the runs are
as large as those recorded in Table 8.7 the difference cannot be of any
practical significance whatever.   Taking the first of the recorded runs as
an example, the assumption that the last piece was good implies that
$n = 8100$ pieces had to be produced to get $G = 6496$ good pieces and that
the value of n/G was therefore $8100/6496 = 1.247$.   If in fact the last nine
pieces were all defective and the 6496th good piece was actually the
8091st piece produced rather than the 8100th, the value $8091/6496$ of the
ratio n/G is reduced only to 1.246.

Accordingly we are quite justified in using the ratios in the last
column of Table 8.7 *as if* they were the ratios n/G for the seven past production runs; and since these ratios are the only quantitative evidence
available for assessment of the distribution of the random variable $\tilde{n}$ in
the new run, we must use them in this assessment in one way or another.
The fact that the evidence is in ratio form will make it more convenient to
proceed by first defining a new random variable rho as

$$\tilde{\rho} = \frac{\tilde{n}}{G}$$

and assessing a probability distribution for $\tilde{\rho}$ on the new run.   Once this
distribution has been assessed it will be easy to derive from it the distribution of $\tilde{n}$ in which we are directly interested.

8.2.2   Relevance of the Recorded Values of $\tilde{\rho}$

Before we start to assess a probability distribution for $\tilde{\rho} = \tilde{n}/G$ on
the basis of the recorded values taken on by that variable in past runs, we

must ask whether all these values are directly relevant to the present run. If, for example, the very high value 1.412 recorded for the last of the seven past runs can be explained by the fact that exceptionally tight tolerances were required on that particular part and if the tolerances on the part about to be made are materially looser, we should pay little or no attention to this recorded value in assessing the distribution of $\tilde{\rho}$ on the new run. The same principle would apply if the material of which any of the old parts were made differed from the material to be used for the new part in such a way that it could be predicted that $\tilde{\rho}$ would have a higher or lower value on the new run than it did on the old run. In general:

> If there is any observable difference between the conditions surrounding an old run and those surrounding the new run which leads to a *predictable* difference in the values of $\tilde{\rho} = \tilde{n}/G$ on the two runs, we must either discard the evidence of the old run in question or else adjust the recorded ρ to conform to the conditions under which the new run will be made.

In what follows we shall assume that the manufacturer has consulted his production engineers and shop foremen and has been told that there is no way of *predicting* the difference between the ρ which will be experienced in the new run and the ρ which has been experienced in any of the old runs.

8.2.3   *The Implications of Length of Run; Process ρ vs. Observed ρ*

Having determined that all the seven ρ's recorded on past runs are relevant to the probability distribution of $\tilde{\rho}$ on the new run, we are tempted to proceed immediately to assess the distribution of $\tilde{\rho}$ by treating the seven recorded ρ's as fractile estimates in exactly the same way that we assessed a probability distribution for the random variable "demand" in Section 6.4 by treating recorded demands as fractile estimates. There is one marked difference between the two problems, however, and we must consider the implications of this difference before we proceed further. In Section 6.4 we were assessing a distribution for the number of units $\tilde{z}$ which would be demanded in *one day* on the basis of recorded values of $\tilde{z}$ each of which gave the number of units which had been demanded in *one day*. In our present problem we are assessing a distribution for the random variable $\tilde{\rho}$ in a run intended to produce $G = 5000$ good pieces on the basis of values of this ratio recorded in runs which gave quite different numbers of good pieces, and even though $\tilde{\rho}$ is the *ratio* of number required to number good we feel intuitively that the required number of good pieces may have some bearing on the probability distribution which it is reasonable to assign to $\tilde{\rho}$.

If all the observable factors affecting a production process—part design, setup, material, condition of tools, etc.—are held constant, and if the process has no tendency to produce defectives in long streaks, then the occurrence of defectives can be likened to the occurrence of aces when a die (fair or deformed) is rolled repeatedly under constant conditions. Since a different part was manufactured on each of the seven runs recorded in Table 8.7 and still a different part is to be manufactured on the new run, we may think of the manufacturer's problem in terms of the following analogy. We are presented with a very large number of deformed dice and from these we select eight which *look* exactly alike. We then take seven of these eight dice and with each one perform a single experiment which consists of rolling the die until a predetermined number G of non-aces (good pieces) has been obtained, counting the number n of rolls required, and recording the ratio $\rho = n/G$. On the basis of this record we wish to assess a probability distribution for the ratio $\tilde{\rho}$ which will be required to obtain $G = 5000$ non-aces with the eighth die.

Now very broad experience leads us to believe, as we saw already in Section 1.6, that when any one die is rolled repeatedly under constant conditions the die-rolling *process* is characterized by a single, definite fraction of aces which it will produce *in the long run;* but experience also leads us to believe that the fraction of aces actually observed in any *finite* number of rolls will usually differ by some amount from this long-run fraction. We can equally well think of the die-rolling process as characterized by a *long-run ratio ρ of total rolls n to non-aces G,* and experience then tells us that if we roll the die until some finite number of non-aces has been obtained the observed ratio ρ will usually differ by some amount from the long-run ratio which characterizes the process as such. It follows that we may regard the total variation among the seven ρ's recorded in Table 8.7 as being composed of two separate parts:

1. Variation due to differences among the long-run ρ's of the seven processes;
2. Variation due to differences between the ρ actually observed on each run and the long-run ρ of the corresponding process.

It also follows that when we assess a probability distribution for the ρ which will be experienced in production of the new part, we may think of this distribution as a quantitative expression of a total uncertainty which is composed of two separate parts:

1. Uncertainty concerning the long-run ρ which will characterize the process of producing the new part;
2. Uncertainty concerning the difference between this long-run ρ and the ρ which will actually be experienced in obtaining the specified finite number of good pieces.

It is important to distinguish between these two kinds of variation or two kinds of uncertainty because *the second kind depends on G whereas the first kind does not.* If we are going to roll a die or produce parts until only a very small number of non-aces or good parts have been obtained, the ρ of this finite experiment may easily differ quite widely from the long-run ρ of the process as such; but if the specified value of G is very large, we feel quite sure that the ρ which is actually observed will be quite close to the long-run ρ of the process.   More generally, we feel that the higher the value of G, the less uncertainty we should have about the difference between the ρ which will actually be experienced and the long-run ρ of the process.

It follows immediately that in the general case we *cannot* obtain a valid probability distribution for the $\tilde{\rho}$ of a future run by simply smoothing a record like Table 8.7 in which the G's are all different, since such a record provides no valid evidence for assessment of the second kind of uncertainty in a run with *any* specified G.   Nor can we in the general case obtain a valid distribution of the long-run process $\tilde{\rho}$ itself from such a record without first in some way eliminating from it the variation due to differences between the ρ's in the record and the corresponding process ρ's.   In the particular problem before us, however, Table 8.7 shows (1) a *very great amount of variation among the observed ρ's* at the same time that (2) all the G's are so high that we feel intuitively that *each observed ρ must almost certainly be very close to the corresponding process ρ*.   We are tempted to conclude that by far the largest part of the variation in the observed ρ's must be due to difference among the process ρ's themselves, and in the next part of the course we shall prove that this intuition is correct: *differences between the observed ρ's of Table 8.7 and the corresponding process ρ's cannot account for more than a negligible fraction of the total variation among the observed ρ's.*

This means that in this particular problem smoothing the recorded ρ's will give us a reasonable probability distribution for the $\tilde{\rho}$ which will characterize the *process* of producing the new part.   It also means that it will be legitimate to treat this distribution of the process $\tilde{\rho}$ as a distribution of the $\tilde{\rho}$ which will actually be experienced in producing a finite number of good parts *provided* that this number is so large that uncertainty about the difference between the process ρ and the ρ of the finite experiment is negligible.   This condition is met by the $G = 5000$ which we are assuming in our example, but we could *not* use the distribution which we are about to assess as a distribution of the ρ to be experienced in a run intended to make a few dozen or even a few hundred good parts.

8.2.4   The Distribution of the Process $\tilde{\rho}$

We now proceed to assess the distribution of the long-run $\tilde{\rho} = \tilde{n}/G$ which will characterize the *process* of manufacturing the new part, following exactly the same procedure that we used in Section 6.4.   We first array the values of $\tilde{\rho}$ shown in Table 8.7 in order of size: 1.205, 1.236, 1.247, 1.312, 1.340, 1.394, 1.412.   We then treat the first of these seven values as a preliminary estimate of the $1/(7 + 1) = .125$ fractile, the second as a preliminary estimate of the .250 fractile, etc., plot each of these preliminary estimates as an X in Figure 8.1, and fit a smooth curve which represents our assessment of the probability distribution of $\tilde{\rho}$. Because this random variable describes the *long-run* ratio of $\tilde{n}$ to G, it can have any value whatever and is not restricted to certain "discrete" values in the way that the random variable "demand" is restricted to the integral values 0, 1, 2, etc.   There is, so to speak, no "space" between one possible value of $\tilde{\rho}$ and the next, and consequently there is no difference between $P(\tilde{\rho} < \rho)$ and $P(\tilde{\rho} \le \rho)$.

The assessment represented by the curve of Figure 8.1 rests not only on the seven preliminary estimates but also on the judgment that the probability distribution should be smooth and the judgment that whereas there is a small probability that the ρ of the new part is considerably worse than the worst of the seven in the record, there is no probability at all that it is very much better than the best of the seven in the record.   In a real situation such judgments would be based on engineering knowledge.

8.2.5   The Cumulative Distribution of $\tilde{n}$

We can now obtain a probability distribution for the $\tilde{n}$ of the manufacturer's current problem, i.e. for the number of pieces which must be produced to yield exactly $G = 5000$ good pieces, by using the distribution of the long-run $\tilde{\rho} = \tilde{n}/G$ assessed in Figure 8.1 *as if* it were a distribution of the ratio $\tilde{n}/G$ to be experienced on this particular run.   We remind the student that this is legitimate only because G is so large that uncertainty about the difference between the ρ of this run and the long-run ρ of the process is negligible in comparison with uncertainty about the long-run ρ itself.

To convert from $\tilde{\rho}$ to $\tilde{n}$, all that we need to do is to relabel both axes of Figure 8.1 and to change the scale on the horizontal axis: multiplying each $\rho = n/G$ on the horizontal axis by $G = 5000$ we obtain the corresponding n.   Because $\tilde{n}$ can take on only integral values, we label the vertical axis $P(\tilde{n} < n + \frac{1}{2})$ to show that in principle we should read $P(\tilde{n} < n)$ one-half unit to the left of n; in practice the successive n's are so close together that we cannot distinguish between n and $n + \frac{1}{2}$ and we may therefore take the height of the curve at any n as giving either $P(\tilde{n} < n)$ or $P(\tilde{n} \le n)$.

8.2.6   The Noncumulative Distribution of $\tilde{n}$

In principle the probability that $\tilde{n}$ has any particular value n can be obtained from Figure 8.1 by using the relation

$$P(\tilde{n} = n) = P(\tilde{n} < n + 1) - P(\tilde{n} < n).$$

If, however, we try to obtain a probability like $P(\tilde{n} = 6000)$ in this way, we find that we cannot actually read the difference between $P(\tilde{n} < 6001)$

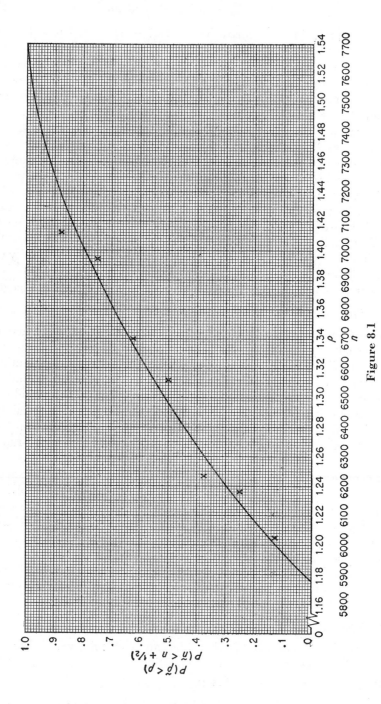

Figure 8.1

148

and $P(\tilde{n} < 6000)$ on the chart.   We must therefore proceed as we did in Section 6.4.3, first obtaining a *grouped* distribution of $\tilde{n}$ from Figure 8.1 and then smoothing this grouped distribution.

The first step is to define the brackets we are going to use.   We select brackets 100 units wide as being wide enough to allow us to determine the total probability of the bracket with good accuracy and yet narrow enough to avoid excessively large changes in probability per unit width from one side of the bracket to the other.   To facilitate reading Figure 8.1 we choose round numbers for the edges of the brackets wherever possible—the only exception is the first bracket, whose left edge is determined by the point at which the curve reaches the horizontal axis.

We then proceed in Table 8.8 just as we did in Table 6.5.   The probability of each bracket is the difference between the cumulative probability at its left edge and the cumulative probability at the left edge of the next bracket.   Thus the .088 in column 3 is .214 − .126, and so forth. In the last column of the table we compute the average probability per unit width within the bracket by dividing the total probability as shown in column 3 by the width of the bracket as shown in column 1.

Table 8.8

Bracket	Cumulative probability at left edge	Total probability of bracket	Probability per unit width
5880–5899	0	.025	.00125
5900–5999	.025	.101	.00101
6000–6099	.126	.088	.00088
6100–6199	.214	.083	.00083
6200–6299	.297	.076	.00076
6300–6399	.373	.070	.00070
6400–6499	.443	.068	.00068
		etc.	

Values of $P(n)$ for all n could now be obtained as in Section 6.4.3 by first plotting a histogram of the grouped distribution of Table 8.8, the height of the bar for each bracket being the probability per unit width shown in the last column of the table, and then smoothing this grouped distribution.   The smooth curve would give $P'(n)$ for all n; and since the width of the bar for any individual n is 1, $P(n)$ would be numerically equal to $P'(n)$.

8.2.7   *The Ratio* $P(\tilde{n} = n)/P(\tilde{n} < n)$

We shall not actually go through the smoothing process required to obtain individual $P(n)$ because what we really need for our present application is values of the ratio $P(n)/P(\tilde{n} < n)$ and these can be obtained by a more direct smoothing procedure which we shall now describe.

If we did smooth a grouped histogram representing Table 8.8, the height of the smooth curve at the *mid-point* of each bracket would be almost exactly equal to the height of the corresponding bar of the unsmoothed histogram, i.e. to the probability per unit width shown in the last column of Table 8.8; and since $P(n)$ is numerically equal to $P'(n)$, this means that we can read $P(n)$ for the mid-point of each bracket directly from Table 8.8.   Values of $P(n)$ obtained in this way are shown in Table 8.9.†

Table 8.9

Bracket	n	$P'(n) = P(n)$	$P(\tilde{n} < n)$	$P(=)/P(<)$
5880–5899	5890	.00125	.01	.125
5900–5999	5950	.00101	.087	.0116
6000–6099	6050	.00088	.170	.00518
6100–6199	6150	.00083	.257	.00323
6200–6299	6250	.00076	.335	.00227
6300–6399	6350	.00070	.410	.00171
6400–6499	6450	.00068	.480	.00142
		etc.		

The value of the ratio $P(n)/P(\tilde{n} < n)$ can now be obtained for all n by first computing this ratio for the mid-point of each bracket and then fitting a smooth curve to the computed values.   The required values of $P(\tilde{n} < n)$ are read from Figure 8.1 and shown in the next to the last column of Table 8.9; notice that these cumulative probabilities apply to the mid-point of each bracket and not to the left edge.   Each $P(n)$ is then divided by the corresponding $P(\tilde{n} < n)$; the resulting ratios $P(=)/P(<)$ are shown in the last column of the table.   Figure 8.2 is obtained by continuing Table 8.9 to cover the whole range of values of $\tilde{n}$, plotting $P(=)/P(<)$ for each mid-point as an X, and fitting a smooth curve to these X's.

8.2.8   Partial Expectations of $\tilde{n}$

Partial expectations of $\tilde{n}$ are obtained from Table 8.8 by the method described in Section 6.5.   The computations are shown in Table 8.10, where the first and third columns are simply copied from Table 8.8.   The "products" are computed by multiplying each mid-point by the corresponding grouped probability, and the last column of the table shows

---

† The n shown for each bracket in Table 8.9 is actually $\frac{1}{2}$ unit above the exact mid-point of the bracket, but it is obvious that a $\frac{1}{2}$-unit change in n makes no material change in $P'(n)$ when each bracket is 100 units wide and the changes in P' from one bracket to the next are as small as those in Table 8.9.

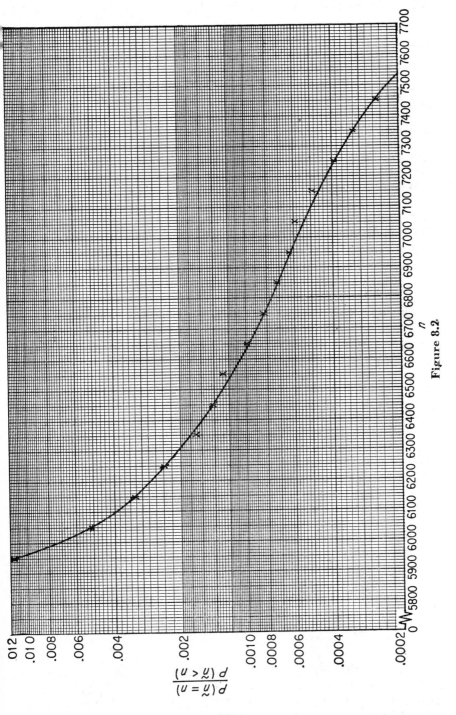

Figure 8.2

151

Table 8.10

Bracket	Mid-point	Grouped probability	Product	Cumulative sum
5880–5899	5890	.025	147	147
5900–5999	5950	.101	601	748
6000–6099	6050	.088	532	1280
6100–6199	6150	.083	510	1790
6200–6299	6250	.076	475	2265
6300–6399	6350	.070	444	2709
6400–6499	6450	.068	439	3148
		etc.		

the cumulative sums of the products.   Each cumulative sum is the partial expectation of $\tilde{n}$ over the range from 0 to the value of $\tilde{n}$ at the *right edge* of the last bracket included in the computation; thus

$$E_0^{5899}(\tilde{n}) = 147, \qquad E_0^{6399}(\tilde{n}) = 2709.$$

Figure 8.3 was obtained by continuing Table 8.10 to cover the whole range of values of $\tilde{n}$, plotting each computed partial expectation against the corresponding n, and fitting a smooth curve to the plotted points. This smooth curve enables us to read partial expectations at points other than the edges of the brackets used in the computation.   Notice that the highest value on the curve gives us the "total" or ordinary expectation of $\tilde{n}$ or the mean of the distribution of $\tilde{n}$:

$$E_0^{7700}(\tilde{n}) = E_0^{\infty}(\tilde{n}) = E(\tilde{n}) = 6550.$$

8.2.9   Solution of an Example

Assume now that the manufacturer whose probability distribution for $\tilde{n}$ is given by Figure 8.1 has the same conditional losses

$$k_o = \$3,$$
$$K_u = \$1000,$$

as the manufacturer of our first example.   We continue to assume that second-order losses are strictly 0.

The *best size of production order* is given directly by Figure 8.2.   We compute

$$\frac{k_o}{K_u} = \frac{\$3}{\$1000} = .003,$$

locate .003 on the vertical scale of Figure 8.2, and read across to the curve and down to 6165 on the horizontal axis.   Since $P(=)/P(<)$ is greater than .003 for *all* units before the 6165th and less than .003 for *all* units after the 6165th, the optimum order size is $Q = 6165$.

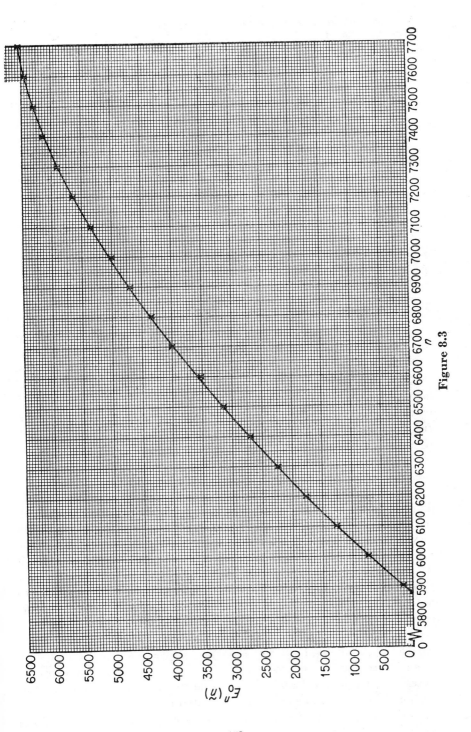

Figure 8.3

153

The *expected loss* of a decision to schedule 6165 pieces into production is obtained by using the formulas given in Section 8.1.5. We first read

$$P(\tilde{n} \leq 6165) = .270$$

from Figure 8.1, compute

$$P(\tilde{n} > 6165) = 1 - .270 = .730,$$

and read

$$E_0^{6165}(\tilde{n}) = 1615$$

from Figure 8.3. We then compute

Expected loss of overage $= \$3[(6165 \times .270) - 1615] = \$150,$
Expected loss of underage $= \$1000 \times .730 = \$730,$
Expected total loss $= \$150 + \$730 = \$880.$

8.3   Second-order Losses

Granted that the probability distribution is correctly assessed, the validity of the methods described above for selecting the best decision and computing expected loss still depends on the accuracy of the assumption that only the losses which will *certainly* be entailed by a rerun need be considered in estimating the loss K_u which will result from a shortage on the initial run. We have pointed out in Section 8.1.2 that an underrun in fact entails a risk of additional loss because the rerun may itself result in an overage or underage; and in principle the expected value of this *uncertain* loss should be added in to the certain loss when we calculate the value of K_u.

Computation of the exact amount of this expected value is extremely difficult, however. Looked at after the initial run has been completed, the second-order losses will depend on the number of good pieces which remain to be produced. If the shortage of good pieces† is very small, the manufacturer will be able to buy virtually complete insurance against a second underage at a very low cost—he can allow several times as many pieces for scrap as he needs good pieces and still the expected loss due to overage will be negligible. If the shortage of good pieces is large, however, such a generous scrap allowance on the rerun would entail a serious expected loss due to overage, and the manufacturer would do better to reduce the allowance and the expected loss of overage even at the expense of an increase in the expected loss of underage. Both these expected losses are part of the true K_u of the initial run, and therefore in order to compute the exact value of K_u for the initial run:

† Notice that this is *not* the "size of underage" $(n - Q)$ as that quantity was defined in Section 8.1.3.

1. We must compute a different conditional expected loss for each possible number of good pieces short, multiply by the probability that the shortage will actually be of this size and add the products; but
2. When we try to compute the conditional loss for any specified number of good pieces short we get into an "infinite regress." The calculation involves the loss which will be incurred if the rerun itself results in an underage, and this loss includes "third-order" losses due to the possibility that the *second* rerun may again result in a underage or an overage.

For this reason it is virtually impossible to find the *exact* optimum Q or the *exact* value of the expected loss in most scrap-allowance problems, but this by no means implies that we cannot find solutions which are so close to exact that they entail no *material* cost of irrationality. In the general case this must be done by a process of successive approximations which is beyond the scope of this course, but in one particular kind of situation which occurs rather frequently in practice it can be shown without detailed calculations that the expected second-order losses are so small relative to the direct cost of scheduling and setting up for a first rerun that they can safely be neglected for all practical purposes. The problem studied in the previous section of this chapter is an example of a situation of this kind.

In this example we saw that *before* the initial run was made, by far the largest part of the manufacturer's uncertainty concerning the ρ which would be experienced on this run was due to uncertainty about the long-run ρ which characterized the *process* of manufacturing the new part; his uncertainty about the difference between the process ρ and the ρ he would experience in getting 5000 good pieces was negligible in comparison. *After* an initial run of several thousand pieces has been made, the situation will be totally different. The results of this run will give the manufacturer almost exact information concerning the long-run ρ of the process, and therefore if a rerun does have to be made *the manufacturer's uncertainty concerning the ρ to be experienced in getting the good pieces still needed will be extremely small in comparison with his original uncertainty.* It follows that even if the G of the rerun is large, he will be able to schedule enough pieces to give him virtually complete insurance against the need for a second rerun and thus a virtually 0 expected loss of underage and still have an expected loss of overage which is negligible in comparison with the direct cost of scheduling and setting up for the first rerun.

Notice very carefully, however, that this line of reasoning applies only when *all* the following conditions are met:

1. The major part of the original uncertainty must be uncertainty about the long-run ρ of the process.

2. The initial run must be so long that its results will remove a very large part of the uncertainty about the process ρ.

3. It must be known in advance that if a rerun is required it will be made under conditions such that the process ρ is *certain* to be the same for the rerun as it was for the initial run.

The last of these three conditions requires particular attention. A rerun will certainly involve new setups of all the machines used in the production process and it may involve a new batch of raw material, new operators, and so forth. Engineering judgment will be required to decide whether the manufacturer can be *sure* that none of these changes will have any substantial effect on the process ρ or whether they must be considered a new source of uncertainty. If the changes do create a substantial amount of new uncertainty, we are *not* in general entitled to treat second-order losses as negligible in planning for the initial run.

PROBLEMS

1. Under the probability distribution of Table 8.3 with k_o = \$3, K_u = \$1000, and assuming that a rerun will come out exactly right:

a. Compute the cost of uncertainty both by the method of Table 8.3 and by the use of the formulas derived in Section 8.1.5.

b. What is the cost of irrationality if a decision is made to issue an order for 13 pieces?

2. Under the probability distribution of Table 8.6 with k_o = \$3 and K_u = \$1000, and assuming that a rerun will come out exactly right, compute expected loss for Q = 13, 14, and 15 and show that it pays to schedule a fourteenth *and* a fifteenth unit even though it does not pay to schedule a fourteenth alone.

3. Under the conditions of Problem 1 except that k_o = \$1.50:

a. What is the best size for the production order?

b. What is the cost of uncertainty?

4. Under the probability distribution of Figure 8.1 with k_o = \$3, G = 5000, and assuming that the true value of K_u is \$1000:

a. Compute the total loss under production orders for Q = 5900, 6000, 6165, 6200, and 6400.

b. Make a graph of loss against the size Q of the production order, fitting a *smooth* curve to the points determined in part a. (The computed points will contain errors because of inaccuracies in reading the various charts and therefore the curve should *not* be put exactly through every point.)

c. *Using this graph*, estimate the extra loss which will be incurred if the production order is 100 units above or below optimum.

d. Suppose that the production manager of the firm faced with this scrap-allowance problem decides that he is tired of the nuisance of shortages on his production runs and instructs his scheduling clerk to schedule enough material to leave only a 1-in-10 chance that a shortage will occur on any run. How many pieces will the clerk schedule for the present run and what is the cost of irrationality of this decision?

5. Under the conditions of Problem 4 except that K_u = \$1500:

a. What is the best size for the production order?

b. What is the cost of uncertainty?

c. What is the cost of irrationality if the production order is based on K_u = \$1000 when in fact K_u = \$1500?

d. Discuss the bearing of your answer to (*c*) on the importance of second-order losses.

6. A production manager has no direct experience whatever with the process he is about to use in producing a specified number of good parts, but on the basis of experience with more or less similar processes he decides that he would bet at the following odds on the fraction defective which will actually be experienced in the run about to be made:

1 to 99 (1 chance in 100) that $f < .65$,
1 to 99 that $f > .85$,
1 to 9 that $f < .70$,
1 to 9 that $f > .80$,
1 to 1 (even money) that $f > .75$ or $f < .75$.

How should he determine how many pieces to schedule if he wishes to bet his company's money consistently with these odds? Make no calculations but list every step in the procedure.

7. All sales made by the retailer of Chapter 6, Problem 2, are made by telephone and the retailer delivers the merchandise to the customer at the end of each day. The retailer decides that in order to maintain customer loyalty he will accept and deliver all orders for the product in question even though the orders exceed the quantity which he stocked at the beginning of the day—if this happens he will have the required additional quantity delivered to him by the wholesaler just before he makes his own deliveries at the end of the day. The wholesaler charges $25 for this special-delivery service.

a. Under the probability distribution for demand which you assessed in answer to Chapter 6, Problem 3 (not 2), how many units should the retailer stock at the beginning of the day?

b. What is the cost of uncertainty?

c. Discuss the similarities and differences between the logic by which the probability distribution for demand was assessed in this case and the logic by which it was assessed in the second example of the present chapter.

8. In July, 1955, the United States Air Force placed a fixed-price procurement contract with the Warner Aircraft Engine Company for 1000 stainless-steel valve assemblies, drawing number AC7036. This was a new, improved design; the assemblies were to be used for field modification of all model Z-16-C engines currently in service and to provide life-of-type spares. The Z-16-C engine was used exclusively by the Air Force and was already out of production. The new valve assembly would fit no other model.

Table 8.11

Lot number	Shrinkage, %	Lot number	Shrinkage, %
1	13	11	14
2	21	12	16
3	20	13	28
4	27	14	25
5	22	15	21
6	21	16	18
7	19	17	21
8	33	18	23
9	26	19	15
10	21	20	26

Production of the valve assemblies called for 26 operations, a large number of which were performed on automatic screw machines. At each stage in the production process, a certain amount of shrinkage occurred owing to breakage, faulty machining, and other causes.   The Warner Company had produced large lots of more or less similar valve assemblies for many other engine models.   Shrinkage losses (fraction defective) for 20 such lots are shown in Table 8.11; the smallest of these lots contained over 5000 pieces.   Although these assemblies varied with regard to dimensions as well as sequence of operations, they were more like drawing AC7036 than any other assemblies on which the Warner Company had shrinkage records.

Total variable labor and material cost per finished assembly was $2.   The total fixed setup cost of the various machines was $1000.

a. How many valve assemblies should Warner schedule into production?

b. What is the expected cost of uncertainty?

c. Discuss the justification of the method by which you assess the probability distribution of the basic random variable.

d. Discuss the justification for neglecting second-order losses in the circumstances of this case.

PART TWO

*Simple Random Processes
and Derived Probabilities*

CHAPTER 9

Conditional and Joint Probability

9.1 Introduction to Part Two of the Course

The probabilities which we have assigned to the events in a payoff or loss table have hitherto all been directly assessed on the basis of experience with the cost-determining events themselves. In problems of inventory control, we have assessed the probability distribution of the random variable "demand" by looking at a historical frequency distribution either of demand itself or of the discrepancy between actual demand and forecast demand. In determining a scrap allowance, we have assessed the probability distribution of the ratio total-to-good by looking at the ratios experienced on previous production runs. The only way in which we have used the mathematical theory of probability was to compute the probability of events such as $\tilde{z} \leq 2$ by adding the probabilities of the events $\tilde{z} = 0$, 1, and 2.

In some cases, however, we have refused to assess probabilities by simply *equating* them to relative frequencies experienced in the past. Our general knowledge of the nature of the factors affecting demand or the factors affecting the ratio total-to-good led us to the conclusion that the probabilities assigned to certain values of the basic random variable should be between those assigned to other values and that the whole distribution should be smooth.

We now begin our study of situations in which our general knowledge of (or beliefs concerning) the factors affecting a cost-determining random variable can be shown to lead to conclusions much more specific than the mere proposition that the probability distribution should be smooth. We glanced briefly at a very special situation of this sort already in Sections 1.5 and 1.7, where we suggested that under certain conditions a manufacturer might reasonably *deduce* the probability that there would be more than 80 defectives among 180 pieces from probabilities assigned to the elementary events of a run of 180 pieces. In most situations direct assignment of probabilities to elementary events will also be extremely difficult, but we shall now see that the probability distribution of the random variable "number defective" in a production run can also be deduced from probabilities assigned to events such as "first piece

160

defective," "second piece defective," and so forth.   A manufacturer who has had little or no experience with production runs of exactly 180 pieces or even with runs of approximately this size will have little confidence in probabilities assessed by the method of Chapter 8, and yet he may have more than enough experience with his process to give him great confidence in the probabilities he assigns to events such as "first piece defective" and therefore in any probabilities which can be shown to be logical consequences of these assignments.

In the present chapter we shall study the basic concepts which underlie the indirect assessment of probabilities; and in order to make these concepts as clear as possible our examples will be simple and artificial ones involving urns and dice.   In the remainder of Part Two of the course we shall apply these concepts to the study of certain kinds of *random processes* which occur with great frequency in practical business applications.   Throughout this part of the course the student should keep in mind the fact pointed out in Section 1.7: the theory of probability can be used either to deduce the *probabilities* of certain events from probabilities assigned to other events or to deduce the *relative frequencies* of certain events from the known or assumed relative frequencies of other events.   Every general proposition we make will be stated both in terms of probabilities and in terms of frequencies; it is up to the student to remember that the two concepts are entirely different and that great caution must be exercised before a probability is equated to a relative frequency *however* the relative frequency has been determined.

9.2   Joint and Conditional Probability

When probabilities are assigned directly to the events in a payoff table, we are dealing with a single set of mutually exclusive events and with a single set of probabilities assigned to these events; our meaning is perfectly clear when we speak of "the" probability of an event.   When probabilities are assessed indirectly, the situation becomes more complex. If two pieces are to be produced on some machine and we wish to assign a probability to the event "two defectives," we may do so by first assigning probabilities to the events "first piece defective" and "second piece defective."   If we do so, it is obvious that we are no longer dealing with a single set of mutually exclusive events: all three of the events just named may occur on a single two-piece run.   A moment's reflection will also show that we may have to deal with more than one probability for the same event: the probability which a reasonable man assigns to the event "second piece defective" may well depend on the quality of the first piece.   In order to avoid confusion in discussing such situations we must introduce the concepts of "joint" and "conditional" probability and with them the concepts of joint and conditional relative frequency.

9.2.1   Joint Probability

The probability that two or more events will *all* occur will be called the *joint* probability of these events.   Thus we may talk about the joint probability of "first piece defective" *and* "second piece defective," or about the joint probability of "rain tomorrow" *and* "demand for 17 pairs of rubbers."

It is important to observe that joint probability is in no sense a new "kind" of probability; it is simply a new way of looking at certain probabilities.   The joint probability of "first piece defective" *and* "second piece defective" is exactly the same thing as the ordinary probability of "two defectives"; the new name simply reflects the new way in which we look at this probability when we try to assess it indirectly rather than directly.

In terms of frequencies rather than probabilities, the *joint relative frequency* of several events is the ratio of the number of trials on which *all the events in question* occur to the total number of trials.

9.2.2   Conditional Probability

The probability which is assigned to an event A when it is known that another event B has occurred, or which *would* be assigned to A *if* it were known that B had occurred, will be called the *conditional* probability of A *given* B.   Thus we may talk about the conditional probability of the event "second piece defective" *given* the event "first piece defective" or about the conditional probability of the event "demand for 17 pairs of rubbers" given that the event "rain tomorrow" occurs.

To see how conditional probability is related to ordinary or unconditional probability, suppose that someone is thinking of betting on one roll of a deformed die with faces 1, 2, and 3 colored red and faces 4, 5, and 6 colored green.   The roll can result in any one of the six *elementary* events described by the numbers 1 through 6 and in either of the *compound* events "red" or "green"; we shall suppose that before the die is rolled this person assigns the probabilities shown in Table 9.1 to the six elementary events and computes the corresponding probabilities of the two compound events also shown in that table.   These are the "ordinary," "simple," or *unconditional* probabilities of this problem.

Suppose now that *after* the die has been rolled this same person is told that the event "red" has occurred but is *not* told which particular one of the three elementary events 1, 2, or 3 has occurred; and suppose that this person now wishes to assign new probabilities taking account of this limited additional information.   Clearly any reasonable man placed in this situation will assign probability 0 to the three elementary events 4, 5, and 6, since these events are impossible given the new information, and will assign a total probability of 1 to the three elementary events 1,

Table 9.1

Elementary event	Compound event	Probability	
1		.10	
2		.10	
3		.20	
	Red		.40
4		.15	
5		.20	
6		.25	
	Green		.60
			1.00

2, and 3, since he knows that some one of these events has occurred. The only question concerns the sharing of the total probability 1 among the three events 1, 2, and 3, and we answer this question by assuming that any reasonable man will do this in such a way that the probabilities which he originally assigned to these events are *all increased in the same proportion*. Since the total probability originally assigned to events 1, 2, and 3 was .4, this assumption implies that the probability assigned to each one of these events must be multiplied by 1/.4; the results are shown in Table 9.2.

Table 9.2

Elementary event	*Probability*
1	$\dfrac{1}{.4} \times .10 = .25$
2	$\dfrac{1}{.4} \times .10 = .25$
3	$\dfrac{1}{.4} \times .20 = .50$
Total ("red")	$\dfrac{1}{.4} \times .40 = 1.00$

The justification for our assumption can now be seen by comparing Tables 9.1 and 9.2. When our hypothetical person originally assigned the same probability .10 to event 1 that he assigned to event 2, he said in effect that he was indifferent between a chance at a prize conditional on event 1 and a chance at the same prize conditional on event 2. Since the information that the event was in fact 1, 2, or 3 in no way favors event 1 over event 2 or vice versa, a person who held this attitude of indifference before this information was received should continue to hold it after the information is received; and this is what he shows by assigning the same probability to events 1 and 2 in Table 9.2. Similarly the original assignments in Table 9.1 showed indifference between the right to receive a certain prize if event 3 occurred and the right to receive the same prize if *either* event 1 or 2 occurred: the .20 probability assigned to event 3 in Table 9.1 equals the total probability of events 1 and 2. Again the new information had no relevance for the *relative* values of these two chances, and again the probabilities of Table 9.2 agree with this fact: the probability .50 assigned to event 3 equals the total probability assigned to events 1 and 2.

Although our discussion has involved the actual effect of information which has already been received, it is obvious that exactly the same arguments hold for the potential effect of information which might be received. The reasonable man we have been discussing would say that *if* he learned that the event "red" had occurred, he *would* then assign to event 1 a probability computed according to the formula

$$\frac{\text{Unconditional probability of elementary event 1}}{\text{Unconditional probability of compound event "red"}} = \frac{.10}{.40} = .25$$

and so forth. Generalizing from this example we may assert that:

If *e* is an elementary event which is contained in a compound event *A*, the only conditional probability which it is reasonable to assign to *e* given *A* is the unconditional probability of *e* divided by the unconditional probability of *A*.

In our example, *e* was the event 1 and *A* was the event "red."

The *conditional relative frequency* of an elementary event is related to its unconditional relative frequency in exactly the same way that conditional probability is related to unconditional probability. Suppose, for example, that the die we have been discussing had in fact been rolled 200 times with the results shown in Table 9.3. By the conditional rela-

Table 9.3

Elementary event	Compound event	Occurrences		Relative frequency	
1		20		.10	
2		20		.10	
3		40		.20	
	Red		80		.40
4		30		.15	
5		40		.20	
6		50		.25	
			120		.60
	Green		200		1.00

tive frequency of event 1 *given* the event "red" we mean the ratio

$$\frac{\text{Number of occurrences of elementary event 1}}{\text{Number of occurrences of compound event "red"}}$$

Using the actual numbers of occurrences given in the third column of Table 9.3 we can compute this ratio directly as $^{20}\!/_{80} = .25$, but we can obtain exactly the same result by using the relative frequencies in the third column: $.10/.40 = .25$. The latter calculation is formally identical to the calculation used in computing conditional probability.

9.3   The Conditional Probability of Compound Events

The example discussed just above shows how a reasonable person will compute the conditional probability of an *elementary* event given that a particular compound event has occurred. We shall now use a simple urn example to show how the same principle can be used to calculate the conditional probability of a *compound* event given that some other compound event has occurred.

One ball is to be drawn from an urn containing 10 serially numbered balls each of which is colored either red or green and in addition is either dotted or striped; the detailed description of the balls is presented in Table 9.4. The elementary events of this trial are the 10 numbers 1 through 10, but we shall be primarily interested in the compound events "red," "green," "dotted," and "striped." Drawing a dotted red ball will be considered as the *joint* occurrence of the events "red" and "dotted" or as the occurrence of the *joint event* "red *and* dotted"; and similarly for the other combinations shown in Table 9.4. We shall

Table 9.4

Serial number	*Description*
1–3	Red and dotted
4	Red and striped
5–6	Green and dotted
7–10	Green and striped

assume that before any knowledge concerning the outcome of this trial is available we have assigned equal probability to all 10 elementary events. The probabilities of the four joint events of Table 9.4 and the probabilities of "red" and "green" can then be computed as in Table 9.5, and by similar logic we can show that the probability of the event "dotted" is $.3 + .2 = .5$; these are the unconditional probabilities of this problem.

Suppose now that the ball is actually drawn from the urn, that we are told that the ball is *red*, and that we wish to revise the .5 probability which we originally assigned to *dotted* in such a way as to take proper

Table 9.5

Elementary event	Probability	Joint event	Probability	Compound event	Probability
1	.1 ⎫				
2	.1 ⎬	Red and dotted	.3 ⎫		
3	.1 ⎭			Red	.4
4	.1 ⎰	Red and striped	.1 ⎭		
5	.1 ⎫				
6	.1 ⎭	Green and dotted	.2 ⎫		
7	.1 ⎫			Green	.6
8	.1 ⎬	Green and striped	.4 ⎭		
9	.1 ⎭				
10	.1 ⎭				
	1.0		1.0		1.0

account of this information. We observe immediately that since we know that "red" has occurred, the probability of "dotted" is now the same thing as the probability of "dotted and red"—"dotted and green" is impossible given the new information. The reasoning of Section 9.2.2 then tells us that we must multiply the probability of every elementary event contained in the event "red" by $1/P(\text{red})$, and this means that the total probability of all the three elementary events contained in "red and dotted" will be multiplied by $1/P(\text{red})$. We conclude that the conditional probability of "dotted" given "red" is

$$\frac{\text{Unconditional probability of "dotted and red"}}{\text{Unconditional probability of "red"}} = \frac{.3}{.4} = .75.$$

Geometrically, this reasoning can be visualized as follows. The original or unconditional probabilities of the various compound and joint events of the problem are represented by areas in Figure 9.1. As soon as we know that "red" has occurred, the area of the "green" bar in this

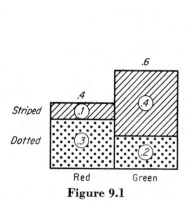

Figure 9.1

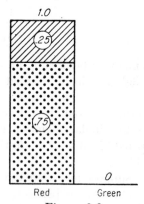

Figure 9.2

figure must be reduced to 0 and the area of the "red" bar increased to 1; the altered diagram is shown as Figure 9.2.   We must, however, leave the *proportions within* the "red" bar unchanged when we change its total area in this way, since our new information gives us no justification for changing these proportions.   Then since the area within the "red" bar corresponding to "dotted" was .3/.4 = .75 of the original area *of the "red" bar*, it becomes .75 of the entire diagram when the "red" bar is enlarged to become the entire diagram as in Figure 9.2.

Before we generalize this example, let us introduce some new notation which will simplify the statement of our results.   In addition to the symbol

P(A): the ordinary, simple, or *unconditional* probability of the event A

we shall henceforth use

P(A|B): the *conditional* probability of the event A *given* the event B; the probability assigned to A when it is known that B has occurred, or which *would* be assigned to A *if* it were known that B had occurred.

P(A,B): the *joint* probability of the events A and B; the probability that *both* A and B will occur.

In the *mathematical theory* of probability, conditional probability is *defined* by the formula

$$P(A|B) = \frac{P(A,B)}{P(B)} \qquad \textit{Mathematical definition of conditional probability}$$

In talking about probabilities assigned to real events in the real world, we defined P(A|B) quite differently, as the probability which a person *would in fact assign* to A if he knew that B had occurred.   Our urn example shows, however, that a reasonable man will always assign conditional probabilities in accordance with the mathematical definition, and therefore *we may use the mathematical definition of conditional probability as a "formula" for assigning conditional probabilities in a real problem.*   Thus when we calculated the conditional probability of "dotted" given "red" we set

$$P(\text{dotted}|\text{red}) = \frac{P(\text{dotted, red})}{P(\text{red})} = \frac{.3}{.4} = .75.$$

Similarly, we would have for the conditional probability of "striped" given "red"

$$P(\text{striped}|\text{red}) = \frac{P(\text{striped, red})}{P(\text{red})} = \frac{.1}{.4} = .25.$$

Geometrically, this is the ratio of the area representing "striped *and* red" in Figure 9.1 to the area representing "red." If we had wanted the conditional probability of "red" given "dotted," i.e. if we had wanted to know what probability should be assigned to "red" after being told that the ball was dotted, we would first have used Table 9.5 or Figure 9.1 to calculate the unconditional probability of "dotted" as .3 + .2 = .5. We would then have had

$$P(\text{red}|\text{dotted}) = \frac{P(\text{red, dotted})}{P(\text{dotted})} = \frac{.3}{.5} = .60;$$

this is the ratio of the area representing "dotted *and* red" in Figure 9.1 to the area representing "dotted."

The distinction between unconditional and conditional *relative frequencies* is shown by the following definitions:

The ordinary or unconditional relative frequency of the event *A* is the ratio of the number of occurrences of *A* to the *total number of trials*.

The conditional relative frequency of *A* given *B* is the ratio of the number of occurrences of *both A and B* to the *number of occurrences of B*.

If balls are drawn repeatedly from an urn, the ordinary relative frequency of "dotted" is the ratio of the number of times a dotted ball is drawn to the total number of draws. The conditional relative frequency of "dotted" given "red" is the ratio of the number of times the ball is *both* dotted and red to the number of times the ball is red.

Table 9.6

Event	Number of occurrences	Relative frequency
Red and dotted	60	.3
Red and striped	20	.1
Red	80	.4
Green and dotted	40	.2
Green and striped	80	.4
Green	120	.6
	200	1.0

To see how conditional relative frequencies of compound events are actually computed, suppose that 200 draws from an urn have actually been made with the results shown in Table 9.6. We can then compute the conditional relative frequency of "dotted" given "red" directly from the numbers of occurrences as $60/80 = .75$, but we can equally well use the ratio of the corresponding relative frequencies: $.3/.4 = .75$. Formally, the latter computation is identical to the computation of conditional probability; again we see that the mathematical "theory of probability" can be used *either* to compute probabilities from other probabilities or to compute frequencies from other frequencies.

9.4   The Multiplication Rule

Although we shall have very frequent occasion to compute conditional probabilities from joint probabilities when we come to Part Three of the course, our interest in Part Two will be in using the definition of conditional probability in reverse—we shall want to start with conditional probabilities which have been directly assigned to certain events and from these to calculate the unconditional probabilities of certain joint events. The so-called multiplication rule for performing such calculations is obtained by applying elementary algebra to the mathematical definition of conditional probability given in the previous section:

$$P(A,B) = P(B) \, P(A|B) \qquad \textit{Multiplication rule}$$

To see how this rule works, suppose that instead of starting with probabilities assigned to joint events in our urn example we had started by assigning the following unconditional and conditional probabilities:

$$P(\text{red}) = .4;$$
$$P(\text{green}) = .6;$$
$$P(\text{dotted}|\text{red}) = \tfrac{3}{4};$$
$$P(\text{dotted}|\text{green}) = \tfrac{1}{3}.$$

We could then have applied the multiplication rule to *compute* such joint probabilities as

$$P(\text{red } \textit{and} \text{ dotted}) = P(\text{red}) \, P(\text{dotted}|\text{red}) = .4 \times \tfrac{3}{4} = .3.$$

The operation of the rule is depicted geometrically in Figure 9.3, which is identical to Figure 9.1 except for the labeling. The bars for "red" and

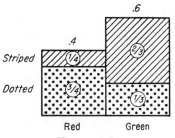

Figure 9.3

"green" constitute respectively .4 and .6 of the total area of the figure. The area representing "dotted *and* red" is ¾ *of the area representing red;* the area representing "dotted *and* green" is ⅓ *of the area representing green.* The calculation of P(red *and* dotted) which was carried out just above amounts simply to saying that the lower left-hand area in Figure 9.3 constitutes ¾ × .4 = .3 of the total area of the diagram.

In terms of *frequencies:* if a red ball is drawn on .4 of *all* draws, and if ¾ *of the red balls* are dotted, then the ball will be *both* red and dotted on ¾ × .4 = .3 of all draws. We have thus computed a joint relative frequency from an unconditional and a conditional relative frequency.

9.5   Statistical Independence

Suppose now that the mix of balls in an urn were such that we assigned the probabilities depicted in Figure 9.4: the unconditional probabilities assigned to "red" and "green" are still .4 and .6 respectively, but the conditional probability of "dotted" given "red" is now ⅓ and identical to the conditional probability of "dotted" given "green." It is obvious that if the dotted area *in each bar* is ⅓ of the area of that bar, then the *total* dotted area is ⅓ of the area of the entire figure. In other words, the *conditional probability of "dotted" given "red" is exactly the same as the unconditional probability of "dotted."*

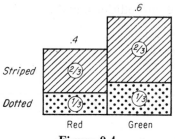

Figure 9.4

In such a situation we shall say that the events "dotted" and "red" are *statistically independent.* More generally, we say that events *A* and *B* are statistically independent if

$$P(A|B) = P(A) \qquad \textit{Condition of statistical independence}$$

By considering ratios of areas in Figure 9.4 the student can easily convince himself that if *A* is independent of *B*, then necessarily *B* is independent of A. The area representing "red" constitutes .4 of the entire diagram and at the same time "red, dotted" constitutes .4 of the total "dotted" area; P(red) = P(red|dotted).

When A is independent of B, the multiplication rule reduces to

---

P(A,B) = P(B) P(A)   *Multiplication rule for independent events*

The student is warned that one of the most common errors in the use of the theory of probability is the application of this form of the multiplication rule to events which are not independent.

PROBLEMS

In addition to studying Chapter 9, the student should review the discussion of the third basic rule of probability in Section 1.3 before attempting to solve these problems.

1. An urn contains four kinds of balls in the mix shown in the table below; you yourself have stirred the contents of the urn thoroughly and will make certain drawings from the urn in such a way that you cannot see the color of the ball before it is drawn.

Description	Number of balls
Red and dotted	2
Red and striped	3
Green and dotted	4
Green and striped	1
	10

    a. If you draw one ball from the urn and without looking at it show it to someone who tells you that it is red, what probability would you then assign to the event "red *and* dotted"? To the event "dotted"? To the event "red *or* dotted"?

    b. If after drawing a ball from the urn and seeing that it is red you are to draw a second ball without replacing the first one, what probability would you assign to the event "second ball green"?

    c. Same as (*b*) except that you have *not* seen that the first ball is red.

    d. Same as (*b*) except that after the first ball is drawn and inspected you replace it in the urn and stir the contents before making the second draw.

    e. Give a frequency justification for your answers to parts *a* through *d*.

    f. If you are to draw two balls from the urn replacing the first ball and stirring the urn before the second is drawn, what probability would you assign to the event "red followed by green"? To the event "green followed by red"? To the event "one red and one green ball"?

    g. Same as (*f*) except that the first ball is *not* to be replaced before the second ball is drawn.

    2. One thousand people are asked whether they listen to classical music on the radio. Each person is also asked whether he has reached his thirtieth birthday and whether he did or did not graduate from high school. The results of the survey are tabulated below. Compute the following relative frequencies of the event "listens to classical music":

Age	High school	Listens	Number
Under 30	Yes	Yes	110
		No	190
	No	Yes	10
		No	90
30 or over	Yes	Yes	55
		No	195
	No	Yes	125
		No	225
			1000

  a. Unconditional.

  b. Conditional given "under 30," given "30 or over," given "graduated," given "not graduated."

  c. Conditional given "under 30 *and* graduated," given "30 or over *and* graduated."

  d. Would knowledge of age be useful in predicting whether a person listens to classical music?

  3. The tolerances for balls used in ball bearings are so tight that the balls cannot be ground exactly to specified size. Instead, they are ground to approximate size, sorted into size groups, and then 100 per cent inspected for correct sizing. Even this process does not always result in adequately accurate classification owing to "inspection fatigue," a well-known phenomenon in 100 per cent inspection.

  A manufacturer of ball bearings has determined by extensive investigations that the first inspection of a lot of 10,000 balls removes about 200 incorrectly sorted balls but that about 50 incorrectly sorted balls remain in the lot. He is thinking of using 200 or 300 per cent inspection (a common practice in this industry) instead of 100 per cent. What improvement in quality do you believe he will obtain if he does this?

  4. *a.* A very carefully made die is to be rolled twice. What expected value would you assign to the right to receive $1 if one or both throws result in an ace? (HINT: Compare Problem 1*f*.)

  b. A very carefully made coin is to be tossed three times. What expected value would you assign to the right to receive $1 if heads occurs on at least one of the three tosses? (HINT: Write out all the elementary events and compute the probability of the only one which is *not* contained in the compound event in which you are interested.)

  c. Two very carefully made coins are tossed together three times. What is the probability that both coins will fall heads on at least one throw?

  5. The XYZ Company manufactures a small cylindrical part used in a precision assembly. The part will be rejected if it does not meet specifications as regards out-of-roundness, taper, and average diameter. The fraction of all parts not meeting these specifications has been:

  Out-of-roundness: .03,
  Taper: .04,
  Average diameter: .05.

  a. What probability would you assign to the rejection of any particular part if you knew that the three kinds of defects are independent? (HINT: Compare Problem 4*b*.)

b. When XYZ has manufactured a lot of these parts, a sample is drawn from the lot and the lot is screened (100 per cent inspected) at a cost of $10 if there is a single defective in the sample. What is the expected cost of screening per lot if the sample consists of a single piece? Of three pieces?

c. How would you in practice determine whether the three kinds of defects are independent?

6. A retailer stocks a product which deteriorates rapidly on the shelf. The product costs the retailer $2; he prices it at $5 on the day it is stocked but reduces the price to $1 on the following day. Product which has not been sold by the end of the second day is scrapped at a total loss. The retailer assigns the probability distributions shown in the table below to demand for the fresh product and demand for the day-old product, and he asserts that because the fresh and day-old products are put to different uses the demand for one is unrelated to the demand for the other. How many units should he stock? (HINT: The events in the payoff table for this problem are of the type "demand for 2 units of fresh *and* demand for 1 unit of day-old.")

Fresh product		Day-old product	
Demand	Probability	Demand	Probability
0	0	0	.1
1	.3	1	.2
2	.4	2	.3
3	.3	3	.3
4+	0	4	.1
		5+	0
	1.0		1.0

CHAPTER 10

The Bernoulli Process: The Binomial Distribution

The output of a great many random processes encountered in practical business problems can be described in terms of a number of *distinct trials* each of which has one or the other of *just two possible results*. Thus an automatic screw machine turns out a number of separate parts which may be classified simply as either good or defective, or the process of drawing a sample of United States housewives yields a number of separate respondents each of whom may be classified simply as a user or a nonuser of instant coffee. In order to have a standard terminology to use in discussing all processes of this kind, we shall call one of the two possible results of each trial a *success* and the other a *failure*. These names are of course completely arbitrary—we can use either name for a defective or for a housewife who uses instant coffee provided that we are consistent in any one problem.

The simplest processes of this kind are those in which the *same probability* is assigned to a success on every future trial and will continue to be assigned *regardless of the outcomes of any future trials*. Such trials are known as *Bernoulli trials with fixed probability*. As we saw in Section 1.6.1, such an assignment of probabilities will be *rational* only if we have adopted a "model" of the process such that we are convinced that *both* the following statements are true:

1. There is absolutely *no pattern* to the occurrences of successes and failures; successes tend to occur with exactly the same frequency in the first as in the last part of a long run; successes tend to be followed by failures exactly as frequently as failures are followed by failures, and so forth.
2. The long-run fraction of successes is *known with certainty*, so that experience with early trials in a sequence will not lead us to change our minds about the value of this fraction.

A process which meets the first condition will be called a *Bernoulli process* and the long-run fraction of successes which characterizes a Bernoulli process will be called the *parameter* of the process; a process meeting both conditions is therefore a *Bernoulli process with known parameter*.

It is trials and processes of this sort which we shall study in this and the two following chapters. The analysis which must be made before we may rationally treat any real, physical process (e.g. an automatic screw machine or a particular method of drawing a sample) as a Bernoulli process with known parameter is somewhat more complex than it might seem at first sight; but rather than discuss this reasoning in the abstract, we shall start by simply *assuming* that we are dealing with situations where adoption of this model of the real process is rational. In the present chapter we shall derive the *binomial* probability distribution for the number of successes in a specified number of Bernoulli trials, and in the next chapter we shall derive the *Pascal* distribution for the number of Bernoulli trials required to obtain a specified number of successes. After we have thus become familiar with the implications of the Bernoulli model, we shall return in Chapter 12 to the question of its suitability in particular real-world situations. We shall then be able to contrast the conditions under which a probability distribution for number of successes or number of trials should be assessed by the method of this chapter, when it should be assessed by the method of Section 8.2, and when still other methods are required.

10.1 A Numerical Example

To make the initial discussion concrete, assume that we wish to assess the probability that exactly two aces will occur in five rolls of a die when the probability of ace on any roll is *and will be* assessed at $\frac{1}{6}$ *regardless of the outcomes of any of these five rolls.* Equivalently, we wish to compute the long-run relative frequency with which two aces will occur in five rolls of a die when aces and non-aces occur *in no predictable pattern* and it is *known* that aces will occur on $\frac{1}{6}$ of the individual rolls in the long run.

We first compute the probability of rolling exactly two aces (A) and three non-aces (N) *in the specified order $AANN$.* Since the probability of an ace on any roll is the same regardless of the results of previous rolls, the events are *independent* by definition; and by the multiplication rule for independent events we have

$$P = \frac{1}{6}\,\frac{1}{6}\,\frac{5}{6}\,\frac{5}{6}\,\frac{5}{6} = \frac{125}{7776}.$$

If we divide an infinite sequence of rolls into groups of 5 consecutive rolls, $\frac{125}{7776}$ of these groups will show the pattern $AANN$.

We next observe that the probability or relative frequency is the same for *any other specified order.* For example, the probability of $NANNA$ is

$$P = \frac{5}{6}\,\frac{1}{6}\,\frac{5}{6}\,\frac{5}{6}\,\frac{1}{6} = \frac{125}{7776}.$$

Since the occurrence of two aces and three non-aces in any specified order and their occurrence in any other specified order are *mutually exclusive* events, we can get the probability of two aces and three non-aces *regardless* of order by adding the probabilities of all the possible orders. The possible orders are

$AANNN$ $NAANN$ $NNAAN$ $NNNAA$
$ANANN$ $NANAN$ $NNANA$
$ANNAN$ $NANNA$
$ANNNA$

or 10 in all.   The probability of two aces in five trials is thus

$$P = 10 \times {}^{125}\!/_{7776} = {}^{1250}\!/_{7776}.$$

If we divide an infinite sequence of rolls into groups of five consecutive rolls, ${}^{1250}\!/_{7776}$ of the groups will contain exactly two aces.

10.2   The Binomial Distribution

Let us now generalize this example by considering the probability of r successes in n trials where the probability of a success is p on any trial. The symbol q will denote the probability of a failure: $q = 1 - p$. *We repeat that we assume that p will remain the same for every one of these n trials regardless of the outcomes of any of them.*

1. The probability of r successes and $(n - r)$ failures *in a specified order* is

$$\underbrace{(p \times p \times p \times \cdots \times p)}_{(r \text{ factors})} \times \underbrace{(q \times q \times q \cdots \times q)}_{(n - r \text{ factors})} = p^r q^{n-r}.$$

2. If we use the symbol C_r^n to denote the *number of possible orders* in which r successes can occur in n trials, then it can be shown that

$$C_r^n = \frac{n!}{r!(n - r)!}$$

where by definition

$$n! = 1 \times 2 \times 3 \times 4 \times \cdots \times n$$

and is read "n factorial."   To cover the cases $r = 0$ and $r = n$, we define

$$0! = 1.$$

3. Since the orders are mutually exclusive, the probability of *exactly* r successes in n trials, *regardless of order*, is

$$P_b(r) = C_r^n p^r q^{n-r} \qquad \textit{Binomial probability}$$

Example.   In the problem of the probability of two aces in five rolls of a die, $n = 5$, $r = 2$, and $p = \frac{1}{6}$.   Substituting these values in the binomial probability formula we have

$$P_b(2) = C_2^5(\tfrac{1}{6})^2(\tfrac{5}{6})^3$$
$$= \frac{5!}{2!3!}\left(\frac{1}{6}\right)^2\left(\frac{5}{6}\right)^3$$
$$= 10(\tfrac{1}{6})^2(\tfrac{5}{6})^3$$
$$= 10 \times {}^{125}\!/_{7776}$$

as before.

10.2.1   *The Random Variable $\tilde{r}$ and the Binomial Distribution*

Although for purposes of analysis we have broken down the output of a random process into a number n of distinct trials, our real interest is

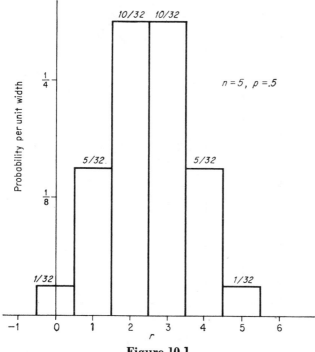

Figure 10.1

not in these individual trials as such but in the "experiment" which consists of all n individual trials taken as a whole. Using S to denote a success and F a failure, we can describe an *elementary* event of such an experiment by a sequence of n symbols of the form $SSFSFS$ . . . , but we are assuming in this chapter that we are interested only in the number r of S's in this sequence and not in the order in which the S's and F's occur. Every conceivable outcome of the experiment will have a definite *value r*, and therefore we may consider any r as a value of a *random variable $\tilde{r}$*.

The symbol $\tilde{r}$ will be used in the remainder of this course to denote the random variable "number of successes" in *any* experiment where the concept of number of successes has meaning.   When the experiment involves a *Bernoulli process with known parameter* and the probability of each *r* can therefore be computed by the binomial formula given above, we shall say that $\tilde{r}$ is a *binomial* random variable.   By using the binomial

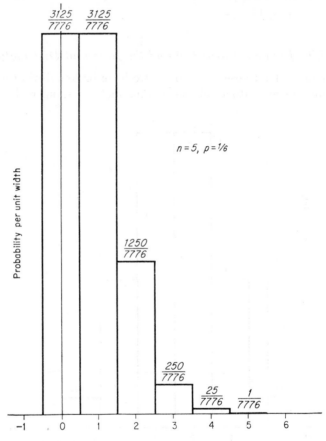

Figure 10.2

formula to compute the probability of every possible number of successes (from 0 to *n*), we arrive at the complete *binomial probability distribution*. The distribution for $n = 5$, $p = .5$ is shown in Figure 10.1 and can be taken as representing the probabilities of various numbers of heads when a "fair" coin is tossed five times.   The distribution for $n = 5$, $p = \frac{1}{6}$ is shown in Figure 10.2 and can be taken as representing the probabilities of various numbers of aces when a "fair" die is rolled five times.

Parameters.   The formula $P_b(r) = C_r^n p^r q^{n-r}$ thus defines, not just one distribution of $\tilde{r}$, but a whole *family* of distributions, one for every possible combination of values of *n* and *p*.   We shall call *n* and *p* the *parameters* of the binomial distribution.   It is only after definite numerical values have been assigned to the parameters that the binomial formula defines a specific distribution of the random variable $\tilde{r}$.   To show the dependence of the probabilities on the parameters n and p we shall often write $P_b(r|n,p)$, which should be read "the probability of r *given* n and p."

10.3   Cumulative Probabilities; Tables of the Binomial Distribution

In many applications we need the probability, not of exactly r successes, but of *r or less* successes or of *more than r* successes or of something of the sort.   Graphically, such probabilities are represented by the *area of a tail of the distribution*.   The probability of three or more successes when $n = 15$, $p = .33$, or $P_b(\tilde{r} \geq 3|n = 15, p = .33)$, is represented by the shaded area in Figure 10.3.

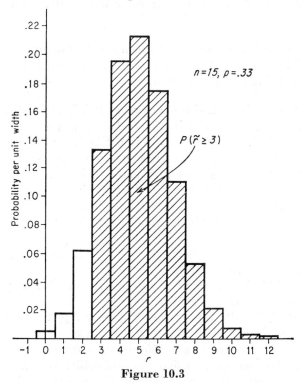

Figure 10.3

Cumulative probabilities can be computed exactly only by computing all the included individual probabilities and adding, and the task becomes very laborious when n is large and the r in "r or more," etc., is not close to either 0 or n.   For this reason tables have been published giving the tail areas directly for certain values of n and p and all the possible values of r; and these tables can also be used to obtain individual probabilities $P_b(\tilde{r} = r)$. A short set of tables of cumulative binomial probabilities is given as Table I.†

10.3.1 The Use of Probability Tables in General

Before using *any* table or chart of cumulative probabilities, the student must examine it to be clear on two points.

1. *Which tail is shown?* Tables may show the area of either the left or the right tail, but they never show both. Recall that the total area of any probability distribution is 1, so that the area of one tail is 1 minus the area of the other tail. The white area in Figure 10.3 is 1 minus the shaded area.

2. *How far does the tail extend?* Tables may show the probability of *r or more* successes, $P(\tilde{r} \geq r)$, or they may show the probability of *more than r* successes, $P(\tilde{r} > \tilde{r})$; and similarly if it is the left tail which is shown.

The various tables and charts which we shall use in this course are not all the same in these respects, although of course any one table or chart is internally consistent.

Table I of the binomial distribution shows $P_b(\tilde{r} \geq r)$, in other words the area *of the right* tail of the distribution *including* the probability of r itself. The value .9167 given opposite $r = 3$ in the table for $n = 15$, $p = .33$ is $P_b(r \geq 3 | n = 15, p = .33)$ and corresponds to the shaded area in Figure 10.3. Other cumulative probabilities and individual probabilities can be very simply obtained as is shown in the following examples for $n = 15$, $p = .33$, the distribution graphed in Figure 10.3.

To find $P_b(\tilde{r} > 3)$: this is the same as $P_b(\tilde{r} \geq 4)$; read .7829 opposite $r = 4$.

To find $P_b(\tilde{r} < 3)$: this is $1 - P_b(\tilde{r} \geq 3)$; read .9167 opposite $r = 3$, and compute $1 - .9167 = .0833$.

To find $P_b(\tilde{r} \leq 3)$: this is $1 - P_b(r \geq 4)$; read .7829 opposite $r = 4$ and compute $1 - .7829 = .2171$.

To find $P_b(\tilde{r} = 3)$: this is $P_b(\tilde{r} \geq 3) - P(\tilde{r} \geq 4)$; read these two probabilities and compute $.9167 - .7829 = .1338$.

To use the tables when $p > .50$, rephrase the problem in terms of $q = 1 - p$. For example, to find the probability that a machine will produce 12 or more defectives in a lot of 15 when the probability is .67 that any individual piece will be defective: look up instead the probability that there will be three or less good pieces when the probability is .33

---

† For very complete tables, see "Tables of the Cumulative Binomial Probability Distribution," *Annals of the Computation Laboratory of Harvard University*, vol. XXXV, Harvard University Press, Cambridge, Mass., 1955.

that any individual piece will be good.   This probability is .2171 as shown above.

PROBLEMS

1. A coin is to be tossed seven times. What probability should be assigned to the following numbers of heads by a person who is firmly convinced that the coin is "fair"?

a. Exactly 3.   *b.* 3 or more.

c. More than 3.   *d.* 3 or less.

e. Less than 3.   *f.* Between 3 and 5 inclusive.

2. An automatic machine is to be used to produce 100 pieces. What probability should be assigned to the following numbers of defectives by a person who is firmly convinced that the machine can be represented as a Bernoulli process producing 10 per cent defectives on the average?

a. Exactly 10.   *b.* 10 or less.

c. Less than 10.   *d.* 10 or more.

e. More than 10.   *f.* Between 10 and 15 inclusive.

3. *Using the same vertical and horizontal scales in both cases*, sketch a smooth curve approximating the histogram of the probability distribution for number defective r in lots produced by a Bernoulli process with $p = .4$

a. When the lot size $n = 10$.   *b.* When the lot size $n = 100$.

The heights of all the bars in the histogram for $n = 10$ should be computed and plotted before the curve is fitted, but in fitting the curve for $n = 100$ it will suffice to compute and plot the heights for every other value of $\bar{r}$ from 30 to 50.

4. *a.* Same as Problem 3 but use *fraction* defective r/n as the horizontal scale rather than number defective r. Remember that the vertical scale of a histogram shows probability *per unit width* and that it is the *area* of the bar which corresponds to probability itself. Thus $P_b(\bar{r} = 3 | p = .4, n = 10) = .2150$ gives the *area* of the bar for $r/n = \frac{3}{10} = .3$. Since the adjacent values of r/n are .2 and .4, the edges of the bar for .3 are at .25 and .35 and the bar has *width* .1. Then since the area of the bar is .215 and its width is .1, its *height* P' is $.215/.1 = 2.15$. Similarly the height of the bar for $r/n = .3$ when $n = 100$ is $.0100/.01 = 1.0$.

b. Can you approximate the binomial distribution for $n = 200$, $p = .3$, by using the distribution for $n = 100$, $p = .3$, and multiplying all values of r by 2?

5. Graph the binomial cumulative distribution $P_b(\bar{r} \leq r)$ for $p = .4$, $n = 10$.

6. *a.* The ABC Company takes 10 successive parts as they are produced by a particular machine and inspects them. If the *machine* is in fact in such a state that it can be treated as a Bernoulli process producing 5 per cent defectives on the average, what is the probability that the pieces drawn for this sample will be good or defective in the order *gggdggdggg*?

b. The XYZ Company draws 10 parts from a lot of 40 purchased parts. If the *lot* is in fact 5 per cent defective, does your answer to (*a*) give the probability that the pieces drawn from the sample will be good or defective in the order *gggdggdggg*? (HINT: What is the probability that the second piece will be good if one good piece has already been removed from the lot?)

7. A certain machine is readjusted by the ABC Company if an inspector finds three or more defectives in a sample of 10 taken from the output of the machine. What is the probability that the machine will be readjusted when it is producing 2 per cent defectives on the average? When it is producing 5 per cent defectives? 10 per cent? 20 per cent? 30 per cent? 40 per cent? 50 per cent? 60 per cent?

Graph the *conditional probability of acceptance* (i.e. the probability that the machine will *not* be readjusted) against the *process per cent defective*, showing per cent defective on the horizontal axis and probability of acceptance on the vertical axis.

182   *Random Processes and Derived Probabilities*

This is an example of a "single-sample decision rule" and its "operating characteristic."

8. The XYZ Company purchases a certain part in lots of 40. A sample of 10 is drawn from each lot and the lot is rejected if the inspector finds three or more defectives in the sample. Does the operating characteristic of Problem 7 give the probability that a lot will be accepted

   a. If the *lot* contains a certain per cent defective?
   b. If the *process* producing the lot produces a certain per cent defective?

9. A process producing transistors can be treated as a Bernoulli process with an average *yield* of 30 per cent: on the average, 30 per cent of the pieces are *good*. What are the probabilities of the following numbers of *defectives* in a lot of 100 pieces?

a. Exactly 70.   *b.* Less than 70.
c. 70 or less.   *d.* More than 70.
e. 70 or more.

CHAPTER 11

The Bernoulli Process: The Pascal Distribution

In Chapter 10 we derived the binomial distribution for the *number of successes in a specified number of Bernoulli trials*. In this chapter we shall derive the Pascal distribution for the *number of Bernoulli trials required to secure a specified number of successes*. We shall then see that the *expectations* of the binomial and the Pascal distributions can be easily obtained from tables in the same way that binomial and Pascal probabilities can be obtained from tables.

11.1 The Pascal Distribution

Suppose that we wish to know the probability that exactly five rolls of a "fair" die will be required to secure two aces—i.e., the probability that the second ace will occur on the fifth roll. We proceed exactly as we did in deriving the binomial distribution: we first get the probability of *one specified order* in which this event can occur and we then add the probabilities of all possible orders.

One possible order in which the event "second ace on fifth roll" can occur is $ANNNA$, and its probability is

$$P = \tfrac{1}{6} \, \tfrac{5}{6} \, \tfrac{5}{6} \, \tfrac{5}{6} \, \tfrac{1}{6} = {}^{125}\!/_{7776}.$$

The probability is the same for any other specified order. For $NNANA$, for example, it is

$$P = \tfrac{5}{6} \, \tfrac{5}{6} \, \tfrac{1}{6} \, \tfrac{5}{6} \, \tfrac{1}{6} = {}^{125}\!/_{7776}.$$

So far the argument is exactly like the one used in deriving the binomial distribution, but there is a difference when we come to counting the number of possible orders. Since by the definition of the problem there *must* be an A in the fifth place, the possible orders are only 4 in number, not 10:

$ANNNA$,
$NANNA$,
$NNANA$,
$NNNAA$.

183

The probability of each of these orders is the same and the orders are mutually exclusive, so that the required probability is

$$P = 4 \times {}^{125}\!/_{7776}.$$

In general, the probability that it will take exactly n trials to secure r successes *in a specified order* is

$$p^r q^{n-r}.$$

Since the rth success must occur on the nth trial, the number of possible orders depends on the arrangement of the first $r - 1$ successes within the first $n - 1$ trials: it is C_{r-1}^{n-1}. Thus the probability that exactly n trials will be required to secure r successes regardless of the positions of the first $r - 1$ successes is

$$P_{Pa}(n) = C_{r-1}^{n-1} p^r q^{n-r} \qquad Pascal\ probability$$

By inserting specific numerical values for r, p, and $q = 1 - p$ in this formula and then computing the probability of every possible number of trials n, we arrive at the complete *probability distribution* of the Pascal random variable $\tilde{n}$.

Parameters. Just like the binomial formula, the general Pascal formula $C_{r-1}^{n-1} p^r q^{n-r}$ defines not one distribution of $\tilde{n}$ but a whole *family* of distributions, one for every possible combination of values of r and p. The quantities r and p are thus the *parameters* of the Pascal distribution of the random variable $\tilde{n}$, just as n and p were the parameters of the binomial distribution of the random variable $\tilde{r}$.

The distributions for $r = 3$ with $p = .2$, .8, and .9 are shown in Figure 11.1. Notice that whereas the binomial variable $\tilde{r}$ must have a value between 0 and n inclusive, the Pascal variable can have any value from r to infinity. Obviously we cannot get r successes in *less* than r trials, but the probability that it will take, say, 1000 trials to secure three successes is not 0 for any value of p other than 0 or 1.

11.2 Tables of the Pascal Distribution

In many applications we need the probability, not that the required number of trials $\tilde{n}$ will have *exactly* some particular value n, but that the required number will be *less than n*, *greater than n*, or something of the sort. Graphically, such probabilities are represented by the *area of a tail* of the distribution—the probability that five or more trials will be required to secure three successes when $p = .2$, .8, or .9 is represented by the shaded areas in Figure 11.1. Again as in the case of the binomial distribution, the labor of computing and summing the areas of the individual bars in a tail can be avoided by use of published tables.

Tables of the Pascal distribution for a few selected values of r and p are shown as Table 11.1. These tables show $P_{Pa}(\tilde{n} \geq n)$, that is the area

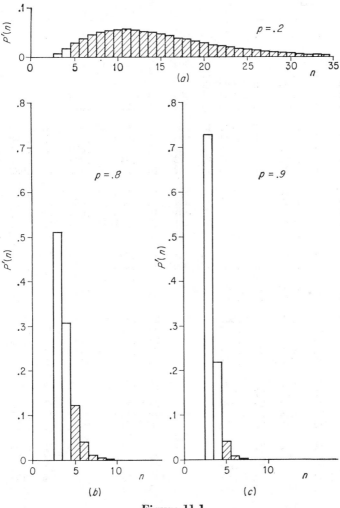

Figure 11.1

of the *right* tail *including* the bar for n itself. Thus $P_{Pa}(\tilde{n} \geq 5 | 3, .8)$, the shaded area in Figure 11.1*b*, is given as .181 opposite $n = 5$ in the table for $p = .8$ and the column for $r = 3$.

Other cumulative probabilities such as $P_{Pa}(\tilde{n} \leq n)$ and individual probabilities $P_{Pa}(\tilde{n} = n)$ can be obtained by procedures just like those described in Section 10.3.1.

Table 11.1
Pascal Distribution
$$P_{Pa}(\tilde{n} \geq n | r, p)$$
$$p = .2$$

r = 1		r = 2		r = 3				r = 4				r = 5			
n	P	n	P	n	P	n	P	n	P	n	P	n	P	n	P
1	1.000					41	.008			41	.028			41	.076
2	.800	2	1.000			42	.007			42	.024			42	.066
3	.640	3	.960	3	1.000	43	.006			43	.021			43	.058
4	.512	4	.896	4	.992	44	.005	4	1.000	44	.018			44	.051
5	.410	5	.819	5	.973	45	.004	5	.998	45	.015			45	.044
6	.328	6	.737	6	.942	46	.003	6	.993	46	.013	6	1.000	46	.038
7	.262	7	.655	7	.901	47	.003	7	.983	47	.011	7	.998	47	.033
8	.210	8	.577	8	.852	48	.002	8	.967	48	.009	8	.995	48	.029
9	.168	9	.503	9	.797	49	.002	9	.944	49	.008	9	.990	49	.025
10	.134	10	.436	10	.738	50	.002	10	.914	50	.007	10	.980	50	.021
11	.107	11	.376	11	.678	51	.001	11	.879	51	.006	11	.967	51	.018
12	.086	12	.322	12	.617	52	.001	12	.839	52	.005	12	.950	52	.016
13	.069	13	.275	13	.558	53	.001	13	.795	53	.004	13	.927	53	.014
14	.055	14	.234	14	.502	54	.001	14	.747	54	.003	14	.901	54	.012
15	.044	15	.198	15	.448	55	.001	15	.698	55	.003	15	.870	55	.010
16	.035	16	.167	16	.398	56	.001	16	.648	56	.002	16	.836	56	.009
17	.028	17	.141	17	.352	57	.000	17	.598	57	.002	17	.798	57	.007
18	.023	18	.118	18	.310			18	.549	58	.002	18	.758	58	.006
19	.018	19	.099	19	.271			19	.501	59	.001	19	.716	59	.005
20	.014	20	.083	20	.237			20	.455	60	.001	20	.673	60	.005
21	.012	21	.069	21	.206			21	.411	61	.001	21	.630	61	.004
22	.009	22	.058	22	.179			22	.370	62	.001	22	.586	62	.003
23	.007	23	.048	23	.154			23	.332	63	.001	23	.543	63	.003
24	.006	24	.040	24	.133			24	.297	64	.001	24	.501	64	.002
25	.005	25	.033	25	.115			25	.264	65	.000	25	.460	65	.002
26	.004	26	.027	26	.098			26	.234			26	.421	66	.002
27	.003	27	.023	27	.084			27	.207			27	.383	67	.001
28	.002	28	.019	28	.072			28	.182			28	.348	68	.001
29	.002	29	.015	29	.061			29	.160			29	.315	69	.001
30	.002	30	.013	30	.052			30	.140			30	.284	70	.001
31	.001	31	.011	31	.044			31	.123			31	.255	71	.001
32	.001	32	.009	32	.037			32	.107			32	.229	72	.001
33	.001	33	.007	33	.032			33	.093			33	.204	73	.001
34	.001	34	.006	34	.027			34	.081			34	.182	74	.000
35	.001	35	.005	35	.023			35	.070			35	.162		
36	.000	36	.004	36	.019			36	.061			36	.143		
		37	.003	37	.016			37	.052			37	.127		
		38	.003	38	.013			38	.045			38	.112		
		39	.002	39	.011			39	.039			39	.099		
		40	.002	40	.009			40	.033			40	.087		

Table 11.1 (*Continued*)

p = .8

r = 1		r = 2		r = 3		r = 4		r = 10		r = 11		r = 15		r = 16	
n	P	n	P	n	P	n	P	n	P	n	P	n	P	n	P
1	1.000									11	1.000			16	1.000
2	.200	2	1.000							12	.914			17	.972
3	.040	3	.360	3	1.000					13	.725			18	.882
4	.008	4	.104	4	.488	4	1.000			14	.498			19	.729
5	.002	5	.027	5	.181	5	.590	10	1.000	15	.302	15	1.000	20	.545
6	.000	6	.007	6	.058	6	.263	11	.893	16	.164	16	.965	21	.370
		7	.002	7	.017	7	.099	12	.678	17	.082	17	.859	22	.231
		8	.000	8	.005	8	.033	13	.442	18	.038	18	.690	23	.133
				9	.001	9	.010	14	.253	19	.016	19	.499	24	.072
				10	.000	10	.003	15	.130	20	.007	20	.327	25	.036
						11	.001	16	.061	21	.003	21	.196	26	.017
						12	.000	17	.027	22	.001	22	.109	27	.008
								18	.011	23	.000	23	.056	28	.003
								19	.004			24	.027	29	.001
								20	.002			25	.013	30	.001
								21	.001			26	.006	31	.000
								22	.000			27	.002		
												28	.001		
												29	.000		

p = .9

r = 1		r = 2		r = 3		r = 4		r = 10		r = 11		r = 15		r = 16	
n	P	n	P	n	P	n	P	n	P	n	P	n	P	n	P
1	1.000									11	1.000			16	1.000
2	.100	2	1.000							12	.686			17	.815
3	.010	3	.190	3	1.000					13	.341			18	.518
4	.001	4	.028	4	.271	4	1.000			14	.134			19	.266
5	.000	5	.004	5	.052	5	.344	10	1.000	15	.044	15	1.000	20	.115
		6	.000	6	.009	6	.081	11	.651	16	.013	16	.794	21	.043
				7	.001	7	.016	12	.303	17	.003	17	.485	22	.014
				8	.000	8	.003	13	.111	18	.001	18	.238	23	.004
						9	.000	14	.034	19	.000	19	.098	24	.001
								15	.009			20	.035	25	.000
								16	.002			21	.011		
								17	.001			22	.003		
								18	.000			23	.001		
												24	.000		

11.2.1   Pascal Probabilities from Binomial Tables

In actual practice, tables of the Pascal distribution as such are not published because the probabilities can be obtained from tables of the binomial distribution.   Although *Table* 11.1 *gives all Pascal probabilities required to solve the required problems assigned in this course*, we shall give the relation between the two distributions in case a student wishes to try his hand at other problems.   The relation rests on the following arguments:

    1. If there are r or more successes in the first n trials, then it took n or less trials to obtain the first r successes.

    2. If, on the contrary, there are less than r successes in the first n trials, then it will take more than n trials to obtain r successes.†

Therefore

$$P_{Pa}(\tilde{n} \leq n | r, p) = P_b(\tilde{r} \geq r | n, p),$$
$$P_{Pa}(\tilde{n} > n | r, p) = P_b(\tilde{r} < r | n, p).$$

For example: the Pascal probability $P_{Pa}(\tilde{n} \leq 5 | 3, .2)$ that five or less trials will be required to obtain three successes when $p = .2$ can be found by looking up the binomial probability $P_b(\tilde{r} \geq 3 | 5, .2)$ that there will be three or more successes in five trials when $p = .2$.   This is given as .0579 by Table I.   We check by observing that

$$P_{Pa}(\tilde{n} \leq 5) = 1 - P_{Pa}(\tilde{n} \geq 6).$$

The probability on the right is given as .942 by the Pascal table in this chapter; and $1 - .942 = .058$, which is the same to three decimal places as the probability given by the binomial table.

11.3   Expectations

11.3.1   Expectations of a Binomial Random Variable

In Table 11.2 the method of Section 5.2.4 is used to compute all partial expectations of the binomial random variable $\tilde{r}$ for the case $n = 5$, $p = .3$, the required probabilities $P_b(r)$ being taken from Table I.   The "complete" or ordinary expectation of $\tilde{r}$—the mean of the distribution of $\tilde{r}$—is 1.500; two of the partial expectations are

$$E_0^1(\tilde{r}) = .360; \qquad E_0^2(\tilde{r}) = .978.$$

---

† Such relations are not quite so obvious as they seem.   It is *not* true, for example, that $\tilde{n} < n$ implies $\tilde{r} > r$.   We can get three successes in less than five trials and still have only three successes in all five trials.

Table 11.2

r	$P_b(r)$	$r\,P_b(r)$	Cumulative sum
0	.168	0	0
1	.360	.360	.360
2	.309	.618	.978
3	.132	.396	1.374
4	.029	.116	1.490
5	.002	.010	1.500
	1.000	1.500	

The labor of computation can be lightened in problems involving expectations by making use of the fact that if $\tilde{r}$ has a binomial distribution, then

$$E_0^r(\tilde{r}) = np\,P_b(\tilde{r} \le r - 1 | n - 1, p) \qquad \textit{Binomial partial expectation}$$

For example: if $n = 5$ and $p = .3$, then

$$E_0^2(\tilde{r}) = 5 \times .3\,P_b(\tilde{r} \le 2 - 1 | n = 5 - 1, p = .3).$$

In the binomial tables for $n = 4$, $p = .3$, we find

$$P_b(\tilde{r} \le 1) = 1 - .348 = .652.$$

We then have for the partial expectation $5 \times .3 \times .652 = .978$, the same result we obtained by direct computation in Table 11.2.

The complete or ordinary expectation of $\tilde{r}$, obtained by summing $r\,P(r)$ for *all possible* r, can be written

$$E(\tilde{r}) = E_0^n(\tilde{r}).$$

Substituting n for r in the formula for the partial expectation we obtain

$$E(\tilde{r}) = np\,P_b(\tilde{r} \le n - 1 | n - 1, p).$$

The probability in this formula is obviously 1 since the number of successes in $n - 1$ trials cannot be greater than $n - 1$, and therefore this result reduces to

$$E(\tilde{r}) = np \qquad \textit{Expected number of successes, binomial distribution}$$

11.3.2   Expectations of a Pascal Random Variable

If the random variable $\tilde{n}$ has a Pascal distribution, its partial expectation is given by the formula

$$E_0^n(\tilde{n}) = \frac{r}{p} P_{Pa}(\tilde{n} \leq n + 1 | r + 1, p) \qquad \textit{Pascal partial expectation}$$

Instead of $E_0^n(\tilde{n})$ we could equally well have written $E_r^n(\tilde{n})$, since $P_{Pa}(n)$
and therefore $n\,P_{Pa}(n)$ is 0 for all n less than r—we cannot get r successes
in less than r trials.

The "complete" or ordinary expectation of $\tilde{n}$—the mean of the
Pascal distribution of $\tilde{n}$—is obtained when all possible values of $\tilde{n}$, from
$n = r$ to $n = \infty$, are included in the expectation. In this case the prob
ability in the formula for the partial expectation becomes $P_{Pa}(\tilde{n} \leq \infty)$
this probability is obviously 1 and therefore

$$E(\tilde{n}) = \frac{r}{p} \qquad \textit{Expected number of trials, Pascal distribution}$$

PROBLEMS

1. A person is firmly convinced that a process producing transistors can be represented as a Bernoulli process with an average *yield* of 20 per cent: on the average,
20 per cent of the pieces are *good*.   What probability should he assign to the proposition that the following numbers of pieces will have to be manufactured in order to
secure five good pieces?
a. Exactly 23.   *b.* Less than 23.
c. 23 or less.   *d.* More than 23.
e. 23 or more.

2. A Bernoulli process is known to produce 10 per cent *defectives*.   What probability should be assigned to the proposition that the following numbers of pieces will
have to be produced in order to secure 15 *good* pieces?
a. Exactly 20.   *b.* Less than 20.
c. 20 or less.   *d.* More than 20.
e. 20 or more.

3. *Using the same vertical and horizontal scales in both cases*, sketch a smooth curve
approximating the histogram of the probability distribution for number of pieces $\tilde{n}$
which must be produced to fill an order when the pieces are produced by a Bernoulli
process with a *yield* of .8 and the order is for
a. 4 good pieces.   *b.* 16 good pieces.

4. *a.* Same as Problem 3 but instead of the total required n use the ratio n/r of
total required to number good as the horizontal scale.   Remember that the vertical
scale should show P′ and not P, and review Chapter 10, Problem 4, before plotting
any points.

b. Can you approximate the Pascal distribution for $r = 500$, $p = .8$, by using the distribution for $r = 5$, $p = .8$ and multiplying all the values of n by 100?

5. According to Chapter 10, Problem 7, the ABC Company readjusts a certain machine if the inspector finds three or more defectives in a sample of 10. It costs $2 to inspect one piece; and since the outcome is certain as soon as the third defective is found, the company decides to reduce the cost of inspection by stopping inspection as soon as the third defective is found. The process will be accepted (i.e., will *not* be readjusted) only if less than three defectives have been found when all 10 pieces in the sample have been inspected.

a. If the process is in fact producing 20 per cent defectives on the average, what is the expected cost of sampling under this plan? Compute (1) by weighting each possible cost by its probability and also (2) by using the formula for the proper partial expectation.

b. Optional: requires use of binomial tables. Using the formula for the proper partial expectation, find the expected sample size given that the process average is 2, 5, 10, 20, 30, 40, 50, and 60 per cent. Plot these expected sizes against the process average.

This is the *ASN* (average sample number) curve of a *partially curtailed single-sample plan.* The plan would be fully curtailed if inspection were stopped as soon as *either* three defectives or eight good pieces were found.

6. In June, 1955, the Warner Aircraft Engine Company received an order for 10 spare ring gears from New England Airlines. The ring gear was the largest and most expensive of the gears in the system which drives the propeller. The Warner Company carried in stock part No. 21573, the gear blanks from which the ring gears would be made. This gear blank was a standard size, used in many airplanes. The number of teeth, however, was nonstandard. When New England Airlines had bought the airplanes in which these gears were used its management had decided that flying requirements peculiar to this airline necessitated a gear ratio slightly higher than standard, and Warner had designed a special gear train accordingly. No other airlines used this ratio, and New England was on the point of replacing its aircraft by a new type with a different engine. Upon inquiry, the production manager of the Warner Company learned that the lot of 10 ring gears would almost certainly last until New England's current aircraft had been entirely replaced.

The gear blank cost Warner about $50 each to make. The first step in the machining process was hobbing. Setup for this operation was very expensive, costing about $500, but the direct cost of hobbing an extra gear was negligible so long as the machine's capacity of 25 gears at one time was not exceeded. After hobbing, each gear was individually subjected to a series of drilling, grinding, and finishing operations, the total cost of which was $90 per gear. The machined gears were then heat-treated at a cost of about $10 per gear, after which they were subjected to a hard- ness test the cost of which was negligible.

Heat-treatment was exceedingly difficult to control. The test for hardness had rigid specifications, and the Warner Company had had considerable difficulty in meet- ing standards on this type of gear in the past. The table on page 192 shows the num- ber of gears put into production and the number passing the hardness test for 10 recent lots of gears made from part No. 21573.

In answering the following questions, assume that the heat-treating process can legitimately be treated as a Bernoulli process with known parameter and assume that if a rerun is required the amount of material scheduled for the rerun will be exactly right.

Number	Number heat-treated	Number passing hardness test
1	20	18
2	16	12
3	16	11
4	18	16
5	10	7
6	15	14
7	20	16
8	12	7
9	19	15
10	14	12

a. If extra material is scheduled as a scrap allowance, how much processing should be done on this material?

b. Give a common-sense reason why the parameter of the process should be estimated by the ratio total-good to total-treated rather than by averaging the recorded fractions good.

c. What is the optimum allowance?

d. What is the cost of uncertainty?

e. What is the cost of irrationality if the production order is 1 unit greater than optimum? 1 unit less?

f. Compute the *range* of values of K_u for which your answer to (*c*) is optimal and discuss the criticality of the assessment of the value of K_u in this case.

g. If 14 pieces are heat-treated, what is the expected number of good pieces short? (As in computing any expectation, list all possible values of the variable "number short," multiply each by its probability, and add the products. Notice carefully that number short means number of good pieces required minus number actually produced on the initial run; it does *not* mean serial number of Gth good piece minus serial number of last piece scheduled on the initial run.)

h. What is the *conditional* expected size of shortage, *given* that a shortage occurs? [HINT: (*g*) asks you to average the total shortage in a long series of runs over all runs; (*h*) asks you to average the total shortage over only those runs in which a shortage occurred.]

7. (Optional)   It was pointed out in Section 8.3 that second-order losses in scrap-allowance problems may legitimately be neglected only under special circumstances but that it is usually extremely difficult to make an exact allowance for these losses. Exact computation *is* possible, however, when both (*a*) the required number of good pieces is small and (*b*) the process producing the pieces is a Bernoulli process with known parameter p.   The nature of the procedure in this case can be suggested by the following hints:

a. If $Q^*(G)$ is the *best* number of pieces to schedule when G good pieces are required on an initial order, it will also be the best number to schedule on any rerun intended to fill out a shortage of G good pieces.

b. If we already know the best number of pieces to schedule when one good piece is required and if we propose to schedule Q pieces when two are required, then

$$C(2|Q) = D(Q) + C^*(1)\, P(1|Q) + C(2|Q)\, P(2|Q)$$
$$= \frac{D(Q) + C^*(1)\, P(1|Q)}{1 - P(2|Q)}$$

where $C(2|Q)$ = total expected cost of filling a requirement for two pieces if Q pieces are scheduled on the initial run and also on any rerun intended to produce two good pieces

$D(Q)$ = total cost (including setup) of manufacturing Q pieces

$C^*(1)$ = *minimum* total expected cost of filling a requirement for one good piece, obtained by scheduling $Q^*(1)$ pieces when one good piece is required

$P(S|Q)$ = probability of a shortage of size S if Q pieces are scheduled on a run intended to produce two good pieces

Compute the optimum production order $Q^*(3)$ to fill a requirement for $G = 3$ good pieces when variable manufacturing cost is \$10 per piece, setup cost is \$1000, and the long-run fraction good of the process is .8.

CHAPTER 12

Conditional Models and Marginal Probability

In the two preceding chapters we have computed probabilities on the *assumption* that it was reasonable to assign the same probability to a success on each of a sequence of future trials and to continue to assign this same probability to the remaining trials regardless of the outcomes of the earlier trials in the sequence. We now turn to examine the conditions under which it *is* reasonable to do this.

12.1 The Definition of a Bernoulli Process

Consider first the process which consists in rolling a die. It has already been remarked repeatedly that broad experience with physical processes of this general nature—not just previous experience with any one particular die—leads us to certain conclusions concerning what would happen if this die and an extremely large number of apparently identical dice were all rolled in the same way an extremely large number of times. Using p to denote the fraction of aces occurring on all rolls of all dice together, we can state the conclusions as follows:

1. Looking at the record of all dice together, we would find that the fraction of aces on all the first rolls was equal to p, the fraction on all the 100th rolls was equal to p, and similarly for all the one-millionth rolls and so forth. The process is *stable*.
2. Looking at the record of any one die, we would find that the fraction of aces on rolls following an ace was equal to p, the fraction of aces on rolls following a run of two aces was equal to p, and similarly for the fraction on rolls following the pattern deuce-trey or any other pattern whatsoever. The individual trials are *independent*.

Because this die-rolling process is believed to meet the two conditions of stability and independence, it is by definition a *Bernoulli process with parameter p*. We remind the student again of the point emphasized in Section 1.6.1: the quantity p describes this process—more strictly, *describes our model of the real process*—in the same sense that another process may be described by the mean diameter of the pieces it produces or by the rms vultage it generates. We shall see later that it is only under certain conditions that the *probability* of a success on a *particular* future trial can be set equal to this parameter p.

Consider next a process which consists of the impact extrusion of aluminum cups from aluminum pellets. Before we may legitimately adopt a Bernoulli model of this process, we must satisfy ourselves that the occurrences of defective cups will meet the same two conditions of stability and independence which we have stated above for the occurrences of aces in die rolling. Very often they will *not* be met in practice.

1. It is quite possible that the process is such that the conditions determining the long-run fraction defective p will not remain the same over time. Two cases must be distinguished.

a. If, for example, the extrusion dies are subject to appreciable wear, the tendency to produce defectives will increase steadily with time. The process is *not stable* and therefore cannot be represented as a Bernoulli process.

b. If, for example, the pellets are themselves produced by a batch process, some batches of pellets may tend to yield more defective cups than others. In this case a Bernoulli model may apply to the processing of any one batch, but no single Bernoulli model (no single value of p) will apply to the entire output of the extrusion process. The process is only *conditionally stable.*

2. It is quite possible that the process is such that defectives tend to be followed by defectives more or less frequently than good pieces are followed by defectives. If, for example, batches of pellets differ in quality and a run is made using pellets from several batches which have not been thoroughly mixed, defectives will tend to occur in streaks. The trials are *not independent* and the Bernoulli model does not apply.

Notice that *the only real distinction between lack of stability and lack of independence lies in the kind of information which indicates a change in the process parameter* p.

1. If we know that p changes with time, the passage of time is "*outside*" *information* which indicates that p has changed and we say that the process is not *stable*. The same thing is true if p changes from batch to batch of raw material and we can identify the batch being used; and in this case we believe vice versa that as long as we *are* using the same batch of material the process *is* (conditionally) stable and can be treated as a Bernoulli process.

2. If, on the contrary, the *only* indication of a change in p is the *output of the process itself,* we say that the trials are not *independent*. If we *cannot* identify a pellet as coming from a particular batch of material, the only evidence that we have come to a group of pellets from a poor batch will be the actual occurrence of defectives.

This discussion should suffice to make it clear that before adopting a

Bernoulli model of any real process we must look not only at the "direct" evidence, i.e. the actual record of previous successes and failures, but also at the "indirect" evidence, i.e. at what we know about the physical mechanism as such. We do not believe that successive rolls of a die are independent because we have rolled that particular die a great number of times and counted fractions of aces—we believe it because we believe that in all such processes the mechanism is such that the occurrence of an ace on one roll neither *affects* the result of the next roll nor *indicates* that the mechanism is in a state which tends to produce a different fraction of aces. If, however, we *do* observe a surprisingly long streak of aces or a surprising number of streaks in rolling some particular die, we ordinarily reconsider our opinion and look for some mechanism peculiar to that die which might account for this behavior.

It is thus very important to exercise due caution before basing decisions on a Bernoulli model of a real process, but it is equally important not to be disturbed by the fact that it is rarely if ever that a real process can be *exactly* represented by a Bernoulli model. In almost all practical decision problems it would be extremely difficult if not flatly impossible to analyze a model which took account of *everything* we know or believe about the real world; and an approximately correct analysis of a problem is far better than no rational analysis at all. We have already seen and we shall continue to see numerous examples of the fact that reasonably small errors in the statement of a problem rarely lead to a decision which is *materially* less profitable than the true best decision.

In some cases, furthermore, a separate, explicit allowance can be made for differences between the actual behavior of a process and the behavior of a Bernoulli model. To give just one very common example: it very often happens that an above-average fraction of defectives is produced while a process is being brought into adjustment after a setup or a tool change. If we can make a separate estimate of the defectives which will be produced in this way, we may well be able to assume a Bernoulli model for the remainder of the run.

12.2 The Parameter of the Process

Suppose, then, that we have satisfied ourselves that some real process can be reasonably well represented by a Bernoulli model: we have still said nothing about the actual numerical value of the process parameter p, the long-run fraction of successes. As we pointed out in Section 1.6, two cases must be sharply distinguished.

12.2.1 Known Parameter

If we have had very great direct experience with some process, we may feel that *for the practical purpose at hand* we *know* the value of the

parameter p which characterizes the process.   If we have rolled a die
tens of thousands of times and have observed that ace came up with relative frequency .15, we will feel *practically* certain that ace will continue to
come up with relative frequency .15 on the average.   If we have observed
that 15 per cent of the last 50,000 pieces turned out by some machine have
been defective and if we have no reason to believe that the condition of
the machine has changed during this time, we may feel *practically* certain
that if no observable changes are made in the condition of the machine in
the future it will continue to turn out 15 per cent defectives on the
average.

In such cases we are justified, as we saw in Section 1.6.1, in assigning
the *probability* .15 to success on any trial in a future sequence and in
continuing to assign this same probability regardless of the outcomes of
the earlier trials in the sequence.   This statement has three separate
implications:

1. As of *now* we assign the same (simple) probability .15 to success
on the last trial of any sequence that we assign on the first, etc. (*stability*).

2. As of *now*, we assign the same (conditional) probability .15 to
success on any trial following a success that we assign on any trial following a failure, etc. (*independence*).

3. We will *continue* to assign this same probability .15 to success on
the later trials in a sequence regardless of the outcomes of the earlier trials
in the sequence (*known parameter*).

The first two implications follow from our conviction that the process
behaves as a Bernoulli process.   The third follows from the fact that *our
past experience with the fraction of successes generated by the process is over-
whelmingly great in comparison with what we can learn by observing a
(relatively) few more trials.*   If, for example, we wish to compute probabilities concerning the outcomes of 10 rolls of the die or a production run
of 10 pieces, we may well feel that we would not *materially* lower our
assessment $p = .15$ even if the first nine trials all resulted in failure or
raise it if the first nine trials all resulted in success.

When and only when all three of these conditions are met, we are
justified in using the binomial formula to compute the probability
of r successes in n trials or in using the Pascal formula to compute
the probability that n trials will be required to produce r successes.

12.2.2   Unknown Parameter

We have just said that we cannot legitimately treat the process
parameter as known and continue to assign the same probability to
success unless our past experience is *overwhelming* relative to the new
experience we will gain in the new sequence of trials we are about to conduct.   If this is not true, then the outcomes of the earlier trials in this

new sequence *should* lead us to modify our estimate of the process parameter *p* and therefore the probability which we subsequently assign to successes. But if this is true, then *the basic assumption underlying the binomial and Pascal distributions is violated, and therefore the probability distribution of r̃ is not binomial and the distribution of ñ is not Pascal.* In this case these distributions give only the long-run relative frequency with which certain events will occur *if* the process parameter *p* in fact has some particular numerical value, and therefore they give only *conditional* probabilities for these events.

This is probably the most common state of affairs when we are trying to apply the theory of probability to practical business problems: our general knowledge of the way a process works convinces us that it is (at least approximately) a Bernoulli process with *some* parameter *p*, but we do not know the value of *p*. Lot-to-lot variation in the machinability of raw material, for example, may prevent us from getting enough experience to *know p* for the material to be used in the next production run even though we are convinced that as long as this batch lasts the process will meet the Bernoulli conditions of stability and independence.

In pure logic, of course, we either know *p* or we do not: if the occurrence of an unbroken string of 1 million successes should change our assessment of the probability of a success on the next trial, then the occurrence of a single success should change our assessment for the following trial by *some* amount. We are really making use of an *approximation* whenever we treat a parameter as known in any practical problem— we are saying that the sequence of trials for which we are computing probabilities is so short that our assessment of *p* could not be changed *materially*, i.e. by enough to affect the decision or the expected costs, and that therefore it is not worth the trouble of taking this change into account at all. Our next problem is to find out how to compute probabilities when the sequence of trials in which we are interested is so long relative to our past experience that the outcomes of the earlier trials of the sequence *could* lead to a material change in our estimate of *p*.

12.3   Allowance for the Two Kinds of Uncertainty; Marginal Probabilities

In any situation where we have adopted a Bernoulli model of a process but do not know the value of the parameter of the process, we can say that we have *two kinds of uncertainty* concerning the random variable r̃ or ñ: the "Bernoulli uncertainty" which we would have if we knew *p*, and additional uncertainty due to the fact that we do not know the value of *p*. A rational probability distribution for r̃ or ñ must take full account of *both* these kinds of uncertainty, and we shall now see how such a probability distribution can be assessed.

12.3.1   *The Random Variable $\tilde{p}$ and Its Probability Distribution*

Consider first an extremely simple example which will bring out the essential points. We are presented with an urn containing three badly deformed dice and are informed that extensive experimentation with these dice has shown that two of them turn up ace with long-run relative frequency $p = .24$ while the other one has $p = .09$. We draw one of the dice from the urn, inspect it carefully, and become convinced that although deformed it will nevertheless meet the Bernoulli conditions of independence and stability: p may not be $\frac{1}{6}$ as it would be in the case of a fair die, but we believe that the fraction of aces following aces will nevertheless be the same as the fraction following non-ace, etc., and that the tendency to produce ace will not change as we make repeated rolls of the die.

In the situation just described, the actual drawing of one die from the three in the urn is a trial with three possible elementary events, two of which give a long-run fraction defective $p = .24$ and one of which gives $p = .09$. The two numbers .24 and .09 are thus *values* assigned to the possible events of a trial and may therefore be considered as values of a *random variable* $\tilde{p}$.

When the parameter of a Bernoulli process is unknown, this parameter becomes the basic random variable in any problem in which the output of the process is involved.

Before we can assign probabilities to the possible events of a roll or rolls of our die, we must first assign probabilities to the possible values of the basic random variable $\tilde{p}$ which characterizes the die-rolling *process* itself. This part of the problem corresponds exactly to the assessment of the distribution of the random variable $\tilde{\rho}$ in Section 8.2—the student will recall that any stable process generating successes and failures in a sequence of distinct trials can be characterized either by the long-run ratio p of successes to trials or by the long-run ratio ρ of trials to successes.

In our present problem the most obvious thing is to argue that since there were three dice in the urn and we know that two of them have $p = .24$ while one has $p = .09$, there is probability $\frac{2}{3}$ that we have a die with $p = .24$ and probability $\frac{1}{3}$ that we have the die with $p = .09$. In other words, we may assign equal probabilities to the three elementary events and from these deduce the probabilities of the events $\tilde{p} = .09$ and $\tilde{p} = .24$ as we did in Section 3.1. We have emphasized repeatedly, however, that *all* available information must be used in assessing any probability; and in this situation the information on the number of dice of each type in the urn is not the only information available, since information can be obtained by inspecting the die which has been drawn. It may well be that the shape of the die is such that it seems highly improbab' that ace would turn up as frequently as it does when a fair die is rolled, and on the basis of this observation we might be willing to bet at odds of four to one, say, that we have in hand the die with long-run fraction .09.

To emphasize the fact that probability assessments should often rest more on judgment than on mere mechanical calculations, we shall assume in what follows that these are in fact the odds which we consider fair: *probability* .8 *is in fact assigned to the event* $\tilde{p} = .09$, and therefore probability .2 is assigned to the event $\tilde{p} = .24$. In algebraic notation:

$$P(\tilde{p} = .09) = .8,$$
$$P(\tilde{p} = .24) = .2.$$

12.3.2   The Marginal Distribution of $\tilde{r}$

Probability of Success on Any One Trial. Consider first the problem of determining the probability that any roll of this die will yield an ace—we shall call this a success. *If we knew* that the process parameter $p = .09$ for this die, we would assign *probability* .09 to a success on one roll, and therefore .09 can be called the *conditional* probability of a success *given* $p = .09$. Similarly .24 is the conditional probability of a success given $p = .24$.

The *unconditional* probability of a success on a single roll is then computed in the way shown in Table 12.1. The probability .072 in the last column is the probability which we assign to the *joint event* that *both* (1) the process parameter or basic random variable $\tilde{p}$ has the value .09 *and* (2) this process yields a success. Similarly the probability .048 in the last column is the probability that *both* (1) $\tilde{p} = .24$ *and* (2) the roll yields a success. Since these two joint events are mutually exclusive, the probability that one or the other will occur is $.072 + .048 = .120$; and since these two joint events represent *all* the possible ways of getting a success, .120 is the probability we must assign to a success.

Table 12.1

Value p of the basic random variable	$P(p)$	Conditional probability $P_b(\text{success}|p)$	Joint probability $P(\text{success},p)$
.09	.8	.09	.072
.24	.2	.24	.048
	1.0		.120

Notice carefully that this probability .120 applies to *any* one roll; it is the probability which we assign to success on the first roll; it is also the probability which *on the basis of the evidence now available* we assign to success on the 100th roll. Notice further that this same number .120 can also be interpreted as the expected value of the basic random variable $\tilde{p}$ itself:

The unconditional probability of a success on a *single* Bernoulli trial is equal to the expected value of the process parameter $\tilde{p}$.

Probability of r Successes in n Trials. Consider next the problem of determining the probability that two successive rolls will both yield successes, $P(\tilde{r} = 2|n = 2)$. If we knew that we had the die with $p = .09$, we would *now* assign probability .09 to success on the first roll, and after the first roll had been made we would assign probability .09 to success on the second roll *regardless of the outcome of the first roll.* The probability that both rolls would yield a success would therefore be $.09^2 = .0081$.

In the actual problem, however, this is only a *conditional* probability *given* $p = .09$, and we denote it by $P_b(\tilde{r} = 2|n = 2, \tilde{p} = .09)$. A similar argument gives $.24^2 = .0576$ as the conditional probability $P_b(\tilde{r} = 2|n = 2, \tilde{p} = .24)$. We then compute the *unconditional* probability $P(\tilde{r} = 2|n = 2)$ as .018 by exactly the same kind of reasoning used in Table 12.1; the work is shown in Table 12.2.

Table 12.2

p	$P(p)$	$P_b(\tilde{r} = 2|p)$	$P(\tilde{r} = 2, p)$
.09	.8	.0081	.00648
.24	.2	.0576	.01152
	1.0		.01800

In Table 12.3 the unconditional probability of *every possible* number of successes in two rolls is computed by the method of Table 12.2,

Table 12.3

r	p	$P(p)$	$P_b(\tilde{r} = r|p)$	$P(r,p)$	$P(r)$
0	.09	.8	.8281	.66248	
	.24	.2	.5776	.11552	
		1.0			.77800
1	.09	.8	.1638	.13104	
	.24	.2	.3648	.07296	
		1.0			.20400
2	.09	.8	.0081	.00648	
	.24	.2	.0576	.01152	
		1.0			.01800
					1.00000

the conditional probabilities $P_b(\tilde{r} = r|p)$ being taken from the binomial tables for $n = 2$. Observe particularly that

The *unconditional* probability of any value of $\tilde{r}$ is simply a *weighted average* of the conditional probabilities of that value of $\tilde{r}$ given each possible value of $\tilde{p}$, the probabilities of the values of $\tilde{p}$ being used as the weights.

Marginal Probability. In Table 12.4 the joint probabilities and totals of Table 12.3 are laid out in a different form. The following points should be particularly observed:

1. The *body* of the table gives the *joint* probability of every possible p, r combination, i.e. of every possible joint event.
2. The *margins* of the table give the *unconditional* probability of every possible p (right margin) and every possible r (bottom margin).

For this reason the unconditional probabilities assigned to the values of $\tilde{p}$ and $\tilde{r}$ in Table 12.4 are often called *marginal* probabilities. A marginal

Table 12.4

p	r			Total
	0	1	2	
.09:	.66248	.13104	.00648	.80000
.24:	.11552	.07296	.01152	.20000
Total	.77800	.20400	.01800	1.00000

probability is simply an unconditional probability computed in a particular way, namely by adding a number of joint probabilities.

Marginal Cumulative Probabilities. Consider next the problem of assessing the probability that there will be 11 or more aces in the first 50 rolls. By the method of Table 12.3 we could compute the marginal probabilities of all numbers from 11 to 50 and add. It is much simpler, however, to consider the occurrence of 11 or more aces as a *single event* and then to compute the probability of this event by the method of Table 12.2. From the binomial tables we find directly that the *conditional* probability of 11 or more successes *given* $p = .09$ is .0043 and that the same probability *given* $p = .24$ is .6822. The marginal probability of 11 or more successes is then computed as approximately .140 in Table 12.5.

Table 12.5

p	$P(p)$	$P_b(\tilde{r} \geq 11|p)$	$P(\tilde{r} \geq 11, p)$
09	.8	.0043	.00344
24	.2	.6822	.13644
	1.0		.13988

Contrast with Binomial Probabilities. In Table 12.1 we showed that the marginal probability of a success on any *one* trial was equal to the expected value of $\bar{p}$; numerically it was .12. Let us now compare the correct probabilities obtained for our problem in Tables 12.3 and 12.5 with the binomial probabilities which we would have obtained if we had assigned probability .12 to ace on *every* future roll *regardless of the outcomes of the earlier rolls in a sequence.*

The results of Table 12.3 are contrasted with binomial probabilities for $n = 2$, $p = .12$ in Table 12.6. The student should notice in particu-

Table 12.6

	Correct probability	Binomial probability
0	.7780	.7744
1	.2040	.2112
2	.0180	.0144
	1.0000	1.0000

lar that *the correct probabilities are higher than the binomial for the extreme values r = 0 and 2 and lower for the middle value r = 1.* A much more striking result of the same kind holds for the probability of 11 or more successes in 50 trials: whereas Table 12.5 shows that in our problem this probability is approximately .140, the binomial probability with $p = .12$ is only .032.

As a still more striking example of the essential point involved in these comparisons, suppose that a two-headed coin is placed in one envelope and a two-tailed coin in another, that we are to choose one of the two envelopes and then toss the coin it contains, and that we assign probability $\frac{1}{2}$ to the event "choose the coin with two heads." Under these circumstances the probability we assign to the event "heads" on one toss of the chosen coin will be $\frac{1}{2}$, just as it would be if we were to toss an ordinary coin which we believed to be "fair." If, however, we are to toss the chosen coin 100 times, the probability distribution which we assign to the random variable "number of heads" will be totally different from the binomial distribution: we will assign probability $\frac{1}{2}$ to each of the extreme values "100 heads" and "0 heads" and 0 probability to all other values.

12.3.3 *Unconditional Expected Value*

Suppose now that we are to roll our deformed die 101 times and that after the rolls have been observed we are to be paid as follows. If ace has occurred once, we shall receive $1; if ace has occurred twice, we shall receive $2; and so forth up to and including a payment of $13 for 13 aces; but if the number of aces is either 0 or above 13, we shall receive nothing. We wish to compute the expected value of this set of conditional payments.

One way of proceeding would be to use the method of Table 12.3 to compute the (marginal) probability of each possible number of aces from 1 to 13; we could then multiply the payment corresponding to each number by the probability of that number and add the products. It is much simpler, however, to proceed as we did when we computed marginal cumulative probabilities: we can compute the *conditional* expected value of the set of payments *given* each of the two possible values of p and then compute the *unconditional* expected value from these conditional values.

Computation of the Conditional Expected Values. If we knew the value of p for the die we have drawn, we could compute the expected value of the set of payments by using binomial tables to find the numerical values of the probabilities in the body of Table 12.7 and substituting these values in the table. Not knowing p, we could compute the conditional expected value for $p = .09$ by substituting the conditional binomial probabilities given $p = .09$ and similarly for $p = .24$.

Table 12.7

r	$P_b(\tilde{r} = r\|p)$	Conditional payment	Expectation given p
0	$P_b(\tilde{r} = 0\|p)$	\$1 $\times$ 0	\$1 $\times$ 0 $\times$ $P_b(\tilde{r} = 0\|p)$
1	$P_b(\tilde{r} = 1\|p)$	\$1 $\times$ 1	\$1 $\times$ 1 $\times$ $P_b(\tilde{r} = 1\|p)$
2	$P_b(\tilde{r} = 2\|p)$	\$1 $\times$ 2	\$1 $\times$ 2 $\times$ $P_b(\tilde{r} = 2\|p)$
. . . .
13	$P_b(\tilde{r} = 13\|p)$	\$1 $\times$ 13	\$1 $\times$ 13 $\times$ $P_b(\tilde{r} = 13\|p)$
			total

These conditional expected values can be obtained much more easily, however, by observing that the total of the last column is simply \$1 times the sum of a set of terms each of which has the form $r\,P(r)$. By definition, this sum is the *partial expectation* of $\tilde{r}$ over the interval $r = 0$ to $r = 13$, so that in our problem the conditional expected value is given by the formula

$$\text{CEV} = \$1\ E_0^{13}(\tilde{r}).$$

Since $\tilde{r}$ is conditionally a binomial variable, we can evaluate the partial expectation by the formula in Section 11.3.1:

$$\begin{aligned}\text{CEV} &= \$1 \times np\ P_b(\tilde{r} \le r - 1|n - 1,p) \\ &= \$1 \times 101p\ P_b(\tilde{r} \le 12|n = 100,\, p).\end{aligned}$$

Substituting the two possible values of $\tilde{p}$ and using the binomial tables to evaluate the probability in the formula we get the two conditional expected values for our problem:

Given $p = .09$,   CEV $= \$101 \times .09 \times .8862 = \$8.06$;
Given $p = .24$,   CEV $= \$101 \times .24 \times .0021 = \$ .05$.

Computation of Unconditional Expected Value. We now look at our problem as follows. If the basic random variable $\tilde{p} = .09$, our whole set of conditional rights can be thought of as a single lottery ticket worth $\$8.06$; if $\tilde{p} = .24$, we have a different ticket worth $\$.05$. We thus know the conditional value of our ticket given each possible value of the basic random variable, and we can therefore proceed as in Table 12.8 to compute the (unconditional) expected value of these conditional (expected) values just as if they were ordinary conditional values.

Table 12.8

p	P(p)	Conditional value	Expected value
.09	.8	$8.06	$6.45
.24	.2	.05	.01
	1.0		$6.46

When Is the Process Parameter Known? We can now state much more clearly than we did before the condition under which the parameter of a Bernoulli process may legitimately be treated as "known with certainty." In virtually *any* real situation we have *some* uncertainty about the value of p, and therefore we should in principle assign a probability distribution to $\tilde{p}$ and compute the unconditional expected cost of each possible decision by the method just described or its equivalent. In other words, we should take a *weighted average* of the conditional profits (or costs or losses) attached to the various possible values of $\tilde{p}$, using the probabilities of the various values as the weights. If, however, the values of $\tilde{p}$ which receive appreciable weights—i.e. the values which are considered at all likely—are all within a very narrow range, the weighted average profit will be nearly the same as the conditional profit attached to some value of $\tilde{p}$ near the middle of the range.

When we treat $\tilde{p}$ as known, we are simply using a short cut to get an approximate answer to our problem; the short cut is legitimate if it is accurate enough to lead to a *decision* which is not materially worse than the decision we would choose as the result of more accurate computations.

12.4 Application to Production Problems

We are now in a position to understand the basic principles under-lying the conditions which determine whether the distribution of $\tilde{r}$ or $\tilde{n}$ in a given practical problem must be assessed by the method of Section 8.2, by use of the simple binomial or Pascal distribution, by the method of marginal probabilities described just above, or by some quite different method. We shall summarize this chapter by stating these conditions even though it sometimes requires statistical theory which we have not studied to decide whether the conditions are or are not met in a given practical situation.

1. *All* of the methods we have studied thus far for assessing the probability distribution of $\tilde{r}$ or $\tilde{n}$ *apply only to Bernoulli processes.* Before applying *any* of these methods to a practical problem we must therefore first make sure that it is reasonable to answer the following two questions in the affirmative.

a. Are the trials *independent?* As we have stated before, the answer to this question usually depends at least as much on expert knowledge of the physical nature of the process as on statistical examination of the pattern of previous successes and failures generated by the process. Quite obviously questions involving the physical nature of the process should be put to a person who is an expert in processes of the sort involved; they are not questions for the statistician. The statistician, on the other hand, is the proper person to examine the record of previous successes and failures, since it is only he who can tell whether or not the streaks of successes or failures in the record are excessive or are only such as might be expected from genuinely independent trials. The method by which this is done is beyond the scope of this course.

b. Is the process *stable?* Again the answer depends partly on knowledge of the general nature of the process and only in part on statis-tical analysis. The production engineer or the master mechanic is the person who will know, for example, whether tool wear is likely to have a material effect on the fraction defective during a run of the size being con-templated. Statistical analysis will be of help only if the fraction defec-tive has been recorded separately for the first and last parts of one or more *long* runs made in the past; in this case these separate fractions defective will show whether there has been substantial variation in p within runs.

2. *If both these questions are answered in the affirmative, then we are dealing in the general case with a Bernoulli process with unknown parameter and we must apply the method of this chapter to allow for both kinds of uncertainty*—the uncertainty concerning $\tilde{p}$ itself and the uncertainty which we would have concerning $\tilde{r}$ or $\tilde{n}$ if we knew $\tilde{p}$. We must start by using our previous experience with the process or similar processes to

assess a probability distribution for $\tilde{p}$ on the proposed run—the method by which we do this will be discussed in a moment—and we must then compute the marginal distribution of $\tilde{r}$ or $\tilde{n}$. There are two *special cases*, however, in which we may disregard one or the other of these two kinds of uncertainty as being *negligible in comparison with the other.*

   a. The answers to Chapter 10, Problem 4, and Chapter 11, Problem 4, suggest that as the run size increases the variability of the *fraction* defective or the *ratio* of total to good decreases; in Chapter 16 we shall learn how we can actually measure this variability and we shall then see that it decreases with the square root of the run size n or the required number of good pieces r. If then the proposed run or required number of good pieces is large *and* at the same time there is considerable uncertainty about the long-run fraction p or ratio $\rho = 1/(1 - p)$, Bernoulli uncertainty may be negligible in comparison with the uncertainty about the process parameter. This was the situation in Section 8.2.

   b. If there is very considerable recorded experience with the process to be used, it may be that there is very little uncertainty concerning the value which p will have during the proposed new run. This will be the case if the fraction defective has been recorded in a fair number of past runs, if there is little variability among these recorded fractions, and if there is no reason to suspect that the conditions surrounding the new run will differ materially from those which surrounded the past runs. If then this recorded variability is small relative to the Bernoulli variability in runs of the size of the proposed new run, it will usually be legitimate to treat the process parameter as known. In this case the distributions of $\tilde{r}$ and $\tilde{n}$ can be obtained directly from the binomial and Pascal distributions as was done in Chapters 10 and 11.

12.4.1   *Practical Assessment of the Distribution of $\tilde{p}$*

   To assess the probability distribution of the long-run fraction defective or process parameter, we must make use of our past experience with the process in question or with similar processes. When there is little or no directly applicable experience, this assessment must be almost wholly subjective, just as the assessment of the probability of ace was wholly subjective in the example discussed in Section 12.3.1 above. When on the contrary we have almost exact knowledge of the values held by $\tilde{p}$ in a fair number of past runs made under conditions which are identical (so far as we know) to the conditions under which the new run will be made, we can assess the distribution by more objective methods, usually by plotting the observed values of $\tilde{p}$ as fractile estimates and fitting a smooth curve to these points. In principle this was what we did in Section 8.2, although for convenience we there smoothed a plot of $\tilde{\rho} = 1/(1 - \tilde{p})$ rather than of $\tilde{p}$ itself.

   Observe, however, that we can never be sure that the fraction defective observed in any run is a true reading on the value of $\tilde{p}$ during that run or that an observed ratio of total to good is a true reading on the value of $\tilde{p}$: no run is ever of infinite length.   The procedure used in Section 8.2 was legitimate because the recorded runs were so long that the *Bernoulli variation in these runs was negligible compared with the variation in $\tilde{p}$.*   It is beyond the scope of this course to discuss the problem of assessing the distribution of $\tilde{p}$ or $\tilde{p}$ when the past record consists of fractions defective in *short runs* or in *small samples* from long runs.

PROBLEMS

1. The following probability distribution is assigned to the process average defective of a machine which can be treated as a Bernoulli process.

p	$P(p)$
.12	.25
.15	.40
.20	.35
	1.00

a. What is the probability that any one piece will be defective?

b. Compute the probability distribution for number of defectives $\tilde{r}$ in a run of three pieces.

c. Compute cumulative probabilities $P(\tilde{r} \geq 20 | n = 100)$ and $P(\tilde{r} < 5 | n = 50)$.

d. Compare the answers to (*b*) and (*c*) with the answers which would have been obtained if the process had had a *known* process average equal to the probability of a defective found in answer to (*a*).

2. Compute the probability distribution for the number of pieces which must be produced in order to obtain four *good* pieces when the production process can be treated as a Bernoulli process and the distribution of the process average fraction *defective* is given by the following table.

p	$P(p)$
.10	.7
.20	.3
	1.0

3. If a baseball player has batted .300 during the season, can you use any method studied thus far to assess the probability that he will get no hits in three times at bat in the next game?   Discuss fully.

4. A person responsible for setting a scrap allowance says that while the historical scrap rate is 10 per cent, this figure is based on very little experience and that he does not feel at all certain that it will hold in the future.   He has no records at all to show variation in scrap rate from run to run.   How should he proceed?

5. If in the situation of Chapter 8, Problem 8, production of 1200 assemblies yielded only 950 good units, what method would you use to compute the distribution of $\tilde{r}$ or $\tilde{n}$ on a rerun intended to fill out the shortage of 50 good units?   Discuss fully but do not make actual computations.

CHAPTER 13

The Poisson Process: The Poisson Distribution

In the previous three chapters we have studied Bernoulli processes which consist of a series of separate trials with a constant probability of success on each trial. In this chapter we shall study a kind of process which cannot usefully be thought of as consisting of a series of separate trials although the probability of a success is still "constant" in somewhat the same sense as in the Bernoulli process. This new kind of process will be called a *Poisson process*.

As an example of a problem involving a Poisson process, consider a machine which is continuously insulating electric wire and which from time to time produces a pinhole defect in the insulation. The machine has produced 1500 defects in the last 1000 feet of wire inspected, or 1.5 defects per foot on the average, and we wish to assess the probabilities that there will be 0, 1, 2, etc., defects in the next 2 feet of wire which the machine will produce.

After carefully investigating the process and failing to discover any "assignable cause" for the defects—i.e. any cause which produces defects in predictable places—most people would be willing to bet that a defect was as likely to occur at any one "point" as at any other: the probability of a defect is *constant from point to point*. The number of "points" on even the shortest piece of wire cannot be counted, however; and although it is probably true that strictly speaking the number of places where a defect may occur is finite, even these "places" cannot be identified or counted *practically*. Consequently we can neither assess the probability of a defect at an individual point by looking at the past ratio of defects to points nor apply the binomial formula to compute the required probabilities of 0, 1, 2, etc., defects in 2 feet.

13.1 The Poisson Distribution

After brooding about infinity for a while, the person responsible for the assessment might decide that one possible way of solving the problem is to use an approximation. The 2 feet of wire can be thought of as divided into a number of fairly short segments—say 10—and each of these can be treated as a Bernoulli trial. Since each segment will be

209

$\frac{2}{10}$ foot long, the average number of defects per segment is 1.5 × .2 = .3; and we would therefore set the probability of a defect on any "trial" at .3. The distribution of the number $\tilde{r}$ of defects in 10 trials or segments could then be computed by simply using the binomial distribution for $n = 10$, $p = .3$.

The difficulty with this idea is that there might be *two* defects in a single segment of the wire, and this violates the assumptions from which the binomial distribution is derived. A piece produced by a punch press is either good or defective but it is never *two* defectives. Suppose, however, that the 2 feet of wire is divided into 100 segments rather than 10 and that the probability of a defect in any segment is set at .03 instead of .3. We might feel fairly confident that the probability of two defects in a segment only $\frac{2}{100}$ foot long is so small that it can be neglected for practical decisions, thus making the assumptions underlying the binomial formula apply. But if reducing the size of the unit which we are going to consider a trial improves the validity of our assumptions, it naturally occurs to us to think of reducing the size still further; and we shall now look systematically at what happens if we do.

Observe first that in both cases described above we divided the 2 feet of wire into a number n of smaller units and then assessed the probability of a defect in a single small unit in such a way that pn always had the same value, 3. The expected number of successes in a binomial distribution is pn, so that what we are doing is going from one binomial distribution to another, *increasing the value of n (number of trials) but decreasing p in such a way that the expected number of successes remains constant.* In Figure 13.1a we show four different binomial distributions all of which have $pn = 3$, and in Figure 13.1b we show the same distributions in cumulative form. The value of n for each distribution is shown in the figure and the values of p correspond as shown in Table 13.1.

Table 13.1

n	p
10	.30
20	.15
50	.06
150	.02

When we examine these two figures we see that the shape of the distribution at first changes substantially with a fairly small change in n but then changes very little for a very large change in n. In both figures it seems that as n increases the distribution approaches a *limiting form.* it looks as if the curve will come closer and closer to this form as we increase n further and further, and it can be proved mathematically that this is true. *There is some value of n above which the difference between the binomial distribution and this limiting distribution is smaller, at all points, than any previously specified amount however small.* This limiting form of

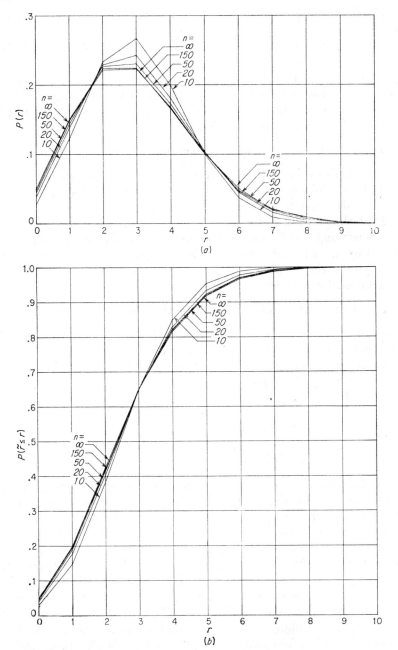

Figure 13.1. Binomial distributions with Poisson limit. $np = 3.$

the binomial distribution is known as the *Poisson* distribution and is shown in the figures with the label $n = \infty$.

Let us now generalize what we have done. We observe first that whereas a Bernoulli process is characterized by the probability of a success on any trial, a Poisson process is characterized by the *expected number of successes per unit of space*. This number is the *parameter* of the Poisson process; it is often called the *intensity* of the process. It will be denoted by the letter kappa: we define

κ: expected number of successes *per unit* of space.

In our example the intensity of the process was $\kappa = 1.5$ defects per unit of length; other Poisson processes may generate $\kappa = 14$ defects per unit of area, $\kappa = 37$ telephone calls per unit of time, etc.

In dealing with a Bernoulli process we wished to find probabilities for various numbers of successes in a specified number of trials which we denoted by n. In dealing with a Poisson process we wish to find probabilities for various numbers of successes in a *specified amount of space* which we shall denote by

t: amount of space within which the successes are to be counted.

In our example the specified space was $t = 2$ feet; in other problems it might be $t = 4$ square feet or $t = 27$ minutes.

In analyzing our example we first computed the *expected number of successes in the specified space;* this was

1.5 defects per foot $\times$ 2 feet = 3 defects.

In general we shall denote such expectations by the symbol

$m = \kappa t$: the expected number of successes in the specified space.

The student must keep clearly in mind the distinction between κ, the expected number of successes *per unit* of space, and m, the expected number of successes in the *space specified* in the problem at hand.

We then considered a series of binomial distributions in all of which the expected number of successes pn had the same value 3 as the m of our problem; and we observed that as p became smaller and n became correspondingly larger these distributions approached a limiting form which depended only on the *product* of the values of κ and t in our example and not on the values of κ and t separately. We could have used the same set of binomial distributions and we would have found the same limit in a problem in which, for example, $\kappa = .001$ and $t = 3000$. In general,

The probability that a Poisson process generating κ successes per unit of space will generate r successes in space t depends only on the product $m = \kappa t$;

it is given by the formula

$$P_{Po}(r) = \frac{e^{-(\kappa t)}(\kappa t)^r}{r!} = \frac{e^{-m}m^r}{r!} \qquad \textit{Poisson probability}$$

where e is a constant equal to 2.718 $\cdots$. The student will not have to use this formula directly since we shall look up Poisson probabilities on a chart rather than actually compute them; but he *should* observe that κ and t occur in the formula *only in the combination* $\kappa t = m$.

13.2 Chart of the Poisson Distribution

The *cumulative* Poisson probability of r *or more* successes, i.e. the area of the *right* tail of the distribution *including* the bar for r itself, is shown in Chart I for values of m from .1 to 30 and for values of $\tilde{r}$ from 1 to 52.† The chart is used in exactly the same way as Table I of the binomial distribution. For example: to find the probability of three or more successes when the expected number of successes is $m = 2$, locate 2 on the horizontal axis, read up to the curve for $r = 3$, and read across to find P = .32.

Individual Poisson probabilities can be read from the same chart by using the relation

$$P(\tilde{r} = r) = P(\tilde{r} \geq r) - P(\tilde{r} \geq r + 1).$$

13.3 Expectations of a Poisson Variable

The mean of any Poisson distribution or ordinary expectation of the Poisson random variable $\tilde{r}$ is obviously equal to the mean of the binomial distributions of which it is the limit:

$$E(\tilde{r}) = \kappa t = m \qquad \textit{Mean of the Poisson distribution}$$

Similarly the partial expectation over the range 0 to r inclusive is the limit of the binomial partial expectation as n increases while np remains equal to m:

$$E_0^r(\tilde{r}) = m\,P_{Po}(\tilde{r} < r | m) \qquad \textit{Poisson partial expectation}$$

† For very extensive tables of the Poisson distribution, see E. C. Molina, "Poisson's Exponential Binomial Limit," D. Van Nostrand Company, Inc., Princeton, N.J., 1942.

13.4 Applicability of the Poisson Model

Since the Poisson model is simply a limiting case of the Bernoulli model, the questions we must ask before using the Poisson distribution to compute probabilities in any real problem are virtually identical to the questions we must ask before using the binomial distribution. These questions were thoroughly discussed in Chapter 12, which the student should review carefully before proceeding further. In particular he should recall that the questions are of two separate kinds: they concern:

1. The applicability of the *model as such.*
2. The extent of our knowledge concerning the *parameter* of the model.

13.4.1 The Definition of the Poisson Process

The conditions defining the Bernoulli process as such were stability and independence, and it is the same two conditions which define a Poisson process. In order to apply them in the new context we need only recall that in deriving the Poisson distribution in the first part of this chapter we assumed that if we divided "space" into small enough segments, we could treat the occurrence of two successes in any one segment as practically impossible. This carries the implication that when successes are generated by a Poisson process,

Successes never occur simultaneously; there is always some measurable interval between any pair.

Provided that this condition is met by a real process, we can think of space or time as being divided into segments or "instants" so short that none of them contains more than one success; and what we are really asserting when we adopt a Poisson model is that these very short segments or instants can be treated as Bernoulli trials. The conditions of stability and independence can then be stated in words identical to those used for a Bernoulli process except that "instant" is substituted for "trial."

Application to a Process Producing Defects. As a first example of the application of the Poisson model to a real process, let us reconsider the machine insulating electric wire which we used as an example at the beginning of this chapter.

1. We must ask ourselves whether we have reason to believe that the process is *stable.* If raw material is supplied in batches, the average number of defects per foot may vary from batch to batch. It may be that a Poisson model applies only conditionally, i.e. to the output of any one batch of material, and not to the entire output of the machine.

2. We must ask ourselves whether the defects are *independent.* If

defects are due in part to inadequately mixed lumps within a batch of raw material, there will be short-run fluctuations in the process parameter; and if this is true there will be more feet of wire with very high numbers of defects and more with very low numbers than there would be if the material were homogeneous (cf. Table 12.6). In this case we cannot use the Poisson model at all, since we cannot know when the process will be operating under one set of conditions and when it will be under another.

Application to Breakage of Machine Parts. As a second example, consider a "process" which generates accidental breakages of some machine part.

1. The process can be considered *stable* only if it is reasonable to believe that both the quantity and the severity of the usage of the part are constant. If there are 100 machine-hours of use in some weeks and 20 in others, the average number of breakages per week will obviously vary, although the number of breakages per machine-hour may be constant. If the use to which the machine is put varies, the Poisson model may apply conditionally under any one kind of usage but not over all. If wear and tear is a factor contributing to breakage, breakages will occur much less frequently in the first hour after a breakage and replacement than they will in the tenth hour and so forth. The same phenomenon can result from a quite different reason, inability to replace a broken part immediately. In this case the machine on which the part is used will be idle for a certain amount of time after a breakage occurs, and no new breakages can occur during this down time.

2. The breakages can be considered *independent* only if we are convinced that once we have allowed for changes in the breakage rate due to *known* changes in conditions of use, there will be no unpredictable changes which affect the mean breakage rate. Variation within a single batch of raw material could result in short-run fluctuations in the mean breakage rate just as it could result in short-run fluctuations in the rate at which defects occur; and if this variation were unpredictable we could not apply a Poisson model even conditionally.

Multiple Sources of Usage. For all these reasons it will be only very rarely that a single machine can be legitimately represented as a Poisson source of parts usage. Usage is much more likely to be Poisson distributed if the part is used on a large number of machines. It is virtually self-evident and it can be proved that:

> If there is a Poisson usage from each of several independent sources, the total usage is Poisson with intensity equal to the sum of the individual intensities.

Even though the intensity of the usage generated by each *individual* source may vary widely over time, the intensity of *total* usage may nevertheless be nearly constant. If enough users are involved, the variations in individual usage rates tend to average out whether they are due to instability or to lack of independence or both.

The implications of this proposition are much broader than they appear at first sight: a Poisson model may represent total usage of a part very accurately even when each individual source of usage is totally unlike a Poisson process. As an example, consider the usage of ordinary light bulbs in a large office building with many thousands of bulbs in service.

If we look at *usage in any individual socket*, it is obvious that there is virtually 0 probability of a failure in the second following the installation of a new bulb and extremely small probability in any second during the first several hundred hours of the bulb's life. After several hundred hours have passed, however, the probability of a failure in the next second begins to rise gradually and ultimately becomes fairly high—if a bulb has already lasted several thousand hours, it is unlikely that it will last much longer. It follows that any *individual* source of usage violates *both* the fundamental conditions defining a Poisson process; if we use κ_t to denote the probability that a bulb t hours old will fail in the next second, the process is *continuously unstable* because κ_t is continuously rising as long as any one bulb is still alive, and events are *not independent* because failure of one bulb means replacement by a new bulb and therefore a drop in κ_t.

If we look now at *total usage* in all the several thousand sockets in the office building of our example, the probability κ that some bulb will fail in the next second is simply the sum of the κ_t's of all the individual bulbs.† When the building is new, κ will be increasing because all the κ_t's will be increasing, and a Poisson model will not apply to total usage any more than it does to usage in an individual socket. If, however, *bulbs are replaced only when they fail*—if there is no *systematic* renewal of bulbs to prevent failures—then the ages t of the bulbs will become more and more thoroughly mixed as time goes on. At any given point of time, some bulbs will have just been installed, some will be a few hundred hours old, and so forth. We would naturally guess, and it can be proved,‡ that *a stage will be reached where the mixture of ages remains approximately stable and therefore the total κ remains approximately stable.* More accurately expressed, a stage is reached where there is an extremely small probability that κ will change by more than an extremely small amount during any specified period of time.

---

† This assumes that the probability of two or more failures in 1 second is 0; the assumption is legitimate because we are using "second" simply as a convenient word for an arbitrarily short interval of time.

‡ On the assumption that bulbs do not fail in some extremely peculiar pattern which creates repeating "cycles" in the mixture of ages.

When this stage is reached, total usage can be quite accurately represented by a Poisson model even though individual sources of usage are still completely non-Poisson.

The student is reminded, however, that this conclusion very definitely rests on the fact that *there is no systematic renewal policy* which installs substantial numbers of new bulbs at the same time.

Demands on Inventory. In problems of inventory control one particular reason for nonapplicability of a Poisson model deserves special attention. The model specifies that successes never occur simultaneously, and therefore the model cannot apply strictly unless *each unit of product is demanded in a separate order.*

Suppose, for example, that a Poisson model does in fact describe the occurrences of the actual breakages of some machine part. If we look at the inventory of spares carried by any one *user* of the part, each breakage will presumably result in an immediate demand on inventory for 1 unit and this demand will therefore be Poisson distributed. If, however, we look at the inventory carried by the *manufacturer* of the part, the Poisson model is much less likely to apply. Rather than order one part at a time, most users will ordinarily wait until they have accumulated a requirement for a quantity of parts and then place an order for this quantity all at one time. Such a demand-generating process is emphatically *not* a Poisson process.

13.4.2   The Intensity of the Process

Even though we have satisfied ourselves that some real process can be reasonably represented as a Poisson process, the (unconditional) *probability* distribution for the number of successes will not be Poisson unless we *know* the value of the process parameter or intensity κ. No further discussion of this point is needed, however; the issues are identical to those which we discussed fully in Chapter 12. The same conditions must be met before we may treat the parameter as known, and the same procedure must be used to compute marginal probabilities when the parameter is not known.

13.5   Approximation of Binomial Probabilities by Poisson Probabilities

Even the most extensive tables of the binomial distribution cover only a limited range of values for the number of trials n, and direct computation of a cumulative binomial probability requires a prohibitive amount of labor when the value of n is so large that it is not in the tables. In such cases we usually resort to some method which will give us an *approximate* value for the required probability, and *under certain condi-*

tions the Poisson distribution can be used to obtain approximations which are more than sufficiently accurate to ensure choice of the best decision.

Since the binomial distribution approaches the Poisson distribution as a limit when n increases while p decreases in such a way as to leave the *expected number of successes pn* unchanged, we can obtain an approximate value for the binomial probability of r or more successes by looking up the Poisson probability of r or more successes when the expected number of successes m has the value pn. In algebraic notation,

$$P_b(\tilde{r} \geq r|n, p) \doteq P_{Po}(\tilde{r} \geq r|m = np).$$

For example, the binomial probability of seven or more successes when $p = .05$ and $n = 100$ is approximated by the Poisson probability of seven or more successes when $m = 5$. From Chart I we find that this probability is .24; the true binomial probability as given by Table I is .234.

From the fact that the Poisson distribution is the limit of the binomial *as n increases while p decreases*, it follows immediately that for *given values of np and r* the approximation will be better the larger the value of n and the smaller the value of p. It is usually said that the approximation will be good "when n is large and p is small," but as is shown by Figure 13.1, accuracy for given n and p varies greatly with r. In Chapter 17 we shall return to this question and systematically examine the accuracy of the approximation for a variety of values of n, p, and r.

When p is very large—i.e. near 1—the probability of a *failure* $q = 1 - p$ will be small, and the Poisson approximation can be used by restating the problem in terms of failures rather than successes. For example, the binomial probability of 95 or more successes when $p = .9$ and $n = 100$ is the same thing as the probability of 5 or less failures when $q = .1$ and $n = 100$, i.e. when the expected number of *failures* is 10. It can therefore be approximated by the Poisson probability $P_{Po}(\tilde{r} \leq 5|m = 10)$, which is given as .067 by Chart I; the true binomial probability is .058.

PROBLEMS

1. What is the probability that a Poisson process producing two defects per minute on the average will produce the following numbers of defects in 1 minute?

a. Exactly 2.   *b.* 2 or less.
c. Less than 2.   *d.* 2 or more.
e. More than 2.

2. What is the probability that the process of Problem 1 will produce the following numbers of defects in 2 minutes?

a. Exactly 3.   *b.* 3 or less.
c. Less than 3.   *d.* 3 or more.
e. More than 3.

3. A shop runs 20 automatic screw machines of identical model and age on a variety of jobs all of which put about the same load on the machines. All machines are run 40 hours a week. If on the average there are 10 machine breakdowns in a

40-hour week and if breakdowns are repaired in a negligible amount of time, what probability would you assign to the occurrence of two or more breakdowns in the same 8-hour shift? Why is the repair time relevant to the problem?

4. During "normal peak hours" the East Central Insurance Company's PBX telephone switchboard receives 180 requests per hour for an outside trunk line. Analysis of the times at which calls were placed over a period of several months shows no discernible pattern *within* the normal peak hours. What probability would you assign to the occurrence of more than six requests for an outside line during a single minute of a normal peak hour?

5. *Using the same vertical and horizontal scales in both cases*, graph the probability distribution for number of defects produced by a Poisson process averaging .5 defect per foot:

  a. In a run of 2 feet.

  b. In a run of 8 feet.

6. Same as Problem 5, but use *defects per foot* as the horizontal scale rather than number of defects. (This means defects per foot in the 2- or the 8-foot run, not in an "infinitely long" run.)

7. Graph the Poisson *cumulative* distribution $P_{Po}(\tilde{r} \leq r)$ for $m = 4$, making the graphs in stepped form rather than in the form of Figure 13.1b.

8. Assuming that the *number of orders received* has a Poisson distribution and that the mean *number of units demanded* is 4 per week, graph the distribution of *number of units demanded in 1 week*

  a. If each order is for 1 *unit*.

  b. If each order is for 2 *units*.

9. Von Bortkiewicz published the following data on the numbers of men killed by a horse kick in each of 10 Prussian army corps in each of the 20 years 1875 to 1894, i.e. the number of deaths in each of 200 corps-year combinations.

Deaths	Absolute number of corps-years
0	109
1	65
2	22
3	3
4	1
	200

The total number of deaths is 122, or an average of .61 per corps-year. If the deaths had been Poisson distributed, how many corps-years would there have been with 0, 1, 2, etc., deaths?

10. R. D. Clarke published the following data on the number of buzz-bomb hits in 576 areas in the south of London, each area covering ¼ square kilometer.

Hits	Absolute number of areas
0	229
1	211
2	93
3	35
4	7
5 and over	1
	576

Since 440 of the 576 areas were hit only once or not at all, do you think the bombs were being aimed at the areas which were hit more often?

11. Demand for a certain product is Poisson distributed and has averaged 3 units per day. A new package design is introduced; the person responsible for inventory control believes that there is a 70 per cent chance that mean demand will be doubled and a 30 per cent chance that it will be tripled. What is the probability that tomorrow's demand will be:

a. Less than 6 units?   *b.* Less than 5 units?

c. Less than 4 units?   *d.* Exactly 5 units?

12. The product discussed in Problem 11 sells for $5, costs $4, and spoils if it is not sold on the day on which it is stocked.

a. How many units should be stocked under the conditions described in Problem 11?

b. How many should be stocked if it were known that demand would average 6.9 units per day in the long run?

13. A company makes one production run per month of a part used in maintenance of a certain type of heavy-duty equipment. Management believes that about $.10 in storage costs, etc., is lost on each part which is not used during the month in which it is produced. If, on the other hand, the production run is inadequate to meet needs during the month, the additional parts must be made by hand at a cost which exceeds regular production costs by $10 per part. Usage of the part has averaged 25 parts per month. How many units should be produced at the beginning of a month if none is on hand and

a. All usage is accidental and unpredictable?

b. 80 per cent of all usage is regular preventive maintenance and 20 per cent is accidental and unpredictable?

CHAPTER 14

The Poisson Process: The Gamma Distribution

In Chapter 10 we derived the binomial probability distribution for the *number r of successes* in a given number n of trials when the probability of a success was constant from trial to trial; in Chapter 13 we extended this result to obtain the Poisson distribution for the number r of successes in a given space t of time or distance when that space could not be separated into distinct trials but the probability of a success could be considered as constant from "point" to "point." In Chapter 11 we obtained the distribution for the *number n of Bernoulli trials* required to obtain a given number r of successes, and we shall now extend this result also to the case where there are no distinct trials but the probability of a success is constant from point to point. We have introduced the symbol t to denote the fixed "space" of time or distance in which the number of successes was a random variable; we now treat t as a random variable and compute its probability distribution for a fixed number of successes r.

We shall use the same concrete example which we used in Chapter 13. A machine insulating electric wire produces an average of $\kappa = 1.5$ defects per foot, and we seek the probability distribution for the distance l from "here" to the rth defect. We shall start by obtaining the distribution for the distance l from here to the *first* defect, i.e. for the special case $r = 1$.

14.1   Distance to the First Success: the Exponential Distribution

Let us first regard the wire as divided into fifths of feet, treat each fifth as constituting a Bernoulli "trial," and take the probability of a success in any one part as $\kappa/5 = 1.5/5 = .3$. As we saw in Section 11.1, the probability that exactly n trials will be required to obtain *one* success is the probability of a run of $n - 1$ failures followed by a success:

$$P(n) = q^{n-1}p.$$

In Table 14.1 we show the probabilities of various numbers of trials computed by this formula; these probabilities are, of course, the Pascal distribution for $r = 1$, $p = .3$. The last column of the table shows the *distance* corresponding to each number of trials: it is assumed that the success occurs at the *end* of the space corresponding to the "trial" in which it occurs.

Table 14.1

Number of trials n	Probability	Distance, feet, t
1	$.3 = .300$	.2
2	$(.7)(.3) = .210$	.4
3	$(.7)^2(.3) = .147$	.6
4	$(.7)^3(.3) = .103$	.8
5	$(.7)^4(.3) = .072$	1.0
	etc.	

Next we divide the wire into tenths of a foot, setting $p = \kappa/10 = .15$, with the results shown in Table 14.2. The same procedure will give the distribution when the wire is divided into parts of any length; in Figure 14.1 the two distributions computed above and the distribution for division into twenty-fifths of a foot are graphed as histograms.

Table 14.2

Number of trials n	Probability	Distance, feet, t
1	$.15 = .150$	.1
2	$(.85)(.15) = .127$	.2
3	$(.85)^2(.15) = .108$	.3
4	$(.85)^3(.15) = .092$	.4
5	$(.85)^4(.15) = .078$	.5
	etc.	

14.1.1 The Exponential Distribution

Before considering the smooth curve superimposed on each histogram, let us look closely at the histograms themselves. The first bar on the left in all three graphs has the same height, 1.5, but the three probabilities are *not* the same. The vertical scale shows, not probability, but *probability per unit width*, and the widths of the three bars are not equal. In the first graph, the width corresponds to $1/5$ foot, so that the first bar represents a probability of .3. In the second graph the width is $1/10$, so that the first bar represents a probability of .15. In the bottom graph the first bar represents probability .06.

This explains why the height of the histogram at any specified value t does not approach 0 as we subdivide further and further, even though the actual probability that l will have any specified value does approach 0. What actually seems to happen as the subdivision becomes finer is that the height of the histogram at any t comes closer and closer to the height of the smooth curve at that t, and it can be proved that this is true.

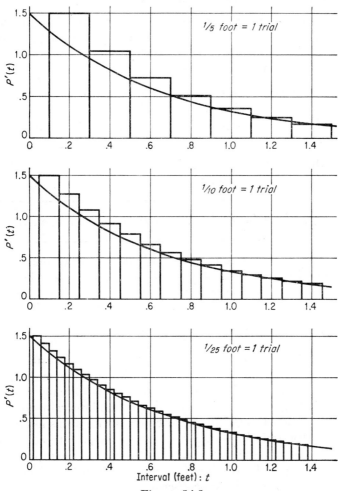

Figure 14.1

The limiting form depicted by this smooth curve is known as the *exponential distribution* defined by the formula

$$P'(t) = \frac{1}{\mu} e^{-t/\mu},$$

where

$$\mu = \frac{1}{\kappa}.$$

The quantity μ (mu) is the one *parameter* of the exponential distribution; the underlying Poisson *process* is characterized equally well by the value of *either* κ or $\mu = 1/\kappa$.

14.1.2   Intervals between Successes

It is a basic assumption of the Poisson model, as it is of the Bernoulli model, that successes are *independent*.   This implies that the distribution of the distance $\tilde{l}$ to the first success is the same no matter where we begin measuring the distance, and therefore

The distribution of the length of the *interval* between two adjacent Poisson successes is identical to the distribution of the distance from "here" to the first success; it is exponential with parameter $\mu = 1/\kappa$, where κ is the intensity of the Poisson process.

Since κ is the mean number of successes per unit of space, $\mu = 1/\kappa$ is the *mean space between successes* and therefore

––

$E(\tilde{l}) = \mu$ *Expected length of interval, exponential distribution*

––

Because the distribution of the length of interval between adjacent successes is identical to the distribution of the distance from "here" to the first success, μ is also the expected distance from "here" to the first success.

14.1.3   Probabilities under a Continuous Distribution

At the end of the limiting process which leads to the exponential distribution we arrive at a "histogram" with infinitely many bars each of which has zero width; the random variable $\tilde{l}$ is formally regarded as capable of taking on any value whatever in the interval 0 to ∞ rather than being restricted to certain definite values within this interval in the way that all the random variables we have studied hitherto have been restricted to the values 0, 1, 2, etc.   For this reason the exponential distribution is said to be *continuous* whereas the distributions we have studied previously are said to be *discrete*.

Because the bars of the limiting histogram have zero width, they have zero area; the probability that a variable with a continuous distribution will have *exactly* any specified value is formally regarded as zero even though this event is *not* regarded as *impossible*.   This is why the formula for the exponential distribution gives only *probability per unit width* at the point t, i.e. the height of the curve at the point t, and cannot give the actual *probability* of the value t in the way the binomial or Poisson formula gives the probability of the value r or the Pascal formula gives the probability of the value n.

This notion that every possible value of a random variable such as distance between two defects has zero probability is of course a pure fiction introduced only for mathematical convenience. In the real world, the very concept of the value of a quantity such as "distance" is meaningless until we have specified the procedure by which the value will be measured; and the values which can be obtained by reading *any* measuring instrument are *discrete*. If the instrument by which we measure the distance between two defects is capable of giving the reading .46 foot, then we should assign a definite, nonzero probability to this value of the random variable "distance." If on the other hand the instrument is *not* capable of giving this reading (e.g. because it measures only to the nearest tenth of a foot) then we must regard this value as strictly impossible.

Given a particular measuring procedure, the "exact" distribution which it would be reasonable to assign to a measured random variable would be represented by a histogram with one bar for every value which is capable of being measured, and to make sense of a continuous distribution such as the exponential we must regard it simply as a convenient way of getting the approximate height of each of these bars without having to go to the trouble of specifying each one individually.

In cases such as the one we have taken as an example, the "exact" distribution is really Pascal and the exponential distribution is used simply as a convenient way of approximating a Pascal distribution with extremely small p just as we saw in Section 13.5 that the Poisson distribution is often a convenient approximation to the binomial distribution with extremely small p.

This implies that to calculate the probability that a random variable such as distance between two defects will have a specific value such as .46 foot we must calculate the approximate area of the corresponding bar of the true histogram, and to do this we must multiply the *width* of this bar as determined by the characteristics of the measuring instrument by the approximate *height* of the bar as given by the exponential distribution. If we define the symbol "delta t" by

δt: the space between two adjacent possible values of the random variable $\tilde{t}$, as determined by the characteristics of the measuring instrument,

then

$$P(\tilde{t} = t) = \delta t\, P'(t).$$

Suppose, for example, that we measure the distance with an instrument which is capable of reading to a fiftieth of a foot, so that $\delta t = .02$ is the width of any bar in the histogram. From Figure 14.1 we read that the height of the curve at $t = .46$ is $.75$, and we then compute the probability that the measured distance will be .46 foot as

$$P(\tilde{t} = .46) = .02 \times .75 = .015.$$

To find the probability that the distance between two defects will be greater or less than some specified value, i.e. to find the area of a tail of the true histogram, we could in principle compute the area of every included bar in the way just described and then add the products. Fortunately, however, we do not have to go to this trouble, any more than we have to compute the areas of a large number of bars in order to get tail probabilities for a binomial, Pascal, or Poisson random variable. We shall see later in the chapter that we can use published tables to get the area of a tail of the continuous exponential distribution, and we can take this area as a direct approximation to the area of the tail of the histogram.

14.2 Applicability of the Poisson Model and the Exponential Distribution

In some real-world situations we have strong a priori or "theoretical" reason to believe that a process generating successes will behave according to the Poisson model. Some examples of such situations were given in Section 13.4—if we believe that a certain part breaks purely by accident and not as the result of gradual wear, and if the part is subjected to usage of constant severity, we will conclude that breakages will occur in accordance with the Poisson model. Similarly it seems reasonable a priori to assume that the fact that one telephone subscriber puts in a call at one instant will have no appreciable effect on the factors which will determine whether another subscriber puts in a call at the next instant, and therefore it is reasonable a priori to treat telephone calls as generated by a Poisson process. Although the intensity of this process will vary with the day of the week and the time of day, it will be nearly constant over reasonably short periods of time.

Usually, however, our a priori or theoretical reasons for believing that a given process must behave as a Poisson process will be far from conclusive. Thus we can argue that the factors tending to cause an accident in a mine *may* be constant over time and therefore that accidents *may* be Poisson distributed, but before we can be at all sure in any particular case we must compare the available historical evidence on that particular case with the implications of the Poisson model. There are two possible ways of making such a comparison:

1. We can cut the entire recorded space or time into a large number of blocks or segments of equal size, count the *number of successes r* in each block, and compare the resulting frequency distribution of the random

variable $\tilde{r}$ with a *Poisson distribution* having the same mean number m of successes per block.

2. We can measure the *interval* t between each success and the next, make a grouped frequency distribution of the lengths of the intervals, and compare this distribution of the random variable $\tilde{t}$ with an *exponential distribution* having the same mean interval μ between successes.†

The first of these two methods was used in Chapter 13, Problems 9 and 10, because the original data in those problems consisted of the numbers of successes in predetermined blocks of time or space, but whenever the actual lengths of intervals have been recorded the second method is usually more convenient. It is applied in Figure 14.2 to show that in

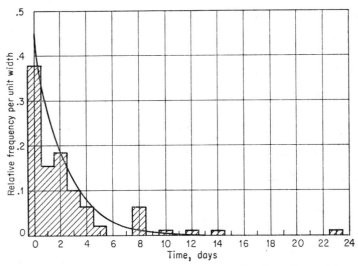

Figure 14.2. **Time between accidents in one district of a mine.** (*Data from Biometrika*, **1952**, *p.* 169.)

one particular mine the intervals between accidents in fact had a nearly exponential distribution, and it follows that the Poisson model will give a good approximation to the actual occurrence of future accidents in this mine as long as the conditions underlying the historical record remain essentially unchanged.

In many situations we observe that intervals are exponentially distributed even though there is almost no a priori reason at all to think

---

† To calculate the ordinate of the fitted exponential curve, we first compute the quantity $v = t/\mu$, then find the value of e^{-v}, and finally divide this value by μ to get $P'(t)$ according to the exponential formula. The value of e^{-v} can be found in several ways. Tables of e^{-v} exist, and the curve labeled $r = 1$ in Chart III can be interpreted as a graph of e^{-v} (vertical axis) against v (horizontal axis). The value of e^{-v} can also be found by looking up the antilogarithm of $-v$ in a table of logarithms to the base e or by looking up the antilogarithm of $-.4343v$ in a table of logarithms to the base 10.

that they are generated by a Poisson process. A very well-known example is the duration of local telephone calls not made from pay stations. To argue a priori that these durations must have an exponential distribution, we would have to assert that the "process" which ultimately leads people to end a telephone conversation is of such a nature that the tendency to hang up does not increase at all as the conversation proceeds—remember that in the Poisson model the probability of a success in any instant is completely independent of what has happened in all previous instants. Such an assumption is of course absurd, and yet it has been observed that the durations of such telephone calls do in fact have an almost exactly exponential distribution. Similarly it is often found that the time required to serve customers at a ticket window or

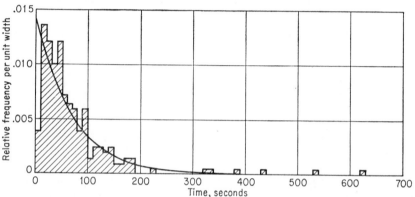

Figure 14.3. Service time at a tool crib. (*Data from Operations Research*, **1955, p. 414.**)

mechanics at a tool crib has an exponential distribution even though we cannot give any strong theoretical arguments to prove that this must be so. An example of a nearly exponential distribution of service times at a particular tool crib is shown in Figure 14.3.

14.3   Distance to the *r*th Success or Sum of *r* Intervals; the Gamma Distribution

The probability distribution for the time or distance $\tilde{t}$ from now to the *r*th Poisson success, or for the interval between one Poisson success and the *r*th following success, can be arrived at by exactly the same kind of limiting process which resulted in the exponential distribution. To find the distribution for the space before the third success, for example, we could simply recalculate Tables 14.1 and 14.2 using Pascal probabilities for $r = 3$ instead of Pascal probabilities for $r = 1$; the histograms would again approach a smooth curve as the space was divided into smaller and smaller parts.

Whatever the value of r—the required number of successes—the limiting distribution is given by the formula for the *gamma distribution:*

$$P'(t) = \frac{1}{\mu} \frac{e^{-(t/\mu)}(t/\mu)^{r-1}}{(r-1)!},$$

where μ is the mean length of *one* interval as before. This distribution has *two* parameters, μ and r. When $r = 1$, it reduces to the formula for the exponential distribution as given in Section 14.1.1: the exponential distribution is simply the special case $r = 1$ of the gamma distribution.

Sums of Poisson Intervals. The total interval from one success to the rth following success can obviously be regarded as the *sum* of the lengths of r intervals between adjacent successes. Since Poisson events and intervals are independent of past history, the distribution of the sum of *any* r intervals, not necessarily adjacent, has the same distribution as the distance from one success to the rth following success.

14.3.1   The Standardized Gamma Distribution

If we were to try to produce tables or charts of the gamma distribution defined by the formula given just above, we would have to have one table or curve for every possible combination of its two parameters μ and r, just as binomial tables must contain one table for every combination of the two parameters n and p. If, however, we agree that in any problem involving a gamma distribution we will *measure all lengths in units such that the mean length of one interval is one unit*, the parameter μ will have the value 1 in all problems and we will need only one table or curve for each value of r.

Suppose, for example, that we want to know the distribution of the total length l of r intervals when the mean length of one interval is $\mu = 2$ inches. Substituting 2 for μ in the formula for the gamma distribution as given above, we obtain

$$P'(t) = \frac{1}{2} \frac{e^{-(t/2)}(t/2)^{r-1}}{(r-1)!}.$$

If now instead of using an inch as our unit of measurement we use a double-inch, calling 6 inches 3 double-inches, etc., the mean length of an interval becomes 1 unit or double-inch. Using v instead of t to denote a length measured in these special units, the formula for the gamma distribution with 1 substituted for μ becomes

$$P'(v) = \frac{1}{1} \frac{e^{-(v/1)}(v/1)^{r-1}}{(r-1)!} = \frac{e^{-v}v^{r-1}}{(r-1)!}.$$

If the mean length of one interval had been 3 inches, we would have obtained exactly this same final result by measuring in triple-inches; if the mean length of one interval had been 7.3 inches we would have obtained exactly the same result by taking 7.3 inches as our unit of measurement; and so forth.   We therefore define the *standardized* random variable

$$\bar{v} = \frac{\bar{t}}{\mu},$$

and in Chart III we show curves giving the *standardized gamma distribution*

$$P'_g(v) = \frac{e^{-v}v^{r-1}}{(r-1)!}$$

for values of the parameter r from 1 through 5.   The distribution for $r = 1$ can also be called the standardized exponential distribution.

Suppose now that we wish to compute the probability that the total length $\bar{t}$ of $r = 3$ intervals will have the value $t = 10$ when the mean

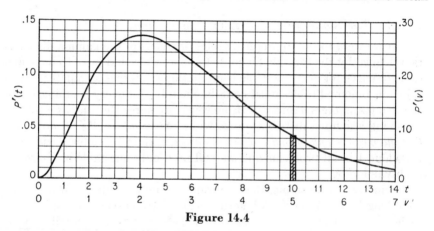

Figure 14.4

length of one interval is $\mu = 2$ inches, and suppose that our measuring instrument gives readings to the fifth of an inch so that each bar in the histogram describing the "true" probability distribution of $\bar{t}$ has width .2 inch.   If we use the scales labeled t and $P'(t)$ in Figure 14.4, this figure gives the natural or *nonstandardized* gamma distribution for $r = 3$, $\mu = 2$ and we can compute the desired probability by exactly the same procedure we followed in computing $P(\bar{t} = .46)$ in Section 14.1.3.   Using the left-hand vertical scale, we read the height of the curve at $t = 10$ as $P'(t) = .042$ and we then compute

$$P(\bar{t} = 10) = \delta t \, P'(10) = .2 \times .042 = .0084.$$

If we use the scales labeled v and $P'(v)$ in Figure 14.4, the figure gives the *standardized* gamma distribution for $r = 3$.   Each value of $\bar{t}$ on the horizontal axis is *divided* by $\mu = 2$ to obtain the corresponding value of $\bar{v}$

but at the same time every value of P'(t) on the vertical axis is *multiplied* by $\mu = 2$ to obtain the corresponding P'(v); consequently the area = width × height of any bar under the curve remains unchanged. Taking the shaded bar representing $t = 10$ as an example, its width of .2 inch has become .1 double-inch but its height has become .084 on the P'(v) scale, so that its area remains

$$P(\tilde{t} = 10) = P(\tilde{v} = 5) = \delta v \, P'(v) = .1 \times .084 = .0084$$

as before. In general,

When we standardize any random variable $\tilde{t}$ by dividing by μ, we divide the width of every bar in the underlying histogram by μ; the probability of any particular value t is therefore given by the formula

$$P(\tilde{t} = t) = \frac{\delta t}{\mu} P'_g(v) \qquad v = \frac{t}{\mu} \qquad \textit{Gamma probability}$$

If we wish to know the probability that the sum of five Poisson intervals will have total length 15 minutes when the mean length of one interval is 4 minutes and time is measured to the hundredth of a minute, we compute

$$v = \frac{t}{\mu} = \frac{15}{4} = 3.75,$$

use the curve for $r = 5$ in Chart III to find $P'_g(3.75) = .194$, and compute

$$P(\tilde{t} = 15) = \frac{.01}{4} .194 = .000485.$$

14.3.2 The Cumulative Gamma Distribution

We often wish to know the probability that an interval or sum of intervals will be less than some amount or greater than some amount. Such tail probabilities can be obtained from Chart I, where the curve for each value of r shows the cumulative probability $P_g(\tilde{v} < v|r)$. In terms of Chart III, this is the area under the curve for the specified parameter r to the *left* of the specified value v of the variable. Chart I used as a chart of the gamma distribution is thus our first example of a chart or table showing *left*-tail cumulative probabilities.†

† For very extensive tables of the gamma distribution, see K. Pearson, "Tables of the Incomplete Γ-Function," Biometrika Office, London, 1951. To find $P_g(\tilde{v} < v|r)$ from these tables, compute $u = v/\sqrt{r}$ and $p = r - 1$ and then look up $I(u,p)$. Gamma probabilities can also be found from tables of the Poisson distribution by using the relation

$$P_g(\tilde{v} < v|r) = P_{Po}(\tilde{r} \geq r|m = v),$$

for the derivation of which compare Section 11.2.1.

Example. We wish the probability that the total length of three intervals will be less than $t = 10$ feet when the mean length of one interval is 2 feet, i.e.

$$P(\tilde{t} < 10 | r = 3, \mu = 2).$$

The logic of the procedure we shall use to evaluate this probability can best be understood by looking back at the graph of the distribution for $r = 3$, $\mu = 2$ shown in Figure 14.4. The required probability of all values t *less than* 10 is the total area of all the bars in the underlying histogram *to the left* of the shaded bar, which represents the value $t = 10$ itself, and this area can clearly be approximated by the area under the smooth curve to the left of the left edge of the bar for $t = 10$. In principle, therefore, we should proceed by (1) determining the value of $\tilde{t}$ at the *left edge* of the shaded bar, (2) converting this value of $\tilde{t}$ to the corresponding value of $\tilde{v} = \tilde{t}/\mu$, and (3) using Chart I to find the area to the left of this value of $\tilde{v}$.

To follow this procedure we would, of course, have to know the fineness with which measurements will be made, since it is this which determines the width of the bar for $\tilde{t} = 10$ and thus the location of the left edge of this bar—if measurements are made to the hundredth of a foot, the left edge of the bar for $t = 10$ feet is at $10 - .01/2 = 9.995$ feet, and so forth. The figure makes it clear, however, that in most practical problems there is no need to go to the trouble of calculating the width of a bar when we seek a *cumulative* probability. If instead of evaluating the area to the left of the *left edge* of the bar for $t = 10$ we evaluate the area to the left of the *center* of this bar, our error will amount to half the area of the bar. This error area will obviously be negligible *in comparison* with the remainder of the tail unless either the specified t is extremely close to 0 or the measurements are so coarse that the width of each bar is really substantial. In the former case we can evaluate the area of each of the individual bars in the tail; in the latter case the gamma approximation to the underlying histogram will be no good no matter how we use it.

We therefore proceed as follows. We first express the specified value $t = 10$ in terms of v by computing

$$v = \frac{t}{\mu} = \frac{10}{2} = 5.$$

We then use Chart I to evaluate

$$P_g(\tilde{v} < 5 | r = 3)$$

by locating the specified value $v = 5$ on the horizontal axis of the chart, reading up to the curve for $r = 3$, and over to find $P = .88$ on the vertical axis.

14.4 Expectations of a Gamma Variable

We saw in Section 14.1.1 above that the mean of the exponential distribution is equal to its parameter $\mu = 1/\kappa$, and from this we can easily deduce the mean of the gamma distribution. If we look at the gamma distribution as the distribution of the *sum of the lengths of r intervals* each one of which has expected length μ, it is clear that

$$E(\tilde{t}) = r\mu \qquad \textit{Expected length of r Poisson intervals}$$

Although the physical meaning of the expected length of an interval or of r intervals is perfectly clear intuitively, it will be well to stop to look at the mathematical meaning of the expected value of a random variable with a continuous distribution. In Section 5.2.3 we defined the expected value of a random variable as the number which results from multiplying every possible value of the variable by its probability and adding the products, and this would seem to lead to some difficulties when we are dealing with a variable such that every individual value is formally regarded as having probability 0 (cf. Section 14.1.1).

Even though the probability of any particular value of a continuous random variable is 0, we know how to calculate the probability that it will lie *between* two different values, and therefore we can get an approximate value for any expectation by first deriving a grouped distribution from the continuous distribution and then proceeding as we did in Section 6.5. As an example, let us compute $E_0^4(\tilde{t})$ when $\tilde{t}$ has a gamma distribution with parameters $\mu = 2, r = 3$; this is the distribution graphed corresponding to the t and $P'(t)$ scales of Figure 14.4. We arbitrarily select brackets $\frac{1}{2}$ unit wide on the t scale and then proceed as shown in Table 14.3.

Table 14.3

Bracket	Mid-point	P' at mid-point	Grouped probability	Product
0–.5	.25	.003	.0015	.000
.5–1.0	.75	.024	.0120	.009
1.0–1.5	1.25	.052	.0260	.032
1.5–2.0	1.75	.080	.0400	.070
2.0–2.5	2.25	.103	.0515	.116
2.5–3.0	2.75	.119	.0595	.164
3.0–3.5	3.25	.130	.0650	.211
3.5–4.0	3.75	.135	.0675	.253
				.855

$P'(t)$ is read for the mid-point of each bracket from Figure 14.4 and is then multiplied by the .5 width of the bracket to give the approximate area or probability of the bracket. This grouped probability is then multiplied by the mid-point to obtain the product in the last column and these products are added to find $E_0^4(\tilde{t}) = .855$ approximately.

A still better approximation could be found by using still narrower brackets but fortunately this labor is unnecessary. It can be shown by calculus that as the brackets are made narrower and narrower the result of computing *any* gamma expectation by the method of Table 14.3 will come closer and closer to the value given by the formula

$$E_0^t(\tilde{t}) = r\mu \, P(\tilde{t} < t | r + 1, \mu).$$

This formula can easily be evaluated if we express the probability in terms of the standardized variable $\tilde{v} = \tilde{t}/\mu$:

$$E_0^t(t) = r\mu \, P_g\left(\tilde{v} < \frac{t}{\mu}\middle| r + 1\right) \qquad \textit{Gamma partial expectation}$$

For our example, $t = 4$, $r = 3$, $\mu = 2$. We compute

$$v = \frac{t}{\mu} = \frac{4}{2} = 2,$$

use Chart I to find

$$P_g(\tilde{v} < 2 | r = 3 + 1) = .143,$$

and compute

$$E_0^4(\tilde{t}) = 3 \times 2 \times .143 = .858.$$

14.5 Approximation of Pascal Probabilities

We saw in Section 13.5 that when p is small the Poisson distribution can be used to obtain very good approximations to binomial probabilities. Under the same condition the gamma distribution can be used to approximate Pascal probabilities.

Suppose that we wish to find the probability that 100 or less Bernoulli trials will be required to secure four successes when $p = .05$. If we imagine that each Bernoulli trial takes 1 unit of time—say 1 minute—this is the probability that 100 or less minutes will be required to secure four successes when the mean number of successes per minute is .05. The mean interval between successes is then $1/.05 = 20$ minutes and if the successes were generated by a Poisson rather than a Bernoulli process, the probability would be

$$P_g(\tilde{v} < {}^{100}\!\!/_{20} | r = 4) = .74$$

by Chart I.   The exact value of the Pascal probability

$$P_{Pa}(\tilde{n} \leq 100 | r = 4, p = .05)$$

is found by looking up $P_b(\tilde{r} \geq 4 | n = 100, p = .05)$ in Table I, where it is given as .742.

PROBLEMS

1. In a Poisson process averaging two defects per foot, distance being measured to a hundredth of a foot, what is the probability that the distance from one defect to the next will be

   a. Less than 3 inches?

   b. More than 9 inches?

   c. Exactly .6 foot?

2. Same as Problem 1 but for the distance from one defect to the fourth following defect.

3. In a Poisson process averaging three deaths by horse kick per year, what is the probability that a year will go by without a death by horse kick?

4. If parts fail by a Poisson process at a rate of one every 8 weeks, if there are two spare parts in inventory, and if a new supply will arrive in 12 weeks, what is the probability that production will be stopped for lack of spare parts for a week or more?

5. If 8 of the 12 weeks lead time of Problem 4 have gone by and only one part has broken, what is the probability that the process will be stopped for a week or more

   a. If the part broke 1 day after the date of Problem 4?

   b. If the part broke 1 day before the end of the 8 weeks?

6. If on the average a Bernoulli process produces one defective in 500 pieces, what is the probability that the fifth defective will occur

   a. Before 3000 pieces have been produced?

   b. As the 3000th piece produced?

   c. After 3000 pieces have been produced?

7. If $\frac{1}{100}$ of 1 per cent of all postings made in a bank are erroneous:

   a. What is the expected number of postings which will be made before the fifth error occurs?

   b. What is the probability that the fifth error will occur after more than 70,000 postings have been made?

8. Sales of a certain product have been Poisson distributed with an average daily volume of 5 units but because of a recent price change the average daily volume is no longer known. If it is guessed that there is one chance in four that the price change will reduce average sales by 20 per cent, two chances in four that the reduction will be 40 per cent, and one chance in four that it will be 60 per cent, what is the probability that a stock of 10 items will last less than two full days?

CHAPTER 15

Min-Max Inventory Control

15.1 Definition of the Problem

15.1.1 The Cost of Carrying Inventory

In the inventory problems studied in earlier chapters, the reason for avoiding too large an inventory was a risk of spoilage which resulted from the fact that all units not sold before a specified date would have to be scrapped or sold at a price below cost. If the cost of spoilage is regarded as a cost of carrying inventory, then in this situation the cost of carrying a unit is some *fixed amount* (or zero) if it is carried less than some specified length of time and a larger *fixed amount* if it is carried longer than this.

We now take up the different kind of problem which arises when the cost of carrying a unit in stock is *proportional* to the time it is carried, which means that for the whole inventory the cost per unit of time is proportional to the size of the inventory. The most common costs which are exactly or approximately of this nature are the cost of capital tied up in inventory, the cost of warehouse space and maintenance, and insurance. Even the cost of spoilage is often much closer to being proportional to time stored than to being of the all-or-none character assumed in earlier chapters. Particularly when obsolescence is involved, it is often a good approximation to assume either (1) that the *actual value* of a piece declines steadily over time, so that there is a *loss certain* which is roughly proportional to the time the item is on the shelf, or (2) that the risk of incurring a loss of fixed amount (cost less scrap value) increases with time, so that there is an *expected loss* which is roughly proportional to the time the item is on the shelf. In such situations obsolescence can also be represented by a charge per unit of time which is added to the charge per unit of time for capital, storage, etc.

15.1.2 The Cost of Shortage

In previous chapters we have considered only situations where the cost of shortage was a certain amount *per unit* short. In this chapter we shall study inventory control not only in situations where the cost of shortage is of this nature but also in situations where the cost of shortage is proportional to the *time* during which the shortage persists.

15.1.3   Inventory Control under Certainty

Two separate decisions may be involved in placing an order for replenishment of stock, whether this order is placed by a purchaser with a vendor or by a production-control department with the shop:
1. The *date* on which to place the order,
2. The *quantity* to order.

If demand could be predicted with certainty and if the lead time between placing an order and receipt of the goods ordered could be predicted with certainty, orders would be placed so that each new lot would arrive at the exact instant that it was needed.   Only two kinds of costs would then have to be considered in determining the date of ordering and the quantity ordered.   The annual cost of carrying inventory would *increase* in proportion to the order quantity, since the average inventory obviously increases with the size of the purchase lot.   On the other hand, the annual costs of ordering or setup, receiving, payment of invoices, etc., are proportional to the number of orders and would therefore *decrease* in inverse proportion to the order quantity.   It is a very simple matter to find the *economic lot size* or order quantity which minimizes the total of these two kinds of cost; and once the lot size is fixed, the interval between orders is simply the lot size divided by the rate at which sales occur.

The analysis would be essentially unchanged if for administrative reasons it were desirable to place orders at intervals other than the "most economic" intervals.   If, for example, the economic lot size implied an interval of 1.37 months between orders but it was more convenient to place all orders for a given item on the same day of each month, the cost of monthly orders and of bimonthly orders would be computed and the schedule with the lower cost would be chosen.   Under certainty, inventory *control* is reduced to ordering a fixed quantity on predetermined dates.

15.1.4   Assumption of Known Lead Time

Two kinds of uncertainty may enter into an inventory problem and render inapplicable the simple system of control described above.

1. There may be uncertainty concerning the *quantity which will be demanded* during any given time period.
2. There may be uncertainty concerning the *lead time* which will elapse between the date on which an order is placed and the date on which the new lot of product will actually arrive.

The problem of inventory control when *both* demand and lead time are uncertain is beyond the scope of this course, but in many situations there is *substantial* uncertainty concerning only one or the other.   Since our purpose in this course is to give examples of the application of probability theory rather than to exhaust the problem of inventory control, we shall study only one of the two cases.

We shall study the problem of control in the face of uncertainty concerning demand; we shall assume that lead time is known with certainty.

15.1.5 The Poisson Model of Demand

In the kind of inventory problem studied in previous chapters, analysis was much simplified by the fact that every decision was completely independent of previous decisions. The *date* at which each order was placed was out of the purchaser's control, and the *stock on hand* when each new order arrived was zero regardless of the quantity received in the previous order. This meant that the only decision required was the quantity and that the expected cost of any decision depended solely on the probability distribution for demand during a single time period.

Once storage is possible, however, this is no longer true. The time required to dispose of any number of units depends, not on the probability distribution of demand during a single, fixed period of time, but on the distributions for demand in a whole series of periods. Consequently analysis of the costs is extremely complex if the probability distribution for demand is changing with time. In this chapter we shall consider the problem of inventory control under only the simplest possible form of uncertain demand: we assume that:

1. The probability distribution for number of units demanded in a period of any given length is the *same for all future time periods*. It is the same for next week as for the week starting a year from now, the same for next month as for the following month, etc.
2. The distributions for any two time periods are *independent*. A high demand in any one hour or any one month will not lead the person responsible for inventory control to lower his forecast of demand for the next hour or month.
3. The *average* demand is *known with certainty*. The person responsible for inventory control would be willing to bet at very long odds that the average demand in a long series of future periods would be very close to some specified number.

The first two statements amount to asserting that demand will be treated as generated by a *Poisson process* with *parameter constant over time*, and the third says that there is no serious uncertainty about the *value* of this parameter.

15.2 The Two Basic Systems of Inventory Control

When demand is uncertain, it is clearly undesirable to fix *both* the ordering dates and the order quantity in advance. If sales are higher than expected and inventory is depleted more rapidly than expected, we will want either to order sooner or to order more than we originally planned. On the other hand, it is almost always administratively undesirable to leave *both* these decisions open and in need of continuous reanalysis. Some kind of trigger is needed which will automatically call attention to the need to do something about a given item, and the two basic systems of inventory control are distinguished by the choice of the trigger.

1. In a *min-max system* of inventory control, the order quantity is fixed once and for all but the date at which each order is to be placed is determined by the stock on hand.
2. In a *system with fixed ordering dates*, the dates at which the orders are to be placed are fixed once and for all but the quantity to order on each occasion is determined by the stock on hand.

We shall study only the min-max system, since analysis of the fixed-date system leads to very heavy arithmetic when lead time is not zero. Even without a complete analysis of both systems, however, we can determine the conditions under which each should be used, and we shall do so before proceeding with the detailed study of the min-max system.

Suppose that the "purchaser" is free to place an order whenever he chooses, that it costs no more to place an order at one time than at another, and that lead time will be the same whenever the order is placed. Under our basic assumption that high or low demand in one time period does not tend to be followed by either high or low demand in the next, the only new evidence which we need consider in deciding when and how much to order is the number of units currently in stock. If stock fell to 6 units on July 7 last and if stock fell to 6 units today, then whatever action was rational on July 7 last is rational today.

This line of reasoning clearly implies that *under the stated conditions* we should:

1. Determine the economic *order quantity* once and for all.
2. Place an order for this quantity whenever the stock on hand falls to a predetermined level known as the *reorder point.*†

In other words, *the min-max system is preferable to the system with fixed ordering dates whenever* (1) *lead time is the same regardless of order date,* (2) *placing of orders at irregular dates entails no substantial extra cost, and* (3) *recent history is of no use in predicting demand.*

The fixed-date system *may* be preferable when any one of these three conditions is violated. In many situations the purchaser is *forced* to order on fixed dates because he is not free to place orders when he

† We remind the student that the Poisson model of demand implies that stock will fall by 1 unit at a time: cf. Section 13.4.1.

chooses, or—what amounts to the same thing—because there are specified "closing dates" and it is the time between these closing dates and
delivery which is constant rather than the time between placing the
order and delivery. This was true in all the problems studied in earlier
chapters: bread had to be stocked daily, and so forth. Shops often operate on a "cycled" basis such that an order for any part of a certain class
will be delivered so many days after the end of the *month* in which the
production order is placed, regardless of the *day* on which the order is
placed.

Another common reason for ordering on fixed dates is a desire to
revise predictions of future demand on the basis of a careful study of
past demand. The fixed dates then simplify the problem of scheduling
the time of the personnel capable of making such a review, or it may be
felt that the review should be made more frequently than it would be if it
occurred only when a reorder point was reached. This is reasonable
enough when it is true that something can be learned about future demand
from the recent history of demand, i.e. when the probability distribution
is *not* of the sort assumed in this chapter. It may be remarked, however,
that mere random fluctuations in demand can easily be mistaken for
"trends" and that the assumption that nothing useful can be learned
from recent history is probably justified more often than it is made.

15.3   Physical Behavior of the Min-Max System

A min-max control system for any item is completely defined by the
values of two parameters:

Q: the *order quantity*, to be the same on all orders.

R: the *reorder point*, an order to be placed as soon as the stock falls
to R units.

Under our assumptions concerning lead time and the distribution of
demand, the situation in which the system operates is fully defined by
two additional parameters:

L: the known *lead time* between placing an order and receipt of
delivery.

μ: the *mean interval between successive demands*, the reciprocal of
mean demand per unit of time, also assumed known.

If lead time were zero—if goods were delivered instantaneously when
an order was placed—then in spite of uncertainty concerning demand the
economics of inventory control under a min-max system would be
identical to the economics of control when demand can be forecast with
certainty. Carrying costs would be minimized by setting the reorder
point R at zero, so that each new lot would arrive an instant after the last

piece in the old lot was sold.   The best value for Q—the economic lot size—would be calculated in exactly the same way that it is calculated under certainty, by balancing the costs which increase with order quantity against the costs which increase with order frequency.

If, on the contrary, lead time is not zero, then whatever the reorder point it will not be true in general that the new lot will arrive at the instant that the last piece in the old lot is sold.   Rather than make a direct attack upon the rather complicated effect which this has on costs, we shall start by analyzing the "physical behavior" of a min-max system with known nonzero lead time.   The analysis becomes very complex if the order quantity Q is smaller than the reorder point R (as it may well be when usage is low and lead time is long), since in this case there will be several orders outstanding at any one time, each of them placed at a different time and due in at a different time.   Therefore we now introduce one further restriction:

We consider only the case where the order quantity Q is greater than the reorder point R.

15.3.1   The Fifo "Assumption"; Shelf Stock, Reserve Stock, and Overlap

Our analysis of the behavior of the min-max system can be greatly simplified by treating it *as if* the inventory is physically handled on a strict Fifo (first in first out) basis.   We shall therefore "assume" that *if the new lot arrives while there is still stock on hand, the new lot will be left intact in its container until the last piece of this old stock is sold.*   We shall use the term *shelf stock* for the old stock which is open for sale on the shelf and the term *reserve stock* for the new stock held in an unopened container (if any).   We shall refer to any time during which there is both old and new stock on hand as a *period of overlap.*

It should be obvious that this "assumption" is nothing but a convenient way of *visualizing* the problem.   All costs will in fact be the same, and the results of our analysis will apply without modification, whether the inventory is in fact handled in this way or not.

15.3.2   The Min-Max Cycle

Over a long period of time there will be many orders placed and many lots received and opened.   In order to analyze this long-run behavior we shall cut it up into a series of *cycles*, determine what *may* happen in any *one* cycle, and then determine what happens *on the average* over *all* cycles or what can be "expected" to happen in one cycle.   A cycle can be defined in various ways: as running from the placing of one order to the placing of the next, from receipt of one lot to receipt of the next, or from the opening of one lot to the opening of the next.   If our analysis is correct we must get the same results whichever of these definitions we use, and the last of them will be the most convenient.

Let us therefore look at what *may* happen in a min-max cycle between the *opening* of one lot and the *opening* of the next.   Since there is probability 0 that the new lot will arrive at the exact instant that the last piece

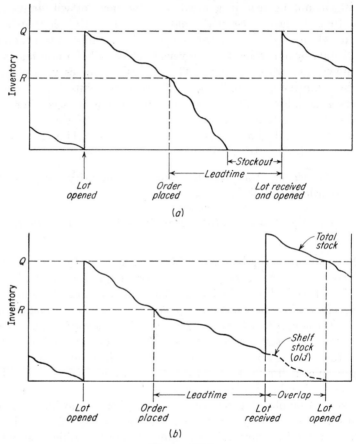

Figure 15.1

in the old lot is sold, we may assume that the behavior of inventory during this cycle will correspond to one or the other of the two sketches in Figure 15.1.   *Either*

a. The last piece from the old lot will have been sold before the new lot arrives, so that there is a *period of stockout, or*

b. Some unsold pieces from the old lot will be left over when the new lot arrives, so that there is a *period of overlap.*

The figures make it clear that in *either* of the two cases we may subdivide the cycle into *two major parts:*

1. Time from opening the first lot to placing the order for the next.
2. Time from placing the order to opening of the ordered lot.

The figures also make it clear that in *either* of the two cases the second of the two major parts can be further subdivided in *either of two ways:*

    a. Time to sell the last R pieces in the old lot plus period of stockout if any.

    b. Lead time plus period of overlap if any.

Our objective is to determine the average or *expected value of the following times:*

    1. *Average shelf time*, i.e. the time that the "average piece" is carried on the shelf after the container has been opened; this determines the cost of carrying shelf stock.

    2. *Overlap time*, which determines the cost of carrying reserve stock intact in its container.

    3. *Time out of stock*, which determines the cost of stockouts.

We now proceed to compute these times in the order listed.

    1. *Average Shelf Time.* It is clear from Figure 15.1a that a new lot *may* be opened immediately after a period of stockout, and the expected time during which a piece from the new lot will remain on the shelf depends on what happens to orders received during this period of stockout. It is obvious that if such orders are canceled or lost, the new stock will last longer than if the orders are back-ordered and filled from the new lot as soon as it is received. In this chapter we shall study only the former case:

    We assume that unfilled orders are lost and have no effect on future demand.

Notice that unsatisfied demands are "lost" in effect not only when

    1. An unsatisfied "customer" buys elsewhere or fills his need by substitution or "local manufacture,"

but also when

    2. A stoppage occurs as soon as the last piece is withdrawn from inventory, with the result that no unsatisfied demands *can* occur.†

† This applies particularly to spare parts. Notice that in this case a part actually in use on a machine must be counted as part of the inventory, so that usage stops as soon as the last part "in inventory" breaks. If inventory is defined as including only the *spare* parts, one breakage may occur *after* the inventory has fallen to 0, and if it does the demand *will* be back-ordered and filled as soon as a new supply arrives, thus invalidating our analysis.

The expected shelf time for the items in a lot is now exceedingly easy to compute. By our "Fifo assumption," no piece from a new lot is put on the shelf until the last piece in the old lot is sold, and then all Q pieces are put on the shelf simultaneously. Since the expected time between successive demands for single units is μ, the expected shelf time for the first piece to be sold is μ, the expected shelf time for the second is 2μ, etc., and the expected shelf time for the last piece to be sold is $Q\mu$. The *average* expected shelf time for the Q pieces in the lot is thus

$$\frac{1}{Q}(1 + 2 + \cdots + Q)\mu$$

and it can easily be shown that this gives

$$\text{Average shelf time} = \frac{Q+1}{2}\mu$$

2. *Expected Period of Overlap.* If one piece of old stock remains unsold when the new lot is received, the expected time before it is sold is μ regardless of how long it has already been on the shelf, since Poisson events are independent of past history. If two units remain unsold when the new lot arrives, the conditional expected time before both are sold is 2μ, and so forth. Under our "Fifo assumption," these times are the conditional expected values of the period of overlap during which both old and new stock is on hand. *The total expected overlap will therefore be equal to μ times the expected number of pieces left over when the new lot arrives.*

This means that our first task is to compute the expected number of pieces which will be left over when the new lot arrives. We shall derive the method of computation by first considering a specific numerical example in which

$R = 3$, the reorder point;
$L = 8$ weeks, the lead time;
$\mu = 4$ weeks, the mean interval between demands.

The expected number of demands during the lead time L is then

$$m = \frac{L}{\mu} = \frac{8}{4} = 2.$$

The probability distribution for the number of units *demanded* during the lead time can now be obtained from Chart I; it is shown in the first two columns of Table 15.1. The conditional number of pieces left over when the new lot arrives is the number R on hand at the beginning of the lead time less the number sold during the lead time; the number sold is either the number demanded or the number R on hand, whichever is less.

The expected number left over is computed for this example in the last column of Table 15.1. Inspection of the individual entries in this

Table 15.1

Demand r	$P_{Po}(\tilde{r} = r \mid m = 2)$	Number left over	Expected value
0	.135	(3 − 0)	.135 × 3 − .135 × 0
1	.271	(3 − 1)	.271 × 3 − .271 × 1
2	.271	(3 − 2)	.271 × 3 − .271 × 2
3 = R	.180	(3 − 3)	.180 × 3 − .180 × 3
4+	.143	(3 − 3)	0
	1.000		.857 × 3 − 1.353

column shows that the *first term of the total* is $3\,P_{Po}(\tilde{r} \leq 3)$ while the *second term* 1.353 is the sum of $r\,P(r)$ for all r from 0 to 3 inclusive and is therefore $E_0^3(\tilde{r})$. Generalizing this example we obtain the formula

$$\text{Expected number left over} = R\,P_{Po}(\tilde{r} \leq R) - E_0^R(\tilde{r}).$$

Substituting the formula given in Section 13.3 for the partial expectation of a Poisson variable we obtain

$$\text{Expected number left over} = R\,P_{Po}(\tilde{r} \leq R) - m\,P_{Po}(\tilde{r} < R).$$

Because Chart I gives right- rather than left-tail probabilities it will be simpler to write this in the form

$$R[1 - P_{Po}(\tilde{r} > R)] - m[1 - P_{Po}(\tilde{r} \geq R)]$$
$$= (R - m) + [m\,P_{Po}(\tilde{r} \geq R) - R\,P_{Po}(\tilde{r} > R)],$$

and because the term in the brackets on the right will occur so frequently in what follows we shall give it the name $g(R)$ (read: g of R):

$$g(R) = m\,P_{Po}(\tilde{r} \geq R) - R\,P_{Po}(\tilde{r} > R) \qquad \textit{Definition of } g(R)$$

We can thus write

$$\text{Expected number left over} = (R - m) + g(R),$$

and because the expected time to sell each piece left over is μ we have

$$\text{Expected overlap} = \mu[(R - m) + g(R)]$$

The quantity $(R - m)$ is usually known as the *safety stock*, since it is the amount by which the quantity on hand when the order is placed exceeds the *expected* demand before delivery of the new lot. The expected overlap thus consists of the expected time to sell off the safety stock plus an additional amount which will be explained in a moment.

3. *Time Out of Stock.* We have already seen that the *actual* time from placing an order to opening of the new lot may be broken down in either of two ways:

a. Time to sell the last R pieces in the old lot plus period of stockout if any.

b. Lead time plus period of overlap if any.

This implies that if we average over all possible cycles, the resulting *expected* time between ordering and opening may be broken down in either of these same two ways:

a. Expected time to sell R pieces plus expected time out of stock.

b. Lead time plus expected overlap.

Since the expected time between ordering and opening must be the same no matter how we subdivide it in our thinking, we may equate a to b. In a, the time to sell R pieces is $R\mu$ by the definition of μ. In b, the lead time is equal to μm by the definition $m = L/\mu$; and therefore

$$\mu m + \text{expected overlap} = \mu R + \text{expected TOS}.$$

Thus

$$\text{Expected overlap} = \mu(R - m) + \text{expected TOS};$$

and comparing this equation with the formula given above for the expected overlap, we see that we have identified the previously unexplained term in that formula:

$$\text{Expected TOS} = \mu g(R)$$

Looking back at the definition of $g(R)$, we see that as the reorder point R is raised, the probabilities in $g(R)$ approach 0: the expected time out of stock approaches 0 and the expected overlap approaches $\mu(R - m)$. With a high enough reorder point, shortages will never occur and the expected delay between receipt and opening of the new lot is simply the expected time required to sell the safety stock of $R - m$ pieces. We also see that when $R = 0$, $g(R)$ reduces to $m\,\mathrm{P}_{Po}(r \geq 0) = m$, the expected time out of stock reduces to $\mu m = L$, and the expected overlap reduces to 0. If there is no stock on hand when the order is placed, the time out of stock is obviously the lead time L and the new order will be opened immediately on receipt.

15.4 Total Expected Cost under a Min-Max System

We now proceed to use our knowledge of the physical behavior of a min-max system to analyze the economics of such a system. In so doing, it would be very awkward to work exclusively with either costs in the strict sense—i.e., actual cash flows—or with opportunity losses as defined in Chapter 7. We shall therefore work out the sum of the *costs* of ordering and of carrying inventory and the *losses* due to stockouts, but to simplify our language we shall refer to all of these indiscriminately as "costs" and we shall call their sum the total "cost" of the system.

As notation we shall continue to use the parameters Q, R, L, and μ in the sense of the previous section and in addition we define the cost parameters

K: cost of placing one order, receiving, payment, etc.
k_o': cost of carrying one piece in inventory per unit of time.
k_u': "cost" (loss) of out-of-stock condition per unit of time.

When the cost of shortage is proportional to the *number of units short*, the expected cost per unit of time is the cost per unit divided by the expected time between demands. If we use k_u for the loss *per unit* short as in earlier chapters, then

$$k_u' = \frac{k_u}{\mu}.$$

15.4.1 The Individual Expected Costs

The real utility of our "Fifo assumption" (Section 15.3.1) is that it permits us to split the carrying costs incurred on any lot into two parts:

1. Cost of carrying the lot intact from the time the lot is received to the time it is opened.

2. Cost of carrying individual pieces from the time the lot is opened until each piece is sold.

Since the cost per unit of time of carrying one piece is k_o', the cost per unit of time of carrying an entire lot of Q pieces is $k_o'Q$. The expected cost in the first of the two categories above is thus $k_o'Q$ times the expected overlap or time from receipt to opening of the lot:

Cost of overlap $= k_o'Q\mu[(R - m) + g(R)]$

If the reorder point R were high enough to make $g(R)$ zero, the expected cost of overlap would be simply $k_o'Q\mu$ times the "safety stock" $(R - m)$, and the term $k_o'Q\mu(R - m)$ is often called the *cost of carrying safety stocks*. Notice, however, that although the safety stock may be negative and therefore the so-called cost of carrying safety stock may be negative, the cost of overlap is never less than 0. The cost of overlap is strictly 0 only when the reorder point R is 0 and the "safety stock" is $(0 - m) = -m$. *The so-called cost of carrying safety stock will be a good approximation to the cost of overlap only when the reorder point is so high that the expected time out of stock is negligible.*

After the lot has been opened and placed on the shelf, the expected time during which the "average piece" will remain on the shelf is $\frac{1}{2}(Q + 1)\mu$. The expected cost of carrying this "average piece" is therefore $\frac{1}{2}k_o'(Q + 1)\mu$, and the expected total for all Q pieces in the lot is Q times this. Since this cost depends only on the lot size Q and not on the reorder point, it is usually known as the cost of "lot-size inventory":

$$\text{Cost of lot-size inventory} = \frac{1}{2}k_o'Q(Q + 1)\mu$$

The expected cost of stockouts is the cost k_u' per unit of time out of stock multiplied by the expected value of this time:

$$\text{Cost of stockouts} = k_u'\mu g(R)$$

15.4.2   Total Expected Cost per Cycle

Adding all these costs plus the cost of ordering K, we have for the *expected total cost per cycle*

$$k_o'Q\mu[(R - m) + g(R)] + \frac{1}{2}k_o'Q(Q + 1)\mu \qquad \text{inventory}$$
$$+ k_u'\mu g(R) \qquad \text{shortage}$$
$$+ K \qquad \text{ordering}$$

Regrouping the terms we obtain an expression more convenient for computation:

Expected TCPC
$$= K + k_o'Q\mu[\tfrac{1}{2}(Q + 1) + (R - m)] + (k_u' + k_o'Q)\mu g(R)$$

The first term is the cost of ordering. The second is the cost of "lot-size" inventory plus the so-called "cost of safety stocks." The last term shows the effect of out of stock, which creates both the cost of shortage and the difference between the true cost of overlap and the so-called cost of safety stocks.

15.4.3   Total Expected Cost per Unit of Time

In order to compute expected cost per unit of time we must divide the expected cost per cycle by the expected length of a cycle. As we can see in Figure 15.1, any cycle from the opening of one lot to the opening of the next can be broken down into at most two parts:

1. The time required to sell the Q pieces in the first lot;
2. The time out of stock if any.

The expected value of the former of these two times is obviously $Q\mu$, the expected value of the latter has been shown to be $\mu g(R)$, and therefore

Expected length of cycle $= Q\mu + \mu g(R)$.

We can now obtain the expected cost per unit of time by dividing the formula for expected cost per cycle by this formula for expected length of cycle. To simplify computation we divide both the numerator and the denominator of the resulting fraction by μ; the *expected total cost per unit of time* is then

Expected TCPUT
$$= \frac{K/\mu + k'_o Q[\tfrac{1}{2}(Q+1) + (R-m)] + (k'_u + k'_o Q)g(R)}{Q + g(R)}$$

15.5 Selection of the Best R for Given Q

We now take up the problem of finding the values of Q and R which will minimize expected cost per unit of time. We shall first see how to find the best R for given Q, and we shall then take up the more complex problem of finding the best value for Q.

15.5.1 *Incremental Effect of the jth Unit on the Min-Max Cycle*

Suppose that we have decided that the reorder point R shall be at least some number which we shall call $(j - 1)$ and that we wish to determine the effect of increasing the reorder point by 1 unit, i.e. to the value j. We shall refer to this as "adding the jth unit to the reorder point." *The physical behavior of a min-max system will be affected by addition of the jth unit in three ways.*

1. The *expected overlap* or time between receipt and opening of a new lot will be increased by $\mu \, \mathrm{P}_{Po}(\tilde{r} < j)$, since $\mathrm{P}_{Po}(\tilde{r} < j)$ is the probability that the jth unit will be left over when the new lot arrives and μ is the expected delay resulting from each piece left over.

2. Looking at the formula for expected overlap with $R = j$,

$$\mu(j - m) + \mu g(j),$$

we see that addition of the jth unit obviously increases the term $\mu(j - m)$ by the amount μ. Since the total overlap actually increases by only $\mu \, \mathrm{P}_{Po}(\tilde{r} < j)$, as we have just shown, addition of the jth unit means that the second term, which is the *expected time out of stock*, is *decreased* by $\mu - \mu \, \mathrm{P}_{Po}(\tilde{r} < j) = \mu \, \mathrm{P}_{Po}(\tilde{r} \geq j)$.

3. The *expected time between orders* is $Q\mu$ plus the expected time out of stock and is therefore *decreased* by $\mu \, P_{Po}(\tilde{r} \geq j)$.

15.5.2   Economic Effect of the jth Unit

The *cost of overlap* is $k'_o Q$ times the expected overlap and is therefore *increased* by $k'_o Q\mu \, P_{Po}(\tilde{r} < j)$. The *cost of shortage* is k'_u times the expected time out of stock and is therefore *decreased* by $k'_u\mu \, P_{Po}(\tilde{r} \geq j)$. Since the other costs (the cost of ordering and the cost of lot-size inventory) are unaffected by a change in the reorder point, adding the jth unit will reduce expected cost *per cycle* if

$$k'_0 Q\mu \, P_{Po}(\tilde{r} < j) < k'_u \mu \, P_{Po}(\tilde{r} \geq j).$$

By using the relation $P(\tilde{r} < j) = 1 - P(\tilde{r} \geq j)$, this condition can be put in either of two more convenient forms

$$P_{Po}(\tilde{r} \geq j) > \frac{k'_o Q}{k'_o Q + k'_u} \qquad P_{Po}(\tilde{r} < j) < \frac{k'_u}{k'_u + k'_o Q}$$

The R which minimizes cost per cycle will be equal to the highest j which satisfies these conditions; the second form of the condition should be compared with the condition given in Section 7.6.3 for another kind of inventory problem.

Remember, however, that what the businessman wants to minimize is not his cost per cycle but his long-run total cost or—what amounts to the same thing—his cost *per unit of time*. When orders are placed at predetermined dates, the two objectives are equivalent, but under a min-max system they are not. We have just seen that addition of the jth unit decreases the expected length of cycle by $\mu \, P_{Po}(\tilde{r} \geq j)$, this reduction in length of cycle tends to *increase* the cost per unit of time, and this effect *may* outweigh the effect of the reduction which the jth unit makes in cost per cycle.

In principle, therefore, we must check the true optimality of the R which minimizes cost per cycle by evaluating cost per unit of time with this value of R and also with the next lower value. If cost per unit of time is *higher* with reorder point $R = j - 1$ than with reorder point $R = j$, then $R = j$ is in fact the best reorder point. If the cost with $j - 1$ is *lower* than the cost with j, we must try $j - 2$ and so forth until we have bracketed the best reorder point. In actual practice, however, the benefit derived from this refinement will usually be extremely small. It is likely to be important only when the costs are such that the best control system calls for an expected time out of stock which is substantial compared with the expected time to use up one lot of material.

Example. Failures of a certain machine part occur once every 4 weeks on the average and are Poisson distributed. The part is purchased in lots of 12 at a delivered cost of \$18.20 per unit. It costs \$25 to prepare and place an order, make out receiving papers, etc., on delivery, and process the invoice through accounts payable. The cost of carrying parts of this type in inventory is figured as 30 per cent per annum of their value at delivered cost. If a part fails when no spare is on hand, a replacement part is manufactured in the toolroom at a cost of \$50. The inventory is controlled by a min-max system, and we wish to determine the reorder point. The lead time from the instant the stock clerk reports that the reorder point has been reached to the instant the new lot is available for use is 8 weeks. From these data we compute the parameters of the problem:

$$Q = 12;$$
$$L = 8 \text{ weeks};$$
$$\mu = 4 \text{ weeks};$$
$$K = \$25;$$
$$k_o' = \frac{30\%}{52} \$18.20 = \$.105 \text{ per week};$$
$$k_u = \$50 - \$18.20 = \$31.80 \text{ per unit short};$$
$$k_u' = \frac{k_u}{\mu} = \frac{\$31.80}{4} = \$7.95 \text{ per week out of stock};$$
$$m = \frac{L}{\mu} = \frac{8}{4} = 2.$$

Cost per cycle will be reduced by adding the jth unit if

$$P_{Po}(\tilde{r} \geq j | m = 2) > \frac{k_o' Q}{k_o' Q + k_u'} = \frac{\$.105 \times 12}{\$1.26 + \$7.95} = .137.$$

From Chart I we find that $P_{Po}(\tilde{r} \geq 4) = .143$ while $P_{Po}(\tilde{r} \geq 5) = .053$, so that a reorder point of $R = 4$ will minimize cost per cycle.

We next evaluate *cost per unit of time*, which means that we take account of the effect of the reorder point on the expected length of cycle. We have already seen that with $R = 4$, $P_{Po}(\tilde{r} \geq R) = .143$ and $P_{Po}(\tilde{r} > R) = .053$. Then

$$g(R) = m\, P_{Po}(\tilde{r} \geq R) - R\, P_{Po}(\tilde{r} > R)$$
$$= (2 \times .143) - (4 \times .053) = .074,$$
$$\frac{K}{\mu} = \frac{\$25}{4} = \$6.25,$$
$$k_o' Q = \$.105 \times 12 = \$1.26,$$
$$\tfrac{1}{2}(Q + 1) + (R - m) = 6.5 + 4 - 2 = 8.5,$$
$$k_u' + k_o' Q = \$7.95 + \$1.26 = \$9.21.$$

Substituting these values in the formula in Section 15.4.3 we have

$$\text{Expected TCPUT} = \frac{\$6.25 + (\$1.26 \times 8.5) + (\$9.21 \times .074)}{12 + .074}$$

$$= \frac{\$17.64}{12.074} = \$1.46 \text{ per week:} \qquad R = 4.$$

We next compute the expected cost per week with a reorder point 1 unit lower, $R = 3$. We already have $P_{Po}(\tilde{r} > 3) = P_{Po}(\tilde{r} \geq 4) = .143$, and Chart I gives $P_{Po}(\tilde{r} \geq 3) = .323$. Thus

$$g(R) = (2 \times .323) - (3 \times .143) = .217,$$
$$\tfrac{1}{2}(Q + 1) + (R - m) = 6.5 + 3 - 2 = 7.5,$$
$$\text{Expected TCPUT} = \frac{\$6.25 + (\$1.26 \times 7.5) + (\$9.21 \times .217)}{12 + .217}$$

$$= \frac{\$17.70}{12.217} = \$1.45 \text{ per week:} \qquad R = 3.$$

The numerator (cost per cycle divided by μ) has been increased by $\$17.70 - \$17.64 = \$.06$, but the increase of $12.217 - 12.074 = .143$ in the denominator (length of cycle divided by μ) has reduced cost *per week* by $\$1.46 - \$1.45 = \$.01$.

It is left to the student as an exercise to show that if the reorder point is decreased to 2, *both* the numerator and the cost per week are increased, the former to $\$19.43$ and the latter to $\$1.55$. The best reorder point for $Q = 12$ is $R = 3$; the best "safety stock" $(R - m)$ is one piece.

15.6   Selection of the Best Q

Having seen how to find the best reorder point for any given order quantity, we now turn to the final problem of determining the best order quantity. Basically we must proceed by trial and error, finding the best R and minimum cost for each of a series of values of Q until we hit upon the best one. We shall see, however, that our choice of values of Q to try can be guided in such a way that an exact answer or a more than adequate approximation can be found very quickly.

What we wish to do is find the values of Q and R which minimize the expression in Section 15.4.3 above for expected total cost per unit of time. We have already seen that when Q is given, it is very easy to find the value of R which minimizes the *numerator* of this expression; and minimizing the numerator would minimize the whole expression were it not for the effect of the term $g(R)$ in the denominator. The tedious part of finding the best R for given Q was the checking and adjusting for the effect of this term. We shall see presently that if this term were absent from the denominator it would also be very easy to find the best value of Q for given R; and we shall therefore proceed in two stages:

1. Find the Q and R which would be best if the term $g(R)$ in the denominator were absent;
2. Correct these approximate optima to allow for the effect of this term.

15.6.1 The Approximate Solution

Dropping $g(R)$ from the denominator of the expression in Section 15.4.3, we have for the *approximate* cost per unit of time

$$\frac{K/\mu + k'_o Q[\tfrac{1}{2}(Q+1) + (R-m)] + (k'_u + k'_o Q)g(R)}{Q}$$

$$= \frac{K/\mu + k'_u g(R)}{Q} + \frac{1}{2}k'_o(Q+1) + k'_o[(R-m) + g(R)].$$

Except for the effect of the omitted term, the costs *per unit of time* of ordering and of shortage vary inversely with Q, the cost of lot-size inventory varies directly with Q, and the cost of overlap inventory is independent of Q. By use of the differential calculus it can be shown that the above expression will be minimized if

$$Q^2 = \frac{K/\mu}{\tfrac{1}{2}k'_o} + \frac{k'_u}{\tfrac{1}{2}k'_o}\, g(R)$$

We shall start by guessing a value for R and using this formula to find the best Q for this R. We then put this Q in the condition for adding the jth unit to R:

$$P_{Po}(\tilde{r} \geq j) > \frac{k'_o Q}{k'_o Q + k'_u} = \frac{Q}{Q + k'_u/k'_o}$$

and find the best R for this Q. We then repeat the process starting from this new R and continue until no further improvement can be made in this way.

Example. In our previous example we arbitrarily set $Q = 12$. We shall now reexamine this problem and find the best value of Q. The basic data were:

$L = 8$ weeks,

$\mu = 4$ weeks,

$\dfrac{K}{\mu} = \$6.25,$

$k'_o = \$.105$ per unit per week,

$k'_u = \$7.95$ per week,

$m = \dfrac{L}{\mu} = 2.$

$\dfrac{K/\mu}{\tfrac{1}{2}k'_o} = 119,$

$\dfrac{k'_u}{k'_o} = 75.7$

$\dfrac{k'_u}{\tfrac{1}{2}k'_o} = 151,$

As our initial guess at a good value for R we take the expected demand during the lead time, which is $m = 2$ units.

First Approximation. With $R = 2$:

$$g(R) = m\, \mathrm{P}_{Po}(\tilde{r} \geq R) - R\, \mathrm{P}_{Po}(\tilde{r} > R)$$
$$= (2 \times .594) - (2 \times .323) = .542,$$
$$Q^2 = 119 + (151 \times .542) = 201,$$
$$Q = \sqrt{201} = 14,$$
$$\frac{Q}{Q + k_u'/k_o'} = \frac{Q}{Q + 75.7} = \frac{14}{89.7} = .156,$$
$$\mathrm{P}_{Po}(r \geq 3 | m = 2) = .323 > .156,$$
$$\mathrm{P}_{Po}(r \geq 4 | m = 2) = .143 < .156.$$

The first-approximation solution is $Q = 14$, $R = 3$.

Second Approximation. With $R = 3$:

$$g(R) = (2 \times .323) - (3 \times .143) = .217,$$
$$Q^2 = 119 + (151 \times .217) = 152,$$
$$Q = \sqrt{152} = 12,$$
$$\frac{Q}{Q + 75.7} = \frac{12}{87.7} = .137,$$
$$\mathrm{P}_{Po}(r \geq 4) = .143 > .137,$$
$$\mathrm{P}_{Po}(r \geq 5) = .053 < .137.$$

The second-approximation solution is $Q = 12$, $R = 4$.

Third Approximation. With $R = 4$:

$$g(R) = (2 \times .143) - (4 \times .053) = .074,$$
$$Q^2 = 119 + (151 \times .074) = 130,$$
$$Q = \sqrt{130} = 11,$$
$$\frac{Q}{Q + 75.7} = \frac{11}{86.7} = .127,$$
$$\mathrm{P}_{Po}(r \geq 4) = .143 > .127,$$
$$\mathrm{P}_{Po}(r \geq 5) = .053 < .127.$$

The third-approximation solution is $Q = 11$, $R = 4$; and since we know that $R = 4$ will lead back to $Q = 11$, we have now done all that we can do by this approximate method.

15.6.2   The Exact Solution

After having found approximations to the best values of Q and R by the method just described, we can find the exact solution by taking a very few values of Q in the neighborhood of the approximate solution and for each one finding the true optimum R and minimum expected cost by the method used in Section 15.5.2 above. In practice, however, this refinement is rarely required. Unless the approximate solution leads to a value of $g(R)$ which is substantial compared with Q, that is to an expected time out of stock which is substantial compared with the time required to use up one lot, restoration of this term to the denominator will have very little effect. We shall go on to find the exact solution of the example above simply to illustrate this point.

Example Continued. With $Q = 12$, we have already seen in Section 15.5.2 that the true best value of R is 3 and that with $R = 3$ the cost is $1.45 per week. With $Q = 11$, $R = 4$ (the last of the approximate solutions):

$$\tfrac{1}{2}(Q + 1) + (R - m) = 6 + 4 - 2 = 8,$$
$$k_o'Q = \$.105 \times 11 = \$1.155,$$

$$k_o'Q + k_u' = \$1.155 + \$7.95 = \$9.105,$$
$$\text{Expected TCPUT} = \frac{\$6.25 + (\$1.155 \times 8) + (\$9.105 \times .074)}{11 + .074}$$

$$= \frac{\$16.16}{11.074} = \$1.46 \text{ per week.}$$

To be sure that we have the lowest cost for $Q = 11$, we must try $R = 3$.

$$\tfrac{1}{2}(Q + 1) + (R - m) = 7,$$
$$\text{Expected TCPUT} = \frac{\$6.25 + (\$1.155 \times 7) + (\$9.105 \times .217)}{11 + .217}$$

$$= \frac{\$16.31}{11.217} = \$1.45 \text{ per week.}$$

Since this cost is lower than the cost with $R = 4$, we must try $R = 2$, but this time we obtain $1.57 as the cost per week. The best R for $Q = 11$ is thus $R = 3$, and the cost of $Q = 11$, $R = 3$ is identical to the cost of $Q = 12$, $R = 3$. *This equality shows that we are at the bottom of the cost curve: no better plan can be found than $R = 3$ and $Q = 11$ or 12.*

Total expected cost per week is shown in Table 15.2 for a variety of combinations of Q and R in the vicinity of the best combinations. This table is a good illustration of the fact that

In most practical problems of decision under uncertainty, reasonably small departures from the optimal decisions have an extremely small effect on total expected cost.

Table 15.2
Total Expected Cost per Week, Dollars

R	Q				
	10	11	12	13	14
2	1.60	1.57	1.55	1.54	1.54
3	1.47	1.45	1.45	1.45	1.46
4	1.47	1.46	1.46	1.47	1.48
5	1.53	1.52	1.53	1.54	1.56

15.7 Opportunity Loss and the Cost of Uncertainty

It would be extremely difficult to lay out a table of conditional opportunity losses for a problem of the kind we are studying in this chapter, and therefore it is not practical to compute expected opportunity loss by taking the expectation of conditional losses. On the other hand, it is very easy to find the expected cost of action under certainty and thus to find the expected loss of any decision by the method of Section 7.3.

15.7.1 Expected Cost under Certainty

Under certainty, there would never be any cost or loss due to stockouts or overlap; each new lot would arrive at the instant the first demand occurred after the exhaustion of the old lot, and the only costs ever incurred would be the cost of ordering and the cost of lot-size inventory. The *cost of ordering* is exactly the same under certainty as under uncertainty, but there is a slight difference in the *cost of lot-size inventory*. Because the new lot arrives at the instant there is a demand for the first piece in it, the expected time on the shelf is 0 for the first piece, 1μ for the second, 2μ for the third, . . . , $(Q - 1)\mu$ for the Qth, so that the average shelf time is

$$\frac{1}{Q} [0 + 1 + 2 + \cdots + (Q - 1)]\mu = \frac{Q - 1}{2}\, \mu.$$

From this we derive (cf. Section 15.4.1)

Cost of lot-size inventory $= \tfrac{1}{2}k_0'Q(Q - 1)\mu.$

There being no stockouts under certainty, the expected length of a cycle is simply $Q\mu$, and we thus obtain (cf. Sections 15.4.2 and 15.4.3)

$$\text{Expected TCPUT under certainty} = \frac{K/\mu + \tfrac{1}{2}k_0'Q(Q - 1)}{Q}.$$

By use of the calculus it can be shown that this cost is minimized by setting

$$Q^2 = \frac{K/\mu}{\tfrac{1}{2}k_0'}.$$

Applying these results to the example discussed in Section 15.6, we obtain for the optimal lot size under certainty

$$Q^2 = \frac{\$6.25}{\tfrac{1}{2} \times \$.105} = 119,$$
$$Q = \sqrt{119} = 11.$$

We can then compute

$$\text{TCPUT under certainty} = \frac{\$6.25 + (\tfrac{1}{2} \times \$.105 \times 11 \times 10)}{11}$$

$$= \$1.09 \text{ per week.}$$

15.7.2   Expected Loss and the Cost of Uncertainty

It is now a trivial problem to find the expected opportunity loss of any Q, R combination by subtracting cost under certainty from cost under that combination. Continuing with the same example, we see in Table 15.2 that expected cost with $Q = 10$, $R = 2$ is $1.60 per week; expected loss under this policy is therefore $1.60 − $1.09 = $.51 per week.

The *cost of uncertainty* is as usual the expected loss of the *best possible* decision under uncertainty. In Table 15.2 we saw that in our example the lowest possible cost under uncertainty is $1.45 per week, and therefore the cost of uncertainty is $1.45 − $1.09 = $.36 per week.

15.8   Applicability of the Results of This Chapter

The expression for total cost per unit of time in Section 15.4.3 above rests on a series of assumptions made during the course of the derivation. We now collect them together as a summary.

1. Lead time can be treated as known with certainty.
2. Demand is generated by a Poisson process.
3. The intensity of the process (average demand per unit of time) can be treated as known with certainty.
4. Either (a) demands which cannot be satisfied immediately are lost and have no effect on future demand, or (b) no demands can occur when there is no stock on hand.
5. The order quantity Q is greater than the reorder point R.

The meaning of most of these assumptions is quite obvious, but as regards the second and third the student should review the discussion in Section 13.4. Many "formulas" which have been publicized as panaceas for almost any problem of inventory control under uncertainty rest on the same basic assumption of a Poisson demand with known intensity which was made in this chapter. Such panaceas tend to be adopted in one situation because they are reported to have "worked" in another, but this is scarcely a rational basis for a decision. *A reasonable policy for inventory control can be determined only by consideration of what is known about the characteristics of demand and by analysis of a model which represents these characteristics with reasonable accuracy.*

One qualification must be attached to this final statement, however, and the qualification is an important one. If we abandon the Poisson model, we must—if we wish to be rational—adopt and analyze a more complex model. If the changes in actual inventory policy which result from improved knowledge are small, this reanalysis may well fail to reduce expected cost enough to pay for itself. We have already seen that when the Poisson model applies, the extra cost due to reasonably small departures from the best Q and R adds almost nothing to total expected cost. We have seen the same thing in our study of the effect of small departures from optimum scrap allowances, and we shall see the same thing repeatedly in other kinds of problems later in the course. If then in any inventory problem the exact model—the one which corresponds exactly to the beliefs of the responsible person—differs only slightly from a Poisson model, we suspect: first, that the exact solution for Q and R will differ only slightly from the values derived from the Poisson model; and second, that the extra expected cost due to using the Poisson Q and R instead of the best values will be negligible. In such a situation the course of action which minimizes the total of *all* costs, including the cost of analysis, may well be to follow the policies dictated by the simple Poisson model.

PROBLEMS

1. Compute the expected number of pieces left over at receipt of a new lot when the reorder point is 2 units, the lead time is 2 weeks, and demand averages .3 unit per week:

    a. By the method of Table 15.1.

    b. By use of the formula $R - m + g(R)$.

2. How large is the "safety stock" in the situation of Problem 1?

3. Compute the expected time of overlap for the situation of Problem 1.

4. For this same situation with $Q = 20$, compute:

    a. Expected time out of stock.

    b. Expected length of cycle.

Since there is no overlap if the old stock *is* all sold before the new lot arrives and there is no stockout if the old stock is *not* sold, how can their expected values both be positive?

5. If in the situation of Problems 1 to 4 it costs $2 per week to carry an item in inventory while $6 is lost every time it is impossible to satify a demand, compute the expected cost per cycle of:

    a. "Safety stock."   *b.* Overlap inventory.

    c. Lot-size inventory.   *d.* Unsatisfied demand.

Which of these four items must be omitted in adding to get *total* expected cost per cycle?

6. Assuming that it costs $10 to place and process each order, compute the total expected cost *per cycle* and the total expected cost *per week* in the situation of Problem 5.

7. Verify the statement at the end of Section 15.5.2 that with $Q = 12$ and $R = 2$ the expected cost per week is $1.55 for the example in the text.

8. In August, 1956, the Gridley Machine Works was short of capital owing to a rapid expansion of business during the year. The company's treasurer asked all departments to keep inventories to a minimum; he announced that every dollar's worth of inventory kept for a year cost the company 30 cents in storage charges and opportunities lost through lack of availability of capital.

At the same time, management was concerned about rising costs in the purchasing and accounting departments. A careful investigation including a time study had shown that the directly traceable cost (clerical labor, mail, and supplies) of placing, receiving, inspecting, and paying for an order amounted to about $15 per order. The total cost, including both departmental and general burden, came to about $25 per order.

Gridley's heavy machinery was subjected to unusual stresses, and breakage of parts often resulted. The company's experience on its Hynes heavy-duty engine lathe was fairly typical. Gridley owned one such machine, which was in almost constant use; part XB411 had broken 72 times in the past 5 years. The failures seemed to be caused by accidental stresses rather than by gradual wear; at least, the shop foreman stated that he was completely unable to predict when a failure would occur.

A very large part of the products manufactured by Gridley required some machining on the Hynes lathe, and if the part on the machine broke when no spare was on hand, a replacement was manufactured immediately in the toolroom. Although the part cost only $20 when bought from Hynes, production in the toolroom cost about $100 owing to the lack of specialized tools and fixtures. There was a 2-month lead time on all parts supplied by Hynes.

Find the optimum min-max inventory policy for Gridley and compute the cost of uncertainty. (HINT: Inventory in this problem should be defined to *exclude* the part actually in use on the lathe. Why?)

CHAPTER 16

Measures of Dispersion: The Variance and the Standard Deviation

In Chapter 5 we saw that for some purposes we did not need to know the full detail of a frequency or probability distribution because we could reach the best decision or compute the expected cost of any decision by knowing only the proper measure of the *location* of the distribution on the horizontal axis. For some other purposes the distribution can be replaced by a measure of its "spread," "scatter," or *dispersion*, or by such a measure together with a measure of location.

By far the most important measures of the dispersion of probability distributions are the variance and its square root, the standard deviation; and these are the only measures which we shall study in this course. We shall, however, begin our study of the variance and standard deviation as summary measures in the same way that we began our study of measures of location: we shall first define and compute them from a complete list of actually observed values, and we shall then show how to compute them from relative frequencies or probabilities.

16.1 Definition of the Variance and Standard Deviation

It naturally occurs to us that the dispersion of a set of values might logically be measured by

1. Selecting some *central value* such as the mean,
2. Computing the *absolute magnitude of the difference* between this central value and each individual value in the set,
3. *Averaging* these "absolute deviations."

Actually, however, it turns out that very few practical problems can be solved by use of the particular measure of dispersion defined by these operations.

16.1.1 The Variance

A much more useful measure is obtained if instead of averaging the deviations themselves we average the *squares of the deviations*, and accordingly we define the

Variance of a set of values: the arithmetic average of the *squares* of the differences between the individual values and the mean value.

As an example, let us use the data of Table 5.1. The mean of the values in this table is 2.7, and therefore the variance is $\frac{1}{10}[(2 - 2.7)^2 + (4 - 2.7)^2 + (0 - 2.7)^2 + (2 - 2.7)^2 + (4 - 2.7)^2 + (3 - 2.7)^2 + (3 - 2.7)^2 + (1 - 2.7)^2 + (3 - 2.7)^2 + (5 - 2.7)^2] = \frac{1}{10}(.49 + 1.69 + 7.29 + .49 + 1.69 + .09 + .09 + 2.89 + .09 + 5.29) = 20.10/10 = 2.01$.

16.1.2 The Standard Deviation

The variance measures the dispersion of a set of values in rather peculiar units. The variance of the set of values of number defective computed just above comes out as 2.01 defectives-squared; the variance of a set of heights of men would come out in inches-squared or something of the sort. It is often more convenient to have a measure of dispersion which is in the same units as the variable itself—in number of defectives or in inches or feet. Therefore we very commonly use as our measure of dispersion the

Standard deviation: the square root of the variance.

The standard deviation of the values of number defective in our example is $\sqrt{2.01} = 1.42$.

16.2 Computation of the Variance from Relative Frequencies or Probabilities

The variance of a set of values can be computed by using their *relative frequencies* as *weights* in exactly the same way that the mean is computed by the use of relative frequencies as weights. The student should review the procedure for computation of the mean as described in Section 5.2.2 before proceeding further in the present chapter.

Let us reexamine the computation of the variance of the values in Table 5.1 as we carried it out above. If we rearrange the data in order of increasing value of the variable we have Table 16.1. The variance is the *average* square, or $20.10/10 = 2.01$.

Instead of writing down two identical rows for the value 2, three rows for 3, and two rows for 4, we can get the same result by writing the square of each value of the deviation once and weighting it by the number of times that the value occurs. This is done in Table 16.2, and again we get the variance by dividing the *sum of squares* by the *sum of the weights*, i.e. by the total number of occurrences. Furthermore we will still get exactly the same result if, instead of dividing the total of the last column by 10, we divide each of the individual products by 10; and instead of doing that, we can divide each of the numbers of occurrences by 10

Table 16.1

Value of the random variable	Deviation	Deviation squared
0	−2.7	7.29
1	−1.7	2.89
2	− .7	.49
2	− .7	.49
3	+ .3	.09
3	+ .3	.09
3	+ .3	.09
4	+1.3	1.69
4	+1.3	1.69
5	+2.3	5.29
		20.10

Table 16.2

Value of the random variable	Deviation	Deviation squared	Number of occurrences	Product
0	−2.7	7.29	1	7.29
1	−1.7	2.89	1	2.89
2	− .7	.49	2	.98
3	+ .3	.09	3	.27
4	+1.3	1.69	2	3.38
5	+2.3	5.29	1	5.29
			10	20.10

Table 16.3

Deviation squared	Number of occurrences divided by 10	Product
7.29	.1	.729
2.89	.1	.289
.49	.2	.098
.09	.3	.027
1.69	.2	.338
5.29	.1	.529
	1.0	2.010

before computing the products. The last three columns of Table 16.2 would then be as shown in Table 16.3; and since the sum of the weights is now 1, the variance is simply the total in the last column.

We now observe that the entries in the second column of Table 16.3 are simply the relative frequencies of the corresponding values of the random variable, and generalizing we conclude that

The variance is computed from a frequency distribution by computing the squared deviations from the mean of the distribution, weighting them by their relative frequencies, and adding these products. Since relative frequencies always add to 1, the sum of the weights is 1 and there is no need to divide by it to get the weighted average.

No new problems arise when we wish to compute the variance of a probability distribution:

The variance of a probability distribution is computed by using the probabilities in exactly the same way that relative frequencies are used in computing the variance of a frequency distribution.

When the random variable is *continuous*, the variance can be approximated by constructing a grouped distribution and treating all the probability in a bracket as belonging to the value of the variable at the midpoint of the bracket. The true variance is defined as the limit of this approximate value as the brackets become narrower and narrower.†

Notation. It is standard practice to use the symbol σ (sigma) to denote the standard deviation of a random variable; when necessary, we shall add the name of the variable in parentheses. Thus:

$\sigma(\tilde{z}) =$ standard deviation of the random variable $\tilde{z}$,

$\sigma^2(\tilde{z}) =$ variance of the random variable $\tilde{z}$.

16.3 Mean and Variance of a Sum of Random Variables

In the great majority of the problems which we shall encounter in the remainder of this course we shall need to know the expectation and variance of a random variable which is the *sum* of a number of other random variables—e.g., the mean and variance of the total length of three intervals when the length of each individual interval is itself a random variable. There is never any difficulty in finding the *expectation* of such a sum when the expectations of the individual variables included in the sum are known, since it can easily be proved that

The expectation of a sum of random variables is the sum of their individual expectations.

In symbols:

$$E(\tilde{x} + \tilde{y} + \tilde{z} + \cdots) = E(\tilde{x}) + E(\tilde{y}) + E(\tilde{z}) + \cdots$$

Any random variables

† Cf. Section 14.4 on the *mean* of a continuous distribution.

This proposition applies to *all random variables without restriction*, and it appeals immediately to our intuition. The expected total length of three intervals is simply the sum of the expected lengths of the three individual intervals.

We shall now state a somewhat similar proposition about the *variance* of a sum of random variables, but before even stating it we call attention to the fact that *this* proposition does *not* apply to *all* sums of random variables. It does apply, however, when the random variables in the sum are *independent*,† and we shall have very frequent occasion to make use of it in this connection. The proposition is the following:

The variance of a sum of independent random variables is the sum of their individual variances.†

In symbols:

$$\sigma^2(\tilde{x} + \tilde{y} + \tilde{z} + \cdots) = \sigma^2(\tilde{x}) + \sigma^2(\tilde{y}) + \sigma^2(\tilde{z}) + \cdots$$
$$Independent\dagger \ random \ variables$$

This is the reason for the great importance of the variance as a measure of dispersion: no other measure of dispersion has this "additive" property.

In particular, the *standard deviation* is *not* additive:

The standard deviation of a sum of random variables is obtained by taking the square root of the variance of the sum.

16.4   Means and Variances of Four Common Distributions

In Chapters 10 to 14 we have studied two simple but extremely important random processes:

1. The *Bernoulli process*, which generates a series of distinct trials with a constant probability of a success on each trial.
2. The *Poisson process*, which generates a "space" in which the probability of a success is constant from "point" to "point."

For each of the two processes we have studied two different probability distributions:

† The proposition actually applies even when the random variables in the sum are *not* independent provided only that they are *uncorrelated*, but the subject of correlation is beyond the scope of this course and we shall have little occasion to deal with sums of random variables which are dependent but uncorrelated.

1. The distribution of the *number of successes* in a specified number of trials or amount of space.

2. The distribution of the *number of trials or amount of space* required to secure a specified number of successes.

We have thus been led to study *four common probability distributions:*

For the Bernoulli process: the *binomial* distribution of $\tilde{r}$ given n and the *Pascal* distribution of $\tilde{n}$ given r;

For the Poisson process: the *Poisson* distribution of $\tilde{r}$ given t and the *gamma* distribution of $\tilde{t}$ given r.

The variance of each of these distributions will be needed later in the course, and we shall now proceed to give the required formulas, proving them where we can without the use of mathematics.

16.4.1 Binomial Distribution

Let us first consider the binomial distribution of the number of successes on *one* trial. If we arbitrarily assign the *value* 1 to a success and the *value* 0 to a failure, we can say that the event of a single trial determines the value of a *random variable* $\tilde{x}$. The *expectation* of this random variable is computed in Table 16.4 in the same way in which we compute the expectation of any random variable, and we find that $E(\tilde{x}) = p$.

Table 16.4

Value of the random variable x	Probability $P(x)$	Expectation $x\,P(x)$
0	q	0
1	$\dfrac{p}{1}$	$\dfrac{p}{p}$

The method of Table 16.3 above can now be used to compute the variance of this random variable $\tilde{x}$. The work is shown in Table 16.5, where the variance is the total of the last column. Since $p + q = 1$, this total reduces to pq.

Table 16.5

Value x of the random variable	Deviation $x - E(\tilde{x})$	Deviation squared	Probability $P(x)$	Product
0	$0 - p = -p$	p^2	q	$p^2 q = p(pq)$
1	$1 - p = q$	q^2	$\dfrac{p}{1}$	$\dfrac{q^2 p = q(pq)}{(p + q)pq}$

The reason for assigning "values" to successes and failures is simply that it permits us to regard the number of successes $\tilde{r}$ in any number n

of Bernoulli trials as *the sum of the values of n random variables* $\tilde{x}_1$, $\tilde{x}_2$, . . . , $\tilde{x}_n$ *describing the individual trials*—if there are three successes in 10 trials, 3 trials have value 1, 7 trials have value 0, and the sum of these 10 values is 3. Consequently the addition theorem for expectations tells us that

$$E(\tilde{r}) = E(\tilde{x}_1) + E(\tilde{x}_2) + \cdots + E(\tilde{x}_n).$$

We have seen that $E(\tilde{x}) = p$, and therefore we have now proved the result which was simply asserted in Section 11.3.1: if n Bernoulli trials all have the same probability p of success, then

$$E(\tilde{r}) = np.$$

Since Bernoulli trials are *independent* by definition, we can also apply the addition theorem for variances to get the variance of the binomial distribution for the number of successes $\tilde{r}$ in any number of trials n with constant probability p. Since the random variable $\tilde{x}$ describing any one trial has variance pq, we have immediately

$$\sigma^2(\tilde{r}) = npq \qquad \textit{Binomial distribution}$$

16.4.2 Poisson Distribution

In Chapter 13 we derived the Poisson distribution with parameter $m = \kappa t$, where κ is the mean number of successes per unit of "space" and t is the amount of space. To do this we considered a binomial distribution with $np = m$ and then observed what happens to this distribution if n increases while p decreases in such a way as to keep $np = m$ constant. Now as p decreases toward 0, $q = 1 - p$ obviously increases approaching 1; and since np remains constant the variance npq of the binomial distribution approaches $np = \kappa t = m$. Thus

$$\sigma^2(\tilde{r}) = \kappa t = m \qquad \textit{Poisson distribution}$$

Notice that *the variance of a Poisson distribution is equal to its mean.*

16.4.3 Pascal Distribution

It can be shown by algebra that the variance of the number of trials $\tilde{n}$ required to secure *one* Bernoulli success is q/p^2. The number of trials required to secure r successes is the sum of r such numbers, and since these r numbers are independent random variables with variances q/p^2,

$$\sigma^2(\tilde{n}) = \frac{rq}{p^2} \qquad \textit{Pascal distribution}$$

16.4.4   Gamma Distribution

It can be shown that the variance of the space $\tilde{l}$ required to secure one Poisson success is μ^2, where $\mu = 1/\kappa$ is the mean space required.† The space required to secure r successes is the sum of r such spaces; and since they are independent random variables with variance μ^2,

$$\sigma^2(\tilde{l}) = r\mu^2 \qquad Gamma\ distribution$$

This distribution of the space $\tilde{l}$ is, of course, the *nonstandardized* gamma distribution which was discussed at the beginning of Section 14.3 and not the standardized distribution discussed in Section 14.3.1.

16.5   Changes of Location and Scale

Very frequently we are interested in the distribution of a random variable each of whose values is obtained by taking a value of some other variable and:

1. Adding (or subtracting) a fixed number, or
2. Multiplying (or dividing) by a fixed number,

or both. Changes of the first sort are known as changes in the *location* of the original distribution; changes of the latter sort are known as changes in the *scale* of the original distribution.

16.5.1   Changes of Location

Suppose that a random variable $\tilde{z}$ has the distribution shown by the left-hand curve in Figure 16.1a, and that we define a new random variable $\tilde{y}$ by

$$\tilde{y} = \tilde{z} + b,$$

where b is a fixed constant. As a concrete example, imagine a set of steel rods of *various* lengths z and a set of couplings all of the *same* length $b = 4$ inches. If one coupling is attached to each rod, the total length of rod plus coupling is the value of the new random variable $\tilde{y}$.

It is obvious that the distribution of $\tilde{y}$, which is shown by the right-hand curve in Figure 16.1a, must be identical in all respects to the distribution of $\tilde{z}$ except that it is shifted along the horizontal axis by the amount $b = 4$ inches. Since every individual value is increased by the same amount b, the average or *mean* of the values is increased by b.

---

† This can be shown either by the use of calculus or by a limiting process like the one used in Section 14.1.1 to derive the *mean* of the exponential distribution from the mean of the Pascal.

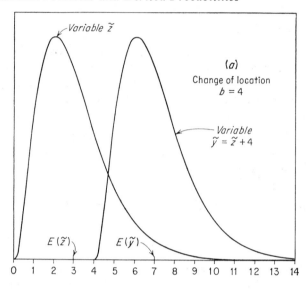

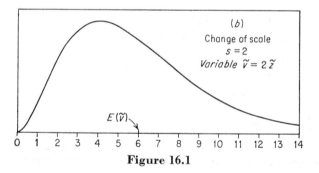

Figure 16.1

Consequently the *differences or deviations between the individual values and their mean* are not changed at all; and since the *variance* is the average of the squares of these deviations, the variance is not changed at all. To summarize:

Adding a fixed amount to or subtracting a fixed amount from every value of a random variable
1. Changes the *mean* of the distribution *by this same amount;*
2. *Has no effect* on the variance or standard deviation.

The Distribution of Residuals. Perhaps the most common problems in which we make use of the two conclusions just stated are problems in which we are interested in the distribution of *the difference between the individual values of some random variable and the expected value of the variable.* Such differences will be called *residuals* and will be denoted by the symbol epsilon: we define

$$\tilde{\epsilon} = \tilde{z} - E(\tilde{z}),$$

where $\tilde{z}$ denotes any random variable in which we are interested. Applied to the distribution of $\tilde{\epsilon}$, our two conclusions become

$$E(\tilde{\epsilon}) = E(\tilde{z}) - E(\tilde{z}) = 0;$$
$$\sigma^2(\tilde{\epsilon}) = \sigma^2(\tilde{z}); \qquad \sigma(\tilde{\epsilon}) = \sigma(\tilde{z}).$$

As an example, consider the random variable "number defective" in a run of n pieces produced by a Bernoulli process with parameter p. The expected number of defectives is

$$E(\tilde{r}) = np,$$

and the residuals are defined by

$$\tilde{\epsilon} = \tilde{r} - np;$$

they are the differences between the *actual* number defective and the *expected* number defective. What we have just shown is that the *expected residual* or mean of the distribution of residuals is 0 while the *variance* $\sigma^2(\tilde{\epsilon})$ and standard deviation $\sigma(\tilde{\epsilon})$ of the distribution of residuals are identical to the variance $\sigma^2(\tilde{r})$ and standard deviation $\sigma(\tilde{r})$ of the original variable "number defective."

16.5.2 Changes of Scale

Consider once again the random variable $\tilde{z}$ which has the frequency distribution sketched in Figure 16.1a and suppose that we define a new variable $\tilde{v}$ by

$$\tilde{v} = s\tilde{z},$$

where s is a fixed positive constant. As a concrete example think of a set of containers of various capacities and let the variable $\tilde{z}$ denote the capacities as measured in *quarts* while $\tilde{v}$ denotes the capacities as measured in *pints*. Then $s = 2$: a container which holds 1.75 quarts holds $2 \times 1.75 = 3.50$ pints.

It is obvious that the distribution of $\tilde{v}$ as sketched in Figure 16.1b will be the same as the distribution of $\tilde{z}$ except that it is *uniformly stretched out:* each value of $\tilde{v}$ is s times as far from $v = 0$ as the corresponding value of $\tilde{z}$ is from $z = 0$. Since every single value in the distribution is multiplied by s, the average or *mean* of the values is multiplied by this same factor s.

It follows that the *difference between any value and the mean* is also multiplied by this same factor s and that the *squares* of these differences are multiplied by s^2. Since the variance is the average of these squared differences, every one of which is multiplied by s^2, the variance is also multiplied by s^2. Then since the standard deviation is the square root of the variance, it follows that the standard deviation is multiplied by s. To summarize:

Multiplying (or dividing) every value in a distribution by the same positive factor s
1. Multiplies (or divides) the *mean* and *standard deviation* by s;
2. Multiplies (or divides) the *variance* by s^2.

Distribution of Standardized Variables. The two conclusions just stated show the following relations between various summary measures of the distributions of the standardized gamma variable $\tilde{v} = \tilde{t}/\mu$ studied in Section 14.3.1 and the corresponding measures of the distributions of the "natural" gamma variable $\tilde{t}$.

$$\mathrm{E}(\tilde{v}) = \frac{1}{\mu}\,\mathrm{E}(\tilde{t});$$

$$\sigma(\tilde{v}) = \frac{1}{\mu}\,\sigma(\tilde{t});$$

$$\sigma^2(\tilde{v}) = \frac{1}{\mu^2}\,\sigma^2(\tilde{t}).$$

If we make use of the results derived in Section 14.4 for $\mathrm{E}(\tilde{t})$ and in this chapter (Section 16.4.4) for $\sigma^2(\tilde{t})$, we can go on:

$$\mathrm{E}(\tilde{v}) = \frac{1}{\mu}\,\mathrm{E}(\tilde{t}) = \frac{1}{\mu}\,r\mu = r;$$

$$\sigma^2(\tilde{v}) = \frac{1}{\mu^2}\,r\mu^2 = r;$$

$$\sigma(\tilde{v}) = \sqrt{r}.$$

16.5.3 Both Changes Together

In Chapter 17 we shall begin our use of an extremely important standardized random variable $\tilde{u}$ defined by

$$\tilde{u} = \frac{\tilde{z} - \mathrm{E}(\tilde{z})}{\sigma(\tilde{z})}$$

where $\tilde{z}$ denotes any random variable in which we are interested. To find the relations between the mean, variance, and standard deviation of $\tilde{u}$ and the corresponding measures of the natural random variable $\tilde{z}$, let us think of each value of $\tilde{u}$ as being calculated in two steps:
1. Compute the residual $\epsilon = z - \mathrm{E}(\tilde{z})$;
2. Compute $u = \epsilon/\sigma(\tilde{z})$.

The first of these steps is simply a *change of location*, and we already know that

$$\mathrm{E}(\tilde{\epsilon}) = 0,$$
$$\sigma(\tilde{\epsilon}) = \sigma(\tilde{z}), \qquad \sigma^2(\tilde{\epsilon}) = \sigma^2(\tilde{z}).$$

The second step is a *change of scale*, the quantity $1/\sigma(\tilde{z})$ playing the role of the factor s in our original discussion of such changes, and therefore

$$E(\tilde{u}) = \frac{1}{\sigma(\tilde{z})}\, E(\tilde{\epsilon}) = \frac{0}{\sigma(\tilde{z})} = 0,$$

$$\sigma(\tilde{u}) = \frac{1}{\sigma(\tilde{z})}\, \sigma(\tilde{\epsilon}) = \frac{\sigma(\tilde{z})}{\sigma(\tilde{z})} = 1,$$

$$\sigma^2(\tilde{u}) = \frac{1}{\sigma^2(\tilde{z})}\, \sigma^2(\tilde{\epsilon}) = \frac{\sigma^2(\tilde{z})}{\sigma^2(\tilde{z})} = 1.$$

16.6 Summary; Conspectus of Formulas

16.6.1 Definitions

The *variance* is the mean of the *squares* of the deviations of a set of values from their mean value.

The *standard deviation* is the square root of the variance.

16.6.2 Additivity

The *expected value* of the sum of any random variables whatever is the sum of the individual expected values.

The *variance* of a sum of *independent* random variables is the sum of the individual variances.†

No other measure of dispersion is additive; the standard deviation of a sum of random variables is obtained by taking the square root of the variance of the sum.

16.6.3 Change of Location

If the same amount b is *added* to every value of a random variable:

The mean of the distribution or expected value of the variable is increased by b.

The variance and standard deviation are unchanged.

16.6.4 Change of Scale

If every value of a random variable is *multiplied* by the same positive factor s:

The mean and standard deviation of the distribution are multiplied by s.

The variance of the distribution is multiplied by s^2.

† See footnote in Section 16 3

16.6.5   Means and Variances of Common Distributions

Bernoulli Process with Parameter p

$$q = 1 - p$$

Binomial distribution: number of successes in n trials $\qquad$ $E(\tilde{r}) = np$

$\sigma^2(\tilde{r}) = npq$

Pascal distribution: number of trials to secure r successes $\qquad$ $E(\tilde{n}) = r/p$

$\sigma^2(\tilde{n}) = rq/p^2$

Poisson Process with Intensity κ

$$\mu = 1/\kappa$$

Poisson distribution: number of successes in space t $\qquad$ $E(\tilde{r}) = \kappa t$

$\sigma^2(\tilde{r}) = \kappa t$

Gamma distribution: space required to secure r successes $\qquad$ $E(\tilde{t}) = r\mu$

$\sigma^2(\tilde{t}) = r\mu^2$

PROBLEMS

1. Show that the mean, variance, and standard deviation of the *fractions defective* in Table 8.7 are respectively .232, .00191, and .0437.

2. Compute the mean, variance, and standard deviation of the *ratios total-to-good* in Table 8.7.

3. One box contains 10 tickets numbered 1, 2, . . . , 10. A second box contains three tickets numbered 3, three tickets numbered 5, and three tickets numbered 7. You draw one ticket from each box and are paid $2 times the sum of the numbers on your tickets. Compute the mean, variance, and standard deviation of each of the following random variables:

a. Number on first ticket.
b. Number on second ticket.
c. Sum of the two numbers.
d. Dollar amount received.

4. The random variable $\tilde{z}_1$ has standard deviation $\sigma(\tilde{z}_1) = 3$. The random variable $\tilde{z}_2$ has standard deviation $\sigma(\tilde{z}_2) = 4$. The two variables are independent.

a. What is the standard deviation of the random variable $\tilde{S} = \tilde{z}_1 + \tilde{z}_2$? (Be careful: are standard deviations additive?)

b. What is the standard deviation of the random variable $\tilde{D} = \tilde{z}_1 - \tilde{z}_2$? [HINT: The *difference* $\tilde{z}_1 - \tilde{z}_2$ can be considered as the *sum* of the random variables $\tilde{z}_1$ and $(-\tilde{z}_2)$. What is the effect of the *negative* scale factor (-1)?]

5. One automatic screw machine is used to produce shafts and another to produce bushings one of which is assembled over each shaft. The mean diameter of the shafts is 1.000 inch; the mean inside diameter of the bushings is 1.002 inches; and the standard deviation of either set of diameters is .001 inch.

a. Compute the mean *clearance* (bushing diameter minus shaft diameter) and the standard deviation of the distribution of clearances on the assumption that assembly is random—i.e., bushings are not *selected* to fit the shafts on which they are placed.

b. What can you say about the clearances if assembly *is* selective?

6. The probability distributions of three random variables $\tilde{x}$, $\tilde{y}$, and $\tilde{z}$ are given in the following table. Compute the mean, variance and standard deviation of each.

x	$P(x)$	y	$P(y)$	z	$P(z)$
0	.29	0	.29	3	.29
1	.49	5	.49	4	.49
2	.16	10	.16	5	.16
3	.05	15	.05	6	.05
4	.01	20	.01	7	.01
	1.00		1.00		1.00

7. Derive formulas for the mean, variance, and standard deviation of the following random variables:

a. $\bar{x} = \tilde{r}/n$, where r is the number of successes in n Bernoulli trials with known parameter p. This random variable $\bar{x}$ (read: x bar) is the *fraction* defective in a production lot.

b. The ratio $\bar{x}/p$, where $\bar{x}$ is defined as in (a); this is the ratio of lot fraction defective to process fraction defective.

c. The ratio $\tilde{n}/r$, where $\tilde{n}$ is the number of Bernoulli trials with known parameter p which are required to secure r successes.

8. *a.* Compute the mean, variance, and standard deviation of the binomial distribution of *number* of defectives $\tilde{r}$ for $p = .232$ and $n = 100$, 1000, and 5000.

b. For these same values of n compute the mean, variance, and standard deviation of the *fraction* defective.

9. *a.* Compute the mean, variance, and standard deviation of the Pascal *number* of trials $\tilde{n}$ for $p = .232$ and $r = 100$, 1000, and 5000.

b. For these same values of r compute the mean, variance, and standard deviation of the *ratio* $\tilde{n}/r$.

10. If $\tilde{p}$ is the unknown *fraction* defective of a Bernoulli *process*, if $\tilde{r}/n$ is the unknown *fraction* defective in a *lot* or run produced by this process, and if we define the residual $\tilde{\epsilon} = \tilde{r}/n - \tilde{p}$, we can write

$$\frac{\tilde{r}}{n} = \tilde{p} + \tilde{\epsilon}.$$

The random variables $\tilde{p}$ and $\tilde{\epsilon}$ are *not* independent, as can easily be seen by remembering that for any *given* p the *conditional* variance of $\tilde{\epsilon}$ is $\sigma^2(\tilde{\epsilon}) = pq/n$, but it can nevertheless be proved that $\tilde{p}$ and $\tilde{\epsilon}$ are *uncorrelated*. Consequently (Section 16.3, footnote)

$$\sigma^2\left(\frac{\tilde{r}}{n}\right) = \sigma^2(\tilde{p}) + \sigma^2(\tilde{\epsilon}):$$

the variance of the lot fraction defective is the variance of the process fraction defective *plus* the Bernoulli variance of the difference between the lot fraction and the process fraction. The variance $\sigma^2(\tilde{\epsilon})$ appearing in this last formula is of course not the conditional variance for given p but the *expected* or *marginal* variance obtained by computing the conditional variance for every possible p and then taking a weighted average of these conditional variances with the probabilities $P(p)$ used as the weights. It can be shown that this expected or weighted-average Bernoulli variance is given by the formula

$$\sigma^2(\tilde{\epsilon}) = \frac{1}{n}\{E(\tilde{p})[1 - E(\tilde{p})] - \sigma^2(\tilde{p})\}.$$

Making use of your answer to Problem 1 above, discuss the legitimacy of neglecting Bernoulli variance in Section 8.2.

CHAPTER 17

The Normal Approximation to Distributions of Sums of Random Variables

Now that we are acquainted with the idea of a continuous distribution and with the definition of the standard deviation of any distribution, we are ready to take up the so-called Normal distribution. This is by far the most important of all probability distributions. Although our beliefs about the real world are never quite so exactly described by the Normal distribution as they sometimes are by such distributions as the binomial or the Poisson, the Normal distribution is an excellent *approximation* to a wide variety of real distributions of great practical importance; and at the same time it is exceptionally manageable mathematically. In this chapter we shall see that under a wide range of conditions the Normal distribution can be used as an approximation to every distribution which we have studied so far, and as the course proceeds we shall find that it can be used as an approximation to still other distributions.

17.1 Behavior of the Binomial Distribution as n Increases

Figure 17.1 shows histograms of the binomial distributions for $p = .1$ and $.5$ and for $n = 10$, 20, and 50. It is obvious from the figure that as n increases the outline of the histogram for either value of p becomes smoother and smoother, but the figure is hard to interpret because both the location and the dispersion of the distributions change as n increases; the values of the mean $E(\tilde{r})$ and the standard deviation $\sigma(\tilde{r})$ of the six distributions are shown in Table 17.1 and indicated graphically in the figure.

Figure 17.2 is drawn to show exactly the same distributions lined up with their means above each other and with the r scales chosen in such a way that the standard deviations of all the distributions are represented by the *same* width on the paper. The *same* smooth curve is superimposed on each of these histograms, and it appears that for either value of p *the histogram approaches this curve as n increases.* It can be proved that this is true: for any value of p there is some value of n above which the differ-

Table 17.1

p = .1			p = .5		
n	E($\tilde{r}$) = pn	$\sigma(\tilde{r}) = \sqrt{npq}$	n	E($\tilde{r}$) = pn	$\sigma(\tilde{r}) = \sqrt{npq}$
10	1	.95	10	5	1.58
20	2	1.34	20	10	2.24
50	5	2.12	50	25	3.54

ence between the histogram and the curve is smaller, at all points, than any specified amount however small.

17.2   The Normal Distribution

The distributions depicted by the smooth curves in Figure 17.1 (not Figure 17.2) are *Normal* distributions defined by the formula

$$P'(r) = \frac{1}{\sigma(\tilde{r}) \sqrt{2\pi}} \exp \left\{ -\frac{1}{2} \left[\frac{r - E(\tilde{r})}{\sigma(\tilde{r})} \right]^2 \right\}.$$

The mean and standard deviation of each of these continuous distributions are E($\tilde{r}$) and $\sigma(\tilde{r})$; i.e. they are equal to the mean and standard deviation of the binomial distribution to which the Normal distribution is fitted. These two quantities are the *parameters* of the Normal distribution, just as r and μ are the parameters of the nonstandardized gamma distribution (cf. Section 14.3); the formula given above thus defines a whole *family* of distributions—one for every possible combination of values of E($\tilde{r}$) and $\sigma(\tilde{r}$).

17.2.1   *The Standardized Random Variable* $\tilde{u}$

The fact that the binomial distribution approaches the Normal distribution as a limiting form means that binomial probabilities can be approximated by use of the Normal distribution when n is large enough. The area of any individual bar in Figure 17.1 can be approximated by multiplying its width, which is 1, by the height of the Normal curve at the center of the bar; the area of all the bars to the left or right of any specified point on the r axis of any one of these histograms is approximated by the area under the Normal curve to the left or right of the same point.

The general form of the Normal distribution as defined by the formula given above is of course of no *practical* use for this purpose, since it is no easier to compute an ordinate or tail area of the Normal distribution than to compute an ordinate or tail area of a binomial histogram, and tabulation of the Normal distribution would be just as difficult as tabulation of the binomial if we had to have a table or chart for every possible Normal curve, i.e. for every possible combination of values for E($\tilde{r}$) and $\sigma(\tilde{r}$). We can get around this difficulty very easily, however, by using the same device which we used in connection with the gamma distribution: we *change the units in which the variable is measured* and in this way obtain a *standardized* distribution which contains fewer parameters. In the case of the gamma distribution we got rid of the parameter μ by using

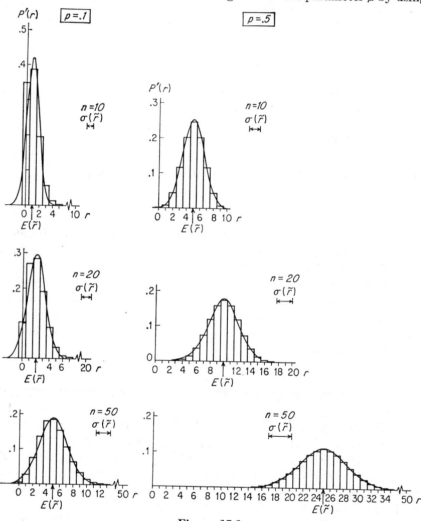

Figure 17.1

the standardized variable $\tilde{v} = \tilde{t}/\mu$; the distribution of this variable has only the one parameter r. In our present problem we can do even better: by using the standardized variable

$$\tilde{u} = \frac{\tilde{r} - \mathrm{E}(\tilde{r})}{\sigma(\tilde{r})},$$

we will end up with a distribution which has no parameters at all.

In addition to values of the "natural" variable $\tilde{r}$, the horizontal axes in Figure 17.2 show the corresponding values of $\tilde{u}$ computed from this definition.   The vertical axes of this figure show values of $P'(u)$ only, not of $P'(r)$.   Figure 17.2 is thus really a set of histograms of *distributions of* $\tilde{u}$ whereas Figure 17.1 is a set of histograms of *distributions of* $\tilde{r}$.   To

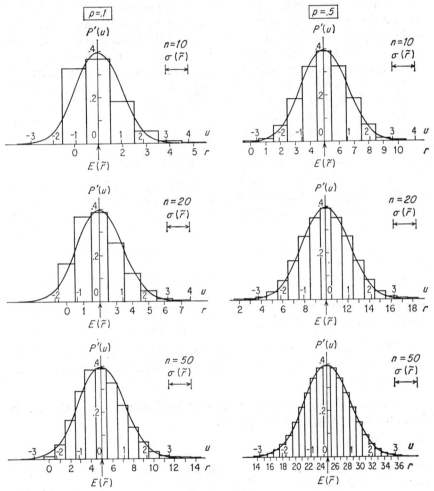

Figure 17.2

understand the differences between the values of $P'(r)$ shown in Figure 17.1 and the corresponding values of $P'(u)$ shown in Figure 17.2, consider the distribution for $n = 10$, $p = .5$—the upper right-hand histogram in each figure—and look at the bar for $r = 5$ $(u = 0)$.

   1. In the r histogram (Figure 17.1), the *height* of the bar for $r = 5$ is shown as .245; its edges are at $r = 4.5$ and $r = 5.5$ so that its *width* is 1; and its *area* is therefore .245 $\times$ 1 = .245.

2. If we had graphed a histogram of the *residuals* $r - \mathrm{E}(\tilde{r})$, this histogram would have looked exactly like the histogram of Figure 17.1 except that all the values on the horizontal scale would have been diminished by $\mathrm{E}(\tilde{r}) = 5$. The widths of the bars would still have been 1 and the heights would therefore have been exactly as shown in Figure 17.1.

3. When the horizontal scale of the histogram for $n = 10$, $p = .5$ was labeled with values of $\bar{u}$ in Figure 17.2, each of these residuals was divided by $\sigma(\tilde{r}) = 1.58$ and therefore the width of each bar was divided by $\sigma(\tilde{r}) = 1.58$: the *width of any bar in this u histogram is* $1/\sigma(\tilde{r}) = 1/1.58$. The *heights* of all the bars in this histogram have therefore been multiplied by this same number $\sigma(\tilde{r}) = 1.58$ in order to keep the areas unchanged: the height of the bar for $u = 0$ is shown in the figure as $1.58 \times .245 = .387$, so that its area is $.387/1.58 = .245$ and identical to the area of the bar for $r = 5$ in the corresponding r histogram of Figure 17.1.

17.2.2   The Standardized or Unit Normal Distribution

If we substitute u for $[r - \mathrm{E}(\tilde{r})]/\sigma(\tilde{r})$ in the formula previously given for the Normal distribution and at the same time multiply the formula by $\sigma(\tilde{r})$ in order to keep the area of every bar unchanged, the formula reduces to

$$\mathrm{P}'_N(u) = \frac{1}{\sqrt{2\pi}}\, e^{-\frac{1}{2}u^2} \qquad \textit{Standardized or unit Normal distribution}$$

This is known as the *standardized Normal distribution;* observe that

The formula for the standardized Normal distribution contains no parameters; it is a unique distribution and not a family of distributions.

We have already considered the standardized random variable $\bar{u}$ in Section 16.5.3, where we showed that

$$\mathrm{E}(\bar{u}) = 0, \qquad \sigma(\bar{u}) = 1,$$

regardless of the values of $\mathrm{E}(\tilde{r})$ and $\sigma(\tilde{r})$. Because the standardized Normal distribution has standard deviation 1, it is also called the *unit Normal distribution*.

17.2.3   Tables of the Standardized Normal Distribution

A table of $\mathrm{P}'_N(u)$, that is of the *ordinates* or heights of the unit Normal curve, is given as Table II.   A table of $\mathrm{P}_N(\bar{u} > u)$, that is of the *area of the right tail* of the unit Normal curve, is given as Table III. Because *the Normal distribution is symmetric about its mean*, these tables have entries only for positive values of $\bar{u}$; ordinates and probabilities for negative u are easily obtained from these as we shall see by some examples.

17.2.4   *The Normal Approximation for Individual Binomial Probabilities*

Suppose that we seek the probability of exactly 30 defectives in a run of $n = 50$ pieces from a Bernoulli process with $p = .5$,

$$P_b(\tilde{r} = 30 | p = .5, n = 50).$$

This is the area of the bar for $r = 30$ in the r *histogram* for $p = .5$, $n = 50$ in Figure 17.1 and this area is *equal* to the area of the corresponding bar for

$$u = \frac{30 - E(\tilde{r})}{\sigma(\tilde{r})}$$

in the corresponding u *histogram* in Figure 17.2. The *width* of this latter bar is easily calculated; its *height* is easily approximated by finding the height of the unit Normal curve at the center of the bar; and the product of width times approximate height will give us an approximation to the *area* we seek. As a preliminary step we compute

$$E(\tilde{r}) = pn = .5 \times 50 = 25,$$

$$\sigma(\tilde{r}) = \sqrt{pqn} = \sqrt{.5 \times .5 \times 50} = 3.54,$$

$$u = \frac{30 - 25}{3.54} = 1.41.$$

Width of the Bar in the u Histogram. The width of the bar for $r = 30$ in the r histogram (Figure 17.1) is 1; its edges are at 29.5 and 30.5. We have already seen that when we transform the r histogram into the u histogram (Figure 17.2), we divide every value of the variable by $\sigma(\tilde{r})$ and therefore we divide the widths of all the bars by $\sigma(\tilde{r})$. The width of any bar in the u histogram for $n = 50$, $p = .5$ is $1/\sigma(\tilde{r}) = 1/3.54$.

Height of the Unit Normal Curve at the Center of the Bar. The center of the bar in which we are interested is located at $u = 1.41$, and to find the height of the unit Normal curve all we need to do is look up $P'_N(1.41)$ in Table II. We find .1476 in the row for 1.4 and the column for .01.

Approximate Area of the Bar. We then have for the approximate area of either bar ($r = 30$ in Figure 17.1 or $u = 1.41$ in Figure 17.2)

$$P_b(\tilde{r} = 30) = P(\tilde{u} = 1.41) \doteq \frac{1}{3.54} \times .1476 = .0416.$$

Generalization. In general, for *any* specified value r of *any* binomial random variable $\tilde{r}$,

$$P_b(r) \doteq \frac{1}{\sigma(\tilde{r})} P'_N \left[\frac{r - E(\tilde{r})}{\sigma(\tilde{r})} \right].$$

Substituting in this expression the formulas for binomial $E(\tilde{r})$ and $\sigma(\tilde{r})$, we have

$$P_b(\tilde{r} = r|n, p) \doteq \frac{1}{\sqrt{npq}} \, P'_N \left(\frac{r - np}{\sqrt{npq}} \right).$$

17.2.5 The Normal Approximation for Cumulative Binomial Probabilities

Suppose next that we seek the probability that the number of successes $\tilde{r}$ will *exceed* the specified number $r = 30$ when $p = .5$ and $n = 50$,

$$P_b(\tilde{r} > 30|p = .5, n = 50).$$

This is the area of that part of the appropriate r *histogram* (Figure 17.1) which lies *to the right of the right edge* of the bar for $r = 30$. This area is *equal* to the area of that part of the u *histogram* (Figure 17.2) which lies to the right of the right edge of the bar for the corresponding value u; it is *approximately* equal to the area in the tail of the unit Normal curve to the right of this edge.

The critical location for our present problem is thus not the center of the u bar corresponding to $r = 30$, which we have seen to be $u = 1.41$, but the *right edge* of this bar. The right edge of the bar for $r = 30$ is at 30.5; using the values

$$E(\tilde{r}) = 25, \qquad \sigma(\tilde{r}) = 3.54$$

which we have already computed, we find that the corresponding edge in the u histogram is

$$u = \frac{30.5 - 25}{3.54} = 1.55.$$

We can then use Table III to find

$$P_N(\tilde{u} > 1.55) = .06057,$$

which is an approximate value for the probability we seek.

Generalization.   In general, for *any* specified value r of *any* binomial variable $\tilde{r}$,

$$P_b(\tilde{r} > r) \doteq P_N \left[\tilde{u} > \frac{r + \frac{1}{2} - E(\tilde{r})}{\sigma(\tilde{r})} \right].$$

The procedure for finding other cumulative binomial probabilities is very similar, except that we do not always *add* $\frac{1}{2}$ to the specified value r: whether we add or subtract the $\frac{1}{2}$ which takes us from the center of a bar to the edge depends on (1) which tail we want and (2) whether the bar for the specified value r is included in the tail or excluded from it. *In case of doubt, sketch a few bars of the histogram.*

17.2.6   Examination of Errors of Approximation

We have already pointed out that when we are seeking approximate values for binomial probabilities:

1. *Both* the Poisson and the Normal approximations improve as n increases.
2. The Poisson approximation improves as p is closer to 0 or 1.

From Figures 17.1 and 17.2 it is apparent that

3. The Normal approximation improves as p is closer to .5.

In Figures 17.3 through 17.6 we illustrate these points by showing the probability distributions and the cumulative distributions $P(\tilde{r} \leq r)$ for

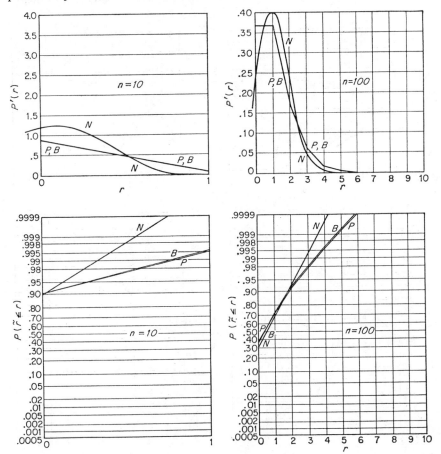

Figure 17.3. Binomial distributions with Normal and Poisson approximations. $p = .01$.

a variety of values of p and n.   In these charts notice one additional fact:

4. The *relative* error due to either approximation becomes greater the farther we go into the tail of the distribution.

17.3   Sums of Independent Random Variables

We pointed out in Section 16.4.1 that the number r of successes in n Bernoulli trials can be looked at as the *sum of the values of n independent random variables with identical probability distributions*.   The result of each trial is a random variable with value 1 if the event of the trial is success, 0 if the event is failure; the "distribution" for any one of the n variables is defined by the same probability p of a success and can be graphed as a histogram with a bar of height p at $r = 1$ and a bar of height

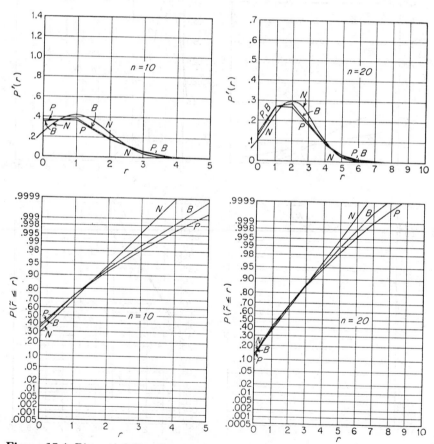

Figure 17.4. Binomial distributions with Normal and Poisson approximations. $p = .1$.

$q = 1 - p$ at $r = 0$. Thus the behavior of $\tilde{r}$ which was graphed in Figures 17.1 through 17.6 can be described as follows:

If $\tilde{r}$ is the sum of n independent two-valued random variables all having the same probability distribution, then as n increases the distribution of $\tilde{r}$ is more and more closely approximated by a Normal distribution with mean $E(\tilde{r})$ equal to the expected value of the sum and with variance $\sigma^2(\tilde{r})$ equal to the variance of the sum.

It is a very remarkable and important fact that this proposition holds for almost *any* sum of independent random variables all having the same probability distribution, *regardless of the nature of this common distribution*. It is true in general that:

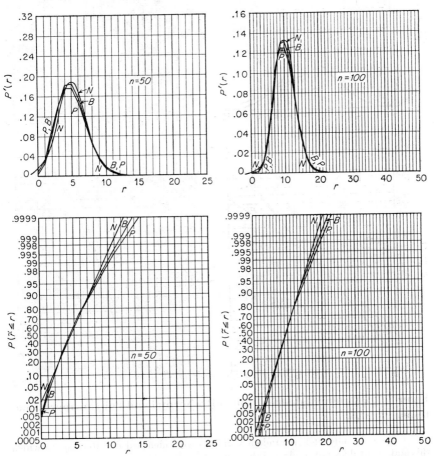

Figure 17.5. Binomial distributions with Normal and Poisson approxima-tions. $p = .1$.

If $\tilde{z}$ is the sum of n independent random variables all having the same probability distribution, then as n increases the distribution of $\tilde{z}$ is more and more closely approximated by a Normal distribution with mean equal to the expected value of $\tilde{z}$ and variance equal to the variance of $\tilde{z}$; and this is true regardless of the nature of the distribution of the individual variables.†

It is this fact which accounts for both the name and the enormous importance of the Normal distribution, since very many of the random variables encountered in practice are in fact sums of independent, identically

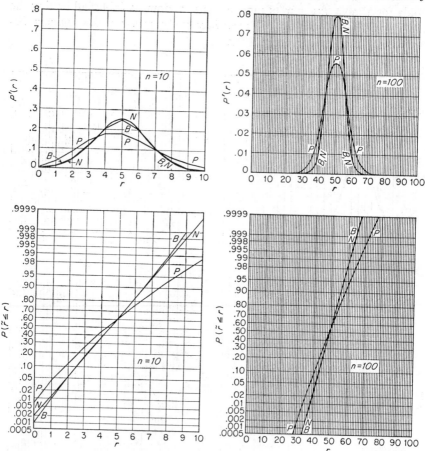

Figure 17.6. Binomial distributions with Normal and Poisson approximations. $p = .5$.

† The only independent random variables with identical distributions to which this statement does not apply are those which have infinite means or standard deviations, and such variables almost never occur in practical business problems. On the other hand, the statement does apply under certain conditions even to sums of independent variables which do not have identical individual distributions.

distributed random variables.† *Provided that the number of such variables included in the sum $\tilde{z}$ is large enough*, probabilities can be approximated by first substituting the standardized random variable

$$\tilde{u} = \frac{\tilde{z} - E(\tilde{z})}{\sigma(\tilde{z})}$$

for the natural variable $\tilde{z}$ and then using tables of the unit Normal distribution.

This proposition is so important that we must stop to examine more closely both its precise meaning and the evidence for its truth; and we shall begin this inquiry by stating the so-called *Central limit theorem*. This famous theorem is a rigorous *proof* that, for random variables $\tilde{z}$ and $\tilde{u}$ defined as we have defined them above,

> For any given u, there is some value of n above which the error in the Normal approximation to $P(\tilde{u} > u)$ is smaller than any previously specified amount however small.

This proof unfortunately does not get us very far, however.

1. It does not tell us how to find the n for any given u and given error.
2. It does not even tell us that if we happen to know the error for one value of n we can be sure that it will be smaller for *any* larger n.

It is in fact not at all difficult to find cases where as n increases the approximation to $P(\tilde{u} > u)$ for some particular u gets worse before it gets better.

Thus our original statement that the approximation becomes closer and closer as n increases must be interpreted as referring to the *over-all* quality of the approximation; and the real evidence for such a qualitative statement is not the Central limit theorem but a great deal of *numerical investigation* of the kind exemplified in Figures 17.3 through 17.6. We shall examine similar charts for other kinds of variables presently; the real utility of the Central limit theorem lies in the subjective assurance it gives us that still other variables would behave in a similar manner. The practical result of all this evidence is this:

> Except when it is extremely important to obtain an extremely exact value for a probability, statisticians *act* as if the Normal approximation improved *continuously* with n; and the businessman may follow their example.

Suppose, for example, that we want a practical evaluation of $P(\tilde{u} > 2)$ in a problem where $n = 25$; and suppose that we happen to know that when $n = 20$ the error in the Normal approximation is less than .03 for all u in the general vicinity of $u = 2$. If an error of .03 is tolerable in our problem, we may use the Normal approximation without further ado.

---

† Or are, what amounts to the same thing, *means* of a number of independent, identically distributed random variables, since the distribution of a mean is the same as the distribution of a sum except for a change of scale.

We now proceed to examine the use and the behavior of the Normal approximation to the three remaining distributions of sums of independent, identically distributed random variables which we have studied so far: the Poisson, the Pascal, and the gamma.

17.3.1   The Poisson Distribution

Consider a Poisson process generating successes at a mean rate κ per unit of space, think of each unit of space as divided into a very large number of very small segments, and let $\tilde{r}'$ denote the random variable "number of defects" in one such segment. Then the number r of successes in any larger space can be thought of as the sum of the values of $\tilde{r}'$ for each of the small segments contained in this space. To be concrete, return to the example of a machine insulating electric wire and think of the wire as divided into segments of length .001 foot. Then the number r of defects in 2 feet, say, of wire can be considered as the sum of the numbers in 2000 segments of length .001 foot.

By the nature of the Poisson process these random variables $\tilde{r}'$ are independent and identically distributed; and as the space in which we count the successes increases, the number of segments increases and therefore the number of summed variables increases. It follows that for any given κ, the Poisson distribution of $\tilde{r}$ approaches Normality as t increases. We know, however, that the Poisson distribution depends only on the product $\kappa t = m$ and not on κ or t separately, and it follows that the closeness of the Normal approximation depends only on m. Consequently the Normal distribution can be used to get an approximation to a Poisson probability when the value of m is large enough. The method of calculating the approximation is identical to the method used in approximating binomial probabilities.

Individual Poisson Probabilities. Suppose that we seek the Poisson probability of *exactly* $r = 22$ successes when the expected number of successes is $m = 30$. We first compute

$$E(\tilde{r}) = m = 30,$$
$$\sigma(\tilde{r}) = \sqrt{m} = 5.48.$$

The *width* of the bar for $r = 22$ in the r histogram is 1, and therefore the width of the corresponding bar in the u histogram is $1/\sigma(\tilde{r}) = 1/5.48$. The center of the bar in the u histogram is at

$$u = \frac{r - E(\tilde{r})}{\sigma(\tilde{r})} = \frac{22 - 30}{5.48} = -1.46.$$

The *height* of the unit Normal curve for negative u is not given in Table II, but by the symmetry of the curve

$$P'_N(-1.46) = P'_N(+1.46).$$

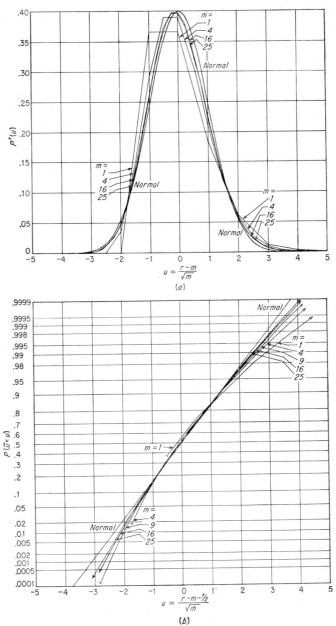

Figure 17.7. Poisson distributions with the Normal approximation

The ordinate on the right is given by the table as .1374, and the *area* or probability we seek is thus

$$P_{Po}(\tilde{r} = 22) \doteq \frac{1}{\sigma(\tilde{r})} P'_N(u) = \frac{1}{5.48} \times .1374 = .0251.$$

Cumulative Poisson Probabilities. Suppose next that we seek the Poisson probability of 22 *or less* successes when $m = 30$. This is a *left-tail* probability which *includes* the bar for $r = 22$. The *right* edge of the bar in the u histogram corresponding to the bar for $r = 22$ in the r histogram is at

$$u = \frac{(22 + \frac{1}{2}) - 30}{5.48} = -1.37$$

and the probability we seek is therefore approximately

$$P_N(\tilde{u} < -1.37).$$

Table III gives only right-tail probabilities, but the symmetry of the Normal curve implies that

$$P_N(\tilde{u} < -1.37) = P_N(\tilde{u} > +1.37)$$

and the latter probability is shown by the table to be .08534.

Examination of Errors of Approximation. In Figure 17.7 we show the Poisson probability and cumulative distributions and the Normal approximations for a series of values of m.[†]

17.3.2   The Pascal Distribution

We have already seen that the number $\tilde{n}$ of Bernoulli trials required to secure r successes can be regarded as the sum of r independent random variables, each one being the number of trials required to secure one success. Hence the Pascal distribution of $\tilde{n}$ approaches Normality as r increases.

Example. The probability that it will take less than 150 trials to secure 48 Bernoulli successes when $p = .25$ is computed as follows.

$$E(\tilde{n}) = \frac{r}{p} = \frac{48}{.25} = 192;$$

$$\sigma^2(\tilde{n}) = \frac{rq}{p^2} = \frac{48 \times .75}{.25^2} = 576;$$

$$\sigma(\tilde{n}) = \sqrt{576} = 24.$$

[†] Notice that we *cannot* judge the Normal approximation to the Poisson distribution from Figures 17.3 to 17.6. When we approximate a binomial probability by a Poisson probability, we use the Poisson distribution with the same *mean* as the given binomial distribution, but this Poisson distribution does *not* have the same *standard deviation* as the binomial it approximates. When we use the Normal distribution as an approximation, we give it *both* the same mean *and* the same standard deviation as the distribution it approximates.

Since we want the area to the left of the left edge of the bar for $n = 150$, we *subtract* $\frac{1}{2}$ in computing

$$u = \frac{(150 - \frac{1}{2}) - 192}{24} = -1.77.$$

From Table III we find

$$P_N(\tilde{u} < -1.77) = P_N(\tilde{u} > +1.77) = .038.$$

The exact value (from binomial tables) is .029.

17.3.3   The Gamma Distribution

The space $\tilde{t}$ required to secure r Poisson successes is likewise the sum of r spaces required to secure one success, and therefore the gamma distribution of $\tilde{t}$ also approaches Normality as r increases.

Individual Gamma Probabilities. Suppose that we seek the probability that it will take *exactly* 3 minutes for 70 Poisson-distributed successes to occur when the mean rate of occurrence is $\kappa = 25$ per minute. We first compute

$$E(\tilde{t}) = r\mu = \frac{r}{\kappa} = \frac{70}{25} = 2.8,$$

$$\sigma^2(\tilde{t}) = r\mu^2 = \frac{r}{\kappa^2} = \frac{70}{625} = .112,$$

$$\sigma(\tilde{t}) = \sqrt{.112} = .335.$$

We now recall from Section 14.3.1 that the gamma distribution which we are approximating by the Normal is itself only an approximation to an underlying discrete distribution described by a *histogram* with one bar for every value t which it is possible to read with the measuring instrument being used.   It is really this histogram which we are approximating when we use the Normal approximation, and we again denote the width of one of the bars in the t histogram by the symbol δt.   The center of the bar in the u histogram corresponding to the bar for $t = 3$ in the t histogram is at

$$u = \frac{3.0 - 2.8}{.335} = .60,$$

and the *height* of this bar is given approximately by Table II as

$$P'_N(.60) = .3332.$$

The *width* of the bar in the u histogram is $\delta t / \sigma(\tilde{t}) = \delta t / .335$, and its *area* is therefore

$$P(\tilde{u} = .60) \doteq \frac{\delta t}{\sigma(\tilde{t})} P'_N(u) = \frac{\delta t}{.335} .3332 = .995\ \delta t.$$

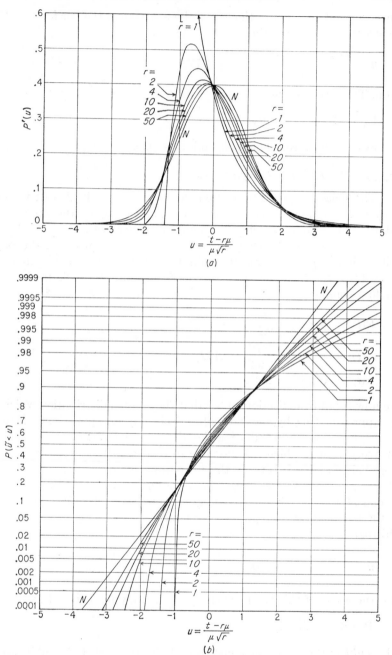

Figure 17.8. Gamma distributions with the Normal approximation.

If the measurements are made to a hundredth of a minute, the probability that the measurement will be exactly 3.00 is .01 × .995 = .00995, and so forth.

Cumulative Gamma Probabilities. Suppose next that we seek the probability that it will take *more* than 3 minutes for 70 successes to occur when the mean rate of occurrence is 70 per minute. This is given approximately by the area of the tail of the unit Normal distribution to the right of

$$u = \frac{(3 + \frac{1}{2}\delta t) - 2.8}{.335}.$$

If measurements are made to the hundredth of a minute, $\frac{1}{2}\delta t = .005$ and u has the value .599; the required probability is then approximately

$$P(\tilde{t} > 3) \doteq P_N(\tilde{u} > .599) = .2746$$

by interpolation in Table III. If we had neglected the .005 width of half of a bar, u would have had the value .597 and interpolation in the table would have given us a probability of .2753. Clearly this kind of difference is not significant in view of the inaccuracies inherent in the use of an approximation to the exact distribution of $\tilde{t}$—the two results are identical to three decimal places—and in general we may neglect half bar widths in computing *cumulative* probabilities when the bars of the underlying histogram are *very narrow*.

Errors of Approximation. Figure 17.8 shows the gamma probability and cumulative distributions and their Normal approximations for a variety of values of the parameter r. It should be observed that the approximation is not very good until r is really quite large.

17.4   Summary

If $\tilde{z}$ is the sum of n independent random variables all having the same probability distribution, then as n increases the over-all distribution of $\tilde{z}$ is more and more closely approximated by a Normal distribution with mean $E(\tilde{z})$ and variance $\sigma^2(\tilde{z})$.

Letting δz denote the width of a bar in the histogram of the exact distribution of $\tilde{z}$, the Normal approximations to the exact probabilities are computed by the following formulas:

$$P(\tilde{z} = z) \doteq \frac{\delta z}{\sigma(\tilde{z})} P'_N(u) \qquad u = \frac{z - E(\tilde{z})}{\sigma(\tilde{z})}$$

$$P(\tilde{z} > z) \doteq P_N(\tilde{u} > u) \qquad u = \frac{(z + \frac{1}{2}\delta z) - E(\tilde{z})}{\sigma(\tilde{z})}$$

If $\bar{z}$ is a random variable which can take on only the integral values 0, 1, 2, etc., $\delta z = 1$ and the factor $\frac{1}{2}\delta z = \frac{1}{2}$ should not be neglected if we want accurate cumulative probabilities. If $\bar{z}$ is a variable which has a nearly continuous distribution, the factor $\frac{1}{2}\delta z$ may usually be neglected in computing cumulative probabilities.

PROBLEMS

A. Exercises on Computation with the Normal Distribution

1. Find the following ordinates and areas of the unit Normal distribution. In some cases it will be necessary to use the symmetry of the distribution: sketch the distribution, locate the ordinate or area you seek, and then locate an equal ordinate or area which can be found in the tables.

a. $P'(0)$.	*b.* $P(\bar{u} > 0)$.	*c.* $P'(+2)$.
d. $P'(-3)$.	*e.* $P'(-3.26)$.	*f.* $P(\bar{u} > +1)$.
g. $P(\bar{u} > +1.87)$.	*h.* $P(\bar{u} < -2)$.	*i.* $P(\bar{u} > -2)$.
j. $P(\bar{u} < +2)$.	*k.* $P(\bar{u} < -3)$.	*l.* $P(\bar{u} < +3)$.

2. Use the Normal approximation to evaluate the following binomial probabilities for $n = 2500$, $p = .2$.

a. $P(\bar{r} = 530)$.	*b.* $P(\bar{r} \geq 530)$.
c. $P(\bar{r} > 530)$.	*d.* $P(\bar{r} < 530)$.

3. Use the Normal approximation to evaluate the following Pascal probabilities for $r = 7290$, $p = .9$.

- *a.* $P(\bar{n} = 8160)$.
- *b.* $P(\bar{n} > 8160)$.
- *c.* $P(\bar{n} < 8040)$.

4. Use the Normal approximation to evaluate the following Poisson probabilities for $\kappa = 3$, $t = 12$.

- *a.* $P(\bar{r} = 30)$.
- *b.* $P(\bar{r} \leq 30)$.
- *c.* $P(\bar{r} > 30)$.

5. Use the Normal approximation to evaluate the following gamma probabilities for $r = 100$, $\mu = 8$.

- *a.* $P(\bar{t} = 1040)$.
- *b.* $P(\bar{t} \geq 1040)$.
- *c.* $P(\bar{t} \leq 560)$.

6. Use the Normal approximation to evaluate the following partial expectations:

- *a.* Binomial $\bar{r}$ over the interval 0 to 20 inclusive when $n = 150$, $p = .2$.
- *b.* Pascal $\bar{n}$ over the interval 100 to 150 inclusive when $r = 100$, $p = .9$.
- *c.* Poisson $\bar{r}$ over the interval 0 to 20 inclusive when $\kappa = .2$, $t = 150$.

B. Choice of Approximations

7. Use Figures 17.3 to 17.6 to decide how you would evaluate each of the following binomial probabilities with the tables and charts available to you. Write down the formula for the approximating probability but do not actually make any arithmetical computations.

a. $P(\bar{r} = 2 \mid n = 25, p = .02)$.	*b.* $P(\bar{r} = 6 \mid n = 25, p = .40)$.
c. $P(\bar{r} = 24 \mid n = 25, p = .98)$.	*d.* $P(\bar{r} \leq 2 \mid n = 100, p = .05)$.
e. $P(\bar{r} \geq 6 \mid n = 100, p = .15)$.	*f.* $P(\bar{r} > 20 \mid n = 100, p = .30)$.
g. $P(\bar{r} < 6 \mid n = 1000, p = .01)$.	*h.* $P(\bar{r} \leq 150 \mid n = 1000, p = .2)$.

8. Decide how you would evaluate each of the following Pascal probabilities with the tables and charts available to you. Write down the formula for the approximating probability but do not actually make any arithmetical computations.

a. $P(\tilde{n} = 600 | r = 5, p = .01)$.

b. $P(\tilde{n} > 6000 | r = 50, p = .01)$.

c. $P(\tilde{n} \geq 50 | r = 30, p = .5)$.

C. Applied Problems

9. A process producing small capacitors has averaged 5 per cent defective over the past several weeks. If you are convinced that the process behaves as a Bernoulli process and that the process average is stable, what probability would you assign to the following events?

a. There are more than 120 defectives in a run of 2000.

b. More than 2100 pieces have to be produced in order to obtain 2000 good capacitors.

c. The 2100th capacitor processed is the 2000th good capacitor.

10. A process producing transistors has averaged 60 per cent defective over the past several weeks. On the assumption stated in Problem 9, what probability would you assign to the following events?

a. There are more than 1250 defectives in a run of 2000.

b. More than 5200 transistors have to be produced in order to obtain 2000 good transistors.

c. The 5200th transistor processed is the 2000th good transistor.

11. A telephone exchange receives 2500 calls per hour on the average. What probability would you assign to the event "less than 135 calls in the next 3 minutes"? What assumptions did you make in computing your answer?

12. In Section 15.4.3 we derived a formula for total cost per unit of time under a min-max system of inventory control with Poisson-distributed demand and saw that the probability distribution enters this formula only through the function

$$g(R) = m\,\mathrm{P}_{Po}(\tilde{r} \geq R | m) - R\,\mathrm{P}_{Po}(\tilde{r} > R | m)$$

defined in Section 15.3.2. When m is large we will wish to evaluate $g(R)$ by use of the Normal approximation.

a. Show that the above definition of $g(R)$ is exactly equivalent to

$$g(R) = m\,\mathrm{P}_{Po}(\tilde{r} = R | m) - (R - m)\,\mathrm{P}_{Po}(\tilde{r} > R | m).$$

b. Show that as m increases less and less inaccuracy results if we suppress the $\frac{1}{2}$ in

$$u = \frac{(R + \frac{1}{2}) - \mathrm{E}(\tilde{r})}{\sigma(\tilde{r})}$$

when using the Normal approximation to $\mathrm{P}_{Po}(\tilde{r} > R | m)$.

c. Show that if the $\frac{1}{2}$ is thus suppressed the Normal approximation becomes

$$g(R) = \sigma(\tilde{r})\,[\mathrm{P}'_N(u) - u\,\mathrm{P}_N(\tilde{u} > u)].$$

If we define

$$G(u) = \mathrm{P}'_N(u) - u\,\mathrm{P}_N(\tilde{u} > u)$$

the Normal approximation to $g(R)$ can thus be written

$$g(R) = \sigma(\tilde{r})\,G(u).$$

The function $G(u)$ is tabulated in Table IV.

13. The XYZ Company places an order for a new supply of part AZ-11 when there are 50 units on hand. Lead time is 90 days; usage of the part is Poisson distributed with mean usage known to be $\frac{1}{2}$ unit per day. What is the expected time out of stock?

CHAPTER 18

The Normal Approximation
to Empirical Distributions

So far we have considered the Normal distribution only as an approximation to distributions of sums of *known* numbers of *independent* random variables whose exact distributions are *identical* and *known*. Often the Normal distribution can also be used to approximate the distribution of a random variable which can be regarded as the sum of an unknown number of more or less independent random variables whose exact distributions are completely unknown.

As an example, consider the random variable "diameter" describing shafts produced by some automatic machine. If we measure the actual diameters of a large number of shafts produced under indistinguishable conditions and if we then plot the frequency distribution of these diameters, we often find that this histogram can be very closely fitted by a Normal curve with the same mean and variance. If we observe this empirical fact in some particular case, we can "explain" it by thinking of the variation in the diameters as being the net effect of a very large number of independent causes each of which individually has a very small effect. This explanation rests in part on a provable extension of the Central limit theorem, but it is very important to realize that the Central limit theorem is of absolutely no *practical use* in this case. The distribution of diameters produced on one machine may be almost exactly Normal while the distribution of diameters produced on another machine may be much farther from Normality. We have already argued in Section 6.1 that it is useful to think of variation in demand as the net effect of a large number of independent factors each of which has a very small effect, and yet we all know that distributions of demand are often *very far* from Normal.

Thus the Central limit theorem most definitely does not "prove" that any distribution of this sort will be Normal or even roughly Normal. It only serves to "explain" Normality when Normality is observed, and for this reason we shall not examine the conditions under which this extended version of the theorem theoretically applies. As a purely *empirical* matter, however, it is often justified to use a Normal distribution as an approximation to the true distribution of variables like those we have been discussing. The required justification is simply this:

294

If a Normal curve "fitted" to the available historical data seems on inspection to express the decision maker's judgment concerning the probabilities about as well as any other curve he could fit, then he can rationally compute costs and make decisions on the basis of this Normal distribution.

One particular point should be noticed, however. Because the tails of the Normal distribution never fall to zero, this distribution will virtually *never* reflect any reasonable man's judgment regarding the probabilities of very large or very small values of the variable. In *most* problems these tail probabilities are completely unimportant; but in problems where very small tail probabilities *are* important, serious errors can be made by using the Normal approximation.

18.1   The "Fitting" of a Normal Distribution

18.1.1   Normal-probability Paper

When a historical frequency distribution of the output of some process is available, it is never legitimate to assess the probability distribution for future output as Normal unless the historical distribution is reasonably Normal. We should *never* proceed by simply computing the mean and variance of the historical distribution and then using Normal tables; the data *must* first be graphed and the graph must be carefully examined to see if it is reasonably close to Normal shape.

The easiest way to do this is to convert the historical data into *fractile estimates* in the way described in Section 6.4 and then plot these estimates on Normal-probability paper. The grid of this paper is laid out in such a way that a *cumulative Normal distribution plots as a straight line*. If then a straight line can be drawn to pass reasonably close to all the plotted fractile estimates, the Normal distribution defined by this straight line may rationally be used as the probability distribution for the problem.

As usual, there is no way of stating objectively how close is "reasonably" close. The answer depends on the degree of accuracy required in the answer; and even if this were specified, the only way of finding what error will actually result from use of the Normal approximation in any particular case would be to compute the answer using both the approximate distribution and whatever distribution the decision maker thinks is the best fitting and therefore the "true" distribution for that particular case.

18.1.2   The Reason for Fitting a Normal Distribution

If the probability distribution in some practical problem must be assessed by smoothing historical data, as we have assumed above, and if all that we need to solve the problem is a cumulative probability or the value of a fractile, there is absolutely no advantage in deciding whether or not the distribution can be treated as Normal. We can read probabilities and fractiles just as easily if we fit a curve to fractile estimates plotted on Normal paper as if we fit a straight line. If, however, we need the results of computations which involve the probabilities of many individual values of the variable, there *is* a great advantage in fitting a line or curve which has *some* known mathematical formula. The advantage is simply this: from the known formula for the distribution, it may be possible by mathematical analysis to derive a formula for the required results; and if this can be done, laborious chart reading of the sort described in Chapter 6 will be unnecessary.

Although the businessman certainly does not need to be able to perform his own statistical computations, he does need some understanding of the basic nature of the devices used by the statistician for this purpose —at least enough understanding to be able to distinguish clearly among error, approximation, and magic, and enough to see why the statistician must sometimes ask him whether in his opinion a certain curve is an adequate description of his beliefs. The Normal distribution is by no means the only distribution of known mathematical form which can be fitted to a historical frequency distribution, and in a great many circumstances it is not the best distribution to use. It is, however, the *simplest* distribution which can be used in this way, and it is the only one which can easily be fitted by graphical methods. We shall therefore devote a few pages to examining the way in which the assessment of an empirical probability distribution as approximately Normal can enormously simplify the task of obtaining solutions to practical problems.

18.1.3   Determination of the Mean and Standard Deviation of the Fitted Normal Distribution

If a formula for a summary measure such as a partial expectation is derived from the formula for the Normal distribution, it is obvious that it will involve one or both of the *parameters* of the distribution. We therefore begin by showing how the values of these parameters can be obtained once the distribution has been graphed in cumulative form. The method is best explained by an example, and as an example we shall take the cumulative Normal distribution represented by the line labeled I in Figure 6.6a.

By the symmetry of the Normal distribution, half the area under any Normal curve lies to the right of the mean and half to the left: the mean is equal to the median. The mean of the distribution we are considering is therefore the value z such that

$$P(\tilde{z} < z) = .5.$$

Locating .5 on the vertical axis of Figure 6.6a and reading across to the line labeled I and down to the horizontal axis we find $z = 75$. Thus

$$E(\tilde{z}) = 75.$$

To find the standard deviation we now read one other point on the line as far from the mean as possible. At the extreme right end of the line labeled I we find that the abscissa is $z = 120$ while the ordinate gives $P(\tilde{z} < 120) = .95$. Expressing the value $z = 120$ in standardized form and recalling that the mean of this distribution is 75, our reading of the graph tells us that

$$P_N\left[\tilde{u} < \frac{120 - 75}{\sigma(\tilde{z})}\right] = .95.$$

This is equivalent to

$$P_N\left[\tilde{u} > \frac{45}{\sigma(\tilde{z})}\right] = .05,$$

and our next task is to find the value of $\sigma(\tilde{z})$ which makes this statement true. We look for the probability .05 in the body of Table III and find that the corresponding u is approximately 1.64. The value of $\sigma(\tilde{z})$ must therefore be such that

$$\frac{45}{\sigma(\tilde{z})} = 1.64,$$

and we compute

$$\sigma(\tilde{z}) = \frac{45}{1.64} = 27.4.$$

18.2   Uses of the Fitted Normal Distribution

We now give some examples to illustrate the way in which the fitting of a distribution of known mathematical form simplifies calculations based on the distribution. Because such procedures are only intended to give reasonable approximations and do not pretend to mathematical exactitude, *we shall simplify our computations of cumulative probabilities by neglecting the ½ which takes us from the center to the edge of a bar.*

18.2.1   *Sums of Independent Normal Variables*

A very important and extremely convenient property of Normal random variables is the following:

The sum of any number of independent Normal random variables has a Normal distribution.

This is *not* a "limiting" property true only for large numbers of variables and it is *not* restricted to variables having the same distribution, i.e. the same mean and standard deviation. It applies to any number of independent variables each of which has any Normal distribution.†

Application. Suppose that the design for a certain assembly calls for placing five different gears side by side and inserting them between two bearings. The design thickness of each of the five kinds of gears is 1.300 inches; and although even substantial departures from design thickness in any individual gear will have no harmful effects, the *total* thickness of the five gears in each assembly must be closely controlled. Using T to denote the total thickness of the five gears in an assembly, there will be interference with the bearings if $T > 6.52$ inches and there will be excessive play if $T < 6.48$ inches. The required control can be obtained by using selective assembly, i.e. by measuring all individual gears and seeing to it that an oversize gear in any assembly is offset by one which is undersize, but this procedure is very expensive and the production manager would like to know what fraction of all assemblies would be defective if ordinary nonselective assembly were used.

Each of the five gears will be manufactured on a different machine. Performance-capability studies of the five machines to be used in the operation have shown that each one can be set up with such accuracy that the *average* thickness of all the gears it produces will be practically identical to the design thickness; but because of the inherent play in the machines the thicknesses of the individual gears produced by any one of them will vary around the design or mean thickness. Frequency distributions of the output of each machine have been made and the standard deviations of these distributions have been computed with the results shown in Table 18.1.

Table 18.1

Machine	Standard deviation, inches
A	.004
B	.003
C	.004
D	.007
E	.002

Since each machine will produce the design thickness on the average and since the expected value of a sum of random variables is the sum of the individual expected values, we can conclude immediately that

$$E(\tilde{T}) = 5 \times 1.300 \text{ inches} = 6.500 \text{ inches.}$$

If assembly is nonselective, the fact that one gear in an assembly is oversize makes it neither more nor less likely that another gear in the same assembly will be oversize or undersize; and since the variance of a sum of

† A sum of Normal random variables may be Normal even when the variables are *not* independent, but the conditions under which this is true are beyond the scope of this course.

independent random variables is the sum of the individual variances, we can compute

$$\sigma^2(\tilde{T}) = \sigma_A^2 + \sigma_B^2 + \cdots + \sigma_E^2$$
$$= .000016 + .000009 + .000016 + .000049 + .000004$$
$$= .000094;$$
$$\sigma(\tilde{T}) = \sqrt{.000094} = .0097 \doteq .010.$$

Thus we know the mean and standard deviation of the distribution of total thicknesses; but *unless we know the "shape" of this distribution we still cannot compute any probabilities.*

Suppose, however, that frequency distributions of the outputs of the five machines show that the thicknesses produced by any one machine have a roughly *Normal* distribution: then we know immediately that the sum of five such thicknesses will be Normally distributed. Neglecting the difference between the center and the edge of any bar in the T histogram for the reason given at the beginning of Section 18.2, we compute

$$P(\tilde{T} > 6.52) \doteq P_N\left(\tilde{u} > \frac{6.520 - 6.500}{.010}\right) = P_N(\tilde{u} > 2.00) = .023.$$
$$P(\tilde{T} < 6.48) \doteq P_N(\tilde{u} < -2.00) = .023.$$

Nonselective assembly will result in about 5 per cent defectives. If the cost of correcting a defective is less than 20 times the extra cost of selective assembly, nonselective assembly should be used.

18.2.2   Fractiles

Although fractiles of a Normal distribution which has been fitted graphically can be read directly from the graph, as we have already said, we shall encounter problems later in the course where we require fractiles of a Normal distribution whose mean and standard deviation have been determined by other procedures. We therefore digress from our immediate purpose to show how fractiles of a Normal distribution with given mean and standard deviation can be found from tables.

To find the $.f$ fractile of a Normal distribution with mean $E(\tilde{z})$ and standard deviation $\sigma(\tilde{z})$, all that we have to do is use Table III to find the value u which is the $.f$ fractile of the unit Normal distribution and then compute the value z which corresponds to this u. Both steps are extremely simple; the only trick to remember is that Table III is a *right-tail* table and therefore gives probabilities complementary to those involved in the definition of fractiles.

Suppose for example that the random variable $\tilde{z}$ has a Normal distribution with mean 95 and standard deviation 20 and that we wish to find $F_{.6}$ of this distribution. By definition, $F_{.6}$ is the value z such that

$$P(\tilde{z} < z) = .6;$$

because of the continuity of the Normal distribution $P(\tilde{z} < z) = P(\tilde{z} \leq z)$ and there will be some z for which the probability is exactly .6. This z is found by first finding the

$$u = \frac{z - E(\tilde{z})}{\sigma(\tilde{z})}$$

such that

$$P_N(\tilde{u} < u) = .6; \qquad \text{i.e. such that} \qquad P_N(\tilde{u} > u) = .4.$$

The closest probability to .4 in Table III is .4013, corresponding to

$$u = .25,$$

and this is close enough for the kind of approximation we are now using. Multiplying both sides of the equation relating u to z by $\sigma(\tilde{z})$ and adding $E(\tilde{z})$ to both sides we obtain

$$z = E(\tilde{z}) + u\sigma(\tilde{z}).$$

Substituting the values of $E(\tilde{z})$ and $\sigma(\tilde{z})$ assumed for our example and the value $u = .25$ which is the .6 fractile of the unit Normal distribution, we have

$$F_{.6} = 95 + (.25 \times 20) = 100.$$

Application. Suppose that a certain item costs \$2, sells for \$5, and spoils if it is not sold on the day it is stocked, so that the loss per unit of overage is $k_o = \$2$ and the loss per unit of underage is $k_u = \$5 - \$2 = \$3$. Suppose further that the probability distribution for demand has been assessed as roughly Normal with mean 95 units and standard deviation 20 units. By Section 7.6.3 we know that the best act is to stock all units up to and including the $k_u/(k_u + k_o)$ fractile, and we therefore compute

$$\frac{k_u}{k_u + k_o} = \frac{\$3}{\$3 + \$2} = .6.$$

We have already determined that $F_{.6}$ of a Normal distribution with mean 95 and standard deviation 20 is 100; this is therefore the best number of units to stock.

18.2.3   Partial Expectations

The partial expectation of any Normally distributed variable $\tilde{z}$ over the interval $\tilde{z} = -\infty$ to $\tilde{z} = z$ can be shown by calculus to be

$$E_{-\infty}^{z}(\tilde{z}) = E(\tilde{z})\, P_N(\tilde{u} < u) - \sigma(\tilde{z})\, P_N'(u) \qquad \textit{Normal partial expectation}$$

where as usual

$$u = \frac{z - E(\tilde{z})}{\sigma(\tilde{z})}.$$

Application to Computation of Expected Loss. Suppose now that we wish to compute expected loss under a decision to stock Q units in the example discussed just above. By the formulas in Section 7.5.2,

Expected loss due to overage $= k_o[Q\,P(\tilde{z} \le Q) - E_0^Q(\tilde{z})],$
Expected loss due to underage $= k_u[E_{Q+1}^\infty(\tilde{z}) - Q\,P(\tilde{z} > Q)].$

If now we define

$$u_Q = \frac{Q - E(\tilde{z})}{\sigma(\tilde{z})}$$

and again neglect the ½ which takes us from the center to the edge of a bar, we can substitute in these formulas

$$Q = E(\tilde{z}) + u_Q\sigma(\tilde{z}),$$
$$P(\tilde{z} \le Q) = P_N(\tilde{u} < u_Q),$$
$$P(\tilde{z} > Q) = P_N(\tilde{u} > u_Q).$$

If the Normal distribution of $\tilde{z}$ has a negligible tail to the left of 0, as it must if it is a reasonable distribution of demand, we can evaluate $E_0^Q(\tilde{z})$ by use of the formula for $E_{-\infty}^Q(\tilde{z})$:

$$E_0^Q(\tilde{z}) \doteq E(\tilde{z})\,P_N(\tilde{u} < u_Q) - \sigma(\tilde{z})\,P_N'(u_Q),$$
$$E_{Q+1}^\infty(\tilde{z}) = E(\tilde{z}) - E_{-\infty}^Q(\tilde{z})$$
$$= E(\tilde{z})\,P_N(\tilde{u} > u_Q) + \sigma(\tilde{z})\,P_N'(u_Q).$$

Making these substitutions in the formulas for the two parts of the total expected loss and adding the results we obtain

Expected loss $= (k_u + k_o)\sigma(\tilde{z})\,P_N'(u_Q)$
$$+ [k_o\,P_N(\tilde{u} < u_Q) - k_u\,P_N(\tilde{u} > u_Q)]u_Q\sigma(\tilde{z}).$$

The *cost of uncertainty* is the expected loss of the *best* decision. If we use Q^* to denote the *best* quantity to stock and

$$u^* = \frac{Q^* - E(\tilde{z})}{\sigma(\tilde{z})}$$

to denote the corresponding *best* value of the standardized variable $\tilde{u}$, then (as we have just seen in Section 18.2.2) Q^* and u^* satisfy the conditions

$$P(\tilde{z} < Q^*) = P_N(\tilde{u} < u^*) = \frac{k_u}{k_u + k_o}.$$

If $k_u/(k_u + k_o)$ is substituted for $P_N(\tilde{u} < u_Q)$ in the formula for expected loss given just above, and if 1 minus this value is substituted for

$P_N(\bar{u} > u_Q)$, the two terms inside the brackets cancel each other exactly. Thus in all problems of this type

---

$$\text{Cost of uncertainty} = (k_u + k_o)\sigma(\tilde{z})\, P_N'(u^*).$$

In the example we have been discussing,

$$\sigma(\tilde{z}) = 20, \qquad\qquad k_o = \$2,$$
$$P_N'(u^*) = P_N'(.25) = .3867 \qquad k_u = \$3.$$

Substituting these values in the formula we obtain

$$\text{Cost of uncertainty} = \$5 \times 20 \times .3867 = \$39.$$

PROBLEMS

1. If the bushing and shaft diameters of Chapter 16, Problem 5, are Normally distributed and if random assembly is used, in what fraction of all tries will it be possible to assemble the bushing over the shaft?

2. A probability distribution for a random variable $\tilde{z}$ is assessed by plotting fractile estimates on Normal-probability paper and fitting a straight line to these points. The line shows $P(\tilde{z} < 30) = .01$ and $P(\tilde{z} < 65) = .90$.

    a. Graph the line and find the mean and standard deviation of the distribution.

    b. Compute the partial expectation of $\tilde{z}$ over the interval $z = 0$ to $z = 60$ and over the interval $z = 40$ to $z = \infty$.

3. Suppose that the random variable $\tilde{z}$ whose distribution was graphed in Problem 2 represents daily demand for a product which is stocked daily and spoils if it is not sold by the end of the day on which it is stocked. If each unit of the product costs $2 and sells for $6, compute:

    a. The best number of units to stock.

    b. Expected loss under your answer to (*a*) and also with stocks of 50, 75, 150, and 200 per cent of your answer to (*a*).

    c. Expected profit under certainty (cf. Section 7.3.1).

    d. Expected profit under the same conditions as in (*b*).

4. In July, 1957, the production manager of the Art-Craft Company was about to schedule his production of 1958 desk calendars. Production had to be completed by the end of August in order to free the plant facilities for manufacture of Christmas novelties. The calendars cost $.30 to make and were sold to wholesalers at a price of $1; any calendars remaining unsold at the end of 1957 would have to be scrapped at a total loss. The sales manager advised the production manager that he believed that about 170,000 calendars could be sold this year; the table on page 303 shows a record of the sales manager's forecasts and of actual demand in earlier years.

    a. How many calendars should be produced?

    b. What is the expected profit and the cost of uncertainty?

    c. What is the cost of irrationality of a decision to schedule 170,000 calendars?

5. A manufacturer about to schedule a production run for stock will suffer a loss of $50 for each unit of demand which he fails to satisfy or a loss of $2 for each unit by which his stock exceeds demand. He employs a statistician to forecast demand by regression analysis, i.e. by finding the relation between demand and a number of other variables such as gross national product, freight-car loadings, data on employment in the steel industry, etc. The statistician forecasts a demand for 2700 units; he also

Year	Forecast	Demand
1946	110,000	106,000
1947	105,000	123,000
1948	125,000	121,000
1949	135,000	137,000
1950	130,000	109,000
1951	125,000	124,000
1952	160,000	147,000
1953	160,000	187,000
1954	170,000	165,000
1955	160,000	165,000
1956	165,000	160,000
1957	150,000	158,000

says that if this forecasting process had been used over the past 10 years the *errors* in individual forecasts would have been roughly Normally distributed with mean 0 and standard deviation 570 units.

How many units should be produced and what is the cost of uncertainty?

6. In a scrap-allowance problem of the type studied in Section 8.2, the distribution of the *process* $\tilde{p} = 1/\bar{p}$ is assessed as Normal with mean 1.307 and standard deviation .0745. The loss factors are $k_o = \$3$ and $K_u = \$1000$. Assuming that a rerun will come out exactly right if one is required:

   a. Find the optimum production order Q for each of the following sizes of purchase order: $G = 1000$, 2000, 5000, and 10,000. [Hint: A good deal of trial-and-error computation can be avoided by expressing the ratio $\mathrm{P}(\tilde{n} = Q)/\mathrm{P}(\tilde{n} < Q)$ as a multiple of the ratio $\mathrm{P}'_N(u_Q)/\mathrm{P}_N(\tilde{u} < u_Q)$ and then using Chart IV.]

   b. Compute the optimal *scrap allowance* $(Q - G)$ for each G and express it as a percentage of G.

   c. Compute the *cost of uncertainty* for each G and express it as a percentage of the total *variable* cost (excluding setup) of manufacturing G pieces good or bad.

   d. In language comprehensible to a person who knows no statistics, discuss the effect of order size G as revealed by your answers to (*b*) and (*c*) and make recommendations for manufacturing and pricing policy.

REVIEW PROBLEMS

The following problems constitute a review of the principal economic types of problems which we have studied in the entire course to date.

1. Part XZ714 is produced by the American Rubber Products Company in a large run once every 6 months, setup costs being too high to permit more frequent runs and shelf life being too short to permit less frequent runs. If any parts are left over from an old run when a new run is scheduled, these parts are thoroughly reconditioned at a variable cost of $4 each; storage costs and the cost of capital tied up in inventory for 6 months or less are negligible in comparison with this cost of deterioration. To avoid loss of good will, American Rubber supplies a part of superior quality at no extra charge to the customer if an order is received for part XZ714 and there is no stock on hand. The variable manufacturing cost of this superior part is $23 whereas the variable manufacturing cost of part XZ714 is only $14.

The sales manager of American Rubber does not believe that sales records more than 3 years old should be used in forecasting future demand because the number of machines on which part XZ714 is used was steadily increasing until about 3 years ago.

Since then, however, he believes that the number of such machines in service has scarcely changed and he knows of no other reason why usage of the part should have changed during the past 3 years or should change during the next 6 months.   The number of parts ordered from American Rubber during the last six semiannual periods has been 2231, 2753, 1970, 2256, 2778, and 1436.

  a. How many units should be produced in the next run, including any old units which are reconditioned at that time?

  b. What is the expected cost of uncertainty?

  2. An order is received by the Acme Automatic Machine Company for 10,000 screw-machine parts.   The design of the part is almost identical to that of a standard part made and stocked by Acme, and in the opinion of Acme's production manager the differences should create no new production problems whatever.   The differences do mean, however, that the part cannot be interchanged in use with standard parts. The customer specifies that the full quantity of 10,000 must be delivered but that he will not pay for any overrun and that it is very unlikely that he will reorder.   Acme's production manager estimates that setup for the job will cost $175 and that variable material, labor, and power will run almost exactly $.35 per part.   Of this $.35 the largest part is for material; scrap parts will have a salvage value of about $.20.

  Before sending the production order to the shop Acme's chief scheduler looks up the record of production runs of the standard part which is almost identical to this special part.   The record is as follows:

Lot number	Number produced	Number defective
1	6,850	445
2	10,370	591
3	9,880	701
4	11,260	586
5	8,325	574
6	9,175	422
7	8,640	458

  a. How many units should the scheduler order into production?

  b. What is a fair premium for Acme to add to the price of the standard part in quoting on this special order?

  3. The Acme Automatic Machine Company sells a wide variety of standard steel studs and bolts from stock but will caseharden these studs only to customer order. The casehardening operation is scheduled only once a week, a large variety of parts being treated in a single batch.   There is a certain amount of shrinkage in the process; the table below shows the record for one part number in each of the last four batches hardened.

Part number	Number hardened	Number defective
XZ-712	8,270	935
AZ-961	11,280	1308
ZB-27	7,675	844
XZ-713	8,325	924

Three days before a regular run of the hardening process is to be made, a telephone order is received for 200 casehardened units of part number XZ-718; the customer states that the material is needed rush and that unless delivery of the full quantity is made within 5 days the order will have to be completely canceled. Part XZ-718 unhardened is carried in inventory at a valuation of $.83 each; the price quoted to the customer for the casehardened parts is $3.17 each net. It costs about $725 for each run of the hardening process; the average number of parts hardened per run is about 12,000.

a. The conditional loss due to overage in this problem is identical to that discussed in Section 8.1 but the loss due to underage is not. Why?

b. Derive expressions for the expected *cost* and expected *revenue* of a decision to schedule Q *pieces* into production, and thus derive the expected *profit* of this decision.

c. Derive expressions for the expected cost and revenue of a decision to schedule the Qth *piece* into production.

d. Derive expressions for expected cost, revenue, and profit *under certainty*.

e. How many units should be hardened?

f. What is the expected cost of uncertainty.

4. The Green Garage Corporation contracts for the maintenance of 2000 taxicabs at a fixed price per cab per year and carries a large inventory of spare parts to support this operation. A typical item in the inventory is a certain model of fuel pump which is used at a rate of about 50 per month on the average. When bought in contract quantity from the Hi-Q company, a manufacturer of off-brand replacement parts, the pumps cost $8.97 each plus a flat $275 setup charge which does not depend on the size of the order. The quality of these off-brand pumps is fully equal to that of the original-equipment pumps sold for $14.70 each through the distributor organization of the manufacturer of the cabs; but because Hi-Q does not carry pumps in stock and there is a 3-month lead time on contract orders, Green is forced to buy some of these original-equipment pumps whenever its own inventory runs out. Green has to rent storage space at a rate which amounts to about $.60 per year per pump stored and is so short of capital that it has been forced to borrow considerable sums at 7 per cent interest.

a. Neglecting the effect of the reorder point on the expected length of cycle, find the optimal order quantity and reorder point for this fuel pump.

b. Compare the cost of this policy with the cost of carrying almost no inventory and purchasing original-equipment pumps on a hand-to-mouth basis.

CHAPTER 19

Waiting Lines

Our study of the Poisson process in Chapter 13 enabled us to derive a probability distribution for the number of successes generated by such a process in a unit of length, time, or "space" in general. Provided that the conditions defining a Poisson process are met and provided that the parameter of the process is known, we can use the Poisson distribution to compute the probability that a machine will produce a certain number of defectives in an hour, or that a certain number of tankers will arrive at a dock during one day, or that so many people will ask for an outside line in a minute.

Now defects produced by a machine are permanent, and how many will occur is all we usually need to know. But tankers leave after they arrive, and telephone calls end as well as begin; and we are usually interested, not so much in how many *arrive* during a particular period of time, as in how many are *in existence* at any one time. The fact of importance is how many tankers are lined up waiting to get to the dock, or how many people are waiting for an outside line, or such related facts as the probability of having to wait, the time lost in waiting, and so forth.

19.1 Waiting Lines in General

If the time to load or unload a tanker or to handle a telephone call is known, if the tanker arrivals or requests for telephone service can be strictly scheduled in advance, and if the capacity of the system is adequate, there will be no waiting line and no probability theory is required. In many situations, however, arrivals can be predicted only in terms of probabilities, and when this is true we often need to assess the probability distribution for number waiting or some summary measure of this distribution such as the mean number waiting. We are now dealing with a probability distribution generated by *two separate processes*, one governing arrivals and one governing departures. The distribution is sometimes called the distribution of "number living" when one process produces "births" and the other produces "deaths."

19.1.1 The Steady State of a Waiting Line

The behavior of an *incipient* waiting line is extremely complex because the probabilities themselves keep changing with time. When a

new dock is opened for business, for example, there is obviously probability 0 that the *first* ship will have to wait at all. The probability
that the second ship will have to wait is greater, the probability that
the third ship will wait is greater still, and so forth. In terms of the
number waiting, the probability that there will be no one waiting is obviously lower for the second day of business than for the first, lower still
for the third day, and so forth. Complete analysis of a waiting line
therefore involves an infinite number of probability distributions, each
one of which applies to only a single moment of time.

Fortunately we do not need this kind of complete analysis in most
business problems. If a dock working full time is unable to discharge all
the tankers which arrive, the waiting line will obviously go on growing
indefinitely and the decision implications are clear enough without a
detailed computation of just *how* it will grow. If, on the other hand, the
dock *is* capable of handling all the tankers which arrive, it can be proved
that the probability distribution for number waiting will ultimately
become stable: it reaches what is known technically as a *steady state*.
Notice that this does *not* mean that the *number waiting* will remain constant: it will not. It is only the *probability distribution* of the number
waiting which remains constant.

In rather loose language, the meaning of a steady state can be
expressed as follows. After the line has reached its steady state, then in
every month (or hour or year) we "expect" to have just about d_0 minutes
in which there are 0 individuals waiting, d_1 minutes in which there is
1 individual, etc. Before the line reaches the steady state, the number
d_0 is different in every month, and similarly for d_1, d_2, etc.

In this course we shall deal only with waiting lines in a steady state, and
this qualification should be attached to all statements in the rest of this
chapter.

19.1.2 Conditions Determining the Length of Line

It is intuitively clear that the probability distribution for the number
waiting must depend on four factors:

1. The probability distribution of the time between *arrivals*.
2. The probability distribution of the amount of time required for
   service after a member of the line gets his turn. This is known as
   the *holding time*.
3. The number of *stations* providing service.
4. The "*line discipline*," i.e., the assumptions we make about the
   behavior of members of the line once they are in line. (Do they
   always wait their turn, or do they go elsewhere if the line is too
   long? If there is more than one station, is there a single line so
   that the first to arrive is served first, or are separate lines formed
   in front of each station? And so forth.)

Except under very special sets of assumptions concerning these four factors, waiting lines are impossible to analyze mathematically and must be handled by the "Monte Carlo" method which we shall discuss in the next chapter. We shall nevertheless devote the present chapter to certain special cases which *can* be analyzed mathematically, in part because these cases occur quite frequently in practice, but more especially because the results of this analysis will give us a useful general feeling for the behavior of all waiting lines.

The simplest cases to analyze mathematically, and the only ones which will be discussed in this chapter, involve the following assumptions:

1. The arrivals are Poisson distributed: the probability of an arrival is the same at all instants of time regardless of what has happened in all previous instants;
2. There is a single line with the rule first come, first served, and no customer leaves the line until he has been served.

Given these two assumptions the behavior of the waiting line will be determined by the shape of the distribution of the holding times, which we shall discuss in due course, and by the numerical values of the following parameters:

A: mean time interval between arrivals,
H: mean holding time,
n: number of serving stations or clerks.

The meaning of many of the formulas which describe the behavior of a waiting line will be clearer if the formulas are expressed in terms of certain auxiliary parameters which are simply combinations of the three basic parameters just defined. Since the mean time between arrivals is A, the mean number of arrivals per unit of time is $1/A$, and therefore

$m = H/A$: the relative traffic intensity

is the expected number of arrivals during the mean time required to serve one customer. If there were exactly m stations, the system would have just enough capacity to handle the demands on its service, and therefore

$\rho = m/n$: the degree of capacity utilization

will measure the extent to which the theoretical capacity of the system is actually utilized.

19.2   Exponential Holding Times

The first special case which we shall study is that in which the holding times have an exponential distribution, since it is only when this condition is met in addition to the two listed in the previous section that it is possible to give a simple and yet complete analysis of the behavior of a waiting line with any number of serving stations. We have seen in Section 14.2 that in many practical situations holding times in fact have a distribution which is very close to exponential, and the results which we are about to give for this case have been extensively applied in the telephone industry and elsewhere. We must always remember, however, that when we face a new application we will virtually never have enough understanding of the physical process generating the holding times to be sure a priori that their distribution is exponential; the only way of making sure is actually to measure a large number of holding times and to look at their frequency distribution in the way described in Section 14.2.

19.2.1 The Probability of Delay

The first step in computing any measure of the behavior of a waiting line under the conditions we are now assuming is to compute the probability that an arriving customer will find all n serving stations busy and will therefore have to wait in line before he is served. We shall denote this probability by

$P(D)$: the probability of delay,

and it turns out very conveniently that the mathematical formula for $P(D)$ can be expressed in terms of Poisson probabilities with parameter m:

$$P(D) = \frac{\mathrm{P}_{Po}(\tilde{r} = n|m)}{\mathrm{P}_{Po}(\tilde{r} = n|m) + (1 - \rho)\,\mathrm{P}_{Po}(\tilde{r} < n|m)} \qquad \text{\textit{Exponential holding times}}$$

There is no intuitive "explanation" for the appearance of these particular probabilities in this formula, and in fact the "random variable" $\tilde{r}$ has no real meaning. It simply happens that it is possible to reduce the mathematical expression for $P(D)$ to a form which is equivalent to a combination of formulas for Poisson probabilities, and we do reduce it in this way because this makes it possible to calculate $P(D)$ by use of tables of the Poisson distribution.

Example. Suppose that a certain service facility has $n = 5$ service stations, that the mean time between arrivals is $A = 4$ minutes, and that the mean time required to serve one customer is $H = 18$ minutes. Then the relative intensity of the traffic is $m = H/A = 18/4 = 4.5$ and the degree of capacity utilization is $\rho = m/n = 4.5/5 = .9$. We use Chart I to find

$\mathrm{P}_{Po}(\tilde{r} < 5|m = 4.5) = 1 - \mathrm{P}_{Po}(\tilde{r} \geq 5) = .532,$
$\mathrm{P}_{Po}(\tilde{r} = 5|m = 4.5) = \mathrm{P}_{Po}(\tilde{r} \geq 5) - \mathrm{P}_{Po}(\tilde{r} \geq 6) = .171,$

and we then compute

$$P(D) = \frac{.171}{.171 + (1 - .9).532} = .763;$$

76.3 per cent of all customers will have to wait in line before they are served.

19.2.2   The Probability Distribution of Waiting Time

The probability distribution for the time that any individual customer will have to wait before being served can now be expressed in terms of $P(D)$ and the standardized exponential distribution, i.e. the standardized gamma distribution with parameter $r = 1$. If we define the random variable

$\tilde{t}$: time that a customer waits before service begins,

then right-tail cumulative probabilities for $\tilde{t}$ are given by the formula

$$P(\tilde{t} > t) = P(D) \, P_g \left[\tilde{v} > \frac{t}{H} (n - m) | r = 1 \right] \qquad \begin{array}{l} \textit{Exponential holding} \\ \textit{times} \end{array}$$

For example, suppose that we wish to know the probability that a customer will have to wait more than an hour before receiving a clerk's attention in our example with $n = 5$, $H = 18$ minutes, $m = 4.5$, and $P(D) = .763$. We compute

$$\frac{t}{H} (n - m) = \frac{60}{18} (5.0 - 4.5) = 1.67,$$

use the curve for $r = 1$ in Chart I to find

$$P_g(\tilde{v} > 1.67) = 1 - P_g(\tilde{v} < 1.67) = .188,$$

and then compute

$$P(\tilde{t} > 60) = .763 \times .188 = .143.$$

The student should observe that the formula for the distribution of $\tilde{t}$ implies (1) that the *conditional* distribution of $\tilde{t}$ *given* that the customer is not served immediately is exponential but (2) that the *marginal* distribution of $\tilde{t}$ is *not* exponential—there is a finite probability $1 - P(D)$ that the value of $\tilde{t}$ will be exactly 0. This means that when we wish to compute "the" probability that $\tilde{t}$ will be *less* than a specified amount we *cannot* proceed by simply reversing the inequality signs in the formula; we must first compute the probability that $\tilde{t}$ will be greater than the specified value and then subtract from 1.

19.2.3 The Probability Distribution of Number Waiting

The probability that there will be any specified number of customers waiting their turn for service at any given instant (*not* counting customers actually being served) can also be expressed in terms of $P(D)$. If we define the random variable

$\tilde{w}$: number of customers waiting; the length of the waiting line

then the probability distribution of $\tilde{w}$ is given by the formula

$$P(\tilde{w} > w) = \rho^{w+1} P(D) \qquad \textit{Exponential holding times}$$

In our example with $\rho = .9$ and $P(D) = .763$, the probability that there will be more than three customers waiting for service is

$$P(\tilde{w} > 3) = .9^4 \times .763 = .656 \times .763 = .500.$$

The probability that there will be no one waiting is

$$P(\tilde{w} = 0) = 1 - P(\tilde{w} > 0) = 1 - \rho P(D) = 1 - (.9 \times .763)$$
$$= .313.$$

19.2.4 Mean Number Waiting; Time Lost by Customers

The mean number waiting or mean length of line—the expected value of the random variable $\tilde{w}$—can be shown to be

$$E(\tilde{w}) = \frac{\rho}{1 - \rho} P(D) \qquad \textit{Exponential holding times}$$

Continuing with our example in which $\rho = .9$ and $P(D) = .763$, the mean number of customers waiting to be served is

$$E(\tilde{w}) = \frac{.9}{1 - .9} \times .763 = 6.87.$$

Since the total amount of time spent in waiting by all customers together is equal to the mean number of customers waiting at any one time multiplied by the length of time the line exists, *the total time lost by all customers in one unit of elapsed time is equal to the mean number of individuals in the line.* Thus the formula for $E(\tilde{w})$ also gives the number of man-weeks lost per calendar week by mechanics waiting at a tool crib or the number of tanker-years lost per calendar year because tankers cannot come up to the dock immediately upon arrival. In our example 6.87 customer-hours are lost every hour.

Customer Loss Ratio. While it is the actual time lost by customers which is usually relevant to a *decision* which will affect a waiting line, we can gain a better *understanding* of the behavior of waiting lines by comparing this lost time with the time the customers spend usefully in being served. We therefore define the "dimensionless" *customer loss ratio*

$$R = \frac{\text{time spent by customers in waiting for service}}{\text{time spent by customers in being served}}.$$

The time which "customers" spend being served is obviously equal to the time which "clerks" spend in rendering service, and the amount of time during which the clerks render service during unit elapsed time is simply the number of stations n multiplied by ρ, the fraction of time during which the "average clerk" is busy. We have already seen that the amount of time which customers spend waiting during unit elapsed time is $E(\tilde{w})$, and therefore we can rewrite our definition of the customer loss ratio in the form

$$R = \frac{E(\tilde{w})}{\rho n} = \frac{E(\tilde{w})}{m} \qquad \textit{Definition of customer loss ratio}$$

This definition holds for any waiting line whatever, but the numerical evaluation of $E(\tilde{w})$ in any particular case will of course depend on the conditions affecting the operation of that particular line. Continuing with our example of a line with exponential holding times and $n = 5$, $\rho = .9$, $E(\tilde{w}) = 6.87$, we have

$$R = \frac{6.87}{4.5} = 1.53.$$

Customers on the average spend 1.53 hours waiting for every hour they spend being served.

19.2.5   *General Observations on the Behavior of Waiting Lines*

The Need for Planned Idle Time. Figures 19.1a and b show what happens to the probability that a customer will have to wait and to the amount of time that he must "expect" to wait as the demands on a service facility approach the theoretical capacity of the facility. The more important of the two graphs is of course the second one, and the most striking fact about that graph is this:

As demands for service approach the system's theoretical capacity to render service, the ratio of customer lost time to useful time increases without bound.

If management tries to keep a single-station facility busy 90 per cent of the time, customers will spend 9 hours in waiting for every hour they spend being served. The implications are clear:

> Whenever demands for service occur irregularly and the time required to render service is irregular, management should deliberately allow for a substantial amount of idle time in any service facility.

The Gains from Expanded Facilities. When long waiting lines are observed ahead of some service facility, it is natural to think that it will require a substantial percentage increase in the number of service stations to make a substantial percentage decrease in the length of line. One of the most useful general results of the systematic study of waiting lines is to show that this intuitive belief is usually quite false. Figure 19.1*b* shows that the really sharp increase in the length of line does not occur until the load on the system is quite close to the theoretical capacity of the system, i.e. until the idle time or slack in the system becomes very small. A small percentage increase in the capacity of a heavily loaded system will make a very large percentage increase in the slack and will therefore usually produce a very substantial reduction in the length of the waiting line and the customer lost time.

Suppose, for example, that a four-station line is loaded to 90 per cent of capacity. Figure 19.2*b* shows that customers will lose 2 hours in waiting for every hour that they spend being served. If one more station is added to the facility, the utilization of the resulting five-station system will be $(.9 \times 4)/5$ or just over .7, and Figure 19.2*b* shows that customers at a five-station system with $\rho = .7$ lose only a small fraction of an hour in waiting for each hour spent being served.

The Effect of Pooling Facilities. Another very interesting general result obtained by systematic analysis of waiting lines bears on the gains which can be made by pooling or centralizing a number of service facilities. The common sense of this point is obvious: if 10 clerks are scattered in 10 separate tool cribs, some will be idle while others are faced with long waiting lines, whereas if all 10 are put in a central crib, those who were idle will be able to assist those who were overloaded and the customers will receive faster service. The contribution of theoretical analysis is in the light that it throws on the rather surprising magnitude of the gains to be made in this way.

Suppose first that we have five separate single-station service facilities all loaded to 90 per cent of capacity; we have already seen that the curve for $n = 1$ in Figure 19.1*b* shows that the customers at each of these facilities will spend 9 hours in waiting for every hour they spend being served. Suppose next that the five facilities are pooled into a single 5-station facility; this facility will also be loaded to 90 per cent of capacity,

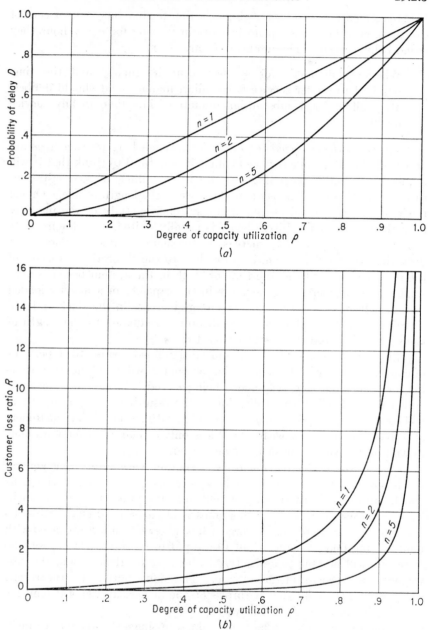

Figure 19.1. **Waiting lines with Poisson arrivals and exponential holding times.**

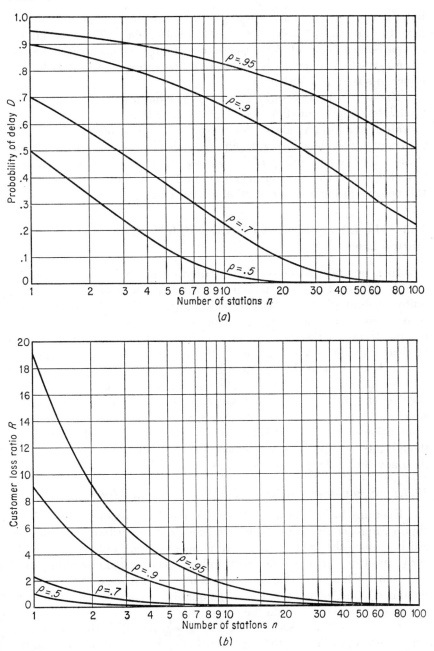

Figure 19.2. **Waiting lines with Poisson arrivals and exponential holding times.**

but the curve for $n = 5$ in Figure 19.1*b* shows that customers will now have to wait only 1.5 hours for every hour of service.   The same kind of comparison can be made for larger values of n by looking at Figure 19.2*b*: when a 20-station facility is loaded to 90 per cent of capacity, the customer loss ratio is less than .5.

Figures 19.1*a* and 19.2*a* show that pooling also has an interesting though less important effect on the probability that a customer will have to wait at all.   In a single-station line the probability of delay is equal to the fraction of time ρ during which the station is busy, but in a multiple-station line the probability of delay is less than ρ.   Although each individual station is free only during a fraction $1 - \rho$ of the time, *some* station will be free during a larger fraction of the time.

19.3   The Effect of Nonexponential Holding Times on a Single-station Line

In a practical situation the distribution of holding times is never exactly exponential, and in many situations the distribution departs quite substantially from the exponential form.   We would therefore like to have some way of getting a feeling for the effect of nonexponential holding times on the behavior of a waiting line, and although mathematical analysis of waiting lines with nonexponential holding times is extremely difficult in the general case of n serving stations, it is possible to give simple formulas for the behavior of a *single-station* line with *any distribution of holding times whatever* provided that *the arrivals are Poisson distributed*.   Since there are a great many practical situations where the assumption of Poisson arrivals agrees very closely with the facts even though the corresponding assumption for the holding times does not, we shall now look briefly at this second special case.

19.3.1   Summary Measures for a Single-station Line

Even in the case of a single-station line it is usually impossible to obtain formulas giving the complete probability distribution of number waiting when the holding times are nonexponential, but what we ordinarily need in a practical decision problem is either the probability that a customer will have to wait or the mean number waiting (the time lost by customers), and fortunately these two quantities are what we *are* able to obtain for any single-station line.

The Probability of Delay.   In a single-station line, the probability that a customer will have to wait before being served depends only on the mean H of the distribution of holding times and not on any other property of that distribution.   The customer will have to wait if the single station is busy when he arrives, and since the station is busy a fraction $H/A = \rho$ of the time,

---

$$P(D) = \rho \qquad \textit{Single-station line; any holding times}$$

We remind the student that this is *not* true of multiple-station lines; the reason was discussed at the end of Section 19.2.5 above.

Mean Number Waiting; Time Lost by Customers. Although the probability of delay depends only on the mean holding time, it is obvious that the number waiting will also depend on the variability of the holding times—long lines tend to form behind a customer who takes a long time being served. We therefore let $\tilde{h}$ denote the random variable "holding time" and define

$\sigma^2(\tilde{h}/H)$: the variance of the ratio of actual holding time to mean holding time.

The mean number waiting in line can then be shown to be

$$E(\tilde{w}) = \frac{\rho^2}{1-\rho} \frac{1 + \sigma^2(\tilde{h}/H)}{2} \qquad \textit{Single-station line; any holding times}$$

---

and for the reason explained in Section 19.2.4 above this formula can also be interpreted as giving the total time lost by customers per unit of elapsed time.

19.3.2   *Comparison of Exponential and Uniform Holding Times*

Looking at the formula just given for $E(\tilde{w})$ in a single-station line, we see first of all that, for a given degree of capacity utilization ρ, the time lost by customers will be least when $\sigma^2(\tilde{h}/H) = 0$, i.e. when holding times are *absolutely uniform*. This confirms our intuitive feeling that customers who require very long service times tend to build up long waiting lines behind them.

At virtually the opposite extreme we have the *exponential* distribution of holding times. We saw in Section 16.5.2 that if a random variable $\tilde{l}$ is the sum of r random variables all having exponential distributions with mean μ, then $\sigma^2(\tilde{l}/\mu) = r$. In our present problem we are dealing with a "sum" which consists of a single random variable, $r = 1$, and therefore $\sigma^2(\tilde{h}/H) = 1$ if $\tilde{h}$ has an exponential distribution. Looking back at the formula for $E(\tilde{w})$, we see that in this case the time lost by customers is exactly double what it is when the holding times are uniform and $\sigma^2(\tilde{h}/H) = 0$.

Most distributions of holding times encountered in practice will have more variability than the uniform but less than the exponential, and the time lost by customers will be between the values obtained by substituting 0 and 1 for $\sigma^2(\bar{h}/H)$ in the formula for $E(\bar{w})$. Unfortunately no such simple quantitative statement is possible for multiple-station lines; all that we can say is that the time lost by customers will usually be "somewhat" below the value given by the formula in Section 19.2.4 above.

PROBLEMS

1. Calculate the relative traffic intensity m and the degree of capacity utilization ρ for a three-station waiting line with the following characteristics:

  a. Mean arrival rate: 9 per minute; mean holding time: .2 minute.

  b. System can serve 75 per hour; 20 arrive per hour.

2. A single-station waiting line has a theoretical capacity of 20 per hour; the mean arrival rate is 18 per hour and is Poisson distributed. What is the probability that a customer will have to wait in line and what is the expected length of line

  a. If the holding time is exponentially distributed?

  b. If the holding time is constant?

  c. If $\sigma^2(\bar{h}/H) = .5$?

3. For each of the three sets of conditions stated in Problem 2, compute:

  a. Total time lost by customers per 8-hour shift.

  b. The expected time lost by an individual customer.

  c. The expected time lost by an individual customer who in fact has to wait in line (part *b* asks you to average lost time over all customers, part *c* to average over only those customers who have to wait).

  d. Customer loss ratio.

  e. Total time lost by clerks per 8-hour shift.

  f. Ratio of time lost by clerks to time spent by clerks in rendering service.

4. In a 10-station waiting line serving 40 Poisson-distributed arrivals per hour with exponentially distributed serving times having a mean of 12 minutes, compute the same quantities computed in Problem 3 and also

  g. The probability that a customer will have to wait more than 15 minutes before service begins.

  h. The probability that there will be three or more customers waiting in line.

5. What is the effect of adding another service station to the 10 described in Problem 4?

6. Holding times for service at a tool crib are exponentially distributed and the mean holding time is 1.6 minutes. The crib is open for business 8 hours a day, and the crib serves almost exactly 250 mechanics every day. Arrivals are equally frequent at all hours of the day.

If a clerk's time is worth $2 an hour and a mechanic's time is worth $8 (including the overhead allocated to machinery which is idle while he is at the crib), how many clerks should management assign to the crib? Do you need any other management information before answering?

7. It has been argued that decisions should not be based on waiting-line theory because it assumes that arrivals and holding times follow a mathematical "law" whereas in real life these things occur "at random." Discuss.

8. Mr. Albert Brooks, the director of public relations for New England Airlines, had heard many complaints from people who had called the company's Boston office for reservations or information and had had to wait, often for considerable periods of time, before they were connected with a reservation clerk. Those persons were particularly exasperated who wanted only some very simple information and yet had to wait several minutes to get a few seconds of a clerk's time. Mr. Brooks believed that delays of this sort directly undermined what he regarded as the airlines' principal competitive advantage, saving time for their customers.

The Boston office of New England Airlines had a large number of trunk lines available to handle incoming calls requesting information and/or reservations. All incoming calls were answered by an operator who gave no information herself but simply routed the calls to extensions manned by reservation clerks. If all reservation clerks were busy the operator asked the caller to wait. As soon as a clerk became free, she was given the call which had been waiting the longest time.

Reservation clerks were paid $3 an hour and the company hesitated to incur the expense of additional clerks, but Mr. Brooks argued that there was a real good-will cost involved in the current delays suffered by customers. Although he was unwilling to give a specific figure for the good-will cost of 1 minute of waiting, he believed that the company's officers would use sound business judgment to decide on the proper number of clerks if they were shown figures on the relation between the number of clerks and the amount of time the average customer would have to wait.

Mr. Brooks decided therefore to obtain as much information as he could on the problem. He requested the four telephone operators who covered the "normal peak hours" of 10 A.M. to 4 P.M. Monday through Friday to record for each incoming call whether the caller was routed directly to a clerk or was asked to wait and whether those who were asked to wait did in fact wait or hung up before being served. The operators did not have enough free time to measure and record the actual time waited on each call.

The operators kept records for 1 week, or five 6-hour "normal peak" periods. During this time there were 21,800 incoming calls, of which 19,500 were delayed. Virtually none of the callers refused to wait until they were finally connected.

On seeing Mr. Brooks's figures, some of the company's officers argued that the situation was hopeless. Ten clerks had been on duty during the entire test period. This was the standard number of clerks for "normal peak hours," and if only about 10 per cent of all calls could be handled immediately by 10 clerks, these officers alleged that it would require an enormous force to handle 90 per cent, say, of the calls without delay. The record showed that calls were evenly distributed over the normal peak hours, so that the question was not one of increasing the force during a few critical hours.

Mr. Brooks was not convinced that such a large increase in the staff would be required, however, and suggested an experiment with 11 or 12 clerks to see what would happen. This turned out to be impossible because there were no extra trained clerks available for the experiment. When the company needed extra clerks for some reason—under unusual weather conditions, for example—people were often taken off other jobs and used as reservation clerks. The job required considerable training and experience, however, and people used in emergencies obviously worked much more slowly than fully trained clerks, so that any experiment in which such substitute clerks were used would be inconclusive.

Discuss the implications of Mr. Brooks's data.

CHAPTER 20

The Monte Carlo Method

We have now studied several types of problems in which *mathematical analysis* can be used to deduce the probability distribution of the cost-determining random variable from given probabilities for a related "basic" variable or variables. In many types of problems, however, such deductions cannot be carried out analytically, and it is therefore a fact of very great practical importance that they can almost always be carried out by *experimentation*. Only mathematical analysis will yield a formula which gives the exact answer to all problems of a given type, but experimentation can always be used to get an approximate numerical answer to a particular problem containing specific numerical data; and we can usually make the approximation as accurate as we need. Solution of problems by experimentation of this sort is known as the Monte Carlo method.

20.1 The Monte Carlo Principle

Suppose that we require the probability distribution for the number of defectives which a machine will produce in a lot of 100 pieces given that the probability that an individual piece will be defective is $\frac{1}{2}$. As we already know, this problem can be solved mathematically, but it can also be solved by the Monte Carlo method and affords the simplest possible illustration of the essential principle of the method.

The principle of the Monte Carlo method is to find some cheap way of making artificial trials the possible events of which have the same long-run frequencies as the events in which we are really interested. We then make a large number of trials and assess the required probabilities on the basis of the relative frequencies with which the various artificial events occur. The problem just stated as an example could be solved by representing the number of defectives in a lot of 100 pieces by the number of heads which occur when 100 fair coins are tossed. Considering one toss of 100 coins as a single "experiment," we would perform this experiment a large number of times, each time recording the number of heads. At the end of the series of experiments we would compute the relative frequency with which each number of heads had occurred, and we would take these

320

relative frequencies as the basis for our assessment of the required probabilities. If the number of experiments had been extremely great and the resulting frequency distribution was very smooth, we might simply equate the probabilities to the observed frequencies. If the frequency distribution looked ragged, we would smooth it before assessing the probabilities.

The operation would be still simpler if we required, not the complete distribution for number of defectives, but merely the probability of some event such as "more than 56 defectives." In this case we would simply record whether each successive experiment did or did not result in more than 56 heads; and after the series of experiments was over we would simply equate the desired probability to the observed relative frequency.

20.2 Practical Monte Carlo Operations

Let us now look very briefly at the two principal devices which are used to carry out Monte Carlo operations in practice: the use of "random numbers" and the combination of mathematical analysis with the Monte Carlo method. We shall continue to use examples which could be completely solved by analysis whenever such examples are the best ones to make a point.

20.2.1 Use of Random Numbers

A table of *random digits* is simply a list of digits from 0 to 9 in the order in which they were generated by a process which is believed to generate the digits independently and with equal relative frequencies in the long run—it is believed, for example, that the digit 3 tends to occur $\frac{1}{10}$ of the time, that $\frac{1}{10}$ of the 3's tend to be followed by a 3, and so forth. A short table of random digits is presented as Table V.†

If we "draw" a digit from such a table in such a way that there is no possibility of preferring certain digits consciously or unconsciously, we will assign probability .1 to each of the 10 possible values 0 to 9. If we draw two digits and regard them as a two-digit number, we will assign probability .01 to each of the 100 possible values 00 to 99, and so forth. If then we wish to make a trial with probability .5 of success, all we need to do is draw a digit from the table and count it as a success if it is between 0 and 4 inclusive, a failure if it is between 5 and 9 inclusive. If we wish to make a trial with probability .037 of success, we draw a three-digit number and count it as a success if it is between 000 and 036 inclusive, a failure if it is between 037 and 999 inclusive. If the required probability were .1286, we would have to draw a four-digit number, and so forth.

† For a very extensive table, see The RAND Corporation, "A Million Random Digits," Free Press, Glencoe, Ill., 1955.

Suppose now that we wish to deduce the probability distribution for number defective in a lot of 100 when the probability that an individual piece will be defective is .037 rather than $\frac{1}{2}$ as in our previous example. We can make an experiment corresponding to one lot by simply reading off 100 three-digit numbers and counting each number below 037 as a defective. This experiment corresponds to *one* toss of 100 coins in our previous example, and a large number of such experiments will generate a frequency distribution for number defective.

20.2.2   Use of Mathematical Analysis

In the extremely simple examples discussed above, each Monte Carlo trial represented a real trial (manufacture of one piece) which had only two possible events the probabilities of which were "basic," i.e. assessed directly from experience. In many problems it is more convenient or even necessary to let the Monte Carlo trials represent more complex trials, the probabilities for the various possible events being obtained from the basic probabilities by mathematical analysis.

Suppose, for example, that we wish to deduce the probability that a machine will produce more than three defects in each of 5 successive feet of wire and that we wish to represent the machine as a Poisson process generating three defects per foot. In order to reduce this problem to one involving trials with probabilities set directly by experience, we would have to think of the wire as divided into extremely small pieces each of which could be considered a Bernoulli trial, and each of these would have to be represented by one Monte Carlo trial. This means that there would have to be a very large number of trials in any one experiment representing 5 successive feet of wire, and a reasonably large number of experiments would mean an extremely large number of trials. The operation would be excessively time-consuming and costly.

We can get around this difficulty if we use the Poisson distribution to obtain the probabilities of zero, one, two, etc., defects in any 1 foot. From Chart I we find that when $m = 3$ the probability of zero defects is .050, the probability of one is .149, of two is .224, etc. We could then make each Monte Carlo trial yield the number of defects in 1 *foot* of wire by drawing three-digit random numbers and interpreting any number from 000 to 049 inclusive as the event "zero defects," any number from 050 to 198 inclusive as the event "one defect," etc., but in the problem we have taken as an example the procedure can be even simpler. Since we are interested only in whether a foot does or does not contain more than three defects, we find from Chart I that $P_{Po}(\tilde{r} > 3|m = 3) = .353$ and we take all numbers from 000 to 352 inclusive as representing the event "more than three defects." Each experiment consists in drawing five three-digit numbers, and the whole experiment counts as *one* "success" if *all five* numbers are below 353. The fraction of all experiments resulting in a success is the basis for assessing the probability that there will be more than three defects in each of 5 successive feet of wire.

Use of Cumulative Intermediate Distributions. Let us use the term "intermediate probabilities" to denote probabilities like the Poisson probabilities in the example just discussed, i.e. probabilities which are derived from the basic probabilities by mathematical analysis and then used as the starting point for a Monte Carlo operation. If the intermediate distribution assigns nonzero probability to a large number of values of the variable, it would be a nuisance to have to write out in advance

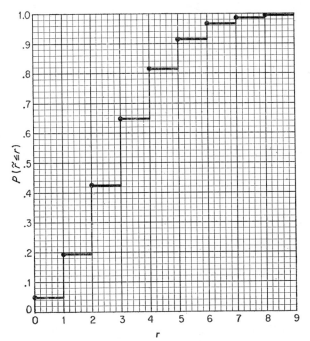

Figure 20.1. Cumulative Poisson distribution, $m = 3$.

which values correspond to which random numbers, and this step can be avoided by using the cumulative form of the intermediate distribution.

Continuing with the example just discussed, we show in Figure 20.1 the cumulative Poisson distribution $P_{Po}(\tilde{r} \leq r | m = 3)$. Suppose now that we draw three-digit random numbers and that the first number drawn is 107. We interpret this as the decimal fraction .107, locate this number on the vertical axis of Figure 20.1, read across to the "curve" and down to the horizontal scale, and find $r = 1$. We then take this trial as resulting in the event "one defective."

The procedure works because the probability that a random number will lead to any given value of the variable is proportional to the height of the "jump" in the graph at that value of the variable, and the height of this jump is in turn proportional to the probability of that value of the variable. Putting the distribution in cumulative form simply accomplishes exactly what we accomplished before by assigning all possible random numbers to values of the variable in proportion to their probabilities. Notice that *it makes no difference whether we use a left-tail or right-tail distribution:* the heights of the jumps at each value of the variable are the same in either case.

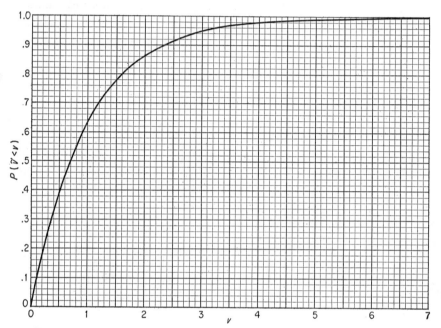

Figure 20.2. Standardized cumulative exponential distribution.

Use of Continuous Distributions. Suppose next that we wish to draw a series of *intervals* between defects in a piece of wire when the defects are Poisson distributed. In this case the "intermediate" distribution is the continuous exponential distribution, but even though the graph of such a distribution contains no jumps it can be used in the same way as Figure 20.1.

Assume first that the mean interval $\mu = 1$. Then the standardized variable $\tilde{v} = \tilde{l}/\mu$ always has the same numerical value as the natural variable $\tilde{l}$, and the graph of the cumulative distribution $P_g(\tilde{v} < v | r = 1)$ shown as Figure 20.2 can be read directly as a graph of the natural distribution $P(\tilde{l} < t | r = 1, \mu = 1)$. Intervals can be drawn from this graph exactly as numbers of successes were drawn from Figure 20.1. If the first random number is 760, we locate .760 on the vertical axis and read across to the curve and down to $t = 1.4$ on the horizontal axis: the length of the interval is 1.4.

The reason the method works in the continuous case can best be understood by looking at the probability of drawing an interval *less than* any specified length rather than at the probability of drawing an interval of *exactly* some specified length. Since there is probability .760 that a three-digit random number will be smaller than 760, the method just described will lead us with probability .760 to assign a value less than 1.4 to the interval: there is probability .760 of "drawing" an interval shorter than 1.4. But by Figure 20.2 this is the probability that an interval will *actually be* shorter than 1.4; and the same correspondence holds for any other length of interval.

When the mean interval μ is not equal to 1, one additional step is necessary. We draw values of the standardized variable $\bar{v}$ from the chart by the procedure described above, and we then convert each value so drawn into the corresponding value of $\bar{t}$. If, for example, $\mu = 2$ and we draw the random number 760 and thus the value $v = 1.4$, we say that we have drawn the value $t = \mu v = 2 \times 1.4 = 2.8$.

20.3 High-speed Computers

In a great many practical business problems, the best—i.e., the most economical—way of applying the Monte Carlo method to get the required answers with the needed accuracy will be to use a pencil and a simple table of random numbers in the way described above. Occasionally there will be a real need for great accuracy in the results and this will require so large a number of experiments that they cannot practically be made by hand. Somewhat more frequently the relation between the basic probabilities and the probabilities or summary measures to be deduced will be so complex that a good deal of calculation must follow each Monte Carlo trial. In such situations hand computation may become unduly slow and cost more than it costs to write and test a "program" which will instruct a high-speed digital computer to do *exactly the same things which would otherwise be done by hand.*

If a computer is used, the basic trials are made by "drawing" random numbers which can either be fed into the machine on cards or tape or be generated by the machine itself. "Intermediate" probability distributions may be stored in the machine and consulted when required, or the machine may compute intermediate probabilities from their formulas. *The machine computes and records the results of the successive experiments and ultimately summarizes them in exactly the same way in which the work would be done by hand.*

20.4 The Proper Number of Monte Carlo Experiments

The basis for assessing any probability by the Monte Carlo method is the relative frequency with which some event occurs in a finite number of "experiments," and it is obvious that this frequency will rarely be exactly equal to the true value of the probability—i.e., to the value which is in fact logically consistent with the basic probabilities from which the analysis started. The same proposition holds, of course, for any summary measure such as the mean of a probability distribution which is computed by the Monte Carlo method. When we design a Monte Carlo procedure we set up a *process* which (we believe) would yield the exact value of the quantity we seek if we made an infinite number of experiments. The experiments we actually make constitute a *sample* of the potentially infinite output of the process, and the results are subject to "sampling error."

The problem of deciding on the proper number of Monte Carlo experiments is thus just one very special case of the problem of deciding on the proper size for a sample. Whenever we base a decision on the evidence of a sample, there is a risk that sampling error will lead us to make a wrong decision. This risk can be reduced indefinitely by increasing the size of the sample, but this costs money and after some point it costs more than it is worth. The remainder of the course will be devoted to the economics of sampling; and by the end of the course we shall know how to determine the economic size for a Monte Carlo run.

PROBLEMS

1. Part XB411 of the Hynes heavy-duty engine lathe was not subject to wear but broke from time to time when subjected to unusually heavy stresses. The lathe was used by two companies, Gridley Machine Works and Burke Appliance. Both companies carried spares for part XB411 in inventory and controlled the inventory by the min-max system. Gridley's order quantity was 4 units; Burke's was 5; both companies had a reorder point so high that the risk of shortage of the part was negligible.

Assuming that Gridley's actual usage of the part was Poisson distributed with $\kappa = 1.2$ per month and that Burke's usage was Poisson distributed with $\kappa = 2$ per month, use the Monte Carlo method to obtain a dated sequence of orders received from Gridley over a 5-year period and a similar sequence of orders from Burke, use these two sequences to compute the total number of units ordered from Hynes in each month of the 5-year period, and compute the frequency distribution of monthly demand. (HINT: The interval between Gridley's orders has a gamma distribution with $r = 4$.)

2. The Great Eastern Steel Corporation operated a dock at a port on the East coast of the United States at which it unloaded iron ore coming by ship from Venezuela. The dock had facilities for unloading two ships at one time. The ships were all of about the same size and type, and it took just about one 24-hour day to unload one. Labor was readily available, and the company was neither forced to pay for a crew's time when there was no ship to unload nor unable to go on a three-shift 7-day basis when the number of arrivals required.

This arrangement had worked out very well for several years. The ships radioed their arrival enough in advance so that a crew was always ready. Not infrequently an arriving ship found both of the dock positions occupied and had to wait before being unloaded, but it was very rarely that the delay amounted to more than a few hours. In September, 1955, however, management became concerned about the fact that the approaching completion of its new steel mill would increase ore requirements and therefore ship arrivals.   About 500 shiploads of ore would be required per year instead of the previous 250, and management was afraid the ships, for which the company paid a charter rate of $1400 a day, would sometimes have to wait a very considerable amount of time before being unloaded.

A study had been made of the possibility of making the arrivals more regular, but it appeared that the variety of conditions encountered during the voyage made this impossible.   (Ships could, of course, be instructed to proceed at slow speed when normal speed would have led to arrivals producing congestion in the harbor.)   A study of past records showed that ships arrived completely unpredictably: equally often at all hours and on all days throughout the year with no apparent pattern.

A study was then made of the possibility of extending the dock or of building a new dock near by.   The study showed that, using the most economical location available, the company would be obliged to spend about $1.4 million to build a one-berth dock and install all necessary equipment such as cranes, rail spurs, etc.   Maintenance of the new facilities would cost about $30,000 a year; operating expenses could be neglected because they depended on the number of ships arriving and not on the number of berths available—no premium was paid to dock crews for working nights or holidays.   The life of the proposed new facilities was estimated at 30 years, and the company's policy was to make no investments which did not earn 30 per cent on the investment before taxes.   The construction of the dock and installation of the facilities could not be completed by the time the new mill was in operation unless it was begun almost immediately.

Should the new dock be built?

PART THREE

The Use of Information
Obtained by Sampling

CHAPTER 21

Revision of Probabilities
in the Light of New Information

21.1 Introduction to Part Three of the Course

Up to now we have relied almost entirely on judgment to tell us how to use our experience with the real world in assessing the probability distribution for a *basic* random variable.   Probability theory has been used only to deduce the distribution of the variable which affects costs directly from a given distribution for some basic variable.   Thus in Part One of the course the distribution of unit demand was assessed by simply taking the frequency distribution of past demand or of past forecast errors and making such modifications as judgment dictated.   In Part Two we used theory to deduce the distribution of number defective from a given distribution of the process average of a Bernoulli process, but the distribution of the process average itself was assessed without the aid of formal theory.

We now turn to situations where part of the available information concerning the basic random variable is of such a nature that the theory of probability *can* be used as an aid to assessing the probability distribution of the basic random variable itself.   In this chapter we shall study the basic principles of this new use of the theory of probability, particularly as it applies to the use of the information in a *sample*.   In the remainder of Part Three of the course we shall apply these principles to a variety of decision problems, extending our knowledge of probability theory when we find this necessary.

21.2 Bayes' Theorem

Before tackling any practical problems in which the theory of probability can be used in assessing the distribution of a basic random variable, let us consider an artificial example which will bring out the basic logic of the procedures we are about to use.   An urn contains 10 balls in the following mix:

1. $\frac{1}{2}$ of all the balls are striped; of these striped balls, $\frac{2}{10}$ are red and $\frac{8}{10}$ are green.

2. ½ of all the balls are dotted; of these dotted balls, $\frac{6}{10}$ are red and $\frac{4}{10}$ are green.

This mix is shown graphically in Figure 21.1; notice that while the numbers *above* the bars give the *unconditional* relative frequencies of striped and dotted balls the numbers *within* the bars are the *conditional* relative frequencies of red and green *given* either striped or dotted. One ball is now drawn from this urn in such a way that we are convinced that every ball had an equal chance of being drawn, and we wish to assess the probability that this ball is striped.

If the only information we have is that given above, then clearly we must assign probability .5 to the event "striped," since we have already assigned equal probability to every elementary event (each individual ball) and we know that half the elementary events are contained in the compound event "striped" (half of all the balls are striped). Suppose, however, that before assessing the probability of "striped" we are given the *additional information* that the ball in question is

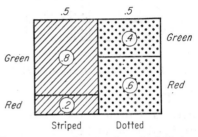

Figure 21.1. Original probabilities.

red. In this case our problem becomes one of assessing the probability that a *red* ball is striped, and we therefore reason as follows.

We originally assigned equal probability to every ball in the urn. The subsequent information that the ball drawn from the urn was red obviously leads us to change this assessment and assign 0 probability to all green balls and therefore to raise the total probability assigned to all red balls to 1, but it gives us no reason whatever to assign a higher probability to any one red ball than to any other and we therefore now assign equal probability to all red balls.   We can then argue that of all the balls in the urn, $.2 \times .5 = .1$ were red striped while $.6 \times .5 = .3$ were red dotted, and therefore that the probability that this red ball is striped is $.1/(.1 + .3) = .25$.

The reasoning can be expressed in terms of relative frequencies as follows.   Suppose that we draw one ball from the urn, record its description, replace the ball in the urn, stir the contents, and then repeat this procedure a great number of times.   Of *all* the balls drawn, about half will be striped; but *if we look only at those occasions on which the ball is red*, only a quarter of *these* balls will be striped.

The same reasoning is represented graphically in Figures 21.2 and 21.3.   We start by reproducing in Figure 21.2 only that part of Figure 21.1 which corresponds to the event "red," since the information that the ball is red means that the rest of Figure 21.1 is now totally irrelevant.

We then produce Figure 21.3 by enlarging Figure 21.2 in such a way that its total area becomes 1; to do this we first calculate the *original* area of each part of Figure 21.2 (the joint probabilities) from the data in Figure 21.1 and then divide the area of each part of Figure 21.2 by the total .4 of these original areas in order to raise the revised area to 1.

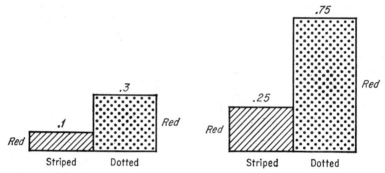

Figures 21.2 (*left*) and 21.3 (*right*). Revision of probabilities.

The calculations can also be laid out in the form of a table like Table 21.1. The events in which we are really interested, striped and dotted, are listed in the first column, and their original probabilities in the second. Notice that these original probabilities are "basic"—they rest on our judgment concerning the process by which the ball was drawn from the urn and in no way depend on the theory of probability. The third column shows the probability of "red" *given* the event "striped" and the corresponding probability given the event "dotted"; again these are "basic" probabilities which rest on judgment and not on the theory of probability.

Table 21.1

Event of interest	Basic probabilities		Computed probabilities	
	Probability of event	Probability of red given the event	Joint probability of event and red	Probability of event given red
Striped	.5	.2	.1	.1/.4 = .25
Dotted	.5	.6	.3	.3/.4 = .75
	1.0		.4	1.00

The theory of probability is then used to compute *revised* probabilities for the events "striped" and "dotted" from these two sets of basic probabilities; the work is shown in the last two columns of the table. We first use the multiplication rule (Section 9.4) to compute the *joint* probabilities of "red *and* striped" and "red *and* dotted" shown in the next to the last column as assessed before it was known that the marble was red. We then use the addition rule to compute the *marginal* probability (Section 12.3.2) of "red" as assessed before it was known that the marble was in fact red; this is the .4 total of the joint probabilities. Finally we apply the definition of conditional probability (Section 9.3) to compute the revised probabilities in the last column of the table.

The logic of this table can be expressed more compactly by the use of algebraic notation. Using S, D, and R to denote the events "striped," "dotted," and "red," we have by the multiplication rule (Section 9.4)

$$P(R,S) = P(S) P(R|S),$$
$$P(R,D) = P(D) P(R|D).$$

The addition rule gives us the marginal probability (Section 12.3.2)

$$P(R) = P(S) P(R|S) + P(D) P(R|D)$$

and the definition of conditional probability then gives (Section 9.3)

$$P(S|R) = \frac{P(S,R)}{P(R)} = \frac{P(S) P(R|S)}{P(S) P(R|S) + P(D) P(R|D)}.$$

This formula is known as *Bayes' theorem*, but it is important to realize that it is really nothing but the mathematical definition of conditional probability as given in Section 9.3 with $P(R)$ written out to show how it is actually calculated. Although the theory of probability can be used as an *aid* in assessing the distribution of a basic random variable, it cannot be too strongly emphasized that theory *by itself* can never determine the probability of any event. As we have emphasized from the outset (Section 1.6.1),

> The theory of probability does not *replace* judgment and experience. Its utility lies rather in the fact that it allows us to *make more effective use* of our judgment and experience by assigning probabilities to those events on which our experience and judgment bear most directly rather than to events which will actually determine costs but with which we have had relatively little direct experience.

21.3 Bayes' Theorem Applied to "Samples"

Our first example of the use of Bayes' theorem to revise probabilities in the light of additional information was chosen to make the underlying logic as obvious as possible rather than to illustrate a common sort of practical use of the theorem. In practical business applications of probability theory the additional information which we wish to consider usually comes from a "sample," and we now proceed to examine three applications of Bayes' theorem in which the information is of this nature.

21.3.1   Samples of Size 1

Suppose that we are presented with an urn containing two kinds of deformed dice.   Half the dice are shaped in such a way that ace will turn up .2 of the time; half the dice are shaped so that ace will turn up .6 of the time.   Using p to denote the fraction of aces which a die would yield in the long run, we can say that $p = .2$ is the *process parameter* of the first kind of dice while $p = .6$ is the parameter of the second kind.

One die is drawn from the urn in such a way that we originally assess at .5 the probability that a die with $p = .2$ has been drawn.   A sample of the die's behavior is then taken by rolling it once; it comes up ace, and we now wish to revise the probability originally assigned to the proposition that the die is one with $p = .2$.

The analysis of the problem is carried out in Table 21.2, which is really identical to Table 21.1.   In terms of an infinite series of trials: if we repeated over and over the process of drawing a die and sampling its behavior by a single roll, we would roll an ace on .4 of all occasions; on

Table 21.2

Value of the basic random variable	Original probability	Conditional probability of sample	Joint probability	Revised probability
.2	.5	.2	.1	.25
.6	.5	.6	.3	.75
	1.0		.4	1.00

.1/.4 = .25 of *these* occasions it would turn out that we had drawn a die with $p = .2$.

Application to a Production Process.   Suppose now that a manufacturer believes that when a certain machine is correctly set up it has a process average fraction defective $p = .2$ but that when a poor job is done the process average is $p = .6$; and suppose further that on the basis of his records of *past* performance the manufacturer assigns probability .5 to the proposition that the setup which has just been made is "correct." Before deciding whether or not to proceed with a production run, the manufacturer obtains additional information on the quality of *this particular* setup by producing and inspecting a sample consisting of one piece of product.   This piece proves defective.

The manufacturer should now assess at .25 the probability that this particular setup is "correct."   The reasoning is identical to that used in the two previous examples.   In terms of an infinite series of trials, the setup is correct on .5 of *all* occasions, but it is correct on only .25 of *those occasions on which the sample piece is defective.*

21.3.2   Samples of Size 2

Suppose next that the manufacturer produces a sample of *two* pieces instead of just one (the die is rolled twice), and suppose that both the sample pieces are defective (both rolls result in ace). The revised probability which the manufacturer should assign to the event "correct setup" ($p = .2$) in the light of *this* evidence is computed in Table 21.3.

Table 21.3

Value of the basic random variable	Original probability	Conditional probability of the sample	Joint probability	Revised probability
.2	.5	.04	.02	.1
.6	.5	.36	.18	.9
	1.0		.20	1.0

The first two columns are identical to those of Table 21.2. The third column shows the conditional probability of getting two defectives (two aces) in a row: if $p = .2$, this probability is $.2^2 = .04$; if $p = .6$, the probability is $.6^2 = .36$. The fourth column gives the joint probability, as evaluated *before* the sample is drawn, of *both* having a setup with the specified value of p (drawing a die with the specified parameter) *and* then producing two defectives (rolling two aces); the total of this column is the marginal or unconditional probability of two defectives as assessed before the sample was taken. The last column is computed from the fourth in the same way as before; the revised probability that the setup is correct ($p = .2$) is .1.

If the entire process of setting up the machine and producing two pieces were repeated over and over, then (on the average) *both* pieces would be defective on 20 out of every 100 occasions. On only 1 of every 10 occasions *with two defectives in the sample* would the setup be of quality $p = .2$; on 9 it would be of quality $p = .6$.

21.3.3   Larger Samples

In the previous examples we have computed the conditional probability of the sample directly from first principles; let us now see how tables of a standard distribution can be used for this purpose. We assume as in Section 21.3.2 that the process average fraction defective p of a certain machine depends on the quality of the setup, but this time we come closer to realism by assuming that p can have any one of ten different values instead of always having one or the other of just two values. The possible values of p are shown in the first column of Table 21.4; the probabilities assigned to these values on the basis of the manufacturer's previous experience are shown in the second column.

Table 21.4

Value of the basic variable p	Original probability $P(p)$	Conditional probability $P_b(\tilde{r} = 4\|n = 50, p)$	Joint probability $P(\tilde{r} = 4, p)$	Revised probability $P(p\|\tilde{r} = 4)$
.01	.30	.0015	.00045	.008
.02	.23	.0146	.00336	.058
.03	.15	.0460	.00690	.120
.04	.10	.0901	.00901	.156
.05	.07	.1360	.00952	.165
.06	.05	.1733	.00866	.150
.07	.04	.1963	.00785	.136
.08	.03	.2037	.00611	.106
.09	.02	.1974	.00395	.069
.10	.01	.1809	.00181	.032
	1.00		.05762	1.000

Suppose now that on one particular occasion the manufacturer runs off a sample of 50 pieces immediately after a setup is made and finds that there are four defectives among them. The conditional probabilities of getting such a sample, given any specified value of p, can be found using the binomial table for $n = 50$; and it is these binomial probabilities $P_b(\tilde{r} = 4|n = 50, p)$ which are shown in the third column of the table. The entry for $p = .04$, for example, is found by looking up

$$P_b(\tilde{r} \geq 4) - P_b(\tilde{r} \geq 5) = .1391 - .0490 = .0901.$$

The remainder of the calculation is carried out exactly as before: the first joint probability is $.30 \times .0015 = .00045$; the first revised probability is $.00045/.05762 = .008$.

21.3.4   Column Totals

Notice carefully the following facts about the column totals in any table like the four we have just studied.

1. The total of the *original* probabilities and the total of the *revised* probabilities must always equal 1; they represent the total probability of all possible values of the basic random variable and the variable is *sure* to have *some* value.

2. The total of the *joint* probabilities will in general be *less than* 1. This is the marginal probability of getting one particular sample "event" (four defectives, or a red ball), and this "event" was *not* sure to happen.

3. The total of the *conditional* probabilities is meaningless; it may be either more than 1 (Table 21.4) or less than 1 (Tables 21.1 to 21.3).

21.4 Definitions

21.4.1 Sample

We are now in a position to see exactly how information obtained from a "sample" differs from the kind of evidence on which probability distributions have been based up to now. In all the examples of this chapter, *the conditional probability which we assigned to the observed sample depended on the value of the basic random variable*—the probability that there would be four defectives among 50 pieces depended on the value of the basic random variable $\tilde{p}$, the process average fraction defective. *It was because of this fact* that we could use the theory of probability to revise the probability distribution of the basic random variable in the light of the observed sample. More generally, the probability distribution assigned to the value of *each* observation in the sample depended on the value of the basic random variable—the conditional probability of the sample as a whole could be computed (or looked up in tables) because the conditional distribution for each observation was given.

21.4.2 Prior and Posterior Probability

Henceforth we shall use the term *prior probabilities* for the probabilities assigned to the values of the basic random variable before some particular sample is taken and the term *posterior probabilities* for the probabilities as revised in the light of the additional information obtained from that sample.

Notice (1) that this is the *only* distinction between prior and posterior probabilities and (2) that the distinction is always *relative to some particular sample*. If the manufacturer of Section 21.3.3 has not taken and is not considering taking any sample, the .30 probability assigned to $p = .01$ in column 2 of Table 21.4 is not a prior probability—it is just a probability. If, on the other hand, two successive samples are taken from the same process, the probabilities posterior to the first sample are the probabilities prior to the second sample. As regards a possible second sample, the value .008 in the last column of Table 21.4 is the *prior* probability that $p = .01$.

In problems where we deal with both a prior and a posterior distribution we shall sometimes use notation of the following sort to keep them distinct:

$P_0(p)$: the *prior* probability that $\tilde{p} = p$; the probability of p on 0 sample evidence.

$P_1(p)$: the *posterior* probability (after *one* sample has been taken) that $\tilde{p} = p$.

$E_0(\tilde{p})$: the mean of the *prior* distribution of $\tilde{p}$.

$E_1(\tilde{p})$: the mean of the *posterior* distribution of $\tilde{p}$.

21.4.3   Likelihood

We shall use the term *likelihood* for the conditional probability of drawing the sample which was actually drawn, given some particular value of the basic random variable. By Table 21.4, the likelihood of four defectives in a sample of 50 given $p = .01$ is .0015. Again we emphasize that the new term is introduced purely for convenience: *a likelihood is a probability in the same sense as any other probability.*

21.5   The Application of Bayes' Theorem

21.5.1   Discrete Prior Distributions

Whenever the prior distribution of the basic random variable is *discrete*, Bayes' theorem can be applied to compute posterior probabilities by following exactly the procedure illustrated in Tables 21.1 through 21.4. The general principle is the same whether the basic variable is the parameter p of a Bernoulli process, the parameter κ of a Poisson process, the fraction of white balls in an urn, or any other unknown quantity whatever.

The nature of the basic random variable affects only the way in which we compute the likelihood of the observed sample. If the basic variable is the parameter p of a Bernoulli process, the likelihood of the observed number of successes is binomial and is found by use of binomial tables or by use of the Poisson or Normal approximations to the binomial distribution. If the basic variable is the parameter κ of a Poisson process, the likelihood of the observed number of successes is Poisson and is found by use of Poisson tables or by use of the Normal approximation to the Poisson distribution. Later on we shall study methods of finding the likelihood of an observed sample for still other kinds of basic variables.

21.5.2   Continuous Prior Distributions

When a random variable represents a quantity which will actually be observed or measured, then (as we saw in Section 14.1.3) the "exact" distribution of this variable must necessarily be discrete. If a measuring instrument is read to the tenth of an inch, we must say that while the values $t = 9.0$ and $t = 9.1$ are possible the value $t = 9.05$ is flatly impossible. When, on the contrary, a random variable represents an unobservable quantity such as the parameter of a Bernoulli or Poisson process, we will usually if not always believe that this variable *may* have any value whatsoever within a certain interval (0 to 1 in the case of $\tilde{p}$, 0 to ∞ in the case of $\tilde{\kappa}$). In other words, the "exact" distribution of a basic random variable—the distribution which accords exactly with our best judgment—will sometimes be *really* continuous, and when this is true Bayes' theorem cannot be strictly applied by the method of Tables

21.1 through 21.4 because the probability (either prior or posterior) that the variable has any particular value *precisely* is 0 (cf. Section 14.1.3). In this case there are two possible ways of obtaining the posterior distribution.

1. The possible values of the variable can be grouped into "brackets" and the total prior probability of each bracket can be assigned to some single value within the bracket, e.g. the mid-point. This procedure reduces the continuous distribution to a discrete one, and we then proceed exactly as if it were a genuine discrete distribution (cf. Section 6.5).

2. We can resort to the integral calculus. In effect, this means nothing more mysterious than finding the *limit* approached by the result of the "bracket method" as the brackets are made narrower and narrower; but in order to do this without making an infinite number of computations we must work with the probabilities in algebraic rather than numerical form.

It is very much worth emphasizing that we very rarely *need* to use the calculus in order to get an accurate answer to a real problem. In a very few very special types of problems the continuity of the prior distribution may play a really essential role, but in the vast majority of practical business problems a discrete prior distribution with sufficiently many brackets will give as accurate an answer as can be desired. If continuous distributions and the calculus *are* used in problems of this sort, they are used for one or both of two reasons which have nothing to do with accuracy.

1. When a solution can be obtained by the calculus, the burden of numerical computation is generally much smaller than when a discrete distribution with many brackets is used; the calculus may be simply an *inexpensive* way of getting an answer to the particular problem in hand.

2. The fact that the calculus solution gives the answer to a whole class of problems in a single formula makes it easy to see the effect of varying certain costs, probabilities, etc., and thus makes it possible to obtain a *general understanding* of a class of problems without computing solutions to large quantities of specific numerical examples.

For either or both of these reasons we may well use a continuous prior distribution as an approximation even when the "true" prior distribution is discrete, just as we have already used the gamma and Normal approximations to compute the probability distributions of counted or measured random variables whose "true" distributions are necessarily discrete.

PROBLEMS

1. Peter is presented with two externally identical urns, one of which contains 10 white balls while the other contains 10 black balls, and he chooses one of the two urns by tossing a fair coin. He will be paid $1 if the chosen urn is the one containing all white balls. What is the expected value of this payment:

a. If Peter must set the price on the basis of only the information given above?

b. If Peter has already drawn one ball from the chosen urn and seen that it is white before he sets the price?

2. Same as Problem 1 except that one urn contains eight white and two black balls, the other contains eight black and two white, and the payment will be made if the chosen urn is the one with eight white and two black.

3. The prior distribution shown in the following table is assigned to the process average fraction defective of a machine which can be regarded as a Bernoulli process.

p	$P(p)$
.01	.6
.03	.3
.05	.1
	$\overline{1.0}$

A sample of 20 pieces is taken from the machine and one defective is found.

a. What was the probability, as evaluated *before* the sample was drawn, of getting the sample which was actually observed?

b. Compute the posterior distribution of $\tilde{p}$.

c. Evaluate $E_0(\tilde{p})$ and $E_1(\tilde{p})$.

4. Same as Problem 3 except that a sample of 80 is taken and 4 defectives are found. Compare the posterior distribution of $\tilde{p}$ with that obtained in Problem 3 and comment.

5. The prior distribution shown in the following table is assigned to the process average fraction defective of a machine which can be regarded as a Bernoulli process.

p	$P(p)$
.15	.6
.20	.3
.25	.1
	$\overline{1.0}$

A sample of 144 pieces is taken from the process and 20 defectives are found. Find the posterior distribution of $\tilde{p}$.

6. The prior distribution shown in the following table is assigned to the average

κ	$P(\kappa)$
.20	.5
.25	.3
.30	.2
	$\overline{1.0}$

number of defects per foot generated by a machine which can be regarded as a Poisson process. A sample consisting of 10 feet of product is taken and 3 defects are found. Find the posterior distribution of $\tilde{\kappa}$.

7. The prior distribution shown in the following table is assigned to the process average fraction defective of a machine which can be regarded as a Bernoulli process.

p	$P(p)$
.05	.6
.10	.2
.15	.2
	$\overline{1.0}$

a. Find the posterior distribution of $\tilde{p}$ after a sample of 10 has been taken and no defective found.

b. Using the result of (*a*) as the prior distribution, find the distribution of $\tilde{p}$ after a second sample of 10 has been taken and 1 defective found.

c. Find the distribution of $\tilde{p}$ if a single sample of 20 is taken and 1 defective found.

CHAPTER 22

Two-action Problems with Linear Costs

As a first example of the use of information from a sample in reaching a decision, we shall consider a problem of choosing between two possible acts when the cost of either act depends on the unknown value of the parameter p of a Bernoulli process.

22.1 Statement of the Problem

A manufacturer has used a particular automatic machine for production of a particular part over a considerable period of time. At the beginning of each production run, the machine is taken down for replacement of worn tools, etc., and then is readjusted by the operator. Experience has convinced the manufacturer that during any one production run the machine behaves as a Bernoulli process, and he knows that when properly adjusted the machine will have a process average fraction defective $p = .01$—it is not within the machine's capability to do better than this, but there is no mechanical reason why it should do worse. It sometimes turns out, however, that the adjustments made by the operator in charge of the machine are not correct and that the machine produces a fraction defective considerably higher than .01.

The entire output of this machine goes directly to the assembly department and the entire output is actually used in the final product, but a defective requires special hand fitting which costs \$.40 per piece. Since a single production run amounts to 500 pieces, this means that a really bad setup leads to a fairly heavy "cost of accepting defective product." These losses can be reduced almost to nothing by having each adjustment checked and corrected by an expert mechanic, since if this is done the process average is always brought down to its minimum value, $p = .01$. The time of the expert mechanic costs \$6, however, and if the machine operator has made a setup which would produce a fraction defective .01, this extra cost would be a complete loss. Even if the operator's setup is slightly worse than .01, the saving in cost of defectives would still not amount to enough to cover the cost of having the adjustment checked and corrected. It is only when the operator's setup is really bad that the \$6 expenditure pays for itself, but the manufacturer must decide whether or not to spend the $6 on the basis of less than perfect information about the quality of the setup.

22.1.1   The Conditional Costs

As usual, the first step in analyzing any problem of decision under uncertainty is to calculate the *conditional* cost which will be incurred under every possible decision for every possible value of the basic random variable. In this problem there are only two possible decisions:

1. Proceed without checking or readjusting the machine; we shall call this a decision to *accept the process;*
2. Have the setup checked and readjusted; we shall call this a decision to *reject the process.*

If the process is *accepted*, the conditional expected number of defectives in the run is $500p$, where p is the value of the process fraction defective. The expected cost of these defectives is $\$.40 \times 500p = \$200\,p$. If the process is *rejected*, the value p will be .01 and the expected number of defectives is $.01 \times 500 = 5$ pieces. The expected cost of these defectives is $2 and the checking and readjustment cost another $6, so that the total is $8. This particular "conditional" cost is not really conditional— it is the same for all p. The conditional expected cost of each possible decision for each possible event p can be shown systematically in a "payoff table"; this is done in Table 22.1, where the asterisks indicate the decision which is conditionally best for each event.

Table 22.1
Payoff Table

Value p of the basic random variable	Act	
	Accept	Reject
.01	$ 2*	$8
.05	10	8*
.15	30	8*
.25	50	8*

As usual, the definition of "cost" is arbitrary to a certain extent: we could, for example, have included the labor and material cost of the 500 pieces in the costs of both decisions for all values of $\tilde{p}$. It is obvious, however, that inclusion of such costs could not affect a rational decision because such costs are *not affected by the decision*. The only costs which need be included are those which, for at least one value of $\tilde{p}$, are *not* the same for every possible decision. These are the *relevant* costs, and the analysis of any decision problem will be much clearer if *all irrelevant costs are excluded.*

22.2   The Better Action without Sampling

22.2.1   The Probability Distribution

Suppose that the manufacturer examines his records of those past production runs for which the setup was *not* checked by a master mechanic and finds the frequency distribution of fraction defective shown in Table 22.2. Since the runs are fairly large (500 pieces), the fraction

Table 22.2
Historical Distribution of Fraction Defective

Fraction defective	*Relative frequency*
.01	.7
.05	.1
.15	.1
.25	.1
	1.0

defective in any run can be taken as roughly equal to the value of the process average p during that run; and if the manufacturer has no information other than this—no reason to think that the operator's skill has changed, etc.—he may reasonably take Table 22.2 as giving the *probability* distribution for the process average $\bar{p}$ in any new run for which the setup is not checked.†

22.2.2   Unconditional Expected Cost

Using the probability distribution of Table 22.2 we can compute the *unconditional* expected costs of the two possible decisions from their conditional expected costs as shown in Table 22.1. The work is carried out in Table 22.3.

Table 22.3
Unconditional Expected Costs

p	$P(p)$	Cost of acceptance		Cost of rejection	
		Conditional	Expected	Conditional	Expected
.01	.7	$ 2	$1.40	$8	$5.60
.05	.1	10	1.00	8	.80
.15	.1	30	3.00	8	.80
.25	.1	50	5.00	8	.80
	1.0		$10.40		$8.00

† In order to simplify the computations, we assume that the process average fraction defective always has one of just four possible values. The only change which a more realistic distribution would make in the analysis would be an increase in the *amount* of arithmetic required to find the solution—there would be no change in the *nature* of the arithmetic.

22.2.3   The Decision

Under the probability distribution assigned to $\tilde{p}$ by the manufacturer on the basis of his *past experience*, the unconditional expected cost of rejection is $2.40 less than the unconditional expected cost of acceptance; he should therefore have the process readjusted by an expert mechanic. In terms of an infinite sequence of trials: costs will average $2.40 less per run if *every* setup is checked by an expert mechanic than if *no* setup is so checked.

22.3   The Better Action after Sampling

Suppose now that, instead of basing his decision to accept or reject entirely on past experience, the manufacturer takes a sample consisting of the first 10 pieces produced after a *particular* setup is made by the operator, inspects this sample, and finds no defective. To keep the arithmetic simple we shall assume that even though 10 pieces have already been produced, a full 500 additional pieces will be produced after the manufacturer decides whether to accept or reject the setup.

22.3.1   The Probability Distribution

The probabilities of Table 22.2 must now be revised to take account of the sample information; the revision is carried out in Table 22.4 by the use of Bayes' theorem in the manner described in Chapter 21, the conditional probabilities $P_b(\tilde{r} = 0|n = 10, p)$ being obtained from the binomial tables.

Table 22.4
Computation of the Posterior Distribution

p	Prior $P(p)$	Likelihood $P_b(\tilde{r} = 0|p)$	Joint $P(\tilde{r} = 0, p)$	Posterior $P(p|\tilde{r} = 0)$
.01	.7	.904	.6328	.881
.05	.1	.599	.0599	.083
.15	.1	.197	.0197	.028
.25	.1	.056	.0056	.008
	1.0		.7180	1.000

22.3.2   Unconditional Expected Cost

The better decision under this revised probability distribution is now found in exactly the same way that we found the better decision under the original distribution. The computations are carried out in Table 22.5, which should be compared with Table 22.3.

Table 22.5
Posterior Unconditional Expected Costs

p	Posterior $P(p)$	Cost of acceptance Conditional	Cost of acceptance Expected	Cost of rejection Conditional	Cost of rejection Expected
.01	.881	$ 2	$1.762	$8	$7.048
.05	.083	10	.830	8	.664
.15	.028	30	.840	8	.224
.25	.008	50	.400	8	.064
	1.000		$3.832		$8.000

22.3.3   The Decision

Under the probability distribution for $\tilde{p}$ assessed by the manufacturer on the basis of *both* his past experience *and* the information that a sample of 10 contained no defectives, the expected cost of acceptance is $4.168 less than the expected cost of rejection; he should therefore accept the operator's setup as is.   In terms of an infinite sequence of trials: costs *on those occasions where a sample of* 10 *is taken and no defective is found* will average $4.168 less per run if *on those occasions* the operator's setup is accepted as is.

22.4   Linear Conditional Costs; Use of the Mean of the Distribution $\tilde{p}$ of

The method of analysis used above is of very general applicability. It can be used to find the unconditional expected cost of any act in any situation where *the conditional cost of the act depends only on the value of the basic variable and on that particular act.*†   Its utility does *not* depend on the number of possible acts or on the way in which the conditional costs vary with the value of the basic random variable.

Certain kinds of problems, on the other hand, have special features which make it possible to use special methods of analysis; and such special methods may have either or both of two advantages over the "standard" method used in the first part of this chapter.   First, the special method may reduce the amount of computation required.   Second, and far more important for the purposes of this course, the special method may bring out much more clearly exactly what aspects of the data are critical for the choice of the best decision.   We shall now see that the example which

---

† We shall see in Chapter 24 that it is sometimes impossible to evaluate the conditional cost of an act such as "accept" or "reject" by looking at that act alone: the cost of the present act sometimes depends in part on how choices among other acts will be made in the future.

we have just discussed has certain peculiarities which make possible such a special method of analysis.

22.4.1 Constant Conditional Cost

The conditional cost of *rejection* in our example is a *constant* \$8 regardless of the value of the basic random variable $\tilde{p}$. The corresponding unconditional cost must therefore have this same value \$8 under *any* probability distribution, and the only reason for going through the form of computing the unconditional cost in Tables 22.3 and 22.5 was to set up a model which can be applied in problems where it is *not* true that the conditional cost of rejection is the same for every p.

22.4.2 Proportional Conditional Cost

The conditional cost of *acceptance*, on the other hand, is strictly *proportional* to the value of $\tilde{p}$ in our example—we saw in Section 22.1.1 above that it amounts to \$200 p. This being so, the unconditional expected cost of acceptance is simply \$200 times the expected value of $\tilde{p}$: we can sum all the terms $p\ \mathrm{P}(p)$ and then multiply by \$200 instead of multiplying each of these terms by \$200 and then summing.

The expected value of $\tilde{p}$ is computed in Table 22.6 for both the prob-

Table 22.6
Expected Value of $\tilde{p}$

p	Prior distribution		Posterior distribution	
	$\mathrm{P}_0(p)$	$p\ \mathrm{P}_0(p)$	$\mathrm{P}_1(p)$	$p\ \mathrm{P}_1(p)$
.01	.7	.007	.881	.00881
.05	.1	.005	.083	.00415
.15	.1	.015	.028	.00420
.25	.1	.025	.008	.00200
	1.0	.052	1.000	.01916

ability distributions of our example; the table shows that

$$E_0(\tilde{p}) = .052,$$
$$E_1(\tilde{p}) = .01916.$$

The unconditional expected cost of acceptance under the prior distribution can then be found by multiplying .052 $\times$ \$200 = \$10.40, the same result which we obtained by the "standard" method in Table 22.3. Under the posterior distribution this same cost amounts to .01916 $\times$ \$200 = \$3.832, the figure we obtained by the "standard" method in Table 22.5.

22.4.3   The Break-even Value of $\tilde{p}$ and the Criterion for Acceptance or Rejection

The real interest of this new method of analysis lies in the fact that it brings out very clearly exactly what it is about the probability distribution of $\tilde{p}$ that actually affects expected cost and the comparative desirability of decisions to accept or reject.

The *conditional* cost of acceptance in our example is \$200 p, and this will be *equal* to the \$8 *conditional* cost of rejection if $\tilde{p}$ has the *break-even value*

$$p_b = \frac{\$8}{\$200} = .04.$$

If we *knew* the value p of $\tilde{p}$, we would:

> Accept if $p < .04$,
> Reject if $p > .04$,
> Be indifferent if $p = .04$.

The results of the discussion in Section 22.4.2 above can now be expressed as follows. *If the conditional cost of rejection is independent of the value of $\tilde{p}$ and the conditional cost of acceptance is proportional to the value of $\tilde{p}$, then exactly this same break-even criterion can be applied to the expected value of $\tilde{p}$ when the true value of $\tilde{p}$ is unknown.* We should:

> Accept if $E(\tilde{p}) < p_b$,
> Reject if $E(\tilde{p}) > p_b$,
> Be indifferent if $E(\tilde{p}) = p_b$.

Notice that this set of conditions holds in exactly the same form whether we are talking about action without sampling or about action after sampling. The *only* difference is that in the former case we apply the conditions to $E_0(\tilde{p})$ whereas in the latter we apply them to $E_1(\tilde{p})$.

22.4.4   Linear Conditional Costs in General

In Figure 22.1 we show the behavior of the *conditional* costs of our example graphically. The cost of rejection is the same \$8 for every p and therefore plots as a horizontal straight line of ordinate \$8. The cost of acceptance is \$200 p and therefore plots as a rising straight line with ordinate \$0 at $p = 0$, ordinate \$20 at $p = .1$, ordinate \$40 at $p = .2$, and so forth. Notice that because such lines represent *conditional* costs they have meaning even for values p which are impossible according to some particular probability distribution. As in Section 5.3.1, we shall say that:

> The conditional cost of a decision is *linear* if the graph of the cost plotted against the basic variable is a straight line *over the entire range of values of the variable which have nonzero probability.*

Although the conditional costs of our example represent only special cases of linear costs (constant cost and proportional cost), it was shown in Section 5.3.1 that in general:

> If the conditional cost of an act is linear, its unconditional cost depends only on the expected value of the basic random variable and is the same as if the variable were known with certainty to have this value.

Notice that *it is only in special cases* that conditional costs are linear. The student must not use the mean instead of the full distribution of the

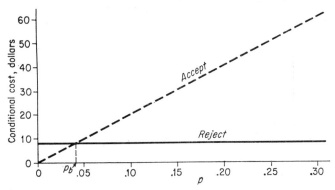

Figure 22.1. Conditional costs.

basic variable in any applied problem unless he has shown that the costs *are* linear in *that particular problem*.

22.5   Expected Opportunity Loss and the Cost of Uncertainty

Whenever sampling is possible the cost of uncertainty becomes of very great interest because it measures the *potential cost reduction obtainable by sampling*. If under a given probability distribution (prior or posterior) the cost of uncertainty is very small, (further) sampling is likely to cost more than it is worth; if the cost of uncertainty is large, (further) sampling may well be worth its cost. We shall lay heavy emphasis on computation of the cost of uncertainty in this part of the course; in Part Four we can then go on to balance the cost of sampling against the expected *reduction* in the cost of uncertainty which results from the sampling. Until we come to this kind of calculation in Part Four, however, no principles will be involved which were not fully discussed in Chapter 7. The remainder of this chapter is simply a review of that chapter.

We have studied two different ways of computing the expected opportunity loss of any act:

1. By computing *conditional opportunity losses* and then taking their expectation;
2. By computing the *expected profit or cost of action under certainty* and then taking the difference between this amount and the expected profit or cost of the act in question.

We shall now see how both methods can be applied to two-action problems.

22.5.1   Computation Using Conditional Losses

The student will recall from Section 7.2.1 that the *conditional opportunity loss* of any act, given a particular value of the basic random variable, is the *difference* between the actual profit or cost of that act and the

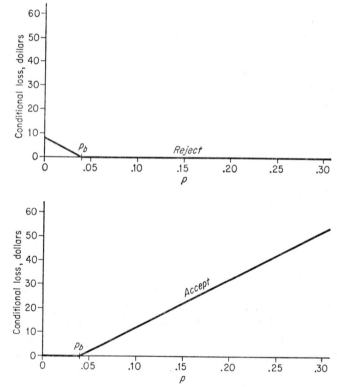

Figure 22.2. Conditional losses.

profit or cost of the act which would be the best possible *for that value o- the variable.*   The loss table shown as Table 22.7 is obtained from the pay-off table shown as Table 22.1 by taking each entry in each row and subtracting from it the starred entry in the same row.

The *unconditional expected losses* of the two possible decisions are now computed in Table 22.8 for the prior distribution of $\tilde{p}$ and in Table 22.9

for the posterior distribution. The calculation is exactly like that in Tables 22.3 and 22.5 except that conditional *losses* are taken from Table 22.7 rather than *costs* from Table 22.1.

Table 22.7
Loss Table

p	Act	
	Accept	Reject
.01	$ 0	$6
.05	2	0
.15	22	0
.25	42	0

Table 22.8
Prior Expected Losses

p	Prior $P_0(p)$	Loss of acceptance		Loss of rejection	
		Conditional	Expected	Conditional	Expected
.01	.7	$ 0	$0	$6	$4.20
.05	.1	2	.20	0	0
.15	.1	22	2.20	0	0
.25	.1	42	4.20	0	0
	1.0		$6.60		$4.20

Table 22.9
Posterior Expected Losses

p	Posterior $P_1(p)$	Loss of acceptance		Loss of rejection	
		Conditional	Expected	Conditional	Expected
.01	.881	$ 0	$0	$6	$5.286
.05	.083	2	.166	0	0
.15	.028	22	.616	0	0
.25	.008	42	.336	0	0
	1.000		$1.118		$5.286

Notice particularly in Table 22.8 that the loss due to accepting under the prior distribution is $2.40 higher than the loss due to rejecting and that *this difference is equal to the difference between the corresponding costs* in Table 22.3; the student should make the same comparison for the posterior distribution.

The *cost of uncertainty* is the *irreducible* loss due to action under uncertainty; it is the *expected loss of the* best *decision for the given prob-*

ability distribution. In our example the cost of uncertainty is $4.20 under the prior distribution, $1.118 under the posterior.

Use of the Mean of the Distribution. We have seen that when the conditional costs of a given decision are linear functions of the basic variable, the unconditional expected cost of the decision can be computed from the mean of the distribution. We warn the student that *unconditional expected loss can almost never be computed in this way because the conditional losses are almost never linear* in the sense defined in Section 22.4.4. The conditional losses for our example are graphed in Figure 22.2; the lines are *not* straight *over the whole range* of values of $\tilde{p}$ which have nonzero probability. Unconditional losses *can* be computed by the use of *partial* expectations, but we shall postpone this subject until we come to the point where this method of computation presents real advantages.

22.5.2 Computation Using the Expected Cost of Action under Certainty

We now proceed to calculate the expected losses in our example by the second of the two methods listed above, i.e. by comparing the expected cost of each decision with the expected cost of action under certainty.

The Expected Cost of Action under Certainty. Without giving the justification for our procedure, which can be found in Section 7.3.1, we proceed in Table 22.10 to compute the expected cost of action under certainty for both the prior and the posterior distributions of our example. The conditional costs in column 2 are the starred entries in Table 22.1 (why?); the expected costs under the two probability distributions are then computed in the usual way.

Table 22.10
Expected Cost under Certainty

p	Conditional cost	Prior distribution $P_0(p)$	Expectation	Posterior distribution $P_1(p)$	Expectation
.01	$2	.7	$1.40	.881	$1.762
.05	8	.1	.80	.083	.664
.15	8	.1	.80	.028	.224
.25	8	.1	.80	.008	.064
		1.0	$3.80	1.000	$2.714

We remind the student once again that, as is well shown by the results of Table 22.10, the "expected cost under certainty" is *not a cost certain:* it depends on the probability distribution. In terms of an infinite sequence of runs, it is the average cost which would be incurred per run *if $\tilde{p}$ varied according to the probability distribution in question but the value of $\tilde{p}$ were known before each run was made.*

Expected Opportunity Loss. The difference between the expected cost of any decision and the expected cost of action under certainty is the expected opportunity loss of that decision. The expected loss due to accepting under the prior distribution is $10.40 (Table 22.3) minus $3.80 (Table 22.10), or $6.60; this same figure was obtained by our other method in Table 22.8. The student should verify the three other expected losses shown in Tables 22.8 and 22.9 by recomputing them in this same way.

PROBLEMS

1. A manufacturer faces a situation of exactly the same sort as the one described in the text but with different data. The run will consist of 1000 pieces. If the machine is set up by an expert mechanic the process average will be .05; the probability distribution for the process average if the machine is set up by the operator is given by the following table. Each defective reaching assembly costs $.30; the cost of

p	$P(p)$
.05	.6
.10	.3
.15	.1
	$\overline{1.0}$

setup by an expert mechanic is $10.

   a. Draw up the payoff table and graph the conditional costs of both acts as functions of p.

   b. From this graph find the *break-even value* p_b, i.e. the value of $\tilde{p}$ at which it makes no difference whether the manufacturer accepts or rejects.

   c. Compute $E(\tilde{p})$ and use it to determine which is the better act.

   d. What is the unconditional expected cost of rejection?

   e. Use $E(\tilde{p})$ to compute the unconditional expected cost of acceptance.

   f. Compute the cost of action under certainty.

   g. Compute the unconditional expected losses of both acts from your answers to (d), (e), and (f).

   h. Draw up the loss table and graph the conditional losses.

   i. Verify your answers to (g) by use of your answer to (h).

   j. What is the probability that if a sample of 20 pieces is drawn it will contain exactly four defectives?

   k. Recompute parts c through i in the light of the additional information that four defectives have been found in a sample of 20 pieces.

2. A commercial photographic concern is about to purchase 100,000 flash bulbs for use during the coming year. A new type of bulb has just been placed on the market and is reported to be more reliable than the present type. The loss in film and labor due to a defective flash bulb averages $2.50. The reliability of the old type is known to be 99.0 per cent; management assigns the probabilities in the following table

Reliability	Probability
.995	⅓
.990	⅓
.980	⅓
	$\overline{1}$

to the reliability of the new type.   What action should be taken and what is the cost of uncertainty:

    a. On this information alone?

    b. If a sample of 500 bulbs of the new type is tested and three defectives are found?

    3. A manufacturer is about to set up a machine for a run of 1000 pieces.   Each defective which occurs in the run will have to be reworked at a cost of $.15 each.   If a defective reaches the assembly department, it will not be detected until the assembly in which it is included fails on final test.   Removal and replacement of the defective then costs an additional $.45 over and above the cost of rework.   Screening the manufactured lot to prevent defectives from reaching assembly costs $25.   On the basis of past experience the manufacturer assigns the following probability distribution to the process average fraction defective which will be produced if the machine is set up by the regular operator in the usual way.   If the machine is very carefully set up by an expert mechanic at an extra cost of $50, the manufacturer can be sure that there will be no defectives, $p = 0$.

p	$P(p)$
0	.2
.1	.7
.2	.1
	1.0

    a. Draw up the cost and loss tables for the three possible decisions: have setup made by expert mechanic, have setup made by operator and screen, have setup made by operator and do not screen.

    b. Determine the best action and compute the cost of uncertainty on the information given above.

    c. Same as (*b*) but on the additional information that four defectives have been found in a sample of 50 taken from the process as set up by the operator.

    (Although this is a three-action problem, it can be analyzed by methods virtually identical to those used for two-action problems of the sort described in the text of this chapter.)

CHAPTER 23

Samples from Finite Populations:
The Hypergeometric Distribution

The samples with which we dealt in previous chapters were drawn from a *random process* in order to obtain evidence on a parameter of that process. We now turn to the study of samples which are drawn from a *finite population* in order to obtain information on the proportion of that population which possesses some specified characteristic. Thus information on the fraction of all United States citizens using a certain product might be obtained from a sample of the population of all United States citizens; or a mail-order company deciding how many to stock of a certain item might use an advance mailing to get information on the proportion of customers on the mailing list for its regular catalogue who will order the item.

In the case of samples from a random process, the sample items were taken *in the order in which they were produced* by the process. The probability distribution for the value of each observation was therefore given directly by the characteristics of the process in terms of the parameter of the process. When, on the contrary, a sample is drawn from an already existing population, it is the *process by which the sample is drawn* that determines the probability distribution for the value of each observation. In this chapter we shall study the process known as *simple sampling without replacement*.

23.1 The Hypergeometric Distribution

As a first example of simple sampling without replacement, consider the following problem. An urn contains 10 balls, 7 white and 3 black. A sample of 5 balls is drawn from the urn, the individual items in the sample being drawn one at a time and kept out of the urn once they are drawn. We shall refer to the drawing of a black ball as a "success," and we wish to determine the probability distribution for the number of successes in the sample.

23.1.1 Unconditional and Conditional Probabilities of a Success on a Given Draw

If the balls are thoroughly mixed before drawing, if there is nothing to distinguish one ball from another except the color, and if the draws are

355

made without looking, a reasonable man will usually conclude that every ball in the urn is equally likely to be drawn and will accordingly assign probability .3 to black on the *first* draw. This *same* probability applies, furthermore, to the event "black" on *any* specified draw if nothing is said about the results of previous draws. If a man is about to draw three balls in a row from the urn, he will assign the same .3 probability to black on the third draw that he assigns to black on the first draw, and we may say that .3 is the *unconditional* probability of a success on *any* draw.

Suppose, however, that we wish to compute the probability that *both* the first two balls will be black. By the rule for computing joint probabilities given in Section 9.4, this probability is the product of the *unconditional* probability of black on the first draw and the *conditional* probability of black on the second draw *given* that the first draw was black; and a reasonable man will *not* assign the same value .3 to this *conditional* probability of black on the second draw which he would assign to the *unconditional* probability of black on the second draw. The fact that one black ball has been drawn from the urn gives him no reason to change his basic belief that every ball in the urn has an equal chance of being selected on the next draw, but the fact that this black ball *has not been replaced* means that the proportion of white and black balls in the urn has been altered. The urn now contains two black and seven white balls, and the probability of drawing a black ball in this situation is $\frac{2}{9}$. If two balls were drawn without replacement from each of an infinite number of urns, the ratio of draws where *both* balls were black to draws *where the first ball was black* would be $\frac{2}{9}$. Other conditional probabilities can be assessed by exactly this same kind of reasoning.

23.1.2 Probability of Exactly Two Successes in a Sample of Five

Following the same general procedure that we used in Chapter 10 to derive the binomial distribution from the probability of a success on any trial, let us now work out the probability that the five draws from our urn will yield exactly two black and three white balls in some specified order, say *BBWWW*.

We have already seen that the probability of black on the first draw is $\frac{3}{10}$ and that, given this result of the first draw, the probability of black on the second draw is $\frac{2}{9}$. There now remain one black and seven white balls in the urn, and the probability of white on the third draw is $\frac{7}{8}$. Continuing in this way we get $\frac{6}{7}$ for the probability of white on the fourth draw and $\frac{5}{6}$ for the probability of white on the fifth draw. We can now apply the multiplication rule for joint probabilities and obtain for the *probability of the joint event BBWWW*

$$\frac{3}{10} \; \frac{2}{9} \; \frac{7}{8} \; \frac{6}{7} \; \frac{5}{6} = \frac{1}{24}.$$

Next we observe that the probability of two black and three white is just the same in *any* specified order. For the order *WBWBW*, for example, we have

$$\tfrac{7}{10}\ \tfrac{3}{9}\ \tfrac{6}{8}\ \tfrac{2}{7}\ \tfrac{5}{6} = \tfrac{1}{24}.$$

As we have already seen in deriving the binomial distribution (Section 10.1), there are 10 possible orders in which two successes can be drawn in a sample of five. Since the orders are mutually exclusive, their probabilities can be added to obtain the probability of two successes *regardless* of order:

$$P(2) = 10 \times \tfrac{1}{24} = \tfrac{10}{24}.$$

23.1.3   *Probability of r Successes in a Sample of n*

We now generalize this example to get the probability of exactly r successes in a sample of n from a finite population described by

N: size of population,

R: number of successes in population.

1. The probability of r successes and $(n - r)$ failures *in a specified order* is

$$\underbrace{\left[\frac{R}{N}\ \frac{R-1}{N-1}\ \frac{R-2}{N-2}\ \cdots\ \frac{R-(r-1)}{N-(r-1)} \right]}_{r \text{ factors}}$$

$$\times \underbrace{\left[\frac{N-R}{N-r}\ \frac{(N-R)-1}{N-(r+1)}\ \frac{(N-R)-2}{N-(r+2)}\ \cdots\ \frac{(N-R)-(n-r-1)}{N-(n-1)} \right]}_{n-r \text{ factors}}.$$

2. The number of mutually exclusive orders is C_r^n, just as in binomial sampling, and therefore we have for the probability of exactly r successes *regardless of order*

$$P_h(r) = C_r^n \left[\frac{R}{N}\ \cdots\ \frac{R-(r-1)}{N-(r-1)} \right]$$

$$\times \left[\frac{N-R}{N-r}\ \cdots\ \frac{(N-R)-(n-r-1)}{N-(n-1)} \right].$$

This formula defines what is known as the *hypergeometric* probability distribution. For computational purposes it is usually written in one or the other of two more convenient forms

$$P_h(r) = \frac{n!\,R!(N-R)!(N-n)!}{r!(n-r)!(R-r)![(N-R)-(n-r)]!\,N!}$$

$$= \frac{C_r^R C_{n-r}^{N-R}}{C_n^N}$$

Hypergeometric probability

23.1.4   Parameters of the Hypergeometric Distribution

The parameters of the hypergeometric distribution in the form given above are n, N, and R. For many purposes, however, it is more convenient to look at the *fraction* R/N of successes in the population rather than at the *number* of successes R. We shall use the same symbol for this fraction that we use for the fraction of successes generated by a Bernoulli process: we define

$$p = \frac{R}{N}.$$

We can think of the parameters of the distribution as being n, p, and N— if we know these three numbers we know n, R, and N, and we are free to express our knowledge in any way we like.

23.1.5   Mean and Variance

The number of successes r can be thought of as the sum of the values of n random variables having the value 0 (failure) or 1 (success). As evaluated before any of the sample items are drawn, the expected value of any one of the n variables is p, and therefore

---

$\mathrm{E}(\tilde{r}) = np$ *Expected number of successes, hypergeometric distribution*

The *mean* of a hypergeometric distribution is thus the same as the mean of a binomial distribution with the same values of n and p; the population size N has no effect.

The *variances* of the two distributions are *not* the same, however. The variance of the hypergeometric distribution can be shown to be

---

$\sigma^2(\tilde{r}) = npq\,\dfrac{N - n}{N - 1}$ *Variance of number of successes, hypergeometric distribution*

It should be observed that this is the binomial variance npq multiplied by a factor which is *always less than* 1 (except when $n = 1$) and which becomes smaller and smaller as the sample size n approaches the population size N. The corresponding expression for the standard deviation is

$$\sigma(\tilde{r}) = \sqrt{npq}\,\sqrt{\frac{N - n}{N - 1}},$$

and the factor $\sqrt{(N - n)/(N - 1)}$ is known as the *finite-population correction*. The reason for the presence of such a "correction factor" and the way in which its value depends on the values of n and N will be examined in more detail later in the chapter.

23.2   The Normal Approximation

It is completely impractical to publish tables of the hypergeometric distribution. The binomial distribution has only two parameters, n and p, and yet it requires a fairly large book to publish tables for sample sizes up to 150. The hypergeometric distribution has *three* parameters, n, p, and N; and tabulation would require a whole book for each value of the population size N. Computation of the probability of any particular number of successes r from the basic formula is not too difficult when one has a table of logarithms of factorials, or better, of logarithms of combinatorials; but computation of cumulative probabilities is usually prohibitive unless either r or $(n - r)$ is very small. When both r and $(n - r)$ are at all large, hypergeometric probabilities are usually computed by some method of approximation, and the Normal approximation is the only convenient one which actually allows for the finiteness of the population.

The procedure for using the Normal approximation is exactly the same as when it is used to approximate a binomial or Poisson probability. To find the probability of an *individual* value r—the area of a single bar in the r histogram—we express r in standard measure as

$$u = \frac{r - \mathrm{E}(\tilde{r})}{\sigma(\tilde{r})}.$$

The height of the corresponding bar in the u histogram is $\mathrm{P}'(u)$ and this is approximately equal to the height $\mathrm{P}'_N(u)$ of the unit Normal curve at this same point u. The area of the bar is found by multiplying this approximate height by the width of the bar, which is $1/\sigma(\tilde{r})$. To find a *tail area* we locate the edge of the tail

$$u = \frac{r \pm \frac{1}{2} - \mathrm{E}(\tilde{r})}{\sigma(\tilde{r})},$$

using $+$ or $-\frac{1}{2}$ according to circumstances, and then find the area $\mathrm{P}_N(\tilde{u} < u)$ or $\mathrm{P}_N(\tilde{u} > u)$ under the Normal curve beyond this edge.

23.2.1   Errors of Approximation

The Central limit theorem stated in Section 17.3 does not apply to the hypergeometric distribution because the variables are *not independent*. For a *given population size N*, it is *not* true that the Normal approximation becomes better and better as the sample size n increases. It *is* true, however, that the approximation improves as n increases if the *sampling ratio* n/N is held constant; and it is also true that the approximation is very good for quite small values of n and quite large values of n/N provided that p is not too far from .5. In Figure 23.1 we show the hypergeometric distributions and the Normal approximation for samples

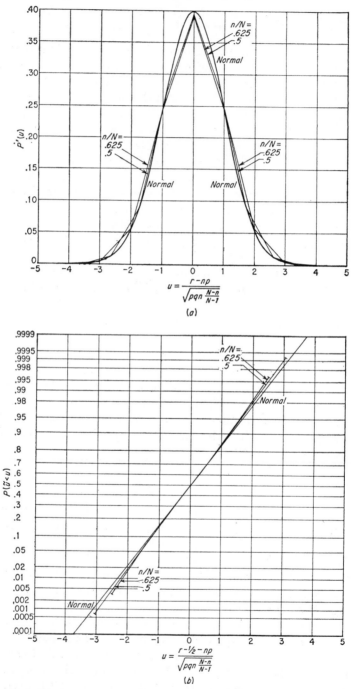

Figure 23.1. Hypergeometric distributions with Normal approximation, $n = 10$, $p = .5$.

of only 10 and two very high sampling ratios: $n/N = .5$ $(N = 20)$ and $n/N = .625$ $(N = 16)$; the parameter p has the value .5 in both cases.

23.3 Application to a Decision Problem

A manufacturer receives a lot of 100 pieces to be used in an assembly. If a defective piece is used in an assembly, the assembly will fail on final test and it will cost \$2 to remove the defective and replace it with a good part. To avoid this cost the manufacturer can inspect all the parts before assembly, but this "screening" operation costs \$.30 per part. Past experience leads the manufacturer to assign the probability distribution shown in Table 23.1 to the fraction defective in the lot. A sample of 30 pieces is taken from this particular lot and five defectives are found.

Table 23.1
Prior Distribution of p

p	$P(p)$
.10	.5
.15	.3
.20	.2
	1.0

To find the posterior distribution we first use the Normal approximation to compute the likelihood of the observed value $r = 5$ for each possible value of $\tilde{p}$. The second column of Table 23.2 shows the expected

Table 23.2
Computation of the Likelihoods

p	$E(\tilde{r}|p)$	$r - E(\tilde{r}|p)$	$\sigma(\tilde{r}|p)$	u	$P'_N(u)$	$P(r|p)$
.10	3.0	+2.0	1.382	+1.45	.1394	.101
.15	4.5	+ .5	1.644	+ .30	.3814	.232
.20	6.0	−1.0	1.842	− .54	.3488	.189

number of defectives $E(\tilde{r}) = np = 30p$ for each p and the next column shows the difference $r - E(\tilde{r}) = 5 - E(\tilde{r})$ between the actual and the expected number. The table then shows the value of $\sigma(\tilde{r})$ with the finite-population correction,

$$\sigma(\tilde{r}) = \sqrt{npq} \sqrt{\frac{N - n}{N - 1}} = \sqrt{30pq} \sqrt{\frac{70}{99}} = 4.605 \sqrt{pq},$$

and using these values of $\sigma(\tilde{r})$ the observed $r = 5$ can be expressed in standard measure as

$$u = \frac{r - \mathrm{E}(\tilde{r})}{\sigma(\tilde{r})}.$$

$\mathrm{P}'_N(u)$ can then be found in Table II and the likelihood of the observed r can be approximated by multiplying the width times this approximate height of the corresponding bar in the u histogram:

$$\mathrm{P}(r) \doteq \frac{1}{\sigma(\tilde{r})} \, \mathrm{P}'_N(u).$$

These likelihoods are then used to compute the posterior distribution of $\tilde{p}$ in Table 23.3 in the usual manner.

Table 23.3
Computation of the Posterior Distribution

p	Prior $\mathrm{P}(p)$	Likelihood $\mathrm{P}(r|p)$	Joint $\mathrm{P}(r,p)$	Posterior $\mathrm{P}(p|r)$
.10	.5	.101	.0505	.32
.15	.3	.232	.0696	.44
.20	.2	.189	.0378	.24
	1.0		.1579	1.00

The conditional costs of the two possible acts reject (screen) and accept (do not screen) are now computed as follows. The 30 pieces in the sample have already been inspected, so that if the lot is *rejected* it will be necessary to screen only the $100 - 30 = 70$ remaining pieces. Since screening costs \$.30 per piece, rejection will cost \$.30 $\times$ 70 = \$21 regardless of the value of the random variable $\tilde{p}$.

Computation of the conditional cost of *acceptance* (not screening) is a little trickier. The number of defectives *originally* in the lot is $Np = 100p$ by the definition of p (Section 23.1.4). Five of these defectives have already been found in the sample, however, and will not be sent to assembly even if the lot is not screened; it is only the $(100p - 5)$ defectives remaining in the uninspected portion of the lot which will give rise to a cost of accepting defective product. Since each of these defectives will give rise to an excess cost of \$2, the conditional cost of acceptance is

$$\$2(100p - 5) = \$200\,p - \$10.$$

These conditional costs are shown for the possible values of the basic random variable $\tilde{p}$ in Table 23.4, together with the conditional losses computed from them in the usual manner. It is left to the student as an exercise to verify the expected losses shown in Table 23.5.

Table 23.4
Payoff and Loss Tables

p	Conditional cost		Conditional loss	
	Accept	Reject	Accept	Reject
.10	$10*	$21	$0	$11
.15	20*	21	0	1
.20	30	21*	9	0

Table 23.5
Expected Loss
Accept $2.16
Reject   3.96

23.4   The Effect of the Finite Population

23.4.1   Relation between the Hypergeometric and Binomial Distributions

The procedure by which we derived the hypergeometric distribution in the first part of this chapter was identical to that by which we derived the binomial distribution in Chapter 10. We used the multiplication rule to get the probability of exactly r successes in some specified order, we observed that the probability of this number of successes was the same in any other specified order, and we multiplied it by the number of possible orders C_r^n to get the probability of r successes regardless of order. For given values of n, p, and r the factor C_r^n is the same for both distributions, so that the difference between them lies entirely in the other factor. This difference, furthermore, is entirely due to the fact that in deriving the binomial probability we took the conditional probability of a success as *constant* and equal to p on every draw, whereas in deriving the hypergeometric probability this conditional probability was equal to p on the first draw but varied on later draws because the proportion of successes remaining in the population was altered by the proportion of successes in the part of the sample already drawn. Let us now examine more closely the magnitude of these changes in the conditional probability of a success and their effect on the hypergeometric distribution.

Suppose first that we draw a sample of 10 from a population of 16 containing eight successes, $p = .5$. The probability of a success on the first draw is .5, just as it would be if we were drawing from a Bernoulli process with $p = .5$. If, however, the first sample item is a success, the probability of a success on the second draw is only $7/15 = .467$; if the first two items are successes, the probability of a success on the third draw is only $6/14 = .429$; and if the first eight items are all successes the probability of a success on the ninth draw is 0. Exactly the same argument would apply if we considered a sample with an unduly large number of failures rather than successes, and we see that

If a sample drawn without replacement from a finite population starts to go "out of line" in either direction, the proportion of successes in the remaining population changes in such a way as to tend to bring the sample back into line.

Suppose, however, that a sample of 10 is drawn from a population of 1000 rather than a population of 16, the fraction of successes in the population still being .5. Even if the first nine sample items are all successes, the probability of a success on the tenth draw is still $^{491}\!/_{991} = .495$, or only a little different from the value .5 which it had on the first draw or the value $^{500}\!/_{991} = .505$ which it would have on the tenth draw if the first nine items had all been failures.

The effect of the finiteness of the population in this second example is thus far smaller than in our first example, and a little thought will show that the magnitude of the effect of the finite population depends essentially on the *ratio* of sample size to population size. If the first 90 draws from a population of 10,000 with $p = .5$ are all successes, the probability of a success on the next draw is $^{4910}\!/_{9910} = .495$, the same as after nine successes have been taken from a population of 1000. Generalizing from this discussion we see that

As the ratio of sample to population decreases, the extent to which the probability of a success changes from draw to draw become smaller and smaller, approaching 0 as the ratio approaches 0.

Now we know that if the probabilities did not change at all from draw to draw, the reasoning which led to the hypergeometric distribution would have led to the binomial distribution. We thus reach the very important conclusion:

As the size of the sample decreases relative to the size of the population, the hypergeometric distribution approaches the binomial distribution with the same n and p.

This is shown graphically in Figure 23.2 for samples from populations with $p = .5$. The figure applies to a single sample size $n = 10$ but a variety of population sizes. The hypergeometric distributions are shown for populations ranging from 16 (sampling ratio $n/N = .625$) to 100 ($n/N = .1$); the corresponding binomial distribution is labeled $n/N = 0$. The figure makes it clear that the effect of the finiteness of the population is already quite small for n/N as large as .2 and very small indeed for $n/N = .1$.

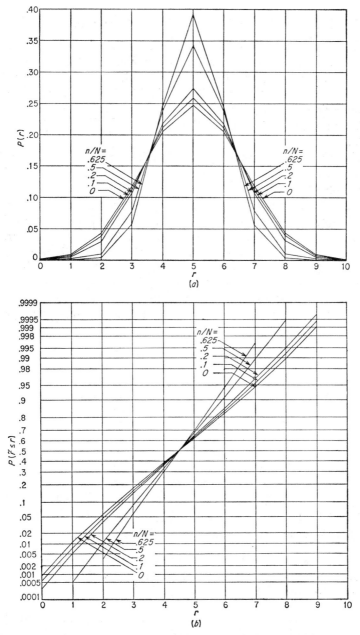

Figure 23.2. Hypergeometric distributions with binomial limit, $n = 10$, $p = .5$.

23.4.2   Behavior of the Finite-population Correction

Figure 23.2 applies only to the special case $n = 10$, $p = .5$; the finite-population correction gives us a convenient method of examining the effect of the sampling ratio n/N in general.   If a sample takes in the entire population, r will necessarily be equal to the number of successes in the population.   This means that the standard deviation of $\tilde{r}$ is *zero*, and this is the value of the correction factor $\sqrt{(N-n)/(N-1)}$ when $n = N$.

The effect of the finite population becomes less as either (1) n decreases with N fixed or (2) N increases with n fixed.   If we look first at a reduction of n with N fixed, the extreme case is a sample of 1.   The finiteness of the population has no effect, and the value of the correction factor is $\sqrt{(N-1)/(N-1)} = 1$.   To see the effect of increasing N with n fixed, let us drop the 1 from the denominator of the correction factor—when N is large, $N - 1$ does not differ appreciably from N.   We can then write the factor in the form $\sqrt{(N-n)/N} = \sqrt{1 - n/N}$, and we see at once that unless n/N is reasonably large the factor will be very close to 1.   The values of the factor for the cases graphed in Figure 23.2 are shown in Table 23.6.   For the extremely high sampling ratio .625 the

Table 23.6
Finite-population Correction

n/N	N	$\sqrt{(N-n)/(N-1)}$
.625	16	.63
.5	20	.73
.2	50	.90
.1	100	.95
0	∞	1.00

hypergeometric distribution has only 63 per cent as much dispersion as the binomial; but for a ratio of .2 it has 90 per cent as much and for a ratio of .1 it has 95 per cent as much.   To sum up:

It is only when a sample drawn without replacement takes in a really substantial fraction of the total population that any attention need be paid to the finiteness of the population.

Percentage Samples.   One of the most common "vulgar errors" concerning sampling is the belief that the reliability of a sample depends upon its *percentage* relationship to the population.   Many businessmen operate sampling inspection plans which call for inspection of a certain percentage of each lot—usually 10 per cent.   Sampling surveys to determine the current value of properties of a utility such as poles, transformers, etc., are often based on a percentage—again usually 10 per cent because public service commissions seem to have accepted this as the proper size.   Our discussion of the behavior of the finite-population correction shows, however, that this policy is completely misguided: *unless the sample takes in a really substantial fraction of the population, its reliability depends on its absolute rather than its relative size.*

23.4.3   Binomial and Poisson Approximations to Hypergeometric Probabilities

The fact that the hypergeometric distribution approaches the binomial as n/N decreases means that when n/N is small enough binomial probabilities can be used as approximations to hypergeometric probabilities.   The binomial probabilities can be taken from tables of the binomial distribution if they are available for the n and p of the problem in hand, or the Poisson approximation to the binomial can be used if the values of n and p are appropriate.

23.5   The Importance of the Sampling Process

As we stated at the beginning of this chapter, the results of this chapter apply when and only when the *sampling process* is:
  1. Simple.
  2. From a finite population without replacement.
We shall now reexamine these two conditions in the reverse order.

23.5.1   Sampling without Replacement

It is essential to realize that it is not the finiteness of the population *as such* which leads to a hypergeometric rather than a binomial distribution of the number of successes: it is the fact that the sampling is *without replacement* from a finite population.   If sampling is simple *with* replacement, the distribution of $\tilde{r}$ is *binomial however small the population may be.*

The Concept of an Infinite Population.   Because of the fact that the binomial distribution is the limit of the hypergeometric as N increases and "approaches infinity" with n fixed, samples from a Bernoulli process are sometimes said to be drawn from the "infinite population" consisting of all the trials which the process "could" generate.

23.5.2   Simple Sampling

Sampling from a number of *objects already in existence* is simple only if the sample items are selected in such a way that the probability which it is reasonable to assign to a success on any draw is equal to the proportion of successes among all items not yet drawn at that time.   Such an assignment will be reasonable only if we are firmly convinced that the selection of the items in the sample has not been influenced, *either con-*

sciously or unconsciously, by any information which may bear on their values. If we know *or suspect* that such information has been used, sampling is not simple and *the results of this chapter do not apply*. Although the methods which must be used when sampling is not simple will not be discussed until Chapter 31, we shall point out here some typical conditions which may make our present methods inapplicable.

In the urn model, sampling is not simple if some of the balls are rougher than others, the person drawing the balls tends to choose either rough or smooth balls by preference, and we either know or suspect that roughness may be associated with color. In a consumer survey carried out to get information on the usage of a certain product, sampling is not simple if interviewers call only once at each household and we suspect that use of the product in question is associated with a tendency to stay at home. In inspection of incoming lots, sampling is not simple if the sample is drawn from the top of the container and we suspect that the parts on top are of different average quality from those on the bottom.

Notice that such problems are *not* restricted to samples drawn in order to obtain information concerning a *finite population*. They can equally well occur in connection with a sample drawn to obtain information concerning a random process if the sample is obtained by drawing a certain number of items from a larger number which have already been produced by the process. If the inspector tends to select defectives in preference to good pieces, it will *not* be rational to set the probability that any sample item will be defective equal to the process parameter p.

PROBLEMS

1. What is the probability of drawing two good pieces and one defective in the order *gdg* by simple sampling without replacement:
    a. From a lot of eight pieces 25 per cent of which are defective?
    b. From a Bernoulli process generating 25 per cent defectives?
2. What is the probability of drawing two good pieces and one defective *regardless of order* under the conditions of Problem 1?
3. What is the probability of drawing two *defectives* and one *good piece* regardless of order under the conditions of Problem 1?
4. What is the probability of drawing *exactly one* defective and the probability of drawing *one or less* defectives in a sample of 10 taken by simple sampling without replacement:
    a. From a Bernoulli process producing 10 per cent defectives?
    b. From a lot of 20 containing 10 per cent defectives?
    c. From a lot of 2000 containing 10 per cent defectives?
5. From Figure 23.2 find the probability of drawing three or less users of instant coffee in a sample of 10 taken by simple sampling without replacement from a population containing 50 per cent users if the entire population consists of
    a. 20 individuals.   b. 50 individuals.
    c. 100 individuals.   d. 10,000 individuals.
6. Find the following hypergeometric probabilities by the best approximation you know and discuss the accuracy of your approximation in each case.

a. 5 or less defectives in a sample of 100 from a lot of 10,000 containing 3 per cent defectives.

b. Exactly 5 defectives in a sample of 100 from a lot of 200 containing 3 per cent defectives.

c. 5 or less defectives in a sample of 100 from a lot of 1,000 containing 1 per cent defectives.

d. Exactly 20 defectives in a sample of 50 from a lot of 200 containing 40 per cent defectives.

e. 3 or less defectives in a sample of 200 from a lot of 50,000 containing 500 defectives.

f. Exactly 50 defectives in a sample of 150 from a lot of 1000 containing 400 defectives.

7. In 1952, W. R. Simmons and Associates conducted a number of interviews on the subject of television viewing for the National Broadcasting Company. The interviews were conducted in the Quad-City area of Davenport, Rock Island, Moline, and East Moline.

a. 72,000 families lived in the area and 5000 were interviewed. What is the finite-population correction?

b. What would the finite-population correction have been if 10,000 families had been interviewed?

c. What would it have been if 5,000 had been interviewed and the population had been 1,000,000 families?

8. For the example in Section 23.3:

a. What is the expected *cost* of rejection? (No computation is necessary.)

b. Compute the expected *cost* of acceptance under the posterior distribution by using the mean of this distribution. (HINT: Review Section 5.3.1 before trying to apply Section 22.4.4.)

c. Compute the posterior expected cost of action under certainty and use it to verify the expected losses in Table 23.5.

d. What is the posterior cost of uncertainty?

9. Part 86Y7 is purchased in lots of 1000 for use in an assembly. If a defective part is included in an assembly, it will have to be removed and replaced at a cost of $5. Screening the lot for defectives costs $.30 per piece. A sample of 50 pieces is taken from the lot and two defectives are found. The frequency distribution of fraction defective in a large number of previous lots is shown in the table below.

Fraction defective	Relative frequency
.05	.7
.10	.2
.15	.1
	1.0

a. What was the probability of this sample result as evaluated before the sample was actually drawn and inspected?

b. What action should be taken and why?

c. What is the cost of uncertainty?

10. The Smith Novelty Company engaged in the business of selling unusual novelty and gift items by direct mail. It used a single mailing list for all offers; the list had been built up and weeded out over many years, and currently consisted of about 30,000 "good prospects," almost all of whom had purchased on two or more occasions.

A large part of Smith's business was in items imported from Europe, where a buyer was permanently stationed. The ordinary procedure was for the buyer to find some item which he believed suitable for the company's business and contract for a lot which was shipped to Smith in the United States in a single shipment. When the merchandise was received, the company would prepare and send out a special mailing. The company was convinced that it was necessary to give a strong "special bargain" flavor to these mailings and therefore invariably restricted sales to "one to a customer."

The chief hazards in Smith's business were two: the risk of being left with a large quantity of unsold merchandise when response to a mailing was poor, and the risk of being short when response to a mailing was unusually good. When merchandise was left over, it was usually wholesaled off to retail bargain outlets at a considerable loss. On the other hand, Mr. James Smith, the owner of the company, felt that a very serious good-will cost was incurred by unfilled customer orders in a business such as his, and when demand exceeded the contract quantity he usually tried to secure additional merchandise off the shelf even if the cost to him of such merchandise was higher than the price paid by the customer.

Smith had been thinking for some time about ways of reducing these losses and had finally concluded that at least in some cases it would be possible and might be profitable to sample his mailing list before ordering any specific quantity from the foreign supplier; the quantity ordered would then be set to correspond with the estimate made from the sample. Doing this would not be altogether simple, however: customers on the sample list would not be willing to wait 3 or 4 months before receiving their merchandise, and the company could not tolerate disgruntled customers because of the importance of repeat business. It would be necessary, therefore, to make two importations: one of a quantity sufficient to satisfy the demand from the sample mailing, and then another to anticipate the demand from the main mailing. Since the initial importation would have to be purchased from the manufacturer's regular stocks at a higher price than that which would be obtained when buying a single contract quantity, and since per-unit shipping costs would be higher on the small quantity, there would be a very real cost involved in the sampling operation.

In June, 1955, the buyer sent over a sample of a blue enameled Dutch skillet which Mr. Smith thought would be an excellent buy. Housewares of this same general category had been offered before, and sales had ranged from 1050 to 2550 units. Smith thought that if this skillet were offered at $3, the sales would be somewhere in this general range but he could not tell just where—one figure seemed about as likely to him as another.

The skillet could be bought from the manufacturer's stock in small quantities at his retail price of $2.75; delivery to the company's premises in the United States by parcel post would cost an additional $.75 per skillet. In a contract quantity and a single shipment by ocean freight the cost would be about $1.50 including delivery. Postage and handling on the mail orders would average about $.50 per sale. Smith believed that skillets remaining unsold after the mailing could be salvaged for about $1.10 each, net of expenses.

a. Simplifying the computations by assuming that Smith assigns equal probability to demands for 1200, 1500, 1800, 2100, and 2400 skillets and 0 probability to all other demands, compute the cost of uncertainty if Smith acts without sampling.

b. Same as (*a*) but after Smith has sent an advance mailing to 200 people and received orders from 10 of them.

c. How could you obtain answers in better accord with Smith's real beliefs? Discuss but do not make any actual computations.

CHAPTER 24

Interdependent Decision Problems; Finite vs. Infinite Populations

Before going on to learn how to analyze new types of problems in which the decision should rest in part on the information obtained from a sample, let us stop to examine a little more closely the conditions under which we may and may not apply the methods of analysis already studied in Chapters 22 and 23. In the present chapter we shall look at two different kinds of problems which arise in the application of these methods. First, we shall see that in some common situations it is impossible to make a rational choice among actions *now* without at the same time adopting a definite plan for making choices which will have to be made in the *future*. Second, we shall see that under certain circumstances we should regard a sample as having been drawn from an *infinite* population even though at first glance it seems obvious that it has been drawn from a *finite* population. Our examples will be taken from the field of quality control because this field offers the clearest and simplest illustrations of the principles involved, but the principles themselves are by no means restricted to applications in this field.

24.1 Independent vs. Interdependent Decisions

As a first example of what we shall call the problem of interdependent decisions we shall take the problem of acceptance sampling when rejected lots are scrapped rather than being screened as they were in the example discussed in Section 23.3.

24.1.1 Acceptance Sampling When Rejected Lots Are Scrapped

A small electrical component used in an assembly is manufactured in lots of about 2500 pieces by a sequence of batch operations. The total fixed cost incurred for each batch produced is $30; variable cost amounts to $.03 per piece. Every effort is made to control the quality of the raw materials and of the work done in each operation, but for reasons which are imperfectly understood some of the finished parts will not work properly in an assembly unless special compensating adjustments are made. Such parts will be called "defectives"; the cost of the adjustments made necessary by one defective averages $3.75.

Beyond the measures already taken to control the quality of the raw materials and the operations in the production process, there is no way of correcting the process when it is generating a high fraction defective. A test has been devised which will identify defectives without actually placing them in an assembly and testing the assembly, but this test subjects each part to very high voltages and even good parts which pass the test are thereby rendered unusable: inspection is *destructive*. The only way of avoiding the costs due to the defectives produced in any batch is therefore to scrap the entire batch.

A quantity of 2500 parts has just been requisitioned by the assembly department. In order to permit sampling the output of the production run, 2520 parts have actually been produced and 20 have been tested; the test has revealed one defective. On the basis of his previous experience with production of this part the manufacturer is convinced that the production process behaves like a Bernoulli process, and before the sample of 20 parts was inspected he had assigned the probabilities shown in the second column of Table 24.1 to the values which the process average defective $\tilde{p}$ might have during the run just made. After learning that the sample from this run contained one defective, he has revised his prob-

Table 24.1
Probability Distributions of Process $\tilde{p}$

p	$P_0(p)$	$P_1(p)$
.01	.60	.42
.03	.20	.28
.05	.10	.16
.07	.07	.10
.09	.03	.04
	1.00	1.00

ability distribution for $\tilde{p}$ as shown in the third column of Table 24.1. The means of the two distributions are:

Prior: $E_0(\tilde{p}) = .0246$,
Posterior: $E_1(\tilde{p}) = .0312$.

The Cost of Acceptance. In this situation the cost of acceptance is exactly like the cost of acceptance in the example analyzed in Chapter 22. The decision to accept or reject affects 2500 pieces, so that the conditional expected number of defectives is $2500p$. Since defectives cost $3.75 each, the conditional expected cost of acceptance is $\$3.75 \times 2500p = \$9375\,p$; and since the conditional cost is thus a *linear* function of p we have immediately

Unconditional cost of acceptance $= \$9375\ E_1(\bar{p}) = \$9375 \times .0312$
$$= \$293.$$

The Cost of Rejection. A complication arises, however, when we try to compute the expected cost of rejection. If the manufacturer accepts, he buys the 2500 parts he needs in assembly for an expected cost of \$293; but if he rejects he in effect obligates himself to obtain the required 2500 pieces by *future* operations, and *on the information given above we cannot compute the expected cost of this obligation.* It quite obviously involves *at least* the cost of manufacturing 2500 more pieces, but for all we know now this second run may also be rejected and a third one made, and so forth: the manufacturing cost which will *ultimately* result from a present decision to reject *depends on future decisions.* The obligation incurred by a present decision to reject also involves some expected cost of accepting the defectives produced on the future run which is finally accepted, and again the amount of the cost depends on the manufacturer's future decisions.

If the manufacturer has already decided that he will *under no circumstances make more than two runs* in order to fill the requirement of the assembly department, then everything is simple. Since the next run is definitely to be accepted if it is made, there is no sense in sampling its product. The run will therefore consist of just the 2500 pieces required in assembly and its manufacturing cost will be $\$30 + (2500 \times \$.03) = \$105$. The information on *run-to-run* variation in $\bar{p}$ provided by the fact that one defective was found in a sample of 20 from the present run is negligible in comparison with the past experience on which the prior distribution of Table 24.1 is based; this prior distribution therefore applies unchanged to the replacement run and the expected cost of the defectives in the replacement run is $\$9375\ E_0(p) = \$9375 \times .0246 = \$231$. Thus on the assumption that the next run will definitely be accepted we have for the total consequences of rejecting the present lot

Unconditional cost of rejection $= \$105 + \$231 = \$336$,

and acceptance of the present run is preferable to rejection by the difference $\$336 - \$293 = \$43$.

The Need for a Decision Plan. Solution of this new kind of problem is thus no more difficult than solution of the kinds of problems discussed in Chapters 22 and 23 *if* the manufacturer has already decided that no more than two runs will be made, but unfortunately this is *not* a rational decision in most situations. If the present run *is* rejected and scrapped, the manufacturer will then be in *exactly the same position that he was in before the present run was made.* If it was rational to sample the present run, it will be rational to sample the replacement run; and if there are any sample results for which it is rational to scrap the product of the present run, it must be equally rational to scrap the product of the replacement run for the same sample results.

Suppose, for example, that the manufacturer decides to make replacement runs until he comes to one with *no* defective in the sample. Such a plan will of course increase the expected manufacturing cost entailed by rejecting the present run above the $105 computed above, but this increase *may* be more than offset by a reduction in the $231 cost of defective product.† This means that it is at least *conceivable* that the total expected cost of rejecting the present lot and making replacement runs until one is found with no defective in the sample *may* actually be less than the $293 cost of accepting the present lot.

Clearly, then, the manufacturer in our present problem *cannot rationally separate the problem of reaching a decision concerning the present run from the problem of reaching decisions on possible replacement runs.* This separation was possible in the problems of Chapters 22 and 23 only because

> In those problems the number of usable pieces produced by the run or obtained from the lot did not depend on the decision which was made, and therefore the costs entailed by a present decision did not depend in any way on future decisions.

In our present problem, the way in which future decisions will be made does affect the costs which will ultimately be entailed by a present decision to reject; and in order to analyze this problem rationally, we must look at it as one of finding *a set of rules for making a whole sequence of decisions in such a way that their total expected cost is minimized.*

Such a problem cannot be analyzed by methods of the kind we are studying at present. In this part of the course we are learning how to evaluate the expected cost of a decision *after a sample has been taken.* Problems involving plans for making a sequence of decisions force us to evaluate the expected cost of *taking a sample and then making a decision;* this will be the subject of Part Four of the course.

24.1.2   Quality Control When Only the Defectives Are Scrapped

The essential point of the example just studied was the fact that *the decision affected the "yield"* which would be obtained from the present run as well as the costs which would be directly incurred. The yield of a decision to accept was 2500 pieces; the yield of a decision to reject was 0.

---

† Notice that *if* the run which is finally accepted is one with $\tilde{p} = .01$, the cost of defective product will be only $9375 \times .01 = \$93.75$; and since there is prior probability .60 that $\tilde{p}$ will in fact have the value .01 on *any one* replacement run, there is at least a good chance that a plan which accepts only runs with no defective in the sample will in fact lead to final acceptance of a run with $\tilde{p} = .01$.

It was this difference in yield which created the interdependence among present and future decisions, and this same essential feature may be present even when rejection does not involve scrapping good as well as bad pieces.

As an example, consider the following problem. A manufacturer is about to make a production run of a certain part. According to the quality of the setup of the machine on which the part is produced, the run will include more or less defectives which *can neither be used in assembly nor reworked and therefore have to be scrapped.* The variable cost of each piece manufactured is $.47 and the scrap value of a piece is $.18, so that there is an out-of-pocket loss of $.29 per defective. The manufacturer is convinced that the machine operates as a Bernoulli process and he assigns the probability distribution shown in Table 24.2 to the process average fraction defective $\tilde{p}$ if the machine is set up by the operator in the usual way. If the setup is corrected by an expert mechanic at an additional cost of $35, $\tilde{p}$ is sure to have its minimum value .10. The machine has

Table 24.2
Prior Probability Distribution

p	$P(p)$
.10	.1
.20	.2
.30	.4
.40	.3
	1.0

just been set up by the regular operator and a sample of 10 pieces produced; the sample contains three defectives. The production run will consist of 500 additional pieces.

Notice that this problem is of exactly the same kind as the problem discussed in Chapter 22 with this one difference: in that problem defectives were *used at extra cost,* whereas in this problem defectives cannot be used and are *scrapped.* We shall now examine the consequences of this difference.

The " Direct" Costs of Acceptance and Rejection. In the light of the prior distribution and the information in the sample, the expected value of $\tilde{p}$ for the operator's setup is .306 as the student should verify. The expected cost directly entailed by acceptance is therefore

$$.306 \times 500 \times \$.29 = \$44.37.$$

If the setup is corrected by the expert mechanic, the expected cost of defectives is $.10 \times 500 \times \$.29 = \$14.50$, and adding in the $35 cost of the mechanic's time we have $49.50 for the expected cost directly entailed by rejection. If this problem were of *exactly* the same nature as the one discussed in Chapter 22, we would conclude that acceptance is better than rejection by the difference $\$49.50 - \$44.37 = \$5.13$.

The Difference in Yield. Observe, however, that *the two possible decisions differ not only in the costs directly entailed but also in yield.* If the manufacturer *accepts*, the expected yield of the run is

$$500 - 500 \, E(\bar{p}) = 500(1 - .306) = 347 \text{ good pieces.}$$

If he *rejects*, the expected yield is $500(1 - .10) = 450$ good pieces. Thus while acceptance can be "expected" to *save* $5.13 in immediate out-of-pocket *expense*, it must also be expected to produce $450 - 347 = 103$ *less good pieces* than a decision to reject.

Now the manufacturer's assembly requirements oblige him ultimately to produce, not a certain number of pieces, but a certain number of *usable* pieces. It follows that if he accepts in this situation, he in effect incurs an obligation to produce the "missing" 103 pieces on some future run, just as he obligated himself to produce and accept 2500 pieces on some future run if he rejected in the first example discussed in this chapter. It is true that we have included the *direct* cost of the missing 103 good pieces in the expected cost of acceptance; but we have *not* allowed for the cost of the defectives which will be produced in the course of obtaining 103 good pieces or for the additional setup and sampling costs which must be charged to the manufacture of these 103 good pieces on a subsequent run or runs.

The exact solution of this problem or of any problem where the decision affects yield as well as cost requires exactly the same methods of analysis as a problem in which rejection involves scrapping an entire lot. As stated before, the development of these methods must be postponed to Part Four of the course.

24.1.3 Approximate Solutions

When we come to Part Four of the course we shall see that the extra computations required to take account of differences in yield as well as cost are fairly laborious, and in *some* problems their effect on the final answers is of no practical interest. Suppose, for example, that we are faced with a problem like the one just studied except that $\bar{p}$ can have values only between .01 and .05. The *cost of acceptance* is proportional to p and therefore will be 5 times as large if $\bar{p} = .05$ as it will if $\bar{p} = .01$. The *number of good pieces*, on the contrary, is proportional to $(1 - p)$ and will be only $(1 - .01)/(1 - .05) = 1.04$ times as large if $\bar{p} = .01$ as it will be if $\bar{p} = .05$. Even if $\bar{p}$ could be as high as .10, the largest possible number good is only $(1 - .01)/(1 - .10) = 1.1$ times as large as the smallest, whereas the highest cost of acceptance is 10 times the lowest.

In such cases we can simply neglect the effect of $\bar{p}$ on number good unless we want extreme accuracy for some special reason. The effect can be neglected even when the ratio of the largest $(1 - p)$ to the smallest is fairly large if at the same time very small probability is assigned to the extreme values. Obviously there can be no rule which will tell us for certain whether or not we can neglect differences in yield in a particular problem, but a little common sense will usually suffice.

24.2   Finite vs. Infinite Populations

We now turn to the second topic of this chapter, the question whether a sample is to be regarded as having been drawn from an infinite or a finite population. We shall start by reviewing the examples which we have already analyzed in Chapters 22 and 23 and in the first part of this chapter.

1. In the examples of Sections 22.1 and 24.1.2, the manufacturer wished to decide whether or not to *correct the process average* of a Bernoulli process. We treated the sample as being drawn from the *process:* we used a prior distribution for the *process average* and we treated $\tilde{r}$ as having a *binomial* sampling distribution.

2. In the example of Section 23.3, the manufacturer wished to decide whether or not to *accept a certain lot* received from a vendor. We treated the sample as being drawn from the *finite* population consisting of this particular lot: we used a prior distribution for the *lot fraction defective* and we treated $\tilde{r}$ as having a *hypergeometric* sampling distribution.

3. In the example of Section 24.1.1, the manufacturer wished to decide whether or not to *accept a certain lot* which had just been manufactured; he had *no control over the process average*. Nevertheless we treated the sample as being drawn from the *process:* we used a prior distribution for the *process average* and we treated $\tilde{r}$ as having a *binomial* distribution.

The first thing to strike the student will no doubt be the apparent inconsistency between the way in which we analyzed the example of Section 23.3 and the way in which we analyzed the example of Section 24.1.1; it looks as if the latter of these two examples involves a finite lot just like the former and should have been analyzed in exactly the same way. What we shall now see is that, although there was no *error* in the logic of our analysis of Section 24.1.1, we did have an *option:* we *could* have analyzed this example in the same way that we analyzed the example of Section 23.3. We shall also see, moreover, that we had similar options in the other cases as well. We could have treated the examples of Sections 22.1 and 24.1.2 as problems involving finite lots, and under certain conditions we could have treated the example of Section 23.3 as a problem involving a process or infinite population.

24.2.1   Equivalence of the Two Methods for a Bernoulli Process

Let us start by reconsidering the examples of Sections 22.1 and 24.1.2, in both of which the manufacturer knew that he was dealing with a Bernoulli process, had some control over the process average, and treated the sample as being drawn from the process.   In both these examples, the sample could equally well have been considered as being drawn from the finite lot which was to be produced if the manufacturer accepted.   The first 10 pieces in this lot are as good a sample of the lot as any other 10 pieces which might have been taken from it, and the fact that the manufacturer could sample the lot before actually incurring the cost of producing it was a piece of economic good fortune which had no bearing on the probabilities involved.   But if the sample is regarded as coming from a finite lot, then it follows necessarily that the number of defectives $\tilde{r}$ must be assigned a hypergeometric probability distribution; and this would make it seem as if this view of the problem would lead to expected costs different from those obtained by treating the sample as coming from a process or infinite population and assigning a binomial distribution to $\tilde{r}$.

The difficulty is resolved as soon as we consider the prior distribution as well as the sampling distribution.   To make the discussion as concrete as possible, we shall talk in terms of an infinite sequence of runs during which the relative frequency of each possible value of the *process* average is equal to its probability as given by the prior distribution in the original statement of the problem.   Each "run" produces one "lot," but *the frequency distribution of the fractions defective in the various* lots *will* not *be the same as the frequency distribution of the process averages during the corresponding* runs.   The point is obvious if we recall that the lot fraction defective would vary from lot to lot because of Bernoulli variation even if the process average remained absolutely fixed during the infinite sequence of runs.   If then the process average varies from run to run, as we are actually assuming, the *total* variation of the lot fraction defective will be the sum of the Bernoulli variation and the variation in the process average.†

Thus if we are to treat the sample in either of these two problems as taken from a particular finite lot rather than from the process in a particular condition, we must use a prior distribution for lot fraction defective rather than the prior distribution for process fraction defective; and in assessing this distribution we must include Bernoulli uncertainty as well as uncertainty concerning the process average.   If we do this correctly, *the extra prior uncertainty concerning the lot fraction defective compared with the process fraction will be just compensated by the extra "tightness" of the hypergeometric sampling distribution as compared with the binomial; the expected costs will be the same whichever method we use.*

Example.   To illustrate the point, suppose that a manufacturer has produced a sample of $n = 2$ pieces in order to decide whether to accept or reject a Bernoulli process before making a "run" of 1 more piece, and

† Cf. Chapter 16, Problem 10.

suppose that he has found $r = 1$ defective in the sample. The sample can be considered as taken either from the process or from a lot of total size $N = 3$. We assume that the prior distribution for the *process* fraction defective shown in Table 24.3 is given, and by applying the methods of Section 12.3.2 we compute the corresponding prior distribution for *lot* number defective R. (It is simply for convenience that we work with lot number defective rather than with lot fraction defective.)

Table 24.3
Prior Distribution

Process average		Lot number defective	
p	$P_0(p)$	R	$P_0(R)$
.1	.5	0	.6205
.2	.5	1	.3135
	1.0	2	.0615
		3	.0045
			1.0000

By applying Bayes' theorem in standard fashion we can combine the prior distributions and the sample result to obtain the corresponding posterior distributions in Table 24.4. The likelihood of the sample is

Table 24.4
Posterior Distribution

Process average		Lot number defective	
p	$P_1(p)$	R	$P_1(R)$
.1	.36	0	0
.2	.64	1	.836
	1.00	2	.164
		3	0
			1.000

computed binomially in the case of $\tilde{p}$, hypergeometrically in the case of $\tilde{R}$. The means of these two posterior distributions are

$$E_1(\tilde{p}) = .164,$$
$$E_1(\tilde{R}) = 1.164.$$

The posterior expected cost of accepting defectives will be proportional to the expected number of defectives in the one-piece remainder of the run or lot. If we look at the problem as one involving the *process*, we say that the decision affects a remaining *run* of one piece and that the expected number of defectives in this run is $1 \times E(\tilde{p}) = 1 \times .164 = .164$. If we look at the problem as one involving the *lot*, we say that the expected number of defectives in the whole lot of three pieces is $E(\tilde{R}) = 1.164$; but since one defective from the whole lot is already in the sample, the expected number of defectives in the remainder of the lot—the part which is to be accepted or rejected—is .164.

24.2.2   Assessment of the Prior Distributions

In actual practice we can never have a historical frequency distribution of true process averages on which to base a probability distribution for process average, and we will only rarely have a historical distribution of lot fractions defective on which to base a probability distribution for this random variable. Usually the record will show only the fraction defective in a *sample* from each lot or run. If these samples are small, the recorded variability in sample fraction defective will include a large amount of Bernoulli variation which must be eliminated when we assess the prior distribution for *either* the lot fraction defective or the process average; and the techniques by which this excess variation can be eliminated in either case are beyond the scope of this course. Our reason for raising the issue of finite vs. infinite populations is therefore not the use which we shall make of the distinction in actually solving problems—we have seen that the difference between the binomial and hypergeometric distributions is negligible in most practical cases anyway. The reason is rather to lay the foundation for two very important general principles which we shall now discuss.

24.2.3   Control of the Output of a Bernoulli Process

Suppose that some productive process has been supplying a sequence of lots of parts of distressingly bad quality—averaging 40 per cent defective, say—but suppose also that there has been considerable lot-to-lot variation around this 40 per cent average. It is very tempting to think that some improvement in the situation can be made by using sampling inspection and rejecting the worst of the lots, but very frequently this is not so. If the lots are small, the whole variation may be Bernoulli variation and the process itself—*whether it belongs to us or to a vendor*—may have a constant process average of 40 per cent. If this is true, then sampling is a total waste of effort. For looking at the problem as we did just above, each lot can be thought of as two separate runs by the process, the first one producing the sample which we inspect, the second one producing the remainder of the lot which is to be either accepted or rejected. If the process average is in fact a constant 40 per cent, variation in the number of defectives in the inspected sample is totally independent of variation in the number of defectives in the remainder of the lot.

In other words: the samples in a situation like this tell us absolutely nothing about the quality of the remainder of the pieces in the lots from which they are taken, and the average quality of the accepted remainders will be neither better nor worse than the average quality of the rejected remainders. If lots are produced by a Bernoulli process, sampling inspection is economically useful only if the *process average* fluctuates from run to run (or if we are uncertain about the process average on a particular run); and this is true whether we have direct control over the process average or the control is entirely in the hands of our supplier. The first of our two general principles is therefore the following:

> Whenever product is produced by a Bernoulli process, the economically rational way of approaching any problem of quality control is to regard it as a problem involving the process average; there is nothing which can be done about Bernoulli variation in lot quality and no money should be spent trying to do anything.

24.2.4   *Quality Control When the Source Is Not a Bernoulli Process*

The second of our two principles is the following:

> When we are *not* justified in assuming that product is the output of a Bernoulli process, we must treat all problems of acceptance and rejection as problems involving finite lots, and we must be sure that the sampling from these lots is *simple.*

The former part of this proposition is obvious—if the process is not a Bernoulli process, the number $\tilde{r}$ of defectives among n successive pieces produced by the process will not have a binomial distribution. The emphasis is really to be put on the second part of the proposition, which is the one that is often overlooked.

Before basing decisions on the assumption that the number of defectives in a sample from any finite lot will have a hypergeometric distribution, we must be sure that we are justified in asserting that the probability that any individual sample item will be defective is equal to the proportion of defectives remaining in the lot at the time this item is drawn. If the lot comes from a process which produces defectives in streaks and if the sample is drawn from the top of the lot container, the number $\tilde{r}$ will most definitely not have a hypergeometric distribution.

PROBLEMS

1. Verify the computation of the posterior distribution in Table 24.1 and its mean $E_1(\tilde{p}) = .0313$.

2. Verify that $E_1(\tilde{p}) = .306$ is the mean of the posterior distribution corresponding to the prior distribution of Table 24.2 and a sample of 10 containing three defectives.

3. Verify the computation of Tables 24.3 and 24.4.

4. The Robinson Abrasive Company manufactured a wide variety of grinding wheels for industrial use. These wheels were subject to extreme stresses; and since breakage could result in severe damage to machinery and injury to machine operators the company was anxious to maintain high-quality output and subjected the wheels to rigorous testing procedures.

The first step in the manufacture of a grinding wheel was to mix bonding material, abrasive, and water until a smooth uniform mixture was obtained and then pour the mixture into molds which were allowed to dry for a period of several days. The dried wheels were then placed on a shaving machine and turned to the desired dimension, bushings were inserted, and the finished product was tested for hardness, toughness, and strength. The strength test consisted in placing the wheel in a protective steel shell and rotating it at a speed 50 per cent greater than the maximum speed which would be used under ordinary operating conditions.

Failure of finished wheels in the strength test could be due to a variety of causes. If the wheels were improperly loaded in the kiln, warping or cracking or internal stresses could result; and on the average, about 5 per cent of all wheels failed on final test for reasons of this sort. The bonding material itself was of variable quality, and sometimes a substantial number of wheels in a single batch would fail because the cohesive strength of the material was inadequate. Although he could not be completely sure of the reason for some of the individual failures, the quality-control supervisor believed that about 70 per cent of all batches had no failures due to the raw material while 20 per cent of the batches had 5 per cent failures for this reason and 10 per cent of the batches had 20 per cent.

In September, 1955, the research department announced that it had developed and had available for immediate use in manufacturing a new bonding material which was much stronger than the old. Wheels made of this material were no better or worse than wheels made of the old material which succeeded in passing inspection, but the failures due to the raw material were completely eliminated and the company intended to purchase no more material of the old kind. At this time the company had on hand enough of the old bonding material to make 1000 grinding wheels 36 inches in diameter; and since there was no test which would give a reliable measurement of the strength of this material other than actually using it to produce finished wheels, the superintendent raised the question whether it ought to be scrapped in order to avoid the risk of wasting money in processing wheels which might fail on final test.

The cost of processing plus the cost of the materials other than the bonding material amounted to $15 per wheel, but enough new bonding material to produce one thousand 36-inch wheels would cost $1000 and the quality-control supervisor suggested that the batch of old material should be tested by actually using some of it in finished wheels before a decision was reached to accept or reject the remainder. He proposed that the test wheels be prepared and processed under carefully controlled conditions, so that the probability of failure due to improper loading would be negligible. They would be given the regular strength test, and a decision to accept or reject the batch would be based on the outcome of this test.

If a sample of 10 wheels is tested and one defective is found, what action should be taken? What is the cost of uncertainty?

5. The Burke Appliance Company manufactured a variety of screw-machine parts which were used in final assembly of its product. Part 684 was a grooved cylindrical shaft which was designed to fit an assembly with close tolerances. The part was used at the rate of about 200,000 a year; it was produced for inventory in lots of 5000, equivalent to a day's run of one machine.

Considerable difficulty was experienced in holding dimensional tolerances on this part, and defectives were causing serious losses. Time studies showed that the interference with a smooth assembly operation caused by each defective reaching the assembly department cost roughly $.25 in addition to the loss due to having to scrap the part. The variable cost of manufacturing one part was $.20; the salvage value of a defective part was $.05.

After examining the company's production records, Mr. Paul O'Brien, the production manager, estimated that when the machine was adjusted in the normal manner there were 6 per cent defectives 50 per cent of the time, 8 per cent defectives 25 per cent of the time, and 12 per cent defectives 25 per cent of the time. Some experimentation had shown that by extremely careful gauging at the start of each run the machine could be set to produce 5 per cent defectives with certainty. The extra cost of this extremely careful setup process was $50 for labor and machine down time. Mr. O'Brien considered both the possibility of having every lot 100 per cent inspected before stocking it in inventory and the possibility of using sample inspection to decide what to do. His studies showed that an inspector paid $3 an hour could inspect 100 pieces per hour. If sampling inspection was used, the delay in the production run would cost an additional $10 in machine and operator idle time.

a. Explain why an exact analysis of this case cannot be made by any method studied thus far and discuss the legitimacy of analysis by approximate methods.

b. Draw up the payoff table for the four possible decisions: reject and screen, reject without screening, accept and screen, accept without screening, and show that two of these four choices can be discarded without further calculation.

c. If a sample of 100 parts is taken and 10 defectives are found, what action should be taken? What is the cost of uncertainty?

CHAPTER 25

Samples from Many-valued Populations; Sufficient Statistics

In Chapters 21 through 24 we have dealt with problems involving the use of the information in a sample from a "population" (finite or infinite) every member of which could be thought of as having the value 0 or 1 (failure or success, good or defective). We shall now proceed to apply exactly the same kind of reasoning to the analysis of problems where members of the sampled population can have any of a wide range of values.

25.1 Discrete-valued Populations: The Pascal Population

Suppose that a sample is to be taken in order to obtain additional information on the process average of some machine which can be treated as a Bernoulli process. Until now we have assumed that such a sample would be taken by collecting a certain number of pieces produced by the process and counting the number of defectives among them, but this sampling procedure is not the only one possible. Instead of taking a *predetermined number of pieces* and letting the number of defectives come out as it may, we can count and inspect the output of the process piece by piece until we have found a *predetermined number of defectives* and let the total number of pieces come out as it may. If r is the specified number of "successes" and n is the number of "trials" actually required to obtain them, the likelihoods $P(\tilde{n} = n|r, p)$ are given by the Pascal distribution for each possible value of the parameter p.

Suppose, for example, that the output of a machine is counted and inspected until $r = 10$ defectives have been found and that the tenth defective turns out to be the $n = $ fourteenth piece produced; and suppose that the distribution of the process average $\tilde{p}$ as assessed *before* this sample was taken was that shown in column 2 of Table 25.1. The likelihoods $P_{Pa}(\tilde{n} = 14|r = 10, p)$ are obtained from Table 11.1; the joint probabilities and the posterior probabilities are then computed exactly as in the problems studied in earlier chapters.

Now if the event success or failure is regarded as occurring at the end

Table 25.1
Computation of Posterior Distribution

p	Prior $P(p)$	Likelihood $P_{Pa}(n|p)$	Joint $P(n,p)$	Posterior $P(p|n)$
.8	.8	.123	.0984	.952
.9	.2	.025	.0050	.048
	1.0		.1034	1.000

of the trial which produces it, then the number of trials after the occurrence of one success to and including the one on which the next success occurs can be considered as the *length of the interval* between these two successes. Looked at in this way, the process generates an infinite population of intervals which may have any value from 1 to ∞ rather than an infinite population of trials which must have one or the other of the two values 0 and 1; and the sample is a sample of size $r = 10$ from this population of intervals rather than a sample of size $n = 14$ from a population of trials. The distribution which describes the *individual* members of the population is the Pascal distribution with parameter $r = 1$. The number of trials from the start of sampling up to and including the trial on which the first success occurs is the value of the first member of the population drawn into the sample. The number of trials from the beginning through the occurrence of the rth success is the *total value of the r items in the sample*, and the sampling distribution of this total value is the Pascal distribution with parameter r; in our example, $r = 10$. The really essential point to observe is the following.

Although this sample was drawn from a population of values ranging from 1 to ∞ rather than from a population consisting only of the values 0 and 1, the information in this sample was used in Table 25.1 in identically the same way that information in samples from two-valued populations was used in earlier chapters.†

25.2 "Continuous"-valued Populations: The Exponential Population

Suppose next that the arrival of mechanics at a certain tool crib is Poisson distributed and that a sample is to be taken in order to gather

---

† Samples of Pascal intervals are sometimes called "inverse" or "sequential" samples but they are really no more inverse and no more sequential than binomial samples. It is true that if the cost of sampling depends on the number of pieces in the sample, then the cost of a sample of r Pascal intervals cannot be known in advance; but situations also arise in which the cost of sampling depends on the number of successes or failures in the sample (e.g., when inspection destroys good pieces as well as bad), and in this case the cost of a binomial sample of n pieces cannot be known in advance.

more information on the parameter μ (or $\kappa = 1/\mu$) of the Poisson process which generates these arrivals; and suppose as in the previous example that instead of observing the process for a fixed amount of time and counting the number of arrivals, we measure the time which elapses until a specified number r of mechanics have arrived. The time between any two successive arrivals is a member of the infinite population of *intervals* which "could" be generated by the process, and we take a *sample of size r* from this population.

The time from the start of sampling to the first arrival is the value of the first member of this population drawn into the sample, and so forth. The *total value* of all items in the sample is the total time t which elapses until the rth arrival. The only difference between this problem and the previous one lies in the fact that intervals between Poisson successes are usually talked about as if they could have any length whatever: the possible values of the members of the population are usually said to be *continuous*. We have already seen, however, that the real distribution of any measured quantity is necessarily discrete and that for such quantities a continuous distribution is simply a convenient mathematical approximation (Sections 14.1.3, 17.3.3). There is absolutely no *real* difference between a discrete population and a so-called continuous population, and consequently there is no difference between the ways in which we use the information in samples from these two kinds of populations.

Suppose, for example, that the prior distribution assigned to $\tilde{\mu}$ is that shown in the two columns of Table 25.2; and suppose that we take a sample of size $r = 5$ (we time until the fifth arrival) and find that the total value of the five sample items is $t = 10.02$ minutes. The likelihood

Table 25.2
Prior Distribution

μ	$P(\mu)$
1.5	.1
1.6	.2
1.7	.3
1.8	.2
1.9	.1
2.0	.1
	1.0

of this value t given any of the possible values of $\tilde{\mu}$ is found by the procedure described in Section 14.3.1. If we take $\mu = 1.5$ as an example, the bar for $t = 10.02$ in the t histogram corresponds to the bar for

$$v = \frac{t}{\mu} = \frac{10.02}{1.5} = 6.68$$

in the v histogram. The *width* of the bar in the t histogram can be called δt; the width of the bar in the v histogram is then $\delta t/\mu$. The *height* of the bar in the v histogram is approximately equal to the height of the standardized gamma distribution with parameter $r = 5$ at the point $v = 6.68$; using the curve labeled $r = 5$ in Chart III we find that this height is .104. The *area* of the bar in either histogram is therefore

$$P(\tilde{t} = 10.02) = \frac{\delta t}{1.5} .104 = .0694 \, \delta t$$

approximately.

The likelihoods for all possible μ are computed in this way in Table 25.3 and these likelihoods are then used in Table 25.4 to compute the posterior distribution of $\tilde{\mu}$ by applying Bayes' theorem in the usual way.

Table 25.3
Computation of Likelihoods

μ	$v = t/\mu$	Height $P'_g(v)$	Width $\delta t/\mu$	Area $P(t\|\mu)$
1.5	6.68	.104	$\delta t/1.5$	.0694 δt
1.6	6.26	.122	$\delta t/1.6$	.0762 δt
1.7	5.89	.139	$\delta t/1.7$	.0817 δt
1.8	5.57	.153	$\delta t/1.8$	.0851 δt
1.9	5.27	.165	$\delta t/1.9$	.0868 δt
2.0	5.01	.175	$\delta t/2.0$	.0875 δt

Table 25.4
Computation of Posterior Distribution

μ	Prior $P(\mu)$	Likelihood $P(t\|\mu)$	Joint $P(t,\mu)$	Posterior $P(\mu\|t)$
1.5	.1	.0694 δt	.00694 δt	.085
1.6	.2	.0762 δt	.01524 δt	.188
1.7	.3	.0817 δt	.02451 δt	.302
1.8	.2	.0851 δt	.01702 δt	.210
1.9	.1	.0868 δt	.00868 δt	.107
2.0	.1	.0875 δt	.00875 δt	.108
	1.0		.08114 δt	1.000

Notice that the unspecified width δt of a bar in the t histogram cancels out in computing the posterior probabilities. Posterior probabilities depend only on the *ratios among* the joint probabilities and are unaffected by any factor which multiplies all these probabilities by the same amount. Notice also, however, that the factor μ by which we divide δt to get the width of the bar in the v histogram does *not* cancel out and must *not* be omitted in the calculations.

25.3   Use of the Normal Approximation

In earlier chapters we have used the Normal approximation to compute likelihoods of an observed sample total r when the sample was drawn from a two-valued population and $\tilde{r}$ had a binomial or hypergeometric distribution. The Normal approximation can be used in exactly the same way to compute the likelihood of a sample total when the sample is drawn from a many-valued population. The procedure has already been explained in Section 17.3.3, but we shall illustrate the point with an example by way of review.

Suppose that in the tool-crib example of the previous section we time the "process" until we have counted $r = 100$ arrivals instead of just 5, and suppose that the elapsed time turns out to be 200.4 minutes instead of 10.02. We have taken a sample of size $r = 100$ from the infinite population of intervals which "could" be generated by the process; the total value of these r items is $t = 200.4$.

Since Chart III does not have a curve for $r = 100$ we cannot use the gamma approximation to the distribution of $\tilde{t}$. Figure 17.8 shows, however, that for $r = 50$ the gamma distribution is reasonably close to Normal; for $r = 100$ it will be closer still, and we are therefore justified in using the Normal approximation to compute the likelihood of $t = 200.4$ for each value of $\tilde{\mu}$. Taking $\mu = 2.0$ as an example, we first put the variable in standard measure as

$$u = \frac{t - \mathrm{E}(\tilde{t})}{\sigma(\tilde{t})} = \frac{t - r\mu}{\mu \sqrt{r}} = \frac{200.4 - 200.0}{2.0 \times 10} = .020.$$

The likelihood is then the area of a bar in the u histogram of *width* $\delta t/\sigma(\tilde{t}) = \delta t/20$ and *height* approximately $P'_N(u) = P'_N(.02) = .3989$; this area is $.3989 \times \delta t/20 = .01994\ \delta t$. The likelihoods for all possible μ are computed in this way in Table 25.5 and the posterior distribution of $\tilde{\mu}$ is then computed in the usual way in Table 25.6.

Table 25.5
Computation of Likelihoods

μ	$u = \dfrac{t - r\mu}{\mu \sqrt{r}}$	Height $P'_N(u)$	Width $\delta t/(\mu \sqrt{r})$	Area $P(t\|\mu)$
1.5	3.360	.0014	.0667 δt	.00009 δt
1.6	2.525	.0165	.0625 δt	.00103 δt
1.7	1.788	.0807	.0588 δt	.00475 δt
1.8	1.133	.2100	.0556 δt	.01168 δt
1.9	.547	.3455	.0526 δt	.01807 δt
2.0	.020	.3989	.0500 δt	.01994 δt

Table 25.6
Computation of Posterior Distribution

μ	Prior $P(\mu)$	Likelihood $P(t\|\mu)$	Joint $P(t,\mu)$	Posterior $P(\mu\|t)$
1.5	.1	.00009 δt	.000009 δt	.00
1.6	.2	.00103 δt	.000206 δt	.03
1.7	.3	.00475 δt	.001425 δt	.18
1.8	.2	.01168 δt	.002336 δt	.30
1.9	.1	.01807 δt	.001807 δt	.23
2.0	.1	.01994 δt	.001994 δt	.26
	1.0		.007777 δt	1.00

25.4   The Concept of a Statistic

We have said repeatedly that the posterior distributions which we have computed were rational in the light of the "information in the sample," but we must now take a little closer look at the justification for this assertion. The total information in a sample consists of *the values of the individual observations in the order in which they were drawn*, but our actual computations of posterior distributions were not based on these individual values. When the sample consisted of a predetermined number of trials drawn from a Bernoulli process or a predetermined amount of "space" taken from a Poisson process, the posterior distribution was based simply on the number r of successes in the sample without regard to order. When the sample consisted of a predetermined number of measured intervals, the posterior distribution was based on the total length n or t of these intervals without regard to even the lengths (values) of the individual intervals, let alone the order in which they occurred.

To illustrate the point, suppose that we draw a sample of five *pieces* from a Bernoulli process and that the pieces turn out in the order *ggdgd*. Strictly speaking, the *likelihood of this particular sample* for any specified value of p is $qqpqp = p^2q^3$; and it is this quantity which we should have multiplied by the prior probability of p to get the joint probability of that p and the *particular* sample we actually observed. What we have actually used for the likelihood in such cases was, however, the probability of two successes in a sample of five, and this probability is $C_2^5 p^2 q^3$ rather than p^2q^3. But because the same factor C_2^5 was present in the joint probability for every possible p, it canceled out when we divided each of these joint probabilities by their total to get the posterior probability of each p.

As a second illustration, suppose that we had set out to draw a sample of two *intervals* from this same Bernoulli process and that the pieces had turned out in this same order *ggdgd*. The length of the first interval or value of the first sample item is then 3; the value of the second is 2. The likelihood of the value 3 is q^2p, the likelihood of the value 2 is qp, and the likelihood of 3 followed by 2 is therefore $(q^2p)(qp) = p^2q^3$. In agreement with common sense, the likelihood of the observed sample is the same whether it is regarded as a sample of five pieces or of two intervals. What we actually used for the likelihood of a sample of Bernoulli intervals in the first part of this chapter was the probability that r intervals would have the observed total value n; in our present example this would be, not p^2q^3, but $C_1^4 p^2q^3$ (Section 11.1). But because the same factor C_{r-1}^{n-1} is present in the joint probability for every possible p, it will cancel out when we divide by the total to get the posterior probabilities.

25.4.1 Definition of a Statistic

Thus what we have really done is use some single quantity such as r, n, or t as a *summary* of the information in a sample, and in the future we shall continue to use such summary numbers rather than work with the individual values of all the items in the sample. We shall use the word "statistic" to denote any such summary—we define:

Statistic: any number computed from the values of the observations in a sample.

The word "computed" as used here is to be understood in the broadest sense. It includes adding the values of the separate observations in the sample to obtain their total, but this may mean nothing more than counting of the "successes" in a sample from a two-valued population or direct measurement of the total length of a sample of intervals or the total weight of a sample of weights without actually measuring and adding the values of the individual members of the sample. The word "computed" also includes mere reporting of the value of the observation which has a particular position in the sample (e.g. the fifth item to be drawn) or which has a particular rank in the sample (e.g. the fifth largest item); and it includes counting the number of sample items which are larger or smaller than some specified value.

A statistic is not necessarily computed *exclusively* from the values of the sample items. The number r of successes or the length t of a sample of intervals is computed in this way, but we also consider $v = t/\mu$ and $u = (r - np)/\sqrt{npq}$ to be statistics even though their values depend on parameters—μ in one case, n and p in the other—as well as on the values of the sample items.

25.4.2 Sufficient Statistics

The two examples just discussed have shown that a posterior distribution based on the statistic r or n in a sample from a Bernoulli process will always be identical to the posterior distribution computed from the values of the individual observations in such a sample. The same arguments would have shown that the same thing is true when a posterior distribution is based on the statistic r or n in a sample from a finite population—the same factor C_r^n or C_{r-1}^{n-1} will be involved that is involved when the population is infinite. By the use of a little more algebra we could have shown that the same statement can be made about a posterior distribution based on the statistic t in a sample from a continuous-valued population of intervals.

A statistic which leads to the same posterior distribution that would be obtained by use of the individual sample values in the order in which they occurred is known as a *sufficient* statistic because the value of such a statistic is sufficient to convey *all* the *relevant* information in the sample.

Notice carefully that *the sufficiency of a statistic depends on our model of the real world.* The statistic r in a binomial sample, for instance, is sufficient *because we have assumed that the value of $\tilde{p}$ does not change from trial to trial.* If we had *not* made this assumption, the order in which the sample items occurred might very well be relevant to our conclusions about the process. Specifically, if we suspected that the value of $\tilde{p}$ might be increasing (owing, say, to wear in the machine), then this suspicion would tend to be confirmed by the fact that the first two pieces were both good whereas two out of the last three were defective. Thus the assertion that a certain statistic is sufficient amounts really to nothing more than an assertion that *a particular short-cut method of computation will give the same result as a particular longer method of computation.* We will get the same result by treating the statistic $\tilde{r}$ as a binomial variable with parameter p that we would get by working with the individual sample values *and assuming that each of these values was a binomial variable with the same p as every other one.*

25.5 Use of the Sample Mean

The only statistic which we have used up to now to summarize a, sample has been the *total value of all the items in the sample* or "sample total." In samples from two-valued populations we assigned the value 0 to a failure and 1 to a success, and the sample total was simply the number of successes r. In samples from many-valued populations, on the other hand, the sample total n or t had to be established by counting or timing, and in later chapters other kinds of measurement will be involved.

It is obvious that any sample can be described exactly as well by stating the *mean* value of all the items in the sample as by stating their *total* value; in order to make use of either piece of information we must know the number of items in the sample, and knowing this we can compute the mean from the total or vice versa. The real reason for using the sample total up to now has been the fact that the tables or charts of the distributions applying to most of our problems happen to be made up in terms of totals rather than means.   Binomial and Poisson tables give probabilities for various values of $\tilde{r}$, Pascal tables give probabilities for values of $\tilde{n}$, and gamma tables give probabilities for values of $(1/\mu)$ times $\tilde{t}$. To avoid confusion we have also worked with the sample total r, n, or t when using the Normal approximation to these distributions, and the means and variances in Section 16.6 all apply to distributions of totals.

The implications of an observed sample are often much more immediately apparent, however, if we look at the sample mean rather than at the sample total.   We are usually interested in the mean of the sampled population, and the value of the sample mean indicates immediately and without calculation which values of the population mean are relatively more and less probable in the light of the sample evidence.   Since it is just as easy to base the actual calculations on the sample mean as on the sample total when the Normal approximation is used, we shall henceforth always use the sample mean in this case.   At the same time we shall make some changes in our notation in order to reduce the number of formulas we shall require.   *When working with the Normal approximation*, we shall henceforth always define:

x: the value of an *individual member* of the population or of an *individual sample item*,

$p = \mathrm{E}(\tilde{x})$: the mean of a two-valued *population*,

$\mu = \mathrm{E}(\tilde{x})$: the mean of a many-valued *population*,

$\sigma^2(\tilde{x})$: the variance of the *individual members* of any population,

n: number of items in a sample; r will not be used in this sense,

r: total value of a sample from a two-valued population,

t: total value of a sample from a many-valued population; n will not be used in this sense,

$\bar{x} = r/n$ or t/n: the sample mean; the mean of the x's drawn in the sample.

The likelihood of an observed value $\bar{x}$ of the sample mean—i.e., the conditional probability $\mathrm{P}(\tilde{\bar{x}} = \bar{x}|\mu)$—is computed by the Normal approximation in exactly the same way that the likelihood of an observed sample total is computed—by first expressing the statistic in standard measure:

$$u = \frac{\bar{x} - \mathrm{E}(\tilde{\bar{x}})}{\sigma(\tilde{\bar{x}})}$$

and then multiplying the width of this bar in the u histogram by the height of the unit Normal curve at its center:

$$\mathrm{P}(\bar{x}) = \frac{\delta\bar{x}}{\sigma(\tilde{\bar{x}})} \, \mathrm{P}'_N(u).$$

Expressions for the mean $\mathrm{E}(\tilde{\bar{x}})$ and variance $\sigma^2(\tilde{\bar{x}})$ in samples from populations of the types we have studied so far can be derived easily enough from expressions already given for the means and variances of the corresponding sample totals. Instead of doing this, however, we shall begin from first principles, partly to review these principles and partly to avoid confusion over notation.

25.5.1   The Mean of the Distribution of the Sample Mean: $E(\tilde{x})$

Provided that the sampling is simple (Section 23.5.2), the value of any one item in a sample from any infinite or finite population is a random variable with expectation equal to the true mean $E(\tilde{x}) = p$ or μ of the population. Since the expected value of a sum of random variables is the sum of their individual expectations, the expected value of the sample total is np or $n\mu$. The sample mean is $1/n$ times the sample total, and therefore its expected value is $1/n$ times the expected value of the total. Thus

$$E(\tilde{x}) = E(\tilde{x}) = p \text{ or } \mu \qquad \textit{Any population, simple sampling}$$

25.5.2   The Variance of the Distribution of the Sample Mean: $\sigma^2(\tilde{x})$

We have defined $\sigma^2(\tilde{x})$ as the variance of the individual *members of the population*, but *provided again that the sampling is simple* we can equally well regard $\sigma^2(\tilde{x})$ as the variance of a *single observation drawn from the population*. In terms of relative frequencies, the distribution which we would get by making an extremely large number of drawings from a population (*with* replacement if the population is finite) and recording the value of each individual observation is identical to the distribution of the population itself.

If now we draw a sample of size n from an *infinite* population (or from a finite population *with* replacement), the values of the n observations are *independent*. The addition theorem for variances (Section 16.3) therefore applies and the variance of the sample *total* ($\tilde{r}$ or $\tilde{t}$) is simply n times the variance of a single observation, or $n\sigma^2(\tilde{x})$. The distribution of the sample *mean* $\tilde{x} = \tilde{r}/n$ or $\tilde{t}/n$ is identical to the distribution of the total except that every value of the random variable is divided by n, and therefore (Section 16.5.2) the variance of the distribution of the mean is $1/n^2$ times the variance of the distribution of the total:

$$\sigma^2(\tilde{x}) = \frac{1}{n}\sigma^2(\tilde{x}) \qquad \textit{Infinite population, simple sampling}$$

If the sample of size n is drawn *without replacement from a finite population*, the sample items cannot be independent for the reason explained in Section 23.1.1. It can be shown that the effect of the finiteness of the population on the variance of the mean of a sample drawn without replacement is the same whether the population is two-valued or many-valued; *provided once again that the sampling is simple*, the variance of the sample mean is always

$$\sigma^2(\bar{x}) = \frac{1}{n} \sigma^2(\tilde{x}) \frac{N-n}{N-1} \qquad Finite\ population,\ simple\ sampling$$

The importance of simple sampling is so great and so often neglected that we revert once more to its meaning. *Sampling is simple if and only if the probability that any sample item will have any specified value is equal to the relative frequency of that value in the entire population at the time the sample item is drawn.* The student is strongly advised to review the discussion of simple sampling in Section 23.5.2.

25.5.3   *The Population Variance* $\sigma^2(\tilde{x})$

The variance $\sigma^2(\tilde{x})$ of the *individual* members of a population or of the value of a sample of size $n = 1$ does *not* depend on whether the population is finite or infinite: it depends only on the *shape of the frequency distribution which describes the population*.

We have already seen that the variance of the individual members of a two-valued finite population is pq just like the variance of the individual values generated by a Bernoulli process. In both cases the distribution can be described by a histogram with two bars and in both cases Table 16.5 applies. Similarly a many-valued finite population may have a distribution which is at least very nearly like the distribution of the output of a many-valued process. In particular, certain types of finite populations often have distributions which are very nearly exponential and resemble a distribution of Poisson intervals; this is often true of distributions of items in inventory by dollar value of the stock of each item or by monthly dollar sales of each item. If such a population *is* approximately exponential with mean μ, its variance $\sigma^2(\tilde{x})$ is approximately equal to μ^2 just as the variance of the lengths of individual Poisson intervals was μ^2 if the mean length of an interval was μ.

Regardless, then, of the reason why the population has the form in question, the variances of the two most important forms of population which we have studied up to now are as given in the table below.

Type of population	Population variance
Two-valued, mean p	pq
Exponential, mean μ	μ^2

PROBLEMS

1. A Poisson process generating pinhole defects in the insulation of electric wire is observed until four defects have occurred; the amount of wire inspected up to this point is 60 feet. If the prior distribution of $\tilde{\mu}$ (the mean distance between defects) is that shown in the following table, what is the mean of the posterior distribution of $\tilde{\mu}$? (Use the sample *total* as the statistic and do *not* use the Normal approximation to its distribution.)

μ	P(μ)
15	.2
20	.3
25	.5
	$\overline{1.0}$

2. In Section 25.3 of the text we discussed the distribution of the *total* $\tilde{t}$ of a sample of 100 intervals from a Poisson process generating intervals with mean length $\mu = 2$ minutes, and we saw that the Normal approximation to the probability that this total will have the value $t = 200.4$ minutes is

$$\frac{\delta t}{\sigma(\tilde{t})} \, \mathrm{P}'_N(u) = \frac{\delta t}{20} \, \mathrm{P}'_N(.02).$$

If the *total* value of a sample of 100 items is 200.4 minutes, the *mean* $\bar{x}$ of the sample values is 2.004 minutes.

  a. Show that the Normal approximation to the probability that $\bar{x}$ will have this value is

$$\frac{\delta \bar{x}}{\sigma(\bar{x})} \, \mathrm{P}'_N(u) = \frac{\delta \bar{x}}{.2} \, \mathrm{P}'_N(.02).$$

  b. Show that if we know that time is measured to one one-hundredth of a minute, so that the width δt of a bar in the t histogram is .01 minute, the width of a bar in the $\bar{x}$ histogram is .0001 minute and the numerical values of the two Normal approximations are the same.

3. Rework Tables 25.5 and 25.6 using the sample mean as the statistic instead of the sample total. (HINT: This exercise requires absolutely *no* computations. All that is required is some changes in column headings, the substitution of the symbol $\delta \bar{x}$ for δt, and division of all the entries in certain columns by a constant which will cancel out in the end.)

4. Same as Problem 3 for Chapter 21, Problem 5.

5. Same as Problem 1 above except that the wire is inspected until the eighty-first defect is found and the mean distance between defects in this sample is 15 feet. Use the sample mean as the statistic. Compare your answer to this problem with your answer to Problem 1 and comment.

6. A company wishes to determine the value of its inventory of spare parts by sampling. The sample will be taken by drawing n part numbers from a list which shows all the 5000 part numbers which are carried in stock. The number of units in stock of each of these n part numbers will be counted and the value of the stock of each part number will then be determined by multiplying the count by the current unit price. It is known that the value of the stock of most part numbers is quite low and that most of the total value of the inventory is tied up in relatively few items. A complete count of the inventory made a year before showed the "J-shaped" distribution graphed as a grouped histogram in Figure 25.1; the smooth curve in the figure is an exponential distribution with the same mean as the actual distribution.

a. Find approximate algebraic expressions for the mean and variance of the *ratio* of the mean value of the n part numbers in the sample to the mean value of the 5000 part numbers in the entire inventory.

b. Using the Normal approximation, decide how large a sample must be drawn if the company wishes to be 99 per cent sure that the sample mean will not differ from the population mean by more than 10 per cent of the true value of the population mean.

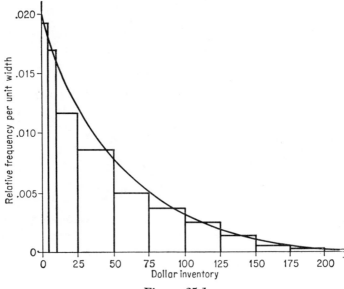

Figure 25.1

CHAPTER 26

Samples from "Normal" Populations
with Known Variance

All the populations, finite or infinite, which we have studied so far have had one very special characteristic: the distribution describing every one was completely defined as soon as we knew the value of a *single* parameter. The heights of the two bars in a histogram describing a two-valued population are defined as soon as we know the value of the fraction p of successes; the curve describing an exponential population is defined as soon as we know the mean μ of the population. It is obvious, however, that *most* populations of many-valued or measured quantities are *not* completely defined by the value of a single parameter. We cannot draw a histogram describing the frequency distribution of diameters of shafts turned out by some machine if all we know about this distribution is its mean.

As a first example of a population requiring more than one parameter for its definition we shall consider a process that is known to generate an infinite population which is approximately Normal in shape† and which therefore is fully defined for most practical purposes by the values of just *two* quantities, the mean $\mu = E(\tilde{x})$ and the standard deviation $\sigma(\tilde{x})$ of its individual members. In this chapter we shall see how to reach a decision when the parameter $\sigma(\tilde{x})$ of a Normal population is known but costs depend on the unknown value of the mean $\mu = E(\tilde{x})$. In the next chapter we shall see how to proceed when the mean is known but costs depend on the unknown value of $\sigma(\tilde{x})$. The additional problems which arise when *both* parameters are unknown will be taken up in Chapter 28.

26.1 Statement of the Problem

A certain chemical is produced from a liquid raw material. The final product must contain at least 3 pounds of constituent X per gallon.

† For the reasons reviewed in Section 25.2, a real population can never be *exactly* Normal and therefore more than two parameters would be required for its *exact* description; this point will be more fully discussed in Chapter 29.

397

With *regular processing*, the amount of constituent X in the final product is 50 per cent of the amount of X in 1 gallon of the raw material. By *special processing* at an extra cost of $400, the yield can be raised to 75 per cent. The X content of the final product is always very precisely measured, and when it is below 3 pounds per gallon the deficit is made up with pure X, which costs $10 per pound. A batch of raw material sufficient to produce 100 gallons of final product is about to be processed, and the manufacturer wishes to decide whether to use regular or special processing. In what follows we shall refer to this as a choice between acceptance and rejection of *regular* processing.

To simplify the discussion, we shall measure the X content of a given lot of raw material in terms of its yield under regular processing, which we shall call the *normal yield* of the material and which we shall denote by the symbol xi:

ξ: yield of the raw material under regular processing.

Thus if there is 5.0 pounds of X in a gallon of raw material, we shall say that its normal yield is $\xi = 2.5$ pounds per gallon. Records of the yields under regular processing of a large number of batches of raw material give the relative frequencies shown in Table 26.1. We assume that the manufacturer has no reason to believe that there has been any change in the factors affecting the quality of the raw material and that he therefore

Table 26.1
Historical Distribution of Normal Yields

ξ	Relative frequency
2.0	.15
2.5	.25
3.0	.60
	1.00

adopts this frequency distribution as his probability distribution for the random variable ξ in the batch about to be processed.

26.1.1 Conditional and Expected Costs and Losses

Special processing at a cost of $400 will produce the required 3 pounds per gallon of X in the final product from raw material having any normal yield shown as possible in the probability distribution of Table 26.1. Since no pure X will have to be added, the total cost of *rejection* will be simply this $400.

If the normal yield is 2.0 pounds per gallon and regular processing is *accepted*, $3.0 - 2.0 = 1.0$ pound of pure X will have to be added per gallon, or 100 pounds for the entire batch. At $10 per pound, this gives a conditional cost of acceptance amounting to $1000. More generally: for any ξ shown in Table 26.1, the amount of pure X which will have to be added is $100(3 - \xi)$ gallons and therefore

Conditional cost of acceptance $= \$10 \times 100(3 - \xi)$
$$= \$3000 - \$1000\ \xi.$$

For $\xi > 3$ the conditional cost of acceptance is 0.

These costs and the corresponding losses are listed in Table 26.2 and graphed in Figure 26.1. Although the cost of acceptance is not linear

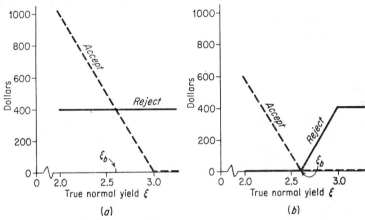

Figure 26.1. (*a*) **Conditional costs;** (*b*) **conditional losses.**

over *all* values of the basic random variable ξ because of the break in the cost of acceptance at the normal yield $\xi = 3.0$, both costs *are* linear over

Table 26.2
Conditional Costs and Losses

ξ	Conditional cost		Conditional loss	
	Accept	Reject	Accept	Reject
2.0	$1000	$400*	$600	0
2.5	500	400*	100	0
3.0	0*	400	0	$400

the whole range of values of ξ *to which nonzero probability is assigned.* The expected costs can therefore be found by use of the mean of the distribution as well as by use of the full distribution; we have

Expected cost of rejection $= \$400$,
Expected cost of acceptance $= \$3000 - \$1000\ E(\tilde{\xi})$.

The student should verify as an exercise that on the basis of prior information alone the marginal expected *losses* are \$115 for acceptance and \$240 for rejection.

26.2 The Sample and the Population

In order to get more information on the quality of the particular batch of raw material about to be processed, nine measurements have been made of its X content.   Although the liquid raw material is itself perfectly homogeneous, so that the true value of ξ is exactly the same in every one of the nine measured samples, the measurements themselves are *not* all the same.   Expressed as estimates of the normal yield of the batch, the measurements are 1.84, 1.75, 1.39, 1.65, 3.53, 1.03, 2.73, 2.86, 1.96; their mean is

$\bar{x} = 2.08.$

As the reported numbers suggest, measurements on the raw material are difficult to make and inaccurate: the fact that an instrument can be *read* to two decimal places does not mean that the measurement is *correct* to two decimal places.   Notice that here as in many practical problems *the variability is in the measuring process itself and not in the object of measurement;* the measurements actually made on the present batch constitute a sample from the *infinite population of "all possible" measurements of a single fixed quantity.*   The sample can also be considered as taken from the *output of a random process* in the same sense that a few pieces turned out by a machine may be a sample from the output of a random process.

In order to determine the characteristics of his measuring process, the manufacturer had previously conducted an extensive investigation. During this investigation numerous measurements were made on each of a large number of batches of raw material and each of these measurements was later compared with a precise determination of the actual yield under regular processing of the batch on which the measurement had been made. Examination of the *residuals* or *errors of measurement* had brought out four important facts:

1. The mean of all the residuals was virtually 0.
2. The standard deviation of all the residuals was .9.
3. The shape of the distribution of the residuals was Normal for all practical purposes.
4a. There was no observable tendency for a high residual to be followed by a high residual, etc.: the errors of measurement were *independent of each other.*
4b. There was no observable relation between the magnitude or sign of the errors made on any one batch and the true yield of that batch; the errors of measurement were *independent of* ξ.

In discussing the Bernoulli and Poisson processes in earlier chapters we have emphasized repeatedly that two kinds of questions must be answered before we may use distributions such as the binomial or the Poisson to compute probabilities:

1. Is the process as such of the type in question?
2. Is its parameter known?

In our present problem we must ask the corresponding questions:

1. Is the process of a known type, and if so what?
2. Are the parameters of this process known?

The results of the manufacturer's investigation as reported above permit us to answer these questions as follows. As applied to *any one* batch of raw material, the measuring process:

1. Is of known type, generating *independent, Normally distributed* values x;
2. Has a mean $\mu = E(\tilde{x})$ *equal to the true normal yield* ξ of the batch being measured;
3. Has standard deviation $\sigma(\tilde{x}) = .9$.

All our subsequent conclusions will depend for their validity on the truth of these three assertions; we have adopted a certain *model* of the real measuring process and our conclusions depend on the validity of the model.

26.3   The Likelihood of the Sample Given μ

The (joint) likelihood of the sample described above is by definition the product of the likelihoods of the nine individual measurements, just as the likelihood of a binomial sample is $p^r q^{n-r}$ (Section 25.4). Since we have adopted a model in which individual measurements have approximately Normal distributions and since the variance of this distribution is known to be $\sigma^2(\tilde{x}) = .9^2$, we know how to compute the likelihood of each measurement given any value of the process or population mean $\mu = E(\tilde{x})$.

26.3.1   Likelihood of an Individual Measurement

The true probability distribution of an individual measurement $\tilde{x}$ for any given μ is a histogram with bars of width $\delta x = .01$, the fineness to which individual measurements can be made. Since the shape of this histogram is roughly Normal, we can approximate the area of a bar by the use of the unit Normal distribution. To do so we find the location of the bar in the u histogram corresponding to the given bar in the x histogram by computing

$$u = \frac{x - \mu}{\sigma(\tilde{x})} = \frac{x - \mu}{.9}.$$

The *width* of this bar in the u histogram is $\delta x/\sigma(\bar{x}) = \delta x/.9$; its *height* is approximately $P'_N(u)$ as read from Table II; and its *area* or likelihood is therefore approximately

$$P(x|\mu) = \frac{\delta x}{\sigma(\bar{x})} P'_N(u) \qquad u = \frac{x - \mu}{\sigma(\bar{x})}.$$

The likelihood of the sample as a whole for any given μ can be evaluated by computing $P(x|\mu)$ for each of the nine x's in the sample and multiplying these nine probabilities together.

26.3.2   Use of the Sample Mean

It can easily be shown, however, that if the individual measurements are treated as Normal and independent and their variance is treated as known, then the sample mean $\bar{x}$ is a sufficient statistic for the sample. The ratio

$$\frac{\text{Likelihood of } \bar{x}}{\text{Joint likelihood of the individual } x\text{'s}}$$

does not depend on the population mean μ, and therefore we will get exactly the same posterior distribution if we base it on the likelihood of $\bar{x}$ as if we base it on the joint likelihood of the nine individual x's. We can save ourselves a good deal of labor and still lose absolutely nothing if we use the sample mean as a summary of all the relevant information in the sample.

It deserves some emphasis that *the truth of the statement that the mean is sufficient in this problem does not depend at all on whether the measurements are in fact Normally distributed:* it depends only on the fact that if we *computed* the individual likelihoods we would do so by use of the Normal approximation. As we pointed out in Section 25.4.2,

To say that a statistic is sufficient is merely to say that a particular short-cut method of computation will give the same result as a particular longer method of computation; it is a statement about arithmetic and not a statement about the real world.

The Distribution of $\bar{x}$. It is virtually obvious that the mean of a sample from an approximately Normal population will have an almost exactly Normal distribution. As we saw in Section 17.3, the distribution of virtually *any* sum of independent identically distributed random variables becomes more and more Normal as n increases. The sample total in our present case is a sum of independent random variables all having the same roughly Normal distribution, so that the distribution of the total is already virtually Normal for $n = 1$; and the distribution of the sample mean is identical to the distribution of the sample total except for a change of scale.

The likelihood of the observed sample mean $\bar{x} = 2.08$ for any given value of the process mean μ is therefore

$$P(\bar{x}|\ \mu) = \frac{\delta\bar{x}}{\sigma(\bar{x})}\ P'_N(u) \qquad u = \frac{\bar{x} - \mu}{\sigma(\bar{x})},$$

where $\delta\bar{x}$ is the fineness to which the sample mean can be measured† and

$$\sigma(\bar{x}) = \frac{\sigma(\bar{x})}{\sqrt{n}} = \frac{.9}{\sqrt{9}} = .3.$$

26.4   The Posterior Distribution of ξ

Likelihoods in terms of μ are of no use to us as such, since the basic random variable of our problem is the *true* normal yield ξ of the batch and not the mean of the measuring process applied to the batch; but *because it has been shown by careful investigation that the process mean μ is equal to the true normal yield ξ* we can compute the likelihood of the sample for any given value of ξ, and this *is* what we need in order to apply Bayes' theorem and thus get the posterior distribution of ξ. It cannot be too strongly emphasized that our insistence on the difference between the *meaning* of μ and the *meaning* of ξ is not due to a desire for logical elegance: *serious mistakes are very often made through failure to inquire whether in fact a measuring process is unbiased.*

We now proceed to compute the likelihood of $\bar{x} = 2.08$ for each possible value of ξ. The work is carried out in Table 26.3, which the student should compare with Table 25.5. In the present problem the factor $\sigma(\bar{x}) = .3$ by which we divide $\delta\bar{x}$ to get the width of the corresponding bar in the u distribution does not vary with the value of the basic random variable, but it did vary in the problem of Table 25.5 and it must never be simply *assumed* that this bar-width factor is the same for all values of the basic random variable.

Table 26.3
Computation of the Likelihoods

$\xi = \mu$	$u = \dfrac{\bar{x} - \mu}{\sigma(\bar{x})}$	Height $P'_N(u)$	Width $\delta\bar{x}/\sigma(\bar{x})$	Area $P(\bar{x}|\xi)$
2.0	+ .27	.3847	$\delta\bar{x}/.3$	.3847 $\delta\bar{x}/.3$
2.5	−1.40	.1497	$\delta\bar{x}/.3$	.1497 $\delta\bar{x}/.3$
3.0	−3.07	.0036	$\delta\bar{x}/.3$	.0036 $\delta\bar{x}/.3$

The posterior distribution of ξ can now be computed in exactly the same way that we have proceeded in earlier chapters; the work is shown

† In our example $\delta\bar{x} = .01/9$, but as usual this factor cancels out and therefore need not be expressed numerically.

in Table 26.4.   It is left to the student as an exercise to show that the posterior expected losses are \$394 for acceptance and \$9 for rejection.

Table 26.4
Computation of the Posterior Distribution

ξ	Prior $P(\xi)$	Likelihood $P(\bar{x}|\xi)$	Joint $P(\bar{x},\xi)$	Posterior $P(\xi|\bar{x})$
2.0	.15	.3847 $\delta\bar{x}/.3$	.0577 $\delta\bar{x}/.3$	.593
2.5	.25	.1497 $\delta\bar{x}/.3$	.0374 $\delta\bar{x}/.3$	.384
3.0	.60	.0036 $\delta\bar{x}/.3$	.0022 $\delta\bar{x}/.3$	.023
	1.00		.0973 $\delta\bar{x}/.3$	1.000

PROBLEMS

1. Verify the statement in Section 26.1.1 that the *prior* expected losses are \$115 for acceptance and \$240 for rejection:

a. By working with the *conditional losses* and the full prior distribution of ξ.

b. By comparing the *expected cost of action under certainty* with the expected *costs* of the two decisions as computed by use of the mean of the prior distribution of ξ.

2. What was the probability, as evaluated *before* the sample described in the text was actually taken, that a sample of nine would yield $\bar{x} = 2.08$?

3. Verify the statement at the end of the chapter that the *posterior* expected losses are \$394 for acceptance and \$9 for rejection.

4. Compute the likelihood given $\xi = 2.5$ of the individual measurement $x = 1.84$:

a. Under all the conditions described in the text.

b. Under these same conditions except that the manufacturer's investigation had shown that the measuring process gave results .3 unit low on the average.

5. Compute the posterior probability distribution and the posterior expected cost of uncertainty for the example of this chapter as they would have been if only the following four measurements of the X content had been made: 3.00, 1.53, 1.30, 2.49.

6. The *median* of a sample of nine from a Normal population has an approximately Normal distribution with a mean equal to the population mean μ and with standard deviation equal to $1.22\sigma(\bar{x})/\sqrt{n}$.

a. Compute the likelihood given $\xi = 2.0$ of the median of the sample described in the text.

b. What advantages and disadvantages can you see in using the median to compute the posterior distribution of ξ in the situation described in the text?

c. The statement that the distribution of the median in this case is approximately Normal does *not* follow from the Central limit theorem or any of the discussion in Chapter 17. Why?

7. In the light of the distinction drawn in this chapter between μ and ξ, what important unstated assumption was made in Section 22.3.1?

CHAPTER 27

Samples from "Normal" Populations with Known Mean

In all problems involving samples which we have studied hitherto, the actual cost which would be incurred as a result of any decision depended on the unknown true value of the *mean* of the population (or, as in the last chapter, on the unknown value of a variable related to the mean of the population). While this is by far the most common kind of problem faced in business practice, it is by no means the only kind. Costs may depend on any of a wide variety of measures of the population, and in this chapter we shall consider a situation where costs depend on its *dispersion* or "scatter."

27.1 Statement of the Problem

The design thickness of a certain part is .360 inch with tolerance ±.010; if a part is thicker than .370 inch or thinner than .350 inch it will not fit in the assembly in which it is to be used. The part is ordinarily manufactured on a high-speed automatic machine, and when the raw bar stock is of proper quality this machine produces thicknesses which are approximately Normally distributed with mean .360 inch and standard deviation .003 inch, so that virtually none of the product is defective. Occasionally, however, a bar is of poor quality and the high-speed machine produces either too large a mean thickness or too great a scatter among individual thicknesses; n either case the result is a substantial number of pieces which are out of tolerance. Each bar yields 1000 pieces and each defective gives rise to losses amounting to $.50, so that a fraction defective .1 implies a loss of $50 on the product of one bar, and so forth. Since the bar stock is too expensive to scrap, the only remedy for this situation is to machine the bar on a heavier but slower machine which can produce with mean .360 inch and standard deviation .003 inch out of *any* material. Use of this machine entails an extra cost of $4.50 for labor and power.

Since there is no way of testing the machinability of a piece of bar stock other than actually processing it on the high-speed machine, the company has adopted a policy of inspecting the first pieces turned out

405

from each bar on this machine. Deviation of the mean thickness from standard is easily detected by a very simple device. The first 20 parts produced from each bar are stacked in a tray which has gauge marks showing the minimum and maximum total thickness which is tolerable. If the thickness of the 20 parts falls outside these limits, the bar is transferred to the heavy-duty machine. Detection of excessive scatter among the individual thicknesses is more difficult, since it requires careful micrometer measurements on the thickness of individual pieces. The company's policy is to make these individual measurements on the last 4 pieces from the test run of 20, and the present chapter will analyze the problem of using these samples of 4 to decide whether or not the bar should be transferred to the heavy-duty machine because of excessive scatter.

Before this sampling policy was adopted the variability of the raw material had been determined by a study in which a very large sample was taken from the product of each of a very large number of bars processed on the high-speed machine. The standard deviation $\sigma(\tilde{x})$ of the individual thicknesses in each sample was computed, and the resulting frequency distribution is shown in Table 27.1. There is no reason to assume that there has been any change in either the average quality or the variability of the bar stock, and this frequency distribution is adopted as a probability distribution for the process standard deviation in the next few runs to be made; this process standard deviation $\sigma(\tilde{x})$ is the basic random variable of our problem and for brevity will be denoted by $\tilde{\sigma}$.

Table 27.1

Standard deviation	Relative frequency
.003	.90
.004	.05
.005	.03
.006	.01
.007	.01
	1.00

27.1.1   The Costs

As usual we must first compute, for each possible value of the basic random variable, the conditional costs of the two possible decisions: accept (do not transfer for scatter) and reject (transfer). The computation of these conditional costs is a little more complex in the present problem than in the problems studied hitherto because the cost of defectives is not in simple *proportion* to the value of the basic variable $\tilde{\sigma}$, but the computation is not at all difficult.

Fraction Defective as a Function of σ. In order to compute the cost corresponding to any value σ of $\tilde{\sigma}$ we must first compute the fraction defective corresponding to that σ, and we do this by making use of the following facts: (1) the population is roughly Normal, (2) its mean μ is known as a result of gauging to have the value .360 inch, and (3) pieces are defective if they are smaller than .350 inch or larger than .370 inch. It follows that the fraction defective for any σ is given by the area beyond these tolerance points in the two tails of the Normal distribution describing the *population*. We thus have for the fraction defective given $\tilde{\sigma} = \sigma$

$$P_N\left(\tilde{u} < \frac{.350 - .360}{\sigma}\right) + P_N\left(\tilde{u} > \frac{.370 - .360}{\sigma}\right);$$

and since these two tail areas are equal,

$$\text{Fraction defective} = 2\,P_N\left(\tilde{u} > \frac{.01}{\sigma}\right).$$

The values of $.01/\sigma$ are shown in column 2 of Table 27.2 and the corresponding fractions defective in column 3.

Table 27.2
Conditional Costs and Losses

σ	$.01/\sigma$	Fraction defective	Cost Accept	Cost Reject	Loss Accept	Loss Reject
.003	3.33	.001	$ .49*	$4.99	$ 0	$4.50
.004	2.50	.012	5.88	4.99*	.89	0
.005	2.00	.046	22.54	4.99*	17.55	0
.006	1.67	.095	46.55	4.99*	41.56	0
.007	1.43	.153	74.97	4.99*	69.98	0

Conditional and Unconditional Costs and Losses. The cost of acceptance is the cost of the defectives which will be produced from that part of one bar which remains after the first 20 pieces have been produced and inspected. The expected number of defectives produced will be 980 times the fraction defective, and their expected cost will be $.50 times that number or $490 times the fraction defective; this cost is shown in column 4 of Table 27.2. If the bar is transferred, σ will be .003, the fraction defective will be .001, and the expected cost of defectives will be $.49. The cost of rejection is this amount plus the $4.50 extra cost of the heavy-duty machine, or $4.99 in all. Finally, the conditional losses are computed in the usual way from the conditional costs and shown in the last two columns. The conditional costs and losses are graphed in Figure 27.1; notice that *the conditional cost of acceptance is not linear and therefore it is impossible to compute the unconditional cost of acceptance from the mean of the distribution of $\tilde{\sigma}$.*

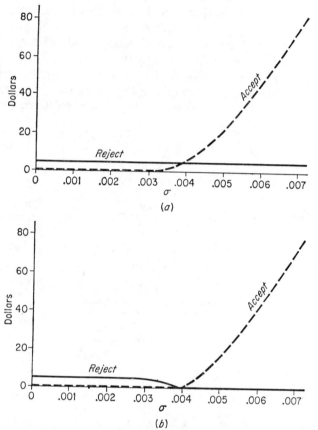

Figure 27.1. (a) **Conditional costs**; (b) **conditional losses**.

The unconditional expected losses of the two possible decisions are computed on the basis of the prior information in Table 27.3. Observe that the calculation is identical to that used in earlier chapters even though we have taken $\tilde{\sigma}$ rather than fraction defective as the "basic" random variable and therefore the costs are nonlinear.

Table 27.3
Unconditional Expected Loss without Sampling

σ	$P(\sigma)$	Loss of acceptance		Loss of rejection	
		Conditional	Expected	Conditional	Expected
.003	.90	$ 0	$0	$4.50	$4.050
.004	.05	.89	.044	0	0
.005	.03	17.55	.526	0	0
.006	.01	41.56	.416	0	0
.007	.01	69.98	.700	0	0
	1.00		$1.686		$4.050

27.2   The Sample and Its Likelihood

Suppose now that a new bar is put on the high-speed machine and the four diameters measured to a "tenth" are .3546, .3673, .3646, and .3537 inch. In deciding whether or not to transfer the bar to the other machine because of excessive scatter, we shall use this evidence in a way which is basically identical to the way in which we have used sample evidence in earlier chapters. We first find the likelihood of the sample for each possible value of the basic random variable ($\tilde{\sigma}$ in our present problem), we then apply Bayes' theorem to revise the probability distribution originally assigned to this variable, and finally we compute the posterior expected losses. In doing all this we shall assume that all *measurements are absolutely without error.* Our problem is thus quite different from the problem of Chapter 26, where the thing measured was fixed and all the variability was in the measurements.

As always, the likelihood of the sample is the product of the likelihoods of the individual members of the sample, and since we are assuming that the population is Normal these individual likelihoods are given by the formula

$$P(x) = \frac{\delta x}{\sigma(\tilde{x})} P'_N(u) \qquad u = \frac{x - \mu}{\sigma(\tilde{x})}$$

where δx is the fineness with which we can measure an individual element —in this case, a diameter. In Section 26.3.1 we saw that we could use this formula to find the likelihood of any x given any μ when $\sigma(\tilde{x})$ was known. In our present problem we can use this same formula to find the likelihood of any x given any $\sigma = \sigma(\tilde{x})$ because μ is known as a result of gauging. Thus for example: the likelihood of the measurement $x = .3673$ given $\tilde{\sigma} = .004$ is

$$P(\tilde{x} = .3673 | \tilde{\sigma} = .004) = \frac{\delta x}{.004} P'_N \left(\frac{.3673 - .3600}{.004} \right).$$

27.2.1   Use of the Statistic $\tilde{s}'$

In the previous chapter we saw that the labor of computing and multiplying together nine separate likelihoods for each μ could be short-cut because we could get the same posterior distribution by basing it on the likelihood of the sample mean: the sample mean is *sufficient* when σ is known. A similar short cut is available in our present problem: it can be proved that the statistic

$$s' = \sqrt{\frac{1}{n} \Sigma (x - \mu)^2}$$

is sufficient when μ is known.†   Notice that this statistic is not quite the

† The notation $\Sigma(x - \mu)^2$ can be interpreted as an instruction to perform the following operations:

    1. Subtract μ from each x in the sample to obtain the corresponding deviation $(x - \mu)$;

same thing as the standard deviation of the values in the sample, which would be $\sqrt{\Sigma(x - \bar{x})^2/n}$ rather than $\sqrt{\Sigma(x - \mu)^2/n}$.

The quantity $\Sigma(x - \mu)^2$ in the present problem is computed in Table 27.4, where all measurements are expressed in thousandths of an inch in order to avoid writing large numbers of zeros. The observed

Table 27.4
Computation of $\Sigma(x - \mu)^2$

$1000x$	$1000(x - \mu)$	$1000^2(x - \mu)^2$
354.6	−5.4	29.16
367.3	+7.3	53.29
364.6	+4.6	21.16
353.7	−6.3	39.69
		143.30

value of s'^2 is thus $143.30/4 = 35.82$ when measurements are expressed in thousandths, and therefore

$$s' = \sqrt{35.82} = 5.98 \text{ thousandths of an inch}$$
$$= .00598 \text{ inch.}$$

The Sampling Distribution of s'. In order to find the likelihood of this observed value of s' we must know the sampling distribution of this statistic, just as we must know the distribution of $\bar{x}$ to compute the likelihood of an observed value $\bar{x}$. It can be shown that *when the population from which the sample is drawn is Normal*, the statistic s' has a distribution given by the formula

$$P'(s') = \frac{ns'}{\sigma^2} P'_g \left[\frac{1}{2} n \left(\frac{s'}{\sigma} \right)^2 \middle| r = \frac{1}{2} n \right]$$

where P'_g is the ordinate of the standardized gamma distribution with parameter $r = \frac{1}{2}n$. Values of $P'(s')$ could thus be obtained from the curve for $r = \frac{4}{2} = 2$ in Chart III of the gamma distribution, but the nuisance of computing ns'/σ^2 and $\frac{1}{2}n(s'/\sigma)^2$ can be avoided by using Chart V, from which the distribution of the ratio s'/σ in samples from a *Normal population* can be read directly. This distribution is known as the $\chi/\sqrt{f}$ distribution (chi over the square root of f).

Looking at Chart V, the student will see that there is actually a whole family of $\chi/\sqrt{f}$ distributions of s'/σ, one for each value of a *parameter f*, just as there is a different gamma distribution for each value of the parameter r. This parameter f will be discussed in Chapter 28; for the moment all that we need to know is that in problems involving the statistic s'

2. Square each of these deviations;
3. Add (Σ) the squares.

defined above its value is equal to the sample size n.†   In computing likelihoods by use of the $\chi/\sqrt{f}$ distribution the student must remember:

1. $P'(s'/\sigma)$ must be read from the curve for the correct value of f.
2. If $\delta s'$ is the width of a bar in the s' distribution, the width of the corresponding bar in the distribution of s'/σ is $\delta s'/\sigma$, so that

$$P(s') = \frac{\delta s'}{\sigma} P'_{\chi/\sqrt{f}}\left(\frac{s'}{\sigma}\bigg| f\right).$$

For example: the likelihood of $s' = .00598$ given $\sigma = .005$ is found by first computing $s'/\sigma = .00598/.005 = 1.20$, reading $P'_{\chi/\sqrt{f}}(1.20) = .77$ on the curve for $f = 4$ in Chart V, and multiplying this height by the width $\delta s'/.005$ to get the area 154 $\delta s'$.

27.3   The Posterior Distribution of $\tilde{\sigma}$

The likelihood of the observed $s' = .00598$ is computed in Table 27.5 for each possible σ and the posterior distribution is then computed in the usual way in Table 27.6.   It is left to the student as an exercise to show that the unconditional expected losses are \$15.37 for acceptance and \$1.52 for rejection.

Table 27.5
Computation of the Likelihoods

σ	s'/σ	Height $P'_{\chi/\sqrt{f}}(s'/\sigma)$	Width $\delta s'/\sigma$	Area $P(s'|\sigma)$
.003	1.99	.02	$\delta s'/.003$	6.7 $\delta s'$
.004	1.50	.30	$\delta s'/.004$	75.0 $\delta s'$
.005	1.20	.77	$\delta s'/.005$	154.0 $\delta s'$
.006	1.00	1.08	$\delta s'/.006$	180.0 $\delta s'$
.007	.85	1.15	$\delta s'/.007$	164.3 $\delta s'$

Table 27.6
Computation of the Posterior Distribution

σ	Prior $P(\sigma)$	Likelihood $P(s'|\sigma)$	Joint $P(s',\sigma)$	Posterior $P(\sigma|s')$
.003	.90	6.7 $\delta s'$	6.03 $\delta s'$	.338
.004	.05	75.0 $\delta s'$	3.75 $\delta s'$	.210
.005	.03	154.0 $\delta s'$	4.62 $\delta s'$	.259
.006	.01	180.0 $\delta s'$	1.80 $\delta s'$	.101
.007	.01	164.3 $\delta s'$	1.64 $\delta s'$	.092
	1.00		17.84 $\delta s'$	1.000

† The distribution of $\tilde{s}'/\sigma$ is known as the $\chi/\sqrt{f}$ distribution because the ratio s'/σ can be written

$$\frac{s'}{\sigma} = \frac{1}{\sigma}\sqrt{\frac{1}{f}\Sigma(x-\mu)^2} = \frac{1}{\sqrt{f}}\sqrt{\Sigma\left(\frac{x-\mu}{\sigma}\right)^2}$$

and χ^2 (chi square) is the standard name for the statistic $\Sigma[(x-\mu)/\sigma]^2$.

PROBLEMS

1. Compute the unconditional *costs* of acceptance, rejection, and action under certainty for the example in the text, and from them compute the cost of uncertainty:

a. Under the prior distribution of $\tilde{\sigma}$.

b. Under the posterior distribution.

2. What was the probability, as evaluated before the sample in the text was actually drawn, that a sample of four would yield $s' = .00598$?

3. Compute the expected value of $\tilde{\sigma}$ under the prior distribution and the conditional cost of acceptance given $\tilde{\sigma} = E(\tilde{\sigma})$. Explain in common-sense language why this cost is not equal to the cost of acceptance computed in Problem 1a and why the latter figure is the correct expected cost.

4. A sample from another bar yields measurements .3640, .3590, .3620, .3590 inch.

a. Should the process be rejected for excessive scatter?

b. What is the expected cost of uncertainty?

5. In earlier chapters we have solved problems of the sort discussed in this chapter by simply counting the number of defectives in the sample and basing the posterior distribution on the binomial likelihood of the observed value of $\tilde{r}$.

a. Use this method to compute the posterior distribution of the fraction defective in the light of the sample described in the text, calculating the binomial likelihoods by use of the binomial formula rather than using binomial tables.

b. How can this posterior distribution differ from that implied by Table 27.6 if both r and s' are sufficient statistics, as it is stated they are?

6. In actual quality-control practice, decisions of the sort described in the text are usually based on the sample *range* (difference between the largest and the smallest value in the sample). What advantages and disadvantages can you see in this method as compared with (a) the binomial method and (b) the method used in the text?

CHAPTER 28

Nuisance Parameters: "Normal" Populations with Both Parameters Unknown

The method of analysis used in Chapters 26 and 27 was identical to the method used in Chapters 21 through 25 even though two parameters were required to describe the population in Chapters 26 and 27 while only one was required in earlier chapters. What all of these problems had in common was the fact that the value of the cost-determining random variable was the only *unknown* parameter in the distribution of the sample observations. We now take up the new problems which arise when the value of the cost-determining random variable is *not* the only unknown parameter. As an example we shall use the simplest possible case, that of an approximately Normal population in which both parameters are unknown.

28.1 Statement of the Problem

In order to focus the discussion on what is really new in this new kind of problem, we shall use the same example of choosing between two kinds of chemical processing that we used in Chapter 26. The sole difference is that we now assume that the manufacturer has *not* previously made a careful investigation of the precision of the measuring process. Instead, we assume that when asked about its precision he says that he has no exact knowledge but that, if he were forced to place bets on the value of $\tilde{\sigma}$,† his experience with similar processes would lead him to bet in accordance with the odds in Table 28.1. On the other hand, we assume

Table 28.1

σ	$P(\sigma)$
.6	.25
.9	.50
1.2	.25
	1.00

that despite the lack of direct evidence on the point the manufacturer

† We continue the practice introduced in Section 27.1 of using the symbol σ by itself to denote $\sigma(\tilde{x})$ when this quantity is a random variable.

believes that repeated measurements would have a nearly Normal distribution and is absolutely sure that they are *unbiased*—i.e., that the mean μ of the infinite population of possible measurements on a single batch is equal to the true normal yield ξ of that batch.

To avoid the need to refer back to Chapter 26, we repeat in Table 28.2 the other basic data of the problem: the prior distribution of the normal yield $\xi = \tilde{\mu}$ and the conditional costs and losses of the decisions to accept and reject.

Table 28.2

$\xi = \mu$	$P_0(\xi)$	Conditional cost		Conditional loss	
		Accept	Reject	Accept	Reject
2.0	.15	$1000	$400*	$600	0
2.5	.25	500	400*	100	0
3.0	.60	0*	400	0	$400
	1.00				

There is one and only one underlying reason why we cannot solve this problem in exactly the same way that we solved the problem when σ was known: the formula for the likelihood of any individual observation

$$P(x) = \frac{\delta x}{\sigma} P'_N \left(\frac{x - \mu}{\sigma} \right)$$

will give *three different* results for any given μ, depending on which of the three possible values σ we use in the formula. Since the likelihood of the sample as a whole is the product of the likelihoods of the individual observations, this means that there will be three different joint likelihoods of the sample for each μ rather than a single joint likelihood as there was in Chapter 26; and if this is true when we work with the individual observations, the same thing must necessarily be true when we summarize them by any *sufficient* statistic or statistics.

Fortunately a very simple device will get us out of this difficulty and permit us to find the required posterior distribution almost as easily when both μ and σ are unknown as when only one of them is unknown. This device consists in first finding the *joint* posterior distribution of $\tilde{\mu}$ and $\tilde{\sigma}$ *together* and then obtaining from this joint distribution the *marginal* posterior distribution of $\tilde{\mu} = \xi$ *alone*. The joint posterior distribution of $\tilde{\mu}$ and $\tilde{\sigma}$ is found by exactly the same procedure we have used previously to find the posterior distribution of a single random variable:

1. We assign a prior probability to every possible μ, σ *combination*.
2. We compute the likelihood of the sample for each μ, σ combination.

3. From the prior probabilities and the likelihoods we compute the posterior probability of each μ, σ combination by applying Bayes' theorem in absolutely standard fashion.

The marginal posterior distribution of $\tilde{\mu} = \xi$ alone is then computed from this joint posterior distribution of $\tilde{\mu}$ and $\tilde{\sigma}$ together in exactly the same way that the marginal distribution of $\tilde{r}$ was computed in Table 12.4 from a joint distribution of $\tilde{p}$ and $\tilde{r}$.

28.2   Solution of the Problem When $n = 1$

Although we shall ultimately work as in earlier chapters with summary statistics rather than with the individual observations in a sample, we shall first explain the basic logic of our new procedure by showing how to compute the marginal posterior distributions when the sample consists of a single observation, $n = 1$. After this has been done we shall see that exactly the same basic method can be applied in working with summaries of a larger sample.

28.2.1   *The Joint Prior Distribution of $\tilde{\mu}$ and $\tilde{\sigma}$*

Since there is no reason to think that a high value of $\tilde{\mu}$ will tend to be accompanied by either a high or low value of $\tilde{\sigma}$, etc., these two variables are *independent* by definition. The joint probability that $\tilde{\mu}$ will have some specified value μ *and* that $\tilde{\sigma}$ will have some specified value σ is then the product of the two simple probabilities. For example: the probability that $\tilde{\mu} = 2.5$ is .25 by Table 28.2; the probability that $\tilde{\sigma} = .9$ is .50 by Table 28.1; therefore the joint probability that $\tilde{\mu} = 2.5$ *and* $\tilde{\sigma} = .9$ is .25 × .50 = .125. The complete joint prior distribution of $\tilde{\mu}$ and $\tilde{\sigma}$ is worked out in this way in Table 28.3.

Table 28.3
Computation of Joint Prior Probabilities

$\mu = \xi$	$P(\mu)$	σ	$P(\sigma)$	$P(\mu,\sigma)$
2.0	.15	.6	.25	.0375
		.9	.50	.0750
		1.2	.25	.0375
			1.00	
2.5	.25	.6	.25	.0625
		.9	.50	.1250
		1.2	.25	.0625
			1.00	
3.0	.60	.6	.25	.1500
		.9	.50	.3000
		1.2	.25	.1500
	1.00		1.00	1.0000

28.2.2   The Likelihood of the Sample

Assume now that a single sample observation is taken and that its value is $x = 1.84$.   In Table 28.4 the likelihood

$$P(\tilde{x} = 1.84) = \frac{\delta x}{\sigma} \, P'_N \left(\frac{1.84 - \mu}{\sigma} \right)$$

is computed for every μ, σ combination.   These computations present nothing whatever that is new.

Table 28.4
Computation of Likelihoods

μ	σ	$u = \dfrac{1.84 - \mu}{\sigma}$	Height $P'_N(u)$	Width $\delta x/\sigma$	Area $P(1.84\mid\mu,\sigma)$
2.0	.6	$-$ .27	.385	$\delta x/.6$	.642 δx
	.9	$-$ .18	.392	$\delta x/.9$	.436 δx
	1.2	$-$ .13	.396	$\delta x/1.2$	.330 δx
2.5	.6	-1.10	.218	$\delta x/.6$	.363 δx
	.9	$-$ .73	.306	$\delta x/.9$	.340 δx
	1.2	$-$ .55	.343	$\delta x/1.2$	.286 δx
3.0	.6	-1.93	.062	$\delta x/.6$	.103 δx
	.9	-1.29	.174	$\delta x/.9$	.193 δx
	1.2	$-$ .97	.249	$\delta x/1.2$	.208 δx

28.2.3   The Joint Posterior Distribution of $\tilde{\mu}$ and $\tilde{\sigma}$

In Table 28.5 we now apply Bayes' theorem in the usual way.   The prior probability of each μ, σ combination is taken from Table 28.3; the likelihood of the sample given this μ, σ combination is taken from Table 28.4; the joint probability of the μ, σ combination *and* the sample is computed by multiplying the prior probability by the likelihood; and the

Table 28.5
Computation of Joint Posterior Probabilities

$\mu = \xi$	σ	Prior $P(\mu,\sigma)$	Likelihood $P(1.84\mid\mu,\sigma)$	Joint $P(\mu,\sigma,1.84)$	Posterior $P(\mu,\sigma\mid1.84)$
2.0	.6	.0375	.642 δx	.0241 δx	.094
	.9	.0750	.436 δx	.0327 δx	.127
	1.2	.0375	.330 δx	.0124 δx	.048
2.5	.6	.0625	.363 δx	.0227 δx	.088
	.9	.1250	.340 δx	.0425 δx	.166
	1.2	.0625	.286 δx	.0179 δx	.070
3.0	.6	.1500	.103 δx	.0154 δx	.060
	.9	.3000	.193 δx	.0579 δx	.226
	1.2	.1500	.208 δx	.0312 δx	.121
		1.0000		.2568 δx	1.000

posterior probabilities are computed by dividing the joint probabilities by their sum.

28.2.4   The Posterior Distribution of $\tilde{\mu}$

From the joint posterior probabilities of all μ, σ combinations in the last column of Table 28.5 we can compute the marginal posterior distributions of both $\tilde{\mu}$ and $\tilde{\sigma}$ by the standard method for computing marginal from joint probabilities; the work is shown in Table 28.6. "*The*" posterior probability that $\tilde{\mu} = \tilde{\xi} = 2.0$ is .269, since this is the total probability that *one or another* of the following three joint events will occur:

$$\tilde{\mu} = 2.0, \qquad \tilde{\sigma} = .6;$$
$$\tilde{\mu} = 2.0, \qquad \tilde{\sigma} = .9;$$
$$\tilde{\mu} = 2.0, \qquad \tilde{\sigma} = 1.2;$$

and these are the *only* events which involve $\tilde{\mu} = 2.0$.

Table 28.6
Computation of Marginal Probabilities

$\mu = \xi$	σ			Total
	.6	.9	1.2	
2.0	.094	.127	.048	.269
2.5	.088	.166	.070	.324
3.0	.060	.226	.121	.407
Total	.242	.519	.239	1.000

28.2.5   Nuisance Parameters

Parameters like σ in this example are known as *nuisance parameters*. We *want* the distribution of the sample values to depend on the parameter μ because it is this relation which enables us to learn something about $\xi = \mu$ from the sample. We do *not* want the distribution of the sample values to depend on any other unknown parameters because this in effect confuses the evidence concerning the value of $\xi = \mu$. But

> If nuisance parameters are present and we want to make full use of all of our information, we have no choice other than to assign them probability distributions and take them into account in our computations.

28.3   Summarization of a Sample When Both μ and σ Are Unknown

Suppose now that instead of a sample consisting of a single observation $x = 1.84$ we have the same sample of nine observations that we had in Chapter 26, the observations having the values 1.84, 1.75, 1.39, 1.65, 3.53, 1.03, 2.73, 2.86, and 1.96.

As always, one way of proceeding is to work directly with the individual observations. For $\mu = 2.0$, $\sigma = .6$, the likelihood (conditional probability) of the observation $x = 1.84$ is $.642\, \delta x$, as shown in the first line of Table 28.4. By making similar computations for each of the other eight observations and multiplying the results together, we would have the joint likelihood (conditional probability) of the whole sample for $\mu = 2.0$, $\sigma = .6$. This likelihood would replace $.642\, \delta x$ at the top of the likelihood column in Table 28.5, and each of the other entries in that column would be similarly replaced by the joint likelihoods of the whole sample given a particular pair of values for μ and σ. The remainder of the calculations would then proceed exactly as before.

28.3.1   Use of the Statistics $\bar{x}$ and s

Fortunately the first and most laborious step in this operation—computation of the joint probability of the whole sample for each pair of values of $\tilde{\mu}$ and $\tilde{\sigma}$—can again be short-cut by working with summaries of the sample rather than with the individual observations. It is almost obvious, however, that the sample *cannot* be summarized by any *single* statistic, since as we already know it requires the statistic $\bar{x}$ to summarize the sample when σ is known and it requires the statistic s' to summarize the sample when μ is known. What we can do is summarize the sample by *two* statistics, the sample mean $\bar{x}$ and the statistic

$$s = \sqrt{\frac{1}{f}\,\Sigma(x - \bar{x})^2}$$

where

$$f = n - 1.$$

Notice carefully that this statistic s differs in *two* respects from the statistic s' used in Chapter 27:

1. The sample mean $\bar{x}$ is used in place of the population mean μ, which is unknown in our present problem.
2. The divisor or *number of degrees of freedom f* is not the sample size n but $n - 1$.

The reason for the name "degrees of freedom" is obvious if we think of a sample of size $n = 1$. In that case $\bar{x} = x$ and $\Sigma(x - \bar{x})^2 = (x - x)^2$ is not "free" to have any value other than 0. The statistic s then has the meaningless value $\sqrt{\frac{1}{0}0^2}$, which expresses the fact that all the information about μ and σ contained in a sample of size $n = 1$ is conveyed by $\bar{x}$, i.e. by the value x of the single observation in the sample.

It can be shown that *when the population is Normal* the two statistics

$\bar{x}$ and s are (1) *independent* and (2) *jointly sufficient*. The first of these properties means that the likelihood of $\bar{x}$ does not depend on the value of s and vice versa. The second means that the ratio

$$\frac{\text{(Likelihood of } \bar{x}) \times \text{(likelihood of } s)}{\text{Joint likelihood of the individual } x\text{'s}}$$

does not depend on either μ or σ, and therefore that we will get exactly the same posterior distributions for $\tilde{\mu}$ and $\tilde{\sigma}$ by working with the joint likelihoods of $\bar{x}$ and s as we would by working with the joint likelihoods of the nine individual x's. We again remind the student that the condition "when the population s Normal" really means "when the probability of the individual observations would be calculated *as if* they were Normal"—we are simply asserting that a particular short method of calculation will give the same results as a particular long method of calculation.

28.3.2　The Sampling Distribution of $\tilde{s}$

It can be shown that *when the population from which the sample is drawn is Normal*, the distribution of the statistic $\tilde{s}$ is given by the formula

$$P'(s) = \frac{fs}{\sigma^2} P'_g \left[\frac{1}{2} f \left(\frac{s}{\sigma} \right)^2 \middle| r = \frac{1}{2} f \right],$$

where P'_g is the ordinate of the standardized gamma distribution with parameter $r = \frac{1}{2}f$. This formula is identical to the formula given in Section 27.2.1 for the distribution of $\tilde{s}'$ except that n is replaced by f. As in the case of $\tilde{s}'$, it is more convenient to use Chart V of the $\chi/\sqrt{f}$ distribution of $\tilde{s}/\sigma$ than to use Chart III of the gamma distribution;† the likelihood of s is then

$$P(s) = \frac{\delta s}{\sigma} P'_{\chi/\sqrt{f}} \left(\frac{s}{\sigma} \middle| f \right).$$

28.3.3　The Likelihood of the Sample

We already know that for this particular sample

$$\bar{x} = 2.08.$$

Recalling that $n = 9$ and therefore $f = 8$ we now compute

$$s^2 = \frac{1}{8}[(1.84 - 2.08)^2 + (1.75 - 2.08)^2 + \cdots] = .6347,$$

$$s = \sqrt{.6347} = .80$$

---

† It is simply the resulting ability to make convenient use of tables or charts like Chart V which explains why in problems like the present one the statistic s is defined with divisor $n - 1$ rather than with divisor n. If the definition had the divisor n, Chart V could be used only by multiplying the statistic by $\sqrt{n/(n - 1)}$ before consulting the chart.

As an example of the use of the two statistics $\bar{x}$ and s we take the case $\mu = 2.0$, $\sigma = .6$. For this value of $\tilde{\sigma}$

$$\sigma(\tilde{x}) = \frac{\sigma}{\sqrt{n}} = \frac{.6}{\sqrt{9}} = .2,$$

$$\frac{s}{\sigma} = \frac{.80}{.6} = 1.33.$$

The conditional probability of $\bar{x}$ is then

$$P(\tilde{x} = 2.08) = \frac{\delta\bar{x}}{\sigma(\tilde{x})} P'_N \left(\frac{2.08 - 2.00}{.2}\right) = \frac{\delta\bar{x}}{.2} .3683 = 1.84 \, \delta\bar{x}$$

and the conditional probability of s is

$$P(\tilde{s} = .80) = \frac{\delta s}{\sigma} P'_{x/\sqrt{f}}(1.33|f = 8) = \frac{\delta s}{.6} .52 = .87 \, \delta s.$$

What we want, of course, is the *joint* probability of $\bar{x}$ and s given $\mu = 2.0$, $\sigma = .6$, since this will represent the joint likelihood of the nine individual observations. Because the probability of $\bar{x}$ is independent of the probability of s, we simply multiply the two probabilities:

$$P(\bar{x}, s|\mu = 2.0, \sigma = .6) = 1.84 \, \delta\bar{x} \times .87 \, \delta s = 1.60 \, \delta\bar{x} \, \delta s.$$

Similar calculations are summarized in Table 28.7 for all possible μ, σ combinations. The student should make sure that he understands the procedure by actually verifying one of the entries in the table. In so doing he should notice that not only the likelihood of s but also the likelihood of $\bar{x}$ varies with σ; and he should further notice that $\sigma(\tilde{x}) = \sigma/\sqrt{n}$ affects *both* the location (and thus the height) *and* the width of the bar for $u = (\bar{x} - \mu)/\sigma(\tilde{x})$.

Table 28.7
Computation of Joint Likelihoods

μ	σ	u	Likelihood of $\bar{x}$	s/σ	Likelihood of s	Joint likelihood
2.0	.6	+ .40	1.84 $\delta\bar{x}$	1.33	.87 δs	1.60 $\delta\bar{x} \, \delta s$
	.9	+ .27	1.28 $\delta\bar{x}$	.89	1.77 δs	2.26 $\delta\bar{x} \, \delta s$
	1.2	+ .20	.98 $\delta\bar{x}$	.67	.71 δs	.70 $\delta\bar{x} \, \delta s$
2.5	.6	− 2.10	.22 $\delta\bar{x}$	1.33	.87 δs	.19 $\delta\bar{x} \, \delta s$
	.9	− 1.40	.50 $\delta\bar{x}$	.89	1.77 δs	.88 $\delta\bar{x} \, \delta s$
	1.2	− 1.05	.58 $\delta\bar{x}$	.67	.71 δs	.41 $\delta\bar{x} \, \delta s$
3.0	.6	− 4.60	.00 $\delta\bar{x}$	1.33	.87 δs	.00 $\delta\bar{x} \, \delta s$
	.9	− 3.07	.01 $\delta\bar{x}$	.89	1.77 δs	.02 $\delta\bar{x} \, \delta s$
	1.2	− 2.30	.07 $\delta\bar{x}$	.67	.71 δs	.05 $\delta\bar{x} \, \delta s$

28.3.4 The Posterior Distribution

The joint likelihoods in the last column of Table 28.7 convey exactly the same information about the sample of nine that the likelihoods in the last column of Table 28.4 conveyed about the sample of one.   In Table 28.8 we proceed to compute the *joint* posterior distribution of $\tilde{\xi} = \tilde{\mu}$ and $\tilde{\sigma}$ by exactly the same procedure that we used in Table 28.5.   The *marginal* posterior distribution of $\tilde{\xi}$ is given by the subtotals in the last column: $P(\tilde{\xi} = 2.0) = .614$, and so forth.

Table 28.8
Computation of the Posterior Distribution

$\xi = \mu$	σ	Prior $P(\xi,\sigma)$	Likelihood $P(\bar{x},s\|\xi,\sigma)$	Joint $P(\bar{x},s,\xi,\sigma)$	Posterior $P(\xi,\sigma\|\bar{x},s)$	
2.0	.6	.0375	1.60 $\delta\bar{x}\ \delta s$	.0600 $\delta\bar{x}\ \delta s$	.144	
	.9	.0750	2.26 $\delta\bar{x}\ \delta s$	.1695 $\delta\bar{x}\ \delta s$	.407	
	1.2	.0375	.70 $\delta\bar{x}\ \delta s$	.0262 $\delta\bar{x}\ \delta s$	.063	
						.614
2.5	.6	.0625	.19 $\delta\bar{x}\ \delta s$	.0119 $\delta\bar{x}\ \delta s$	.029	
	.9	.1250	.88 $\delta\bar{x}\ \delta s$	.1100 $\delta\bar{x}\ \delta s$	.264	
	1.2	.0625	.41 $\delta x\ \delta s$	.0256 $\delta\bar{x}\ \delta s$	.061	
						.354
3.0	.6	.1500	.00 $\delta\bar{x}\ \delta s$	.0000 $\delta\bar{x}\ \delta s$	.000	
	.9	.3000	.02 $\delta\bar{x}\ \delta s$	.0060 $\delta\bar{x}\ \delta s$	.014	
	1.2	.1500	.05 $\delta\bar{x}\ \delta s$	.0075 $\delta\bar{x}\ \delta s$	.018	
		1.0000		.4167 $\delta\bar{x}\ \delta s$		.032
						1.000

It is left as an exercise to show that the expected loss of acceptance is $404 while the expected loss of rejection is $13.   Rejection is the better choice just as it was in Chapter 26, but the uncertainty about $\tilde{\sigma}$ has increased its expected loss from $8 to $13.

PROBLEMS

1. Compute the *prior* expected loss of acceptance for the example of the text. Does uncertainty about $\tilde{\sigma}$ have any effect on this computation?   Why?

2. Given that $\tilde{\mu}$ and $\tilde{\sigma}$ are independent and have the distributions shown in the following table, compute their joint distribution.

μ	$P(\mu)$	σ	$P(\sigma)$
2.2	.20	.7	.25
2.4	.30	.8	.35
2.6	.50	.9	.40
	1.00		1.00

3. Compute the likelihood of the single observation $x = 2.80$

a. For $\mu = 2.2$, $\sigma = .8$.

b. For $\mu = 2.4$, $\sigma = .7$.

4. Given the distributions of Problem 2, compute the joint probability that

a. $\tilde{\mu} = 2.2$, $\tilde{\sigma} = .8$, *and* $\tilde{x} = 2.80$.

b. $\tilde{\mu} = 2.4$, $\tilde{\sigma} = .7$, *and* $\tilde{x} = 2.80$.

5. Verify all values in the sixth line ($\mu = 2.5$, $\sigma = 1.2$) of the following tables:

a. Table 28.5.

b. Table 28.7.

c. Table 28.8.

6. What was the probability, as evaluated before the sample in the text was actually drawn, that a sample of nine would yield $\tilde{x} = 2.08$ *and* $s = .80$?

7. Find the posterior distribution of $\tilde{\sigma}$ on the evidence of the prior distributions and the sample of nine described in the text.

8. Verify the posterior expected losses given at the end of the text.

9. Compute the posterior distribution of $\tilde{\xi}$ and the posterior expected costs of acceptance and rejection for the example in the text as they would be if the measuring process were known to give measurements which are .37 unit high on the average and if the following four measurements of the X content had been made: 3.37, 1.90, 1.67, 2.86. Most of the computations which would be required by this problem can be avoided by starting from the results shown in the following table.

σ	$P(s\|\sigma)$
.6	.85 δs
1.2	.79 δs

ξ	σ	$P(\bar{x}\|\xi,\sigma)$	$P(\bar{x},s,\xi,\sigma)$
2.0	.6	1.28 $\delta\bar{x}$	.0408 $\delta\bar{x}\ \delta s$
	.9	.87 $\delta\bar{x}$	.0724 $\delta\bar{x}\ \delta s$
	1.2		
2.5	.6	.50 $\delta\bar{x}$	.0266 $\delta\bar{x}\ \delta s$
	.9	.58 $\delta\bar{x}$	
	1.2	.52 $\delta\bar{x}$	.0257 $\delta\bar{x}\ \delta s$
3.0	.6	.01 $\delta\bar{x}$	.0012 $\delta\bar{x}\ \delta s$
	.9		
	1.2	.21 $\delta\bar{x}$	.0249 $\delta\bar{x}\ \delta s$

CHAPTER 29

Populations of Incompletely Specified Form; "Large-sample Theory"

In our study of measured (many-valued) populations, we have up to now always assumed that the population with which we are dealing had a *known mathematical form* — Pascal, exponential, or Normal. It was because of this fact that these populations were fully defined by only one or two parameters: given definite values for these parameters, the entire distribution of the population could have been graphed by substituting these values in the mathematical formula for the type of population in question.

In the case of the Pascal population it is possible *in some applications* to maintain that this mathematical form is a virtually exact description of the real physical population. A real physical process *may* actually be known to operate almost exactly as a Bernoulli process, and the Pascal distribution of intervals is a mathematically exact deduction from the basic assumptions of a Bernoulli process. While we did not pretend that the exponential and Normal distributions were *exact* descriptions of the real populations which they represented, they too may in some situations be known to give very close approximations to the heights of the bars in the histogram of the real population. The best example is an exponential population of Poisson intervals, since the nature of the mechanism generating the intervals may be known to operate almost exactly as a Poisson process.

In other cases, however, the evidence for the accuracy of such approximations is much weaker, as in the case of the chemical assaying process discussed in Chapter 26 or the production process discussed in Chapter 27. In these applications there was no really strong a priori or "theoretical" reason to believe that the population was Normal: the proposition rested primarily on the fact that a Normal curve had given a reasonably good fit to a few score observations. In the situation discussed in Chapter 28 the evidence was weaker still. If a measuring process has been so little studied that its standard deviation is not known, the only reason to think that it will generate an approximately Normal population of measurements is the general knowledge that *some* measur-

423

ing processes of more or less the same type do in fact generate such populations.

The student may well inquire why we resort to approximations in such cases instead of using some more exact method of analysis, and the first purpose of this chapter is to answer that question. After it has been answered we shall go on to draw the implications for the analysis of decisions in situations where we have even less evidence on the form of the population than we had in Chapter 28. Such situations are unfortunately more common than not.

29.1   The Exact Description of a Measured Population

The only exact representation of a measured population is a histogram with as many bars as there are possible values of the variable. A complete description of such a histogram would require a statement of the area of every one of the bars but one—the area of one bar can be calculated as 1 minus the area of all the others, just as $q = 1 - p$—so that if there are P possible values of the variable it requires $P - 1$ numbers to describe the histogram. The description does not have to be put in this particular form, of course. Instead of specifying the areas of $P - 1$ bars, we could specify the mean of the population and the areas of any $P - 2$ bars, or the mean and variance and the areas of any $P - 3$ bars, and so forth. *But no matter what set of parameters we choose, it requires $P - 1$ parameters to describe the population completely.*

Suppose now that the costs of various acts depend on the mean μ of some population and that we wish for this reason to compute the posterior distribution of $\tilde{\mu}$ in the light of the evidence supplied by a sample of size n drawn from the population. To do this we must compute the likelihood of the sample for each possible value of $\tilde{\mu}$, and it will therefore be simplest to think of the population as described by the value of $\tilde{\mu}$ and $P - 2$ other parameters. It is fairly obvious that the likelihood of any one observation in the sample will depend on the value of at least one parameter other than μ; and unless there are "tied" observations it follows that the joint likelihood of the n observations in the sample will depend on at least n different parameters in addition to the value of the cost-determining random variable $\tilde{\mu}$.

Unless we know the values of these n other parameters, each one of them is a nuisance parameter exactly as σ was a nuisance parameter in Chapter 28. In that chapter we had to compute the likelihood of the sample for every possible combination of values of $\tilde{\mu}$ and $\tilde{\sigma}$ and then multiply by the prior probability of that combination. If there were n nuisance parameters we would have to do this for every possible combination of values of $\tilde{\mu}$ and all the n nuisance parameters and then multiply by the prior probability of each combination. It is not so much the difficulty of carrying out the actual computations which bothers us, since this might be solved by the use of either more advanced mathematical techniques or high-speed computers. The real difficulty is that assessment of the prior probability of each combination of values of the nuisance parameters requires the use of experience and judgment, and the mind recoils at the prospect of supplying these probabilities.

29.2   Complete vs. Incomplete Models

29.2.1   *Completely Specified Approximate Models*

Thus we *cannot* try to be "exact" when we deal with a measured population where the number of possible values of the variable is at all considerable, and we *must* find some other method of analysis. One possible procedure is the one we have used hitherto. We reduce the problem to manageable proportions by using a model which describes the population *completely* (although not *exactly*) in terms of only a limited number of parameters. The exponential and Normal populations which we have already studied are just two of a wide variety of such models; and although it is beyond the scope of this course to discuss other models in detail, the student should realize that the general principles involved in their use are identical to those involved in the use of the models we have already studied. The joint likelihood of any sample can always be calculated from the likelihoods of the individual observations, since a model of a population is in effect nothing but a statement of the likelihood of any observation given specified values of the parameters. If, however, the sample is to be summarized by sufficient statistics, two problems are involved for each new model: we must first find out what *are* the sufficient statistics and then find tables of or means of computing the sampling distribution of each statistic we need to use.

29.2.2   *Incompletely Specified Models; Use of the Central Limit Theorem*

Although it is not at all hard to find a fairly simple model which will express everything we know or believe about a population, the computation of the exact likelihood of the sample for each possible value of the decision parameter may be quite laborious even when the model is fairly simple. Sufficient statistics do not exist for all models, and even when sufficient statistics exist their distributions may not be tabulated. In all such cases we would be forced to work directly with the likelihoods of the individual observations if we wished to extract *all* the information which the sample contains.

When we are dealing with *very small* samples we are usually forced to use as exact a model as we can, regardless of the computational and other difficulties which this may entail. Our information is so scanty that we cannot afford to waste any of it, whether this information is "prior" information or is contained in the sample. When we have *reasonably large* samples, on the contrary, we are usually able to do nearly as well by relying on the Central limit theorem and not specifying the exact shape of the population at all; and the labor involved will in general be far less. Since most business problems turn on the *mean* of some population, we shall show in the remainder of this chapter how "large-sample theory" can be applied to decisions concerning the mean when the shape of the population is only very roughly specified.

29.3   Decisions Concerning the Population Mean; Population Variance Known

We already know that if several independent random variables all have the same distribution and this distribution has a finite variance, then whatever the shape of this distribution may be, the distribution of the sum of the variables approaches Normality as the number of variables in the sum increases (Section 17.3). Since the distribution of a mean is the same as the distribution of a sum except for a change of scale, this implies immediately that the mean of a sample from a process generating independent observations will have a distribution which approaches Normality as the size of the sample increases provided only that the variance of the values generated by the process is finite—the proposition is independent of the "shape" of the infinite population of observations generated by the process. As for samples drawn *without replacement* from a *finite population*, the Central limit theorem does not apply strictly, since the values of the successive sample items are not independent; but we have seen in discussing the hypergeometric distribution (Section 23.2.1) that samples from a finite two-valued population nevertheless in fact approach Normality as n increases provided that n/N is not too large, and the same thing is true of finite many-valued populations.

Thus provided that the sample is large enough to justify treating the sample mean as Normally distributed and provided that we know the value of the population standard deviation σ, we can compute the posterior distribution of the mean of a population of *any* shape by exactly the same procedure that we used in Chapter 26 to deal with a population of Normal shape. We must, of course, remember to use the finite-population correction in computing $\sigma(\bar{x})$ if the sample is drawn without replacement from a finite population (cf. Section 25.5.2).

29.3.1   Normality of $\bar{x}$

We have already repeatedly examined the Normal approximation to the distributions of the means (or totals) of samples from a wide variety of populations, and we know that the *rapidity* with which the exact distribution of $\bar{x}$ approaches Normality depends on the nature of the population. This means, of course, that we do have to have a model of the population in mind when deciding whether a given sample is large enough to justify the use of the Normal approximation, but for *this* purpose we do not have to have decided on a *complete and detailed* mathematical specification of the model. We can settle the question by looking at the distribution of $\bar{x}$ in samples from mathematically specified populations which correspond *roughly* to the model we have in mind.

Rectangular Populations. One type of nonnormal population which often occurs in business problems is approximately *rectangular:* all values of the variable within a certain limited interval are nearly equally likely, and all values above or below the limits of that interval are nearly or completely impossible. Such populations generally arise as a result of some kind of preselection. Ball bearings which have a roughly Normal distribution when manufactured may be sorted into a number of size groups after manufacture, and if the range of diameters included in any one size group is narrow compared to the natural spread of the process by which the bearings are manufactured, each group will contain just about as many bearings which are just large enough to be included in the group as it contains bearings just small enough to be included. "Stratified" sampling is another common source of rectangular populations. Even though the dollar values of all items in an inventory may have a nearly exponential distribution, we may sample the inventory by taking one sample of all the very-low-value items, another sample of the next higher group of items, and so forth. When this is done, the distribution of any one of the sampled *subpopulations* will be very nearly rectangular.

The curves labeled R in Figure 29.1 show the true probability and cumulative distributions of $\bar{x}$ in samples of size 10 from a rectangular distribution while the curves labeled N show the Normal approximation to these distributions. It is obvious that *even for samples as small as 10 the error in the Normal approximation to the distribution of $\bar{x}$ in samples from a rectangular population is totally negligible.*

Skew Populations. The other most common type of nonnormal population encountered in business problems is asymmetric, or "skew." The exponential distribution is an extreme example of a skew population which we have already encountered both in connection with intervals generated by a Poisson process and as an approximation to many inventory populations actually encountered in practice. In other cases inventory and other empirical populations are quite reasonably well described by some curve of the gamma family shown in Chart III; as we already know, the exponential population is simply the special case $r = 1$ of this family.

The curves labeled E in Figure 29.1 show the true distribution of $\bar{x}$ in

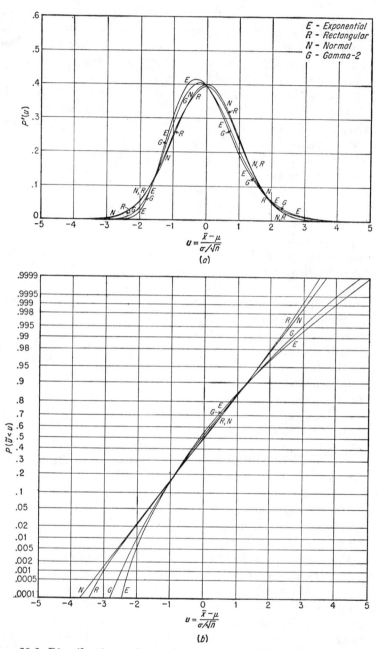

Figure 29.1. Distributions of sample means with Normal approximation, $n = 10$.

samples of size 10 from an exponential population; the curves labeled G show the same information for a gamma population of the shape shown by the curve labeled $r = 2$ in Chart III. Comparing these curves with their Normal approximation, we see that *the effect of skewness on the Normality of the sample mean is much more serious than the effect of rectangularity*—for many purposes it might be rather unsafe to use the Normal approximation for samples this small from populations this skew.†

29.4   Population Variance Unknown: "Large-sample Theory"

Although we rarely if ever really know the variance of the population and therefore of $\tilde{x}$ *exactly*, we very often know enough about the variance to treat it *as if* it were known exactly when costs will depend only on the value of μ.

Exact knowledge of σ is unnecessary when the cost-determining random variable is $\tilde{\mu}$ because uncertainty about σ has only a small or "second-order" effect on the posterior distribution of $\tilde{\mu}$.

As a simple numerical example of the effect of uncertainty about $\tilde{\sigma}$ on the posterior distribution of $\tilde{\mu}$, let us reexamine the problem of Chapter 28, where the uncertainty about $\tilde{\sigma}$ was very great. In that chapter the problem was solved "exactly" by using *all* the available information on $\tilde{\sigma}$—both that expressed by the prior distribution of $\tilde{\sigma}$ and that obtained from the sample through use of the statistic s. The result was the posterior distribution of $\tilde{\mu}$ shown in the column headed "all available evidence" in Table 29.1. The next column, headed $\hat{\sigma} = E_0(\tilde{\sigma})$, shows the

Table 29.1

μ	Prior probability	Posterior probability of μ on basis of		
		All available evidence	$\hat{\sigma} = E_0(\tilde{\sigma}) = .9$	$\hat{\sigma} = s = .8$
2.0	.15	.61	.59	.66
2.5	.25	.36	.39	.33
3.0	.65	.03	.02	.01
	1.00	1.00	1.00	1.00

† The student who is curious about the effect of the skewness of these two populations on larger samples or the effect of a lesser degree of skewness can investigate it by means of Figure 17.8. Since the gamma population with parameter $r = 2$ can be regarded as the distribution of the sample total or mean in samples of size 2 from an exponential population, the mean of a sample of size n from this gamma population is distributed like the mean of a sample of size $2n$ from an exponential population. In general, the mean of a sample of size n from a gamma population with parameter r is distributed like the mean of a sample of size rn from an exponential population.

distribution of $\bar{\mu}$ which we would have obtained if we had treated the mean of the prior distribution of $\bar{\sigma}$ as if it were the known value of $\bar{\sigma}$. Finally we show, in the column headed $\hat{\sigma} = s$, the distribution we would have obtained if we had treated the observed value of the statistic $\bar{s}$ as if *it* were the known value of $\bar{\sigma}$. Examination of Table 29.1 shows that while the three posterior distributions show substantial percentage differences in the probabilities assigned to $\mu = 3.0$, the absolute differences are all quite small and *would have little effect on expected costs* in a situation like that of Chapter 28.

29.4.1   *The Statistic $\bar{t}$ and Its Sampling Distribution*

The impression given by this example can be confirmed in a more systematic way by a different kind of argument.   When the true value of $\bar{\sigma}$ is unknown and an estimate based solely on a sample is to be used in its place, the most common procedure is to take as the estimate the statistic s defined in Section 28.3.1.   When the shape of the population is unspecified it is impossible to say what is the *best* estimate of σ, but at least in most situations the estimate s is probably about as good as any that can be devised.

Suppose then that in some problem we do treat σ *as if* it were known to have the value s even though the true value is actually unknown.   We will compute the likelihood of the observed $\bar{x}$ by use of the Normal approximation, but when we standardize $\bar{x}$ in the usual manner we will *not* get the *true* value of the statistic

$$u = \frac{\bar{x} - \mu}{\sigma(\bar{x})} = \frac{\bar{x} - \mu}{\sigma/\sqrt{n}};$$

what we will get is an "estimate" of u which is usually called

$$t = \frac{\bar{x} - \mu}{s/\sqrt{n}}.$$

What we now want to do is to find some rough way of saying what error this use of an estimate of u rather than u itself may produce in the likelihoods we assign to $\bar{x}$, and we can do this by comparing the sampling distribution of the statistic $\bar{u}$ with the sampling distribution of its estimate $\bar{t}$.

Student's Distribution.   The distribution of $\bar{t}$ will, of course, depend on the shape of the population from which the sample is drawn; and the distribution is unfortunately unknown for most populations.   We can, however, get an idea of the *order of magnitude* of the errors which will arise by treating the observed value of $\bar{t}$ as if it were the true value of $\bar{u}$ by comparing the two distributions for the one well-known case, that of samples from Normal populations.

When a sample is drawn from a Normal population, the statistic $\bar{t}$ has what is known as Student's distribution.   Since the s which occurs in

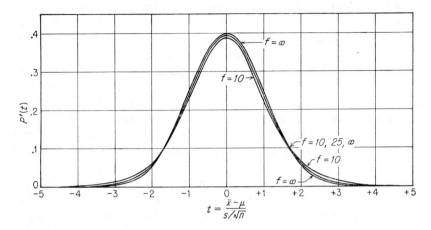

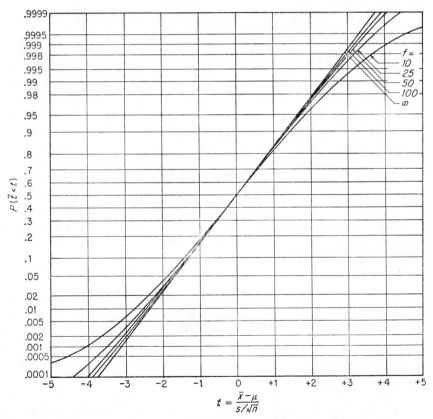

Figure 29.2. Student distributions with Normal limit.

the denominator of t has a $\chi/\sqrt{f}$ sampling distribution which depends on the number f of degrees of freedom (Section 28.3.2), it is clear that *the distribution of $\tilde{t}$ must depend on the number of degrees of freedom on which s is based.* In Figure 29.2 we show the unit Normal distribution of the statistic $\tilde{u}$ (curves labeled $f = \infty$) and the Student distributions of its estimate $\tilde{t}$ for 10, 25, 50, and 100 degrees of freedom. It is clear that fairly substantial errors may be made by treating an estimate s based on only 10 degrees of freedom as if it were the known value of σ; but it is also clear that *the errors will almost certainly be negligible if s is based on 50 degrees of freedom and will be negligible for much smaller values of f in most practical problems.*

Use of the Distribution of $\tilde{t}$. It may seem that we would do better to use the distribution of $\tilde{t}$ for the actual computation of likelihoods when σ is unknown than to use it merely as a way of estimating the errors which we are likely to make computing likelihoods by use of the Normal approximation. In fact, however, such a procedure either is not worth the extra trouble or else is not good enough.

Since the distribution of $\tilde{t}$ depends on both the shape of the population and the number of degrees of freedom on which s is based, we would have to have a whole library of tables instead of a single table if we wished to proceed in this way.† *But if the degrees of freedom are so few that the uncertainty of the estimate $\hat{\sigma} = s$ is serious, we should use our prior information about σ as well as the sample information,* and to do this we must proceed as we did in Chapter 28: mere replacement of the sampling distribution of $\tilde{u}$ by the sampling distribution of $\tilde{t}$ is not good enough. *We are justified in throwing away our prior information on σ only when the uncertainty in s is negligible for the purpose in hand;* and if this is so, then it is not worth the trouble to have and consult a whole book of special tables instead of a single table of the Normal distribution. We may proceed to solve our problem by the use of "large-sample theory," which means nothing more than using estimates of nuisance parameters *as if* they were the known true values of those parameters.

29.4.2   Estimates of σ Based on Several Samples

In many practical situations there will be much more evidence available concerning σ than there is concerning μ. In the chemical-assaying example in its original form (Chapter 26), the manufacturer's entire investigation of the measuring process gave evidence on σ for the current set of measurements even though it gave no information at all on the value of μ.

---

† Although the mathematical form of the distribution of $\tilde{t}$ is not known for most populations, the distribution could be obtained for any population by the Monte Carlo method.

Computation of s′ When the True Values of $\tilde{\mu}$ Are Known. In the example of Chapter 26, the true value of $\tilde{\mu} = \xi$ for each batch used in the investigation of the measuring process was *exactly determined* by measuring the X content of the final product. This meant that the σ^2 of the process could easily be estimated by *averaging the squares of the residuals or differences between each individual measurement and the true μ of the population from which that measurement was drawn* (i.e. the true ξ of the batch on which the measurement was made).

Another way of looking at this procedure is to consider it as a *weighted average* statistic $s′$ as defined in Section 27.2.1. From the n_1 measurements made on the first batch used in the investigation, the manufacturer could compute

$$s_1'^2 = \frac{1}{n_1} \Sigma(x - \mu_1)^2,$$

and similarly for all the other batches. He could then have got the same result he got before by taking a weighted average of these statistics using the number of measurements on which each was based as the weight:

$$s'^2 = \frac{1}{N} (n_1 s_1'^2 + n_2 s_2'^2 + \cdot \cdot \cdot)$$

where N is the total number of measurements made on all batches.

Computation of s When the True Values of $\tilde{\mu}$ Are Unknown. When $\tilde{\mu}$ varies from sample to sample and its true value for each sample is *unknown*, we cannot compute the statistic $s′$ for any sample. We *can* compute the statistic s (Section 28.3.2) for each sample, however, and we can take a weighted average of these statistics s in much the same way that we averaged the $s′$. For the first sample we compute

$$s_1^2 = \frac{1}{f_1} \Sigma(x - \bar{x}_1)^2,$$

where $f_1 = n_1 - 1$ is the number of degrees of freedom; and similarly for the other samples. We then take a weighted average of these statistics *using the number of degrees of freedom as the weights:*

$$s^2 = \frac{1}{F} (f_1 s_1^2 + f_2 s_2^2 + \cdot \cdot \cdot)$$

where F is the total number of degrees of freedom in all the samples.

The weighted average $\bar{s}$ computed in this way has the $\chi/\sqrt{f}$ distribution with F degrees of freedom, and the distribution of $\bar{t}$ based on this $\bar{s}$ has this same number of degrees of freedom. It is very important to observe that

The distribution of $\bar{t}$ depends on the number of degrees of freedom on which its denominator $\bar{s}$ (or $\bar{s}′$) is based; it does not depend on the sample size on which $\bar{x}$ is based.

This is the reason why there was virtually *no* error in treating σ as known in Chapter 26 even though the $\bar{x}$ in which we were interested came from a sample of only nine observations.

PROBLEMS

1. Three assays are made on each of three batches of raw material, resulting in the measurements shown below. Assuming that there is no other information worth consideration, estimate the standard deviation of the measuring process from these data:

Batch 1: 3.225, 0.974, 1.304.
Batch 2: 3.282, 2.125, 2.815.
Batch 3: 6.072, 5.609, 1.477.

2. We shall see later in the course that very good approximate solutions to certain problems involving two-valued populations can be obtained by treating these populations *as if* they had a definite known variance even though the variance actually depends on the population mean p. Suppose then that the parameter p of a Bernoulli process has the prior distribution shown in the following table and that the fraction defective in a sample of 80 turns out to be $\bar{x} = .20$. Compute the likelihoods of $\bar{x}$ and the pos-

p	$P(p)$
.10	.2
.15	.3
.20	.3
.25	.2
	1.0

terior distribution of $\tilde{p}$ by means of the Normal approximation to the distribution of $\tilde{x}$

a. Using the correct population standard deviation $\sigma = \sqrt{pq}$ in computing $\sigma(\bar{x}) = \sigma/\sqrt{n}$ for each value of $\tilde{p}$.

b. Treating the population standard deviation σ as being known to have the value which it actually does have when $p = E_0(\tilde{p})$.

CHAPTER 30

Normal Prior Distributions

30.1 Continuous Prior Distributions

The prior probability distributions which we have used in all examples hitherto have been admittedly very unrealistic. We have said that $\tilde{p}$ must have one of the four values .01, .05, .15, or .25, or that $\tilde{\mu}$ must have one of the three values 2.0, 2.5, or 3.0, even though common sense told us that in any real situation the businessman would consider *all* values in a certain interval as possible and would describe his prior distribution by some kind of smooth curve. The justification for this procedure was simply that the smooth curve representing the businessman's real prior distribution could always be represented by a discrete distribution in which the possible values were very close together and that the methods of analysis which would be used under such a distribution were identical to those used under our extremely simplified distributions.

In many real problems it is actually much more convenient to apply mathematical analysis to a continuous prior distribution in its original form than it is to break it down into a many-valued discrete distribution and use arithmetic. Analysis can be used, however, only if the continuous distribution is expressed by an algebraic formula of a type which is mathematically manageable; it is *not* possible to apply analytical methods to any curve the businessman happens to draw. The businessman, on the other hand, is very unlikely to insist on the exact shape of the prior distribution, and if some convenient formula gives a reasonable-looking curve he is likely to be as willing to act on the implications of this distribution as on those of any other curve he might draw. Accordingly we shall proceed in this chapter:

1. To show by example how continuous prior distributions can be used to facilitate the solution of particular applied problems;

2. To show that in many situations the exact shape of the prior distribution is not at all critical: i.e., to show that substantial changes in the shape of the prior distribution have very little effect on the posterior distribution which actually determines expected costs;

3. To show how the use of continuous prior distributions can contribute to our general understanding of an entire class of problems.

435

30.2   Choice of a Normal Prior Distribution

The one continuous distribution whose use as a prior distribution we shall study in any detail is the Normal.   There are two reasons for this choice.   First: it takes absolutely no mathematical skill to find the Normal distribution which best expresses the judgment of the person responsible for a decision.   Second and much more important: when the basic random variable is the mean of some population, the use of a Normal prior distribution leads under certain conditions to an extremely simple posterior distribution, and we shall see that this posterior distribution is often very nearly exact even when the Normal prior distribution is quite far from being an exact representation of the decision maker's beliefs.

30.2.1   Tail Probabilities

Since the tails of a Normal curve never fall completely to zero, it is true that a Normal prior distribution may flatly contradict the decision maker's belief that certain values of the variable are impossible; and if the assignment of some small probability to impossible values of the variable will really have a material effect on expected costs in the particular problem at hand, then the use of a Normal prior distribution may give very wrong results.   Ordinarily, however, the small tail probabilities have virtually no effect on expected costs; and in many problems the assignment of some small probability to values of the variable which seem "virtually" impossible may actually be very desirable.   If the student thinks back to the problems in which we have used discrete prior distributions, he will immediately recall that any value of the variable which is assigned zero prior probability will necessarily have zero posterior probability regardless of the results of sampling.   When the prior distribution is continuous, the corresponding statement is the following:

> If the total prior probability assigned to all values of a random variable within any particular interval is zero, the posterior probability that the variable lies within this interval will be zero *regardless of the results of sampling.*

In many situations this result may flatly contradict judgment and common sense.

Suppose, for example, that the costs of certain acts will be determined by the true X content of a finished batch of some chemical product, and suppose that on the basis of his experience with previous batches the manufacturer is tempted to assign a prior distribution to the X content which runs only from 0 to 6 pounds per gallon.   If he does this, he is in effect asserting that even if a million very accurate measurements showed an X content of -1 pound per gallon, he would absolutely refuse to believe that the true X content was below 0, and that if the measurements showed an X content of 7, he would absolutely refuse to believe that the true value was above 6. The former of these two results may well make sense, since negative X contents may be meaningless and therefore *impossible* in a strictly logical sense, and the same thing will be true of the upper limit of 6 pounds per gallon if it is *chemically impossible* for this limit to be exceeded. If, however, the upper limit is based merely on experience with previous batches, then the fact that a large number of very precise measurements indicate an X content of 7 pounds per gallon should almost certainly lead the manufacturer to revise his previous opinions and conclude that *this* batch in fact has an X content very close to 7 pounds per gallon; and if he would thus revise his opinions after the sample has been taken, his prior distribution should have assigned enough probability to values above 6 to make this revision automatic.

30.2.2   Fitting a Normal Prior Distribution to a Historical Frequency Distribution

In some situations the evidence on which a prior distribution is to be assessed will consist primarily of a frequency distribution of values actually taken on by the basic random variable in the past. In such situations one way of choosing the proper Normal prior distribution—i.e., of determining the mean and standard deviation of this distribution—is to use the graphical method described in Section 18.1.1. The trouble of plotting the fractile estimates is warranted, however, only if there is real doubt that it is legitimate to use a Normal distribution at all; when this can be taken for granted, there is a much simpler way of proceeding which we shall explain by means of an example.

Suppose that we have received five lots of parts produced by some automatic machine, that the mean diameter of all the shafts in each of the lots has been determined with the results $\mu = 5.681, 5.736, 5.202, 5.362, 5.774$ inches, and that we wish to assess a probability distribution for the random variable $\tilde{\mu}$ describing the mean diameter of the parts in the next lot to be received. Each lot constitutes a population of individual pieces, but we can consider the lots themselves as being individual members of a *superpopulation;* i.e., we can consider the μ of each lot as being drawn from a superpopulation of μ's. The parameters of this superpopulation can then be estimated in the same way that we would estimate the parameters of the population of individual diameters x in any one lot. We simply average the observed μ's to estimate

$$E(\tilde{\mu}) = \tfrac{1}{5}(5.681 + 5.736 + 5.202 + 5.362 + 5.774) = 5.551$$

and we estimate $\sigma(\tilde{\mu})$ in the same way that we estimated $\sigma(\tilde{x})$ in Section 29.4:

$$\sigma(\tilde{\mu}) = \sqrt{\frac{1}{5-1}\left[(5.681 - 5.551)^2 + (5.736 - 5.551)^2 + \cdots\right]}$$

$$= .255.$$

It is true that these "estimates" are rather unreliable when they are based on only five observations, but we shall see later in the chapter that *in many situations* it is simply not worth the trouble to worry excessively about the exact values of the parameters of a prior distribution.

We warn the student to distinguish clearly in his mind between the *superpopulation* of μ's each of which describes one *lot* as a whole and the *ordinary population* of x's describing the diameters of individual *pieces* in any one lot.   In terms of processes rather than populations, the setup mechanic is a *superprocess* with parameters $E(\tilde{\mu})$ and $\sigma(\tilde{\mu})$ which generates a series of μ's each of which characterizes a whole production run; each run is an *ordinary process* with parameters μ and σ which generates a series of x's each of which characterizes a single piece.

30.2.3   *Fitting a Normal Prior Distribution to Purely Subjective Judgments*

In many situations a prior distribution must be assessed without the aid of any historical frequencies at all.   Suppose, for example, that a company has developed a new product but hesitates to put it into production because sales volume may not be sufficient to cover the cost of tooling up for production, let alone allow any net profit.   If management is sensible it will do some field research by taking a sample of potential consumers and the final decision will turn primarily on the evidence obtained from this sample; but the *prior* distribution of the random variable "sales volume" will have to rest purely on marketing judgment.

Suppose then that the executive who must decide whether or not to produce this product says that his best guess is that the average sales per potential customer will be 8 units but thinks that there is only a 50-50 chance that this guess is within plus or minus 2 units of the true value. If he is willing to fill in the details of his probability distribution by using a Normal curve with its peak at 8 units and half of its area between 6 and 10 units, we can determine the parameters of this distribution as follows. The peak of a Normal distribution is at its mean, and therefore

$$E(\tilde{\mu}) = 8.$$

Since the 6-to-10 interval which contains half the total probability is centered on $E(\tilde{\mu})$, the tail of the distribution below 6 and the tail above 10 must each have probability $\frac{1}{4}$ as shown in Figure 30.1.   This implies that $\sigma(\tilde{\mu})$ must have a value such that

$$P(\tilde{\mu} > 10) = P_N\left[\tilde{u} > \frac{10-8}{\sigma(\tilde{\mu})}\right] = P_N\left[\tilde{u} > \frac{2}{\sigma(\tilde{\mu})}\right] = .25.$$

From Table III we find that $P_N(\tilde{u} > .67) \doteq .25$ and we calculate

$$\frac{2}{\sigma(\tilde{\mu})} = .67,$$

$$\sigma(\tilde{\mu}) = \frac{2}{.67} = 3.0.$$

Again we warn the student to distinguish clearly between the probability distribution of the random variable $\tilde{\mu}$ and the frequency distribution of the individual members of the population of which μ is the mean. In our present example the *population* consists of a large number of x's each of which describes the exact number of units that a *particular customer*

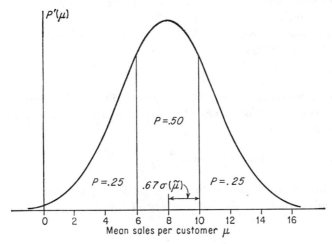

Figure 30.1. Judgmental assessment of a Normal prior distribution.

would purchase; these x's have a definite though unknown *frequency distribution* with mean μ and standard deviation $\sigma(\tilde{x})$. Because total sales and therefore total profit depend on the unknown mean of this population, $\tilde{\mu}$ is the profit-determining random variable of the problem and it is the executive's beliefs about the true value of $\tilde{\mu}$ which are described by a Normal *probability distribution* with parameters $E(\tilde{\mu})$ and $\sigma(\tilde{\mu})$. This latter distribution can be interpreted in terms of a *superprocess* if we recognize that the real *basic* random variable of the problem—the random variable to which probabilities are assigned *directly*—is not $\tilde{\mu}$ but a forecast discrepancy of the kind we studied in Chapter 6, Problems 2 and 3, and in Chapter 18, Problem 4. The executive has asserted in effect that his own mind operates as a random process which in situations like the present one will generate forecasts which are correct *on the average* but which are in error by 2 units or more on 50 per cent of all *individual occasions.*

30.3   The Posterior Distribution When the Prior and Sampling Distributions Are Normal and the Sampling Variance Is Known

We now turn to the problem of determining the posterior distribution of the random variable $\tilde{\mu}$ when the prior distribution of $\tilde{\mu}$ is Normal and the nature of the population and the sample size n are such that the distribution of the sample mean $\tilde{x}$ can be treated as Normal. In principle the computation is carried out by exactly the same method we have used when the prior distribution of $\tilde{\mu}$ was discrete. It is true that there is 0 probability that a continuously distributed random variable will have *exactly* any specified value whatever, but we get out of this difficulty by grouping the possible values of $\tilde{\mu}$ into brackets and assigning all the probability in a bracket to the μ at its mid-point.

As an example, consider the Normal prior distribution with mean and standard deviation

$$E_0(\tilde{\mu}) = 8, \qquad \sigma_0(\tilde{\mu}) = 3$$

which was assessed in Section 30.2.3 above. The total probability which any Normal distribution assigns to all values of $\tilde{\mu}$ in a bracket of width $\delta\mu$ and mid-point μ is

$$P(\mu) = \frac{\delta\mu}{\sigma(\tilde{\mu})} P'_N(u), \qquad u = \frac{\mu - E(\tilde{\mu})}{\sigma(\tilde{\mu})}.$$

Substituting the numerical values of $E_0(\tilde{\mu})$ and $\sigma_0(\tilde{\mu})$ into these formulas and assuming that we choose brackets of width $\delta\mu = .1$ the formulas become

$$P_0(\mu) = \frac{.1}{3} P'_N(u) = .033 P'_N(u) \qquad u = \frac{\mu - 8}{3}.$$

The probabilities of some typical brackets are as shown in Table 30.1.   If

Table 30.1

Bracket	Mid-point μ	$u = \dfrac{\mu - 8}{3}$	Height $P'_N(u)$	Width $\delta\mu/\sigma_0(\tilde{\mu})$	Area $P_0(\mu)$
5.95–6.05	6.00	$-.67$	.319	.033	.0105
6.05–6.15	6.10	$-.63$	.327	.033	.0108
6.15–6.25	6.20	$-.60$	.333	.033	.0110

now a sample were taken and we wished to revise the distribution of $\tilde{\mu}$ to take account of the new evidence, we could treat $\tilde{\mu}$ as having the *discrete* prior distribution given by the second and last columns of Table 30.1 and proceed exactly as we did in Chapter 26 or 28.   If the *population* standard deviation $\sigma(\tilde{x})$ were *known*, we could use the method of Chapter 26; if it were *not* known, we would have to treat it as a random variable, assign it a probability distribution, and then proceed as in Chapter 28.

The real advantage of assigning a Normal prior distribution to $\tilde{\mu}$ lies, however, in the fact that it often makes this heavy computation unnecessary. If $\tilde{x}$ is Normally distributed and the value of $\sigma(\tilde{x})$ is *known*, then by the use of the calculus we can always derive a mathematical formula for the posterior distribution of $\tilde{\mu}$ which gives exactly the same results that the arithmetical method would yield if we worked with very narrow brackets. Even if the value of $\sigma(\tilde{x})$ is *not* known, we can obtain a formula for the posterior distribution of $\tilde{\mu}$ provided that certain other conditions are met, but we shall study only the simpler case where $\sigma(\tilde{x})$ is known. As we saw in Section 29.4, situations where $\sigma(\tilde{x})$ can be treated as known even though μ cannot are by no means rare in actual business practice. Previous experience often gives us considerable knowledge of $\sigma(\tilde{x})$ without telling us anything about μ; and even if $\sigma(\tilde{x})$ is *not* known exactly, we are usually justified in treating a reasonably reliable estimate of $\sigma(\tilde{x})$ *as if* it were the true value when it is μ which will actually determine cost or profit.

30.3.1 *The Posterior Distribution of* $\tilde{\mu}$ *When* $\sigma(\tilde{x})$ *Is Known*

The following result obtained by use of the calculus will be used continually in the remainder of this course. In any problem where

1. The prior distribution of $\tilde{\mu}$ is Normal with parameters $E_0(\tilde{\mu})$ and $\sigma_0(\tilde{\mu})$,
2. The sampling distribution of $\tilde{x}$ is Normal with parameters μ and $\sigma(\tilde{x})$,
3. The value of $\sigma(\tilde{x})$ is known,

the posterior distribution of $\tilde{\mu}$ *is Normal* with parameters

$$E_1(\tilde{\mu}) = \frac{E_0(\tilde{\mu})[1/\sigma_0^2(\tilde{\mu})] + \bar{x}[1/\sigma^2(\tilde{x})]}{1/\sigma_0^2(\tilde{\mu}) + 1/\sigma^2(\tilde{x})}$$

$$\frac{1}{\sigma_1^2(\tilde{\mu})} = \frac{1}{\sigma_0^2(\tilde{\mu})} + \frac{1}{\sigma^2(\tilde{x})}$$

Notice that:

1. The posterior mean is a *weighted average* of the prior mean and the sample mean, the weights being the *reciprocals* of the variances of the two distributions.
2. The *reciprocal* of the posterior variance is the *sum* of the reciprocals of the variances of the prior and the sampling distributions.

Example. In the marketing problem discussed in Section 30.2.3, suppose that the marketing research department makes a thorough investigation of the types of firm which might use the product in question, draws up a complete list of potential customers containing 20,000 names, and from this list draws a sample of size

$$n = 100.$$

A small quantity of the new product is manufactured by hand and offered for sale to the potential customers in the sample; the amount x which each of them purchases is recorded and the values of the 100 x's are summarized by computing the statistics

$$\bar{x} = 5, \qquad s = 7.$$

It would be completely illegitimate to assume that the *population* of 20,000 individual x's has a Normal distribution without careful investigation, but the discussion in Section 29.3.1 shows that the *mean* of 100 observations on almost *any* population will have a very nearly Normal distribution and therefore we may treat $\bar{x}$ as Normally distributed in our present problem—in a real application we could check this assumption by actually looking at the frequency distribution of the 100 x's in the sample to make sure that we were not faced with some extremely peculiar population. To calculate the standard deviation of $\bar{x}$ we must know the standard deviation $\sigma(\bar{x})$ of the 20,000 individual x's in the population. Strictly speaking, the value of $\sigma(\bar{x})$ is not known; but the estimate $s = 7$ rests on $f = n - 1 = 99$ degrees of freedom, and as we saw in Section 29.4.1 this means that it is legitimate to proceed *as if* $\sigma(\bar{x})$ were known to have the value 7. Since the sampling ratio $n/N = 100/20{,}000 = .005$ is extremely small, the finite-population correction is completely negligible and we may compute

$$\sigma(\bar{\bar{x}}) = \frac{\sigma(\bar{x})}{\sqrt{n}} = \tfrac{7}{10}.$$

Recalling that the parameters of the executive's prior distribution were

$$E_0(\tilde{\mu}) = 8, \qquad \sigma_0(\tilde{\mu}) = 3,$$

we can proceed to determine the parameters of the Normal posterior distribution:

$$E_1(\tilde{\mu}) = \frac{8(1/3^2) + 5(1/.7^2)}{1/3^2 + 1/.7^2} = \frac{(8 \times .111) + (5 \times 2.041)}{.111 + 2.041} = 5.15.$$

$$\frac{1}{\sigma_1^2(\tilde{\mu})} = .111 + 2.041 = 2.152;$$

$$\sigma_1(\tilde{\mu}) = \frac{1}{\sqrt{2.152}} = \frac{1}{1.467} = .69.$$

30.3.2   The Concept of Quantity of Information

The really striking thing about this numerical example is the fact that the evidence supplied by the sample has virtually overwhelmed the executive's original beliefs about sales of the new product. Although he originally "expected" that sales would average $E_0(\tilde{\mu}) = 8$ units per potential customer, he now expects to sell only $E_1(\tilde{\mu}) = 5.15$ units per potential customer or scarcely more than the average of the actual sales to the 100 potential customers in the sample. This result is due, of course, to the fact that in computing $E_1(\tilde{\mu})$ the weight $1/\sigma^2(\tilde{x}) = 2.041$ given to $\tilde{x}$ was very large compared to the weight $1/\sigma_0^2(\tilde{\mu})$ given to $E_0(\tilde{\mu})$; and it is natural to think of the disparity between the two weights as a reflection of the fact that the guesstimate $E_0(\tilde{\mu})$ rested on very little solid information about the market for the new product whereas the actual sales to 100 customers constitute a good deal of information.

We can acquire a better feeling for the way in which the prior distribution and the sample evidence combine to determine the posterior distribution by thinking of both $E_0(\tilde{\mu})$ and $\tilde{x}$ as "estimates" of the true μ and thinking of the weights used in the computation of $E_1(\tilde{\mu})$ as actual *measures of the "quantity of information"* underlying these estimates. Therefore *provided that $\tilde{x}$ is Normally distributed with known variance* we define

$$I_{\tilde{x}} = \frac{1}{\sigma^2(\tilde{x})} : \text{the quantity of information summarized by } \tilde{x};$$

and *provided that $\tilde{\mu}$ is Normally distributed* we define

$$I_0 = \frac{1}{\sigma_0^2(\tilde{\mu})} : \text{the quantity of information summarized by } E_0(\tilde{\mu});$$

$$I_1 = \frac{1}{\sigma_1^2(\tilde{\mu})} : \text{the quantity of information summarized by } E_1(\tilde{\mu}).$$

Substituting the first two of these new symbols in the formula for $E_1(\tilde{\mu})$ we have

$$E_1(\tilde{\mu}) = \frac{I_0 E_0(\tilde{\mu}) + I_{\tilde{x}}\tilde{x}}{I_0 + I_{\tilde{x}}}$$

and we can say that

The mean of the posterior distribution of $\tilde{\mu}$ is a weighted average of the prior mean and the sample mean, the weight of each estimate being the quantity of information it summarizes.

Next let us look at the *dispersion* of the posterior distribution of our example. It may seem puzzling at first sight that the posterior standard deviation $\sigma_1(\tilde{\mu}) = .69$ came out less than *either* the prior standard deviation $\sigma_0(\tilde{\mu}) = 3$ or the sampling standard deviation $\sigma(\bar{x}) = .7$, but in terms of quantities of information this result is the most obvious common sense.   The original formula for $1/\sigma_1^2(\tilde{\mu})$ can be written

$$I_1 = I_0 + I_{\bar{x}},$$

and we can say that

> The total information contained in $E_1(\tilde{\mu})$ is the sum of the information contained in $E_0(\tilde{\mu})$ and the information contained in $\bar{x}$.

Thus I_1 is *necessarily* greater than either I_0 or $I_{\bar{x}}$, and therefore

$$\sigma_1^2(\tilde{\mu}) = \frac{1}{I_1}$$

is *necessarily* less than either $\sigma_0^2(\tilde{\mu})$ or $\sigma^2(\bar{x})$.

The real reason why reciprocals of variances are called "quantities of information" in problems of the kind we are now studying is that in the simplest situations

$$\frac{1}{\sigma^2(\bar{x})} = \frac{n}{\sigma^2(\tilde{x})}$$

and it is natural to think of the quantity of information in a sample as being proportional to the number of observations in the sample.   It is by no means true, however, that the quantity of information in an $\bar{x}$ which is Normally distributed with known variance is *always* proportional to the sample size n.   We already know that in samples drawn without replacement from a finite population

$$I_{\bar{x}} = \frac{1}{\sigma^2(\bar{x})} = \frac{n}{\sigma^2(\tilde{x})} \frac{N-1}{N-n},$$

which means that each successive observation contributes *more* information than the previous one;† and in the next chapter we shall study a kind of situation in which each successive observation contributes *less* information than the previous one.   In any case, we remind the student most emphatically that

> It is *only* when the distribution of an estimate $\tilde{z}$ is *Normal with known variance* that the quantity of information in z is usefully measured by $1/\sigma^2(\tilde{z})$.

30.3.3   Disregard of Negligible Prior Information

Suppose now that the executive of our example had decided that his prior information was totally negligible in comparison with the informa-

---

† Let $\sigma^2(\tilde{x}) = 1, N = 3$.   Then there is 1 unit of information in a single observation, 4 units in two observations, and infinite information (perfect knowledge) in three observations.

tion obtained from 100 actual observations on the population whose mean was in question and had therefore set

$$I_0 = \frac{1}{\sigma_0^2(\tilde{\mu})} = 0.$$

The formulas for the parameters of the posterior distribution would then have reduced to

$$E_1(\tilde{\mu}) = \bar{x}$$
$$\sigma_1(\tilde{\mu}) = \sigma(\tilde{\bar{x}}) \qquad I_0 = 0$$

but the numerical values of these parameters would have scarcely been changed. Instead of the value 5.15 for $E_1(\tilde{\mu})$ we would have had 5.00, and instead of the value .69 for $\sigma_1(\tilde{\mu})$ we would have had .70.

In general, it is clear from the way in which the prior and sample informations enter the formulas for the parameters of the posterior distribution that even substantial percentage changes in $E_0(\tilde{\mu})$ will have little effect on the posterior distribution if I_0 is very small compared to $I_{\bar{x}}$ and that substantial percentage changes in I_0 will have little effect if the largest reasonable value for I_0 is small compared to $I_{\bar{x}}$. In such cases the person responsible for a decision will usually be justified in sparing himself the mental agony required for a careful assessment of $E_0(\tilde{\mu})$ and $\sigma_0(\tilde{\mu})$ and basing his posterior distribution entirely on the sample according to the reduced formulas given just above. We shall sometimes refer to such a procedure as adopting a Normal prior distribution with infinite standard deviation.†

"*Total Ignorance.*" Let us be careful, however, to treat this process of disregarding evidence which is *negligible in comparison with other evidence* as what it is and not as something nobler than this. Innumerable attempts have been made to treat the use of a prior distribution with $\sigma_0(\tilde{\mu}) = \infty$ as an "objective" expression of "total ignorance."‡ The argument runs that if we know nothing at all about the value of $\tilde{\mu}$, then all values *must* be equally likely; and a Normal prior distribution with $\sigma_0(\tilde{\mu}) = \infty$ in a certain sense assigns equal probability to all values of $\tilde{\mu}$. The argument is absurd, however, as can easily be seen. If "total ignorance" about $\tilde{\mu}$ implies that all values of $\tilde{\mu}$ are "equally likely," then total ignorance about $\tilde{\mu}^2$ must imply that all values of $\tilde{\mu}^2$ are equally likely.

† Strictly speaking a Normal distribution with infinite standard deviation does not exist because the area under such a curve would be infinite. The values of $E_1(\tilde{\mu})$ and $\sigma_1(\tilde{\mu})$ given by these reduced formulas really describe the *limit* approached by the posterior distribution as $\sigma_0(\tilde{\mu})$ becomes larger and larger.

‡ The assertion that we *should* use such a prior distribution when we are totally ignorant is known as Bayes' postulate. This "postulate" is to be sharply distinguished from Bayes' theorem.

Total ignorance about $\tilde{\mu}$ certainly implies total ignorance about $\tilde{\mu}^2$ and vice versa; but unfortunately it is simply impossible to assign equal probability to all values of $\tilde{\mu}$ and at the same time to assign equal probability to all values of $\tilde{\mu}^2$. Suppose, for example, that we say that it is just as likely that $\tilde{\mu}$ is between 0 and 1 as it is that $\tilde{\mu}$ is between 1 and 2. This necessarily implies that $\tilde{\mu}^2$ is as likely to be between 0 and 1 as it is to be between 1 and 4 and values of $\tilde{\mu}^2$ between 0 and 1 are therefore *three times* as likely on the average as values between 1 and 4.

Thus even if a person responsible for a decision feels himself to be in a state of total ignorance about the value of $\tilde{\mu}$, there is no "objective" way of assigning prior probabilities. He must make up his own mind—he must place his own bets—and when there is no sample evidence available, it is these bets which will be crucial for the decision. *Prior information or prior betting odds can be neglected only when substantial sample evidence is available.*

30.3.4 Nonnormal Prior Distributions

Now that we have seen that the exact *numerical values* of the parameters of the prior distribution are of little importance when $I_{\tilde{x}}$ is large, let us look briefly at the effect of the exact *shape* of the prior distribution on the posterior distribution when $I_{\tilde{x}}$ is large. In Figure 30.2a we show two contrasting prior distributions which we take as examples:

1. A *Normal* prior distribution with mean $E_0(\tilde{\mu}) = 1$ and standard deviation $\sigma_0(\tilde{\mu}) = 1$.
2. An *exponential* prior distribution with the same mean and standard deviation as the Normal.

The exponential distribution is about as violently nonnormal as any smooth distribution can be: it is J-shaped rather than symmetric, and it actually assigns 0 probability to all negative values of the random variable $\tilde{\mu}$.

In the remaining four graphs of Figure 30.2 we compare the *posterior* distributions corresponding to these two prior distributions after samples of four different sizes have been taken. In all four cases we assume that the observed value of the sample mean $\bar{x} = 1$ and that $\sigma^2(\tilde{x}) = 1/n$; it is only the sample size n that differs from case to case. In Figure 30.2b we see that if the sample consists of just one observation, there is a very substantial difference between the two posterior distributions; and in Figure 30.2c we see that the difference would still be quite large if $n = 4$. By the time $n = 9$, however, the difference is becoming much smaller (Figure 30.2d), and it is very small for $n = 25$ (Figure 30.2e). With a sample of 50 or more the difference would be completely negligible for almost all practical purposes.

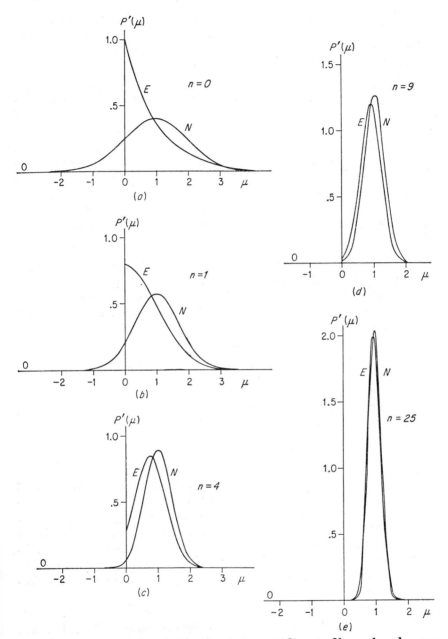

Figure 30.2. Posterior distributions corresponding to Normal and exponential prior distributions.

Although Figure 30.2 is only a study of a special case, the general nature of the conclusions derived from it can easily be seen to hold for *any* prior distribution which is reasonably smooth in the vicinity of the observed sample mean $\bar{x}$. Without trying to express the argument rigorously, we can suggest its nature as follows. The posterior probability that $\tilde{\mu}$ lies within any small interval or "bracket" is roughly proportional to *both* the prior probability of that bracket and the likelihood of $\bar{x}$ given the μ at the mid-point of the bracket. We know that the *likelihood* will be extremely small if the mid-point is more than $4\sigma(\bar{x})$, say, away from $\bar{x}$. As the sample size increases, $\sigma(\bar{x})$ decreases and therefore the likelihood factor restricts the bulk of the posterior probability to a narrower and narrower group of brackets on either side of $\bar{x}$. Ultimately the total width of this group of brackets becomes so small that the *prior* probability of every bracket in the group is virtually the same *regardless* of the shape of the prior distribution as a whole. We conclude that

If the variance of the decision maker's true prior distribution is large compared with the sampling variance of $\bar{x}$, he can simplify his calculations with no material loss of accuracy by substituting the mean and variance of his true prior distribution into the formulas which apply to a Normal prior distribution.

30.4   The Cost of Uncertainty in Two-action Problems with Linear Costs

In Section 18.2.3 we gave the formula for the partial expectation of a Normal random variable:

$$ \mathrm{E}^z_{-\infty}(\tilde{z}) = \mathrm{E}(\tilde{z})\, \mathrm{P}_N(\tilde{u} < u) - \sigma(\tilde{z})\, \mathrm{P}'_N(u), \qquad u = \frac{z - \mathrm{E}(\tilde{z})}{\sigma(\tilde{z})}, $$

and by its use obtained an extremely simple and convenient formula for the cost of uncertainty or expected value of perfect information in *many-action* problems with *proportional losses* when the basic random variable has a Normal distribution. We shall now derive an equally simple formula for the expected value of perfect information in *two-action* problems with *linear costs*, first deriving formulas which apply under any probability distribution and then specializing these to the case of a Normal distribution.

In Figure 30.3 we show the conditional costs and the probability distribution of the basic random variable $\tilde{\mu}$ for a problem of choice between act 1 and act 2. The linear conditional costs are

Conditional cost of act 1 $= K_1 + k_1\mu$,
Conditional cost of act 2 $= K_2 + k_2\mu$.

The two cost lines cross at the *break-even value* μ_b where either action is as good as the other. The probability distribution is of arbitrary shape, but it has been drawn so that its mean $E(\tilde{\mu})$ is *below* μ_b.

30.4.1 Expected Cost under Uncertainty

We already know that when the conditional cost of an act is linear, its expected cost is found by merely substituting $E(\tilde{\mu})$ for μ in the formula for the conditional cost. The proof of this assertion was given in Section 5.3.1, but we shall now restate it as background for our discussion of the value of perfect information.

The height of either cost line in Figure 30.3 above any particular μ on the horizontal axis corresponds to the entry in a payoff table for the

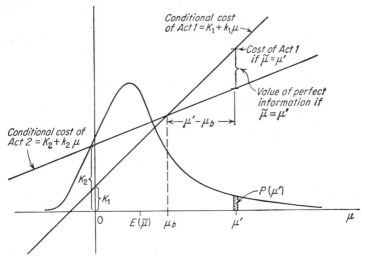

Figure 30.3. Two-action problem with linear costs.

act in question given the particular event $\tilde{\mu} = \mu$. When the probability distribution is continuous we cannot obtain the expected cost of an act by multiplying its conditional cost for *every* possible event or value of $\tilde{\mu}$ by the probability of that event and adding the products, but we can approximate the expected cost to any desired degree of accuracy by converting the continuous distribution into a grouped distribution in the way discussed in Section 30.3. Once this has been done, the expected cost is obtained by multiplying the conditional cost at the mid-point of each bracket by the probability of the bracket and adding the products.

For act 1 the sum obtained in this way can be written

$$\text{Expected cost of act } 1 = \Sigma_\mu (K_1 + k_1\mu)\, P(\mu),$$

where the symbol Σ_μ is an instruction to take every mid-point μ, compute the product $(K_1 + k_1\mu)\, P(\mu)$, and then add the products. Written out in full this summation would look exactly like Table 5.8; and by applying exactly the same reasoning which was used to derive Table 5.9 from Table 5.8 we can break the sum into two separate sums and factor out constant terms to obtain

$$\text{Expected cost of act } 1 = K_1 \Sigma_\mu \, \text{P}(\mu) + k_1 \Sigma_\mu \mu \, \text{P}(\mu).$$

Since the sum of products $\mu \, \text{P}(\mu)$ for all possible μ is by definition the expectation of $\tilde{\mu}$ and the sum of $\text{P}(\mu)$ for all possible μ is necessarily 1,† we may rewrite this result in the form

$$\text{Expected cost of act } 1 = K_1 + k_1 \, \text{E}(\tilde{\mu}).$$

Graphically, this means that the expected cost of either act is given by the ordinate of the conditional-cost line at the point $\mu = \text{E}(\tilde{\mu})$ on the horizontal axis. Since the cost line for act 1 in Figure 30.3 is lower than the line for act 2 at $\mu = \text{E}(\tilde{\mu})$, act 1 is the better act under uncertainty.

30.4.2   Conditional Value of Perfect Information

Assuming that the decision maker whose problem is represented by Figure 30.3 would be rational and choose act 1 if he acted under uncertainty, we now inquire what he would gain if he were given perfect information on μ before acting. Since the act chosen under uncertainty will also be the better act after the event if $\tilde{\mu}$ is *less* than μ_b, advance information that $\tilde{\mu}$ is in fact less than μ_b is worthless—it would have no effect on the decision maker's act. In other words, the *conditional value of perfect information is zero given any μ less than μ_b*. Advance information on the value of $\tilde{\mu}$ would, on the contrary, have real value if $\tilde{\mu} > \mu_b$, since in this case the information would lead the decision maker to choose act 2 instead of act 1 and save the difference in cost. In other words, *given any μ greater than μ_b, the conditional value of perfect information is equal to the difference between the ordinates of the two cost lines at that μ.*

To calculate the magnitude of this difference we start from the fact that the ordinates of the two cost lines are *equal* at the break-even value μ_b. For each unit that we move to the right of μ_b, the cost of act 1 increases by the amount k_1 while the cost of act 2 increases by only the lesser amount k_2, so that the difference between the costs at any point μ is $(k_1 - k_2)$ times the distance from μ_b to that point. Recalling that additional information is valueless if μ is less than μ_b, we have for the conditional value of perfect information

$$\text{Conditional VPI} = \begin{cases} 0 & \textit{if } \mu < \mu_b, \\ \\ (k_1 - k_2)(\mu - \mu_b) & \textit{if } \mu > \mu_b, \end{cases} \qquad \text{E}(\tilde{\mu}) < \mu_b.$$

† Strictly speaking, these statements are true of the limits approached by the two sums as the brackets become narrower and narrower.

The Loss Constant k_t. This formula as it stands would be rather tricky to apply in practice, since it applies only if we use the name act 1 for the act whose cost line has the greater slope. If we reversed the *names* of the acts in Figure 30.3 and with them the meanings of k_1 and k_2, act 2 would be the better act under uncertainty and the conditional value of perfect information would be $(k_2 - k_1)(\mu - \mu_b)$ instead of $(k_1 - k_2)(\mu - \mu_b)$. To get out of this difficulty we define the *loss constant*

$$k_t = |k_1 - k_2|$$

as the *absolute value*† of the difference between the two slopes and rewrite our previous result in the form

$$\text{Conditional VPI} = \begin{cases} 0 & \textit{if } \mu < \mu_b, \\ k_t(\mu - \mu_b) & \textit{if } \mu > \mu_b, \end{cases} \qquad \text{E}(\tilde{\mu}) < \mu_b.$$

Observe that *this formula for the conditional value of perfect information applies just as well when the problem is stated in terms of profit as when it is stated in terms of cost.* For suppose that the two straight lines in Figure 30.3 represent the conditional profits of the two acts rather than their conditional costs. With $\text{E}(\tilde{\mu})$ less than μ_b a reasonable man will now choose act 2 under uncertainty because it has the higher expected profit but the value of perfect information will be exactly the same as in our original problem where he chose act 1 because it had the lower expected cost. Information that $\tilde{\mu}$ is in fact *less* than μ_b will still be valueless because it will not affect the choice of the act and information that $\tilde{\mu}$ is in fact *greater* than μ_b will again alter the act and will increase profit by the same amount that it previously reduced cost, i.e. by the amount $|k_1 - k_2|(\mu - \mu_b)$.

It is left to the student to show that if the probability distribution of Figure 30.3 is replaced by one whose mean $\text{E}(\tilde{\mu})$ is to the *right* of (greater than) μ_b, then whether the figure represents cost or profit

$$\text{Conditional VPI} = \begin{cases} k_t(\mu_b - \mu) & \textit{if } \mu < \mu_b, \\ 0 & \textit{if } \mu > \mu_b, \end{cases} \qquad \text{E}(\tilde{\mu}) > \mu_b.$$

30.4.3   Expected Value of Perfect Information

Under a discrete distribution the *expected* value of perfect information or cost of uncertainty is computed by multiplying the conditional value

---

† The "absolute-value signs" $|\ \ |$ in the definition of k_t are an instruction to take any quantity between them as positive regardless of its algebraic sign. Thus $|-3| = +3$; $|2 - 6| = +4$. Observe carefully, however, that algebraic signs are *not* to be neglected in performing computations *inside* the absolute-value signs. If $k_1 = +2$ and $k_2 = -5$, then $k_t = |(+2) - (-5)| = |+2 + 5| = |+7| = +7$.

for each possible μ by the probability of that μ and adding the products; under a continuous distribution we proceed in the same way except that we must again first cut the μ axis into brackets and assign all the probability in each bracket to the μ at the mid-point.

When $E(\tilde{\mu})$ is less than μ_b, as it is in Figure 30.3, the conditional values and therefore the products are 0 for all μ to the left of μ_b; the summing operation has actually to be carried out only for the μ to the right of μ_b. The product for the typical μ' shown in Figure 30.3 is $k_t(\mu' - \mu_b) \, P(\mu')$, and summing over all μ we obtain as the expected value of perfect information

$$\text{Expected VPI} \; = \; \sum_{\mu=\mu_b}^{\infty} k_t(\mu - \mu_b) \, P(\mu), \qquad E(\tilde{\mu}) < \mu_b.$$

Breaking this expression up in the same way that we broke up the expression for the expected cost of act 1 in Section 30.4.1, we have

$$\text{Expected VPI} \; = \; k_t \left[\sum_{\mu=\mu_b}^{\infty} \mu \, P(\mu) - \mu_b \sum_{\mu=\mu_b}^{\infty} P(\mu) \right], \qquad E(\tilde{\mu}) < \mu_b.$$

The first of the sums inside the brackets is the partial expectation of $\tilde{\mu}$ over the interval μ_b to ∞, the second is the total probability of all μ greater than μ_b, and therefore we may write

$$\text{Expected VPI} \; = \; k_t [E_{\mu_b}^{\infty}(\tilde{\mu}) - \mu_b \, P(\tilde{\mu} \geq \mu_b)] \qquad E(\tilde{\mu}) < \mu_b$$

It is left to the student to show by similar reasoning that when $E(\tilde{\mu})$ is *greater* than μ_b

$$\text{Expected VPI} \; = \; k_t [\mu_b \, P(\tilde{\mu} \leq \mu_b) - E_{-\infty}^{\mu_b}(\tilde{\mu})] \qquad E(\tilde{\mu}) > \mu_b$$

30.4.4   *Value of Perfect Information When the Distribution Is Normal*

The formulas which we have just obtained apply under *any* probability distribution whatever, and the probabilities and partial expectations involved could always be obtained by the graphical and arithmetical methods described in Chapter 6. If, however, the probability distribution is Normal, the computational labor can be greatly reduced by use of the formula for a Normal partial expectation and tables of the unit Normal distribution.

Taking first the case when $E(\tilde{\mu})$ is *less* than μ_b, we put the break-even value μ_b in standard measure by defining

$$u_b = \frac{\mu_b - E(\tilde{\mu})}{\sigma(\tilde{\mu})}.$$

The probability in the formula given above for the expected value of perfect information when $E(\tilde{\mu}) < \mu_b$ can then be written

$$P(\tilde{\mu} \geq \mu_b) = P_N(\tilde{u} > u_b).$$

Using the formula for $E^{\mu_b}_{-\infty}(\tilde{\mu})$ under a Normal distribution and remembering that $P(\tilde{u} < u) = 1 - P(\tilde{u} > u)$ we can evaluate

$$E^{\infty}_{\mu_b}(\tilde{\mu}) = E(\tilde{\mu}) - E^{\mu_b}_{-\infty}(\tilde{\mu}) = E(\tilde{\mu}) - E(\tilde{\mu}) \, P_N(\tilde{u} < u_b) + \sigma(\tilde{\mu}) \, P'_N(u_b)$$
$$= E(\tilde{\mu}) \, P_N(\tilde{u} > u_b) + \sigma(\tilde{\mu}) \, P'_N(u_b).$$

Substituting these two results in the formula for the value of perfect information when $E(\tilde{\mu}) < \mu_b$ and regrouping terms we obtain

$$\text{Expected VPI} = k_t \sigma(\tilde{\mu}) \left[P'_N(u_b) - \frac{\mu_b - E(\tilde{\mu})}{\sigma(\tilde{\mu})} P_N(\tilde{u} > u_b) \right]$$
$$= k_t \sigma(\tilde{\mu}) G(u_b), \qquad E(\tilde{\mu}) < \mu_b,$$

where $G(u)$ is the function tabulated in Table IV.

Taking next the case when $E(\tilde{\mu})$ is *greater* than μ_b we could again obtain the value of perfect information by algebraic operations, but it will be much more instructive to make use of the symmetry of the Normal curve. Figures 30.4a and b show two problems with the same conditional costs as Figure 30.3 but different probability distributions. Both distributions in Figure 30.4 are Normal and both have the same standard deviation $\sigma(\tilde{\mu})$; the only difference is that *the mean $E(\tilde{\mu})$ in Figure 30.4b is exactly as far above μ_b as the mean in Figure 30.4a is* below μ_b.

The expected value of perfect information in Figure 30.4a will be a sum of products of type $k_t(\mu - \mu_b) \, P(\mu)$ for all μ to the right of μ_b and the expected value in Figure 30.4b will be a sum of products of type $k_t(\mu_b - \mu) \, P(\mu)$ for all μ to the left of μ_b. We consider any typical value μ' in Figure 30.4a and choose a μ'' in Figure 30.4b such that the distance $\mu' - \mu_b$ is equal to the distance $\mu_b - \mu''$; this means that the distance $\mu' - E(\tilde{\mu})$ is also equal to the distance $E(\tilde{\mu}) - \mu''$. It is obvious that the *conditional values* are equal,

$$k_t(\mu' - \mu_b) = k_t(\mu_b - \mu'');$$

and the symmetry of the Normal curve means that the probabilities are also equal:

$$P(\mu') = P(\mu'').$$

Consequently the products are equal,

$$k_t(\mu' - \mu_b) \, \mathrm{P}(\mu') = k_t(\mu_b - \mu'') \, \mathrm{P}(\mu'');$$

and since every μ above μ_b in Figure 30.4a can be exactly matched in this way by a μ below μ_b in Figure 30.4b, the expected values of perfect information are exactly equal in the two cases.

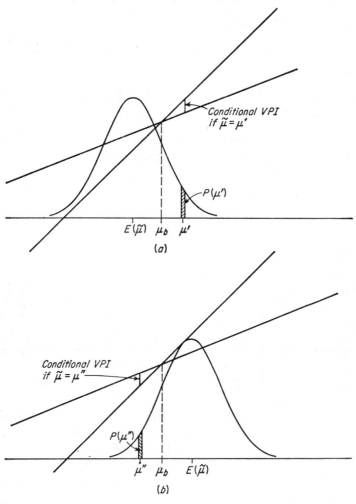

Figure 30.4

We conclude that in any two-action problem with linear costs the expected value of perfect information under a Normal distribution depends on the *absolute magnitude* of the difference between $\mathrm{E}(\tilde{\mu})$ and μ_b but not on its direction or algebraic sign. We therefore define

$$D = \frac{|\mu_b - E(\tilde{\mu})|}{\sigma(\tilde{\mu})} \qquad \textit{Definition of } D$$

and obtain the expected value of perfect information for *any* $E(\tilde{\mu})$ by simply writing D instead of u_b in the formula previously derived for the case where $E(\tilde{\mu}) < \mu_b$:

Expected VPI or cost of uncertainty $= k_t \sigma(\tilde{\mu}) G(D)$
Two-action problem, linear costs, Normal distribution

Example. In the marketing problem we have been using as an example, suppose that it would cost \$500,000 to tool up for quantity production of the new product and that competitive conditions are such that it would have to be priced to yield a margin of \$3.87 above total variable cost. Since μ is defined as average sales *per potential customer* and there are 20,000 potential customers, total unit sales will be $20,000\mu$, total contribution to overhead will be \$3.87 $\times$ $20,000\mu$ = \$77,400 μ, and subtracting out the cost of tooling up we have

Conditional profit of production $= -\$500,000 + \$77,400\ \mu.$

The alternative act is, of course, to do nothing, and obviously

Conditional profit of "do nothing" $= \$0 + \$0\ \mu.$

The loss constant is

$$k_t = |k_1 - k_2| = |\$77,400 - \$0| = \$77,400$$

and the break-even value is given by

$$-\$500,000 + \$77,400\ \mu_b = \$0,$$
$$\mu_b = \frac{\$500,000}{\$77,400} = 6.46.$$

Under the *prior* distribution of Section 30.2.3 with $E_0(\tilde{\mu}) = 8$ and $\sigma_0(\tilde{\mu}) = 3$, the expected profit of a decision to go into production is

$$-\$500,000 + \$77,400\ E_0(\tilde{\mu}) = -\$500,000 + (\$77,400 \times 8)$$
$$= +\$119,200$$

and this is the better act because the expected profit of "do nothing" is obviously \$0. Even the better act under uncertainty involves risk, however, and to evaluate the extent of this risk we compute

$$D_0 = \frac{|\mu_b - E_0(\tilde{\mu})|}{\sigma_0(\tilde{\mu})} = \frac{|6.46 - 8.00|}{3} = |-.51| = .51,$$

use Table IV to find $G(.51) = .1947$, and finally compute

$$\text{Prior cost of uncertainty} = k_t \sigma_0(\tilde{\mu})G(D_0) = \$77,400 \times 3 \times .1947$$
$$= \$45,200.$$

While production is the better act and promises a substantial profit of $119,200, the risk is $45,200 and very serious.

Under the *posterior* distribution of Section 30.3.1 with $E_1(\tilde{\mu}) = 5.15$ and $\sigma_1(\tilde{\mu}) = .69$, the expected profit of a decision to produce is *negative*, since

$$-\$500,000 + (\$77,400 \times 5.15) = -\$101,400,$$

and it is better *not* to produce. To find the risk involved in a decision to drop the entire matter at this point we compute

$$D_1 = \frac{|6.46 - 5.15|}{.69} = 1.90,$$
$$G(D_1) = .01105,$$
$$\text{Posterior cost of uncertainty} = \$77,400 \times .69 \times .01105 = \$590.$$

Unless further sampling is extremely cheap, it is clearly best to consider the matter closed and write off the development of the new product as a total loss.

PROBLEM

1. Mar-Pruf Finishes, Inc., was a relatively small firm operating in a segment of the industrial-finishes market which was dominated by the American Paint and Lacquer Company. Mar-Pruf's research chemists had recently developed a product to compete with American's type A-1 lacquer and the company was trying to decide whether or not to put this product on the market. Some preliminary market research had shown that while some firms considered the new Mar-Pruf product to be superior to American's A-1, the difference was not great enough to permit Mar-Pruf to charge a price appreciably higher than American's price of $8.75 per gallon. On the other hand, any attempt to seize American's market by charging a lower price was almost certain to produce a price war which American was sure to win because of its superior financial resources. It was clear that if the product was to be marketed at all it would have to be marketed at a price of $8.75 per gallon.

Mar-Pruf figured that if it installed the necessary equipment for economical manufacture of the new product it could realize a net contribution (selling price less variable cost of production, selling, and delivery) amounting to about $.40 per gallon; and after considering the amount of time during which a customer could be expected to continue buying the product, Mar-Pruf's management had decided that the discounted present value of the whole stream of future contributions to be expected from a customer who was initially sold on the new product would be about $2 for each gallon-per-year of initial sales. In other words: Mar-Pruf "expected" to realize contributions with a present value of $20 from a customer who started buying at a rate of 10 gallons per year, $50 from a customer who started buying at a rate of 25 gallons per year, and so forth.

Mar-Pruf's hesitation about entering the market with this new product arose from the fact that the total cost of installing and debugging the necessary equipment for volume manufacture plus the cost of the required introductory sales effort would amount to about $600,000, so that unless a sales volume of $600,000/$2 = 300,000 gallons per year could be attained, the introduction of the product would result in a net loss. Mar-Pruf's market research had shown that there were about 10,000 firms who could be considered potential customers for the product, so that the break-even point could also be considered as achieving annual sales averaging 30 gallons per firm. Because of the considerable risk involved in the decision, Mar-Pruf's marketing-research department had drawn a sample of 100 of these 10,000 firms in such a way that each firm had an equal chance of being drawn and had then dispatched salesmen to give free samples of the product to these firms and to ask whether they would buy if it were actually placed on the market and if so how much per year. The results of this survey are shown in simplified form in the table below.

Annual purchase rate	Number of firms
0	60
60	10
90	20
120	10

a. Use the data obtained from the pilot sample to estimate the standard deviation of the population of annual purchase rates. (Each firm's individual annual purchase rate is one member of this population.)

b. Using $\tilde{\mu}$ to denote the mean annual purchases per firm, assess a Normal distribution for $\tilde{\mu}$ which is reasonable in the light of the evidence of the pilot sample, previous evidence being disregarded as negligible.

c. Decide whether Mar-Pruf should or should not go into production if action is to be based on the pilot sample alone, and compute the risk involved in making this decision on this evidence.

d. Recompute part *c* assuming that, before taking the consumer survey, Mar-Pruf management had done its best to assess the market potential and had decided that the most likely average sales rate was 50 gallons per customer per year but that there was only a 50-50 chance that this estimate was within plus or minus 20 units of the true figure.

CHAPTER 31

Biased Measurement and Biased Selection

Our entire discussion of the use of the information summarized by a sample mean has up to now always been based on the assumption that

> If the process by which the sample was obtained were repeated over and over, the average of the means of all the samples thus obtained would be exactly equal to the true value of the random variable which will determine cost or profit.

We shall now examine this crucial assumption more critically and shall find that it is often unwarranted. It would be even closer to the truth to say that the assumption is *never* strictly correct although sometimes it is close enough to the facts to warrant its use as a basis for practical business decisions.

31.1 Measurement Bias: Systematic Error vs. Sampling Error

As a first concrete example of the way in which this assumption may be violated, let us take the problem of measuring the X content of a batch of raw material which we discussed in Chapter 26. The basic random variable in that problem was

ξ: the true X content of a particular batch of raw material,

and our whole procedure for computing the posterior distribution of ξ and thus the posterior expected costs of the two acts under consideration depended on the assumption that *if an infinite number of measurements x were made on this batch, the mean μ of these measurements would be exactly equal to the true X content ξ of the batch.*

31.1.1   Systematic Error

This assumption was justified in Chapter 26 because it agreed with the results of a long and careful investigation of the errors previously generated by the measuring process in question, but it is clear that in many if not most situations an assumption of this sort will *not* be justified. We will, on the contrary, feel quite sure that the mean μ of an infinite number of measurements would *not* be exactly equal to the true value of the quantity being measured, and we therefore define the

> *Systematic* error or "bias" of a measuring *process:* the difference between the true value ξ of the quantity measured and the mean μ of the measurements which would be obtained if the process were applied to this quantity an infinite number of times.

If we use the letter beta to denote the systematic error or bias of a process, this definition can be written more concisely in the form

$$\beta = \mu - \xi;$$

or we can think of the mean of the measuring process as the sum of the true value ξ plus the systematic error β:

$$\mu = \xi + \beta \qquad \textit{Definition of bias or systematic error}$$

31.1.2   Sampling Error

The bias or systematic error of a measuring *process* must be sharply distinguished from what we shall now call the pure

> *Sampling* error of an *individual measurement:* the difference between an individual measurement x and the mean μ of an infinite number of measurements made by the *same process* under the *same conditions.*

Observe very carefully that this definition does not even mention the true value of the quantity being measured. If we use ϵ to denote the sampling error of an individual measurement, the definition can be written

$$\epsilon = x - \mu;$$

or we can think of any individual measurement as the sum of the process mean μ plus the individual error ϵ:

$$x = \mu + \epsilon \qquad \textit{Definition of sampling error}$$

The sampling error ϵ is the *only* kind of error we have considered hitherto.

31.1.3   The Composition of a Measurement

We saw in Section 31.1.1 that the process mean μ can itself be regarded as the sum of the true value ξ plus the bias β. Substituting

$\xi + \beta$ for μ in the last formula above we obtain a formula which shows the *three component parts of any individual measurement:*

$$x = \xi + \beta + \epsilon \qquad \text{\textit{Composition of any measurement}}$$

In words rather than symbols, any measurement can be regarded as the sum of (1) the true value of the measured quantity, (2) the systematic error or bias which would be present in the mean of an *infinite number* of measurements, and (3) the sampling error peculiar to the *individual* measurement.

31.1.4 The Composition of a Sample Mean

Suppose now that we use a measuring process with bias β to make n separate measurements of the same true quantity ξ and compute the mean $\bar{x}$ of these measurements. The computation is represented symbolically in Table 31.1, and two facts are immediately apparent. (1) Because ξ and the systematic error β are constant throughout the series of measurements, they appear unchanged in the average. (2) The

Table 31.1

Serial number	Value x of the measurement
1	$\xi + \beta + \epsilon_1$
2	$\xi + \beta + \epsilon_2$
. . . .	
n	$\xi + \beta + \epsilon_n$
Total	$n\xi + n\beta + \Sigma\epsilon$
Average	$\xi + \beta + \bar{\epsilon}$

sampling errors ϵ, on the contrary, vary from each measurement to the next and what appears in the average is their mean $\bar{\epsilon}$. Symbolically, then,

---

$$\bar{x} = \xi + \beta + \bar{\epsilon} \qquad \text{\textit{Composition of any sample mean}}$$

In words rather than symbols,

Any sample mean can be regarded as the sum of (1) the *true value* of the quantity measured, (2) the *fixed systematic error* or bias of the measuring process, and (3) the *mean of the sampling errors* of the individual observations in the sample.

31.1.5 Populations of True Values vs. Populations of Measurements

In our chemical example the cost of an act depended on the true value ξ of a *single* batch of material; the only "population" involved in the problem was the infinite population of measurements of ξ which the measuring process "could" generate.   In other situations the cost or profit of an act depends on the *mean* of a whole *population of true values*, and we must now distinguish clearly between this population and the population of measurements which "could" be generated by a sampling process.

As an example, let us reconsider the marketing problem which we analyzed in the last chapter.   Profit in this problem depended on the average number of units of a product which would be purchased by each of 20,000 potential customers after the product was put in quantity production and sold in the normal way; information on this average was obtained by drawing 100 of these potential customers and seeing how many hand-made units each one of them actually bought when approached in the course of the sampling procedure.   In order to make the nature of measurement bias in such a problem concrete, let us think of every one of the 20,000 potential customers as represented by a card on which *two* numbers are written:

1. The number of units which that customer would *actually* buy if the product were put in *regular* production and offered for sale in the regular way.   Each of these numbers is a *true value* and we shall denote their mean by

ξ: mean of the population of individual *true values*.

2. The number of units of the hand-made product which that same customer would be *recorded* as buying if he were drawn in the sample and *specially* approached in the course of the marketing-research project. These numbers constitute a population of *potential sample measurements* x and we shall denote their mean by

μ: mean of the population of individual potential *measurements*.

Our original analysis of this problem rested on the assumption that *the mean μ of the population of* 20,000 *potential sample measurements was exactly equal to the mean ξ of the population of* 20,000 *potential purchases under normal conditions*, and it is obvious that this assumption may well be in disagreement with the facts.   To give just two of many possible reasons, the quality of the hand-made product offered to the sample customers may be noticeably different from the quality which can be maintained in the mass-produced product, and each customer may be much more effectively sold when there are only 100 customers to sell than when there are 20,000.   Either cause can produce a substantial difference between (1) the mean sales μ which would result if all 20,000 customers were treated exactly like the 100 sample customers and (2) the mean sales ξ which will actually be realized if the company goes into production.   We shall call the difference $\beta = \mu - \xi$ the *measurement bias* of this sampling procedure.   In most surveys carried out to estimate the market for a new product there is a source of measurement bias which is far more serious than either of the two we have just suggested.   The sampling procedure usually consists in simply *asking* the sample members how many units they think they would buy *if* the product were offered for sale, and it is obvious that the difference β between (1) the mean μ of the *answers which the whole population would give* if asked this question and (2) the mean ξ of the *quantities which would in fact be purchased* may be very serious indeed.

Even though the cost-determining quantity ξ in problems like these is the mean of a population rather than a single, fixed quantity as in our chemical example, the formula

$$x = \xi + \beta + \epsilon$$

for the composition of any sample measurement or observation still applies and has exactly the same meaning as before.   The bias β is the difference between the mean μ of all possible observations and the true value ξ which will determine cost or profit, and the sampling error ϵ is still the difference between μ and the value of an individual sample observation.†   It follows that our previous result for a sample *mean*

$$\bar{x} = \xi + \beta + \bar{\epsilon}$$

also applies in problems where ξ is the mean of a population of true values rather than the true value of a single "thing."

31.2   The Use of Information from a Biased Sample

The basic procedure by which we have hitherto made use of the information in a sample mean consists of three steps:

1. Compute the likelihood of $\bar{x}$ given every possible value of the basic random variable ξ;
2. Multiply the prior probability of each ξ by the likelihood of $\bar{x}$ given that ξ;
3. Divide each of these joint probabilities by their total.

The logic underlying these steps as set forth in Chapter 21 applies just as well when we know or suspect that $\bar{x}$ contains both bias β and sampling error $\bar{\epsilon}$ as it does when we know or assume that it contains only sampling error.   The only effect of known or suspected bias is on the details of the procedure by which we compute the likelihoods in step 1.

---

† Notice that the difference between (1) the *true value* of an *individual* member of the population and (2) the mean ξ of these true values is completely irrelevant to our problem and nowhere enters our discussion.   The *only* thing about the true values which is relevant is their mean ξ.

In some situations the amount of the bias or systematic error β will be *known*, and in this case the distribution of $\tilde{x}$ for any given ξ will be given by the formula

$$\tilde{x} = \xi + \beta + \tilde{\bar{\epsilon}},$$

where the only random variable on the right side is the mean sampling error $\tilde{\bar{\epsilon}}$. In other situations the amount of the bias will be *unknown* so that we must also treat $\tilde{\beta}$ as a random variable and write

$$\tilde{x} = \xi + \tilde{\beta} + \tilde{\bar{\epsilon}}.$$

Starting with the simpler of the two cases, that of known bias, our first step is to study the sampling distribution of the random variable $\tilde{\bar{\epsilon}}$.

31.2.1   Assessment of the Distribution of $\tilde{\bar{\epsilon}}$

Mean and Variance of the Individual Errors $\tilde{\epsilon}$. We have defined an *individual* sampling error $\epsilon = x - \mu$ as the difference between an individual measurement x and the mean μ of either (1) the infinite number of measurements which "could" be made by a measuring process *under constant conditions* (Section 31.1.1) or (2) an entire finite population of potential measurements made by a sampling process operating *under constant conditions* (Section 31.1.5). Figure 31.1a shows the frequency distribution of such a population (infinite or finite) of potential x's, and Figure 31.1b shows the frequency distribution of the corresponding population of potential ϵ's. Part a of the figure can also be interpreted as the probability distribution of the random variable $\tilde{x}$ representing the value of one individual measurement "drawn" from the population of potential measurements; part b can also be interpreted as the probability distribution of the random variable $\tilde{\epsilon}$ representing the value of one individual sampling error "drawn" from the population of potential errors. The mean $\mu = E(\tilde{x})$ of the population of x's shown in part a of the figure is the sum of *some* fixed value ξ of the quantity being measured and *some* fixed value β of the bias of the measuring or sampling process, but for our present purposes we are not interested in these values as such; all that we care about is that

> The measurements are made under conditions such that the *sum* $\mu = \xi + \beta$ is *fixed;* in other words, the measurements are drawn from a *single, fixed* population of potential x's with mean μ.

The two important things to observe about the relation between the distribution of $\tilde{x}$ and the distribution of $\tilde{\epsilon}$ are these:

1. Because each ϵ is *defined* as the difference between an individual x and the mean μ of the fixed population of x's, *the mean of the ϵ's is 0 by definition and in absolutely all circumstances.*

2. In all other respects the distribution of $\bar{\epsilon}$ is *identical* to the distribution of $\bar{x}$ *for a fixed* μ. In particular, the *variance of* $\bar{\epsilon}$ is equal to the variance of $\bar{x}$ *given a specified* μ.

Since the distributions of $\bar{x}$ with which we dealt in previous chapters were all distributions *for some given* μ, we see that the problem of assessing the variance of $\bar{\epsilon}$ is really just an old problem expressed in a new notation. If

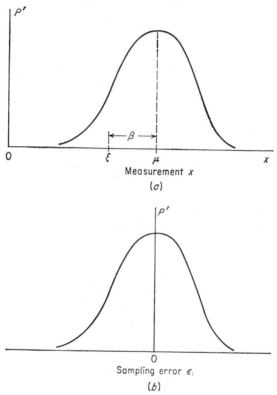

Figure 31.1

we make a number of measurements on a single, *fixed* true value ξ under conditions such that the bias β of the measuring process remains *constant*, then we may say that the process mean $\mu = \xi + \beta$ was *fixed* during the series of measurements and we may use these measurements as data for assessment of the variance of $\bar{\epsilon}$. If the number of measurements is so great that we may take their mean $\bar{x}$ as essentially equal to the true μ of the process, we may compute

$$\sigma^2(\bar{\epsilon}) = \frac{1}{n}\Sigma(x - \mu)^2.$$

If we do *not* have a large enough number of measurements made under constant conditions (*fixed* μ) to justify us in treating their mean $\bar{x}$ as certainly equal to μ, then we may *estimate* the variance of $\bar{\epsilon}$ in the same way that we have always estimated the variance of $\bar{x}$ *for fixed* μ:

$$\sigma^2(\bar{\epsilon}) \doteq s^2 = \frac{1}{n-1} \Sigma(x - \bar{x})^2.$$

This estimate of $\sigma^2(\bar{\epsilon})$ has $f = n - 1$ degrees of freedom, and when f is large the estimate may be treated as if it were the known true value of $\sigma^2(\bar{\epsilon})$.

For the meaning of "large," the student should review Section 29.4.

While it is true that most of the present discussion of the assessment of the variance of $\bar{\epsilon}$ is simply a restatement in different notation of the discussion in Section 29.4, there is one new point to which the student must pay the most careful attention. We may *not* simply assume that the mean $\mu = \xi + \beta$ of a measuring process had the same value during the making of any given set of measurements *simply* because all the measurements were made on the *same true value* ξ. We must also check to make sure that all the measurements in the set were made under *constant conditions*.

If the conditions under which the measuring process operated were *not* constant, then the bias β may have varied even though the true value ξ remained constant; and if this is true, then the "estimate" s^2 will tend to *overstate* the true sampling variance $\sigma^2(\bar{\epsilon})$ because the x's from which s^2 is computed will contain variation due to variation in bias as well as variation due to pure sampling error.

Distribution of the Mean Sampling Error $\bar{\bar{\epsilon}}$. We saw in Table 31.1 that the pure sampling error of a *sample mean*,

$$\bar{\epsilon} = \bar{x} - \mu,$$

can be regarded as the mean of a number of individual sampling errors; and we have just seen that these individual sampling errors can be regarded as having been drawn from a population of potential ϵ's with mean $E(\epsilon) = 0$ and variance $\sigma^2(\bar{\epsilon})$. It follows at once that the mean and variance of the sampling distribution of $\bar{\bar{\epsilon}}$ can be determined by exactly the same reasoning that we used in Section 25.5 to determine the mean and variance of the mean $\bar{x}$ of a number of x's drawn from a population of x's. Just as we did for the x's in Section 25.5,

We assume in what follows that the sampling of the ϵ's is simple— i.e., that the ϵ's drawn from an *infinite* population are *independent* or that every ϵ remaining in a *finite* population has an *equal chance* of occurring as each successive measurement is made.

Our conclusions will in general be invalid if this assumption is violated, although we shall see in Section 31.4.1 that one particular kind of violation can be dealt with by introducing the concept of "selection bias" in addition to the "measurement bias" defined in Section 31.1 above.

Expectation of $\bar{\tilde{\epsilon}}$. Since the mean $\mathrm{E}(\tilde{\epsilon})$ of any *individual* sampling error drawn by simple sampling is 0 by definition and since the expected value of a sum of random variables is the sum of their individual expected values, the expected value of the *total* of the individual ϵ's in any sample is 0 and therefore the expected value of the *mean* of these ϵ's is 0:

$$\mathrm{E}(\bar{\tilde{\epsilon}}) = 0 \qquad Any\ population\ of\ \epsilon\text{'s, simple sampling}$$

Variance of $\bar{\tilde{\epsilon}}$. If the ϵ's in a sample are drawn by simple sampling from an *infinite* population of potential ϵ's (such as the population of ϵ's which "could" be generated by a chemical measuring process), then the ϵ's in the sample are *independent* and the addition theorem for variances (Section 16.3) applies. The variance of the sum of the individual $\tilde{\epsilon}$'s in a sample is the sum of their individual variances or $n\sigma^2(\tilde{\epsilon})$, the distribution of the mean $\bar{\tilde{\epsilon}}$ of these individual errors is the same as the distribution of their sum except that the scale is changed by the factor $1/n$, and therefore (Section 16.5.2) the variance of $\bar{\tilde{\epsilon}}$ is $(1/n)^2$ times the variance of the sum:

$$\sigma^2(\bar{\tilde{\epsilon}}) = \frac{1}{n}\sigma^2(\tilde{\epsilon}) \qquad Infinite\ population\ of\ \epsilon\text{'s, simple sampling}$$

If a sample of ϵ's is drawn without replacement from a *finite* population of potential ϵ's (such as the one discussed in Section 31.1.5), the ϵ's in the sample cannot be independent for the reason discussed in Section 23.1.1; but if the sampling is simple this interdependence is completely accounted for by the so-called "finite-population correction" (Section 25.5) and

$$\sigma^2(\bar{\tilde{\epsilon}}) = \frac{1}{n}\sigma^2(\tilde{\epsilon})\frac{N-n}{N-1} \qquad Finite\ population\ of\ \epsilon\text{'s, simple sampling}$$

Shape of the Distribution of $\bar{\tilde{\epsilon}}$. In most practical situations the exact shape of the distribution of an *individual* sampling error $\tilde{\epsilon}$ will be known very imperfectly for the same reason that the shape of the distribution of an individual measurement $\tilde{x}$ is ordinarily known very imperfectly: it takes a very great amount of historical frequency data to establish these shapes exactly. On the other hand the Central limit theorem applies to the distribution of a *mean* sampling error $\bar{\tilde{\epsilon}}$ just as it applies to any other mean of a number of random variables, and it follows that

> The distribution of $\bar{\tilde{\epsilon}}$ in "large" samples will often be almost exactly Normal even though the distributions of the individual $\tilde{\epsilon}$'s are quite far from Normal.

For the meaning of "large," the student should review Section 29.3.1.

31.2.2   The Distribution of $\bar{\tilde{x}}$ When β Is Known and $\bar{\tilde{\epsilon}}$ Is Normal

Suppose now that we have calibrated a measuring process by making a number of measurements under constant conditions on each of several different true values ξ and suppose that the number of measurements made on each ξ individually was large enough to allow us to treat their mean $\bar{x}$ as equal to the true long-run mean μ of the measuring process as applied to that ξ. Suppose further that this investigation has shown that

1. The difference $\mu - \xi$ was the same for every ξ, so that we are entitled to say that the *bias* $\beta = \mu - \xi$ of the process as applied to any future ξ is *known*.
2. The variance of the *individual* sampling errors $\tilde{\epsilon} = \tilde{x} - \mu$ was the same regardless of the ξ to which the process was applied, so that we can say that the *sampling variance* $\sigma^2(\tilde{\epsilon})$ of the process as applied to any future ξ is *known*.
3. The number of measurements to be made on a new, unknown ξ is large enough to permit the distribution of the *mean sampling error* $\bar{\tilde{\epsilon}}$ to be treated as Normal.

Because the bias β is known, the distribution of the mean $\bar{\tilde{x}}$ of the measurements to be made on the new ξ is given by the model

$$\bar{\tilde{x}} = \xi + \beta + \bar{\tilde{\epsilon}}$$

and the distribution of $\bar{\tilde{x}}$ is therefore the same as the distribution of $\bar{\tilde{\epsilon}}$ except for a change of location. Applying the rules of Section 16.5.1 and remembering that $E(\bar{\tilde{\epsilon}}) = 0$ by definition, we have for the mean and variance of $\bar{\tilde{x}}$:

$$E(\bar{\tilde{x}}) = \xi + \beta + E(\bar{\tilde{\epsilon}}) = \xi + \beta,$$
$$\sigma^2(\bar{\tilde{x}}) = \sigma^2(\bar{\tilde{\epsilon}});$$

and because the distribution of $\bar{\tilde{\epsilon}}$ is Normal,

> The distribution of $\bar{\tilde{x}}$ is Normal.

Computation of Likelihoods. The fact that β is known means that the values of $E(\bar{\tilde{x}})$ and $\sigma(\bar{\tilde{x}})$ as given by these formulas are known once ξ

has been specified, and therefore the likelihood of any observed $\bar{x}$ given any specified ξ can be computed from the usual formula

$$P(\bar{x}|\xi) = \frac{\delta\bar{x}}{\sigma(\bar{x})} P'_N(u), \qquad u = \frac{\bar{x} - E(\bar{x})}{\sigma(\bar{x})}.$$

31.2.3 Unknown Bias: Assessment of the Distribution of $\tilde{\beta}$

We now come to our one really new problem, that of obtaining the distribution of $\bar{x}$ when the bias of the measuring or sampling process is *not* known and must therefore be treated as a random variable; and the first step in the analysis is of course to assign a probability distribution to this new random variable $\tilde{\beta}$. The problems involved in this assessment are no different in principle from the problems involved in assessing the distribution of any other random variable. In some situations there will be a record of the actual values of $\tilde{\beta}$ on previous occasions and we will be able to fit a probability distribution to the historical frequency distribution. In other situations we will have no historical data of this kind and our distribution will have to be based on purely subjective judgment.

Table 31.2

Batch serial number	Average of measurements on the raw material	True X content	Error
1	2.73	2.97	−.24
2	2.53	2.32	+.21
3	2.99	3.03	−.04
4	2.90	3.06	−.16
	etc.		

As an example of a distribution based on actual historical values of $\tilde{\beta}$, suppose that the investigation of the chemical-assaying process discussed in Chapter 26 had *not* shown that the process was unbiased as we there assumed but instead had shown that impurities in the raw material biased the measurements of the X content; and suppose that batch-to-batch variation in these impurities makes it impossible to predict the exact amount of bias which will be present when the X content of the new batch is measured. More specifically, suppose that the investigation had been conducted by making a very large number of measurements of the X content of each of a number of different batches of raw material, that the true X content of each batch had then been measured in the final product, and that the results were of the nature indicated in Table 31.2. Assuming (1) that all the measurements made on any *one* batch were made under constant conditions and therefore contain the same amount of bias, and (2) that the number of measurements on each batch was large enough to allow us to treat their mean as practically equal to the true mean μ of the process as applied to the batch, we may treat the errors in the last column of the table as pure systematic errors β and assess a probability distribution for the $\tilde{\beta}$ of the next set of measurements by converting these β's into fractile estimates and proceeding as in Section 6.4. If the fractile estimates fall reasonably close to a straight line on Normal-probability paper (cf. Section 18.1.1), the probability distribution may be assessed as Normal and its parameters may be determined either by the graphic method of Section 18.1.3 or by the numerical method of Section 30.2.2.

As an example of a distribution of $\tilde{\beta}$ assessed without the aid of historical frequencies, suppose that the marketing executive of the example discussed in Chapter 30 is in fact worried about possible bias due to factors of the sort discussed in Section 31.1.5 above. Frequency data on the actual effect of these factors is obviously unobtainable, and therefore the executive must assess his distribution of $\tilde{\beta}$ in the same way that he assessed his distribution of $\tilde{\xi}$ in Section 30.2.3. Suppose then that he decides (1) that the *most probable* effect of the peculiar conditions surrounding the sample survey is to produce sales which average 2 units *more* per customer than sales would average under normal conditions but (2) that there is *one chance in four* that sales under sample conditions tend to average 2 or more units *less* per customer than sales under normal conditions. In algebraic notation, the executive asserts (1) that the most probable value of $\tilde{\beta}$ is $+2$ but (2) that $P(\tilde{\beta} < -2) = \frac{1}{4}$. If he is willing to fill in the details by use of a Normal curve, we can say that *his distribution of $\tilde{\beta}$ is Normal* with mean equal to the most probable value

$$\mathrm{E}(\tilde{\beta}) = +2$$

and with standard deviation $\sigma(\tilde{\beta})$ such that

$$P(\tilde{\beta} < -2) = P_N\left[\tilde{u} < \frac{-2 - \mathrm{E}(\tilde{\beta})}{\sigma(\tilde{\beta})}\right] = \frac{1}{4}.$$

By the reasoning of Section 30.2.3 this latter condition means that

$$\frac{-2 - \mathrm{E}(\tilde{\beta})}{\sigma(\tilde{\beta})} = \frac{-4}{\sigma(\tilde{\beta})} = -.67,$$

$$\sigma(\tilde{\beta}) = \frac{-4}{-.67} = 6.0.$$

31.2.4   The Distribution of $\tilde{x}$ When $\tilde{\beta}$ Is Unknown and $\tilde{\epsilon}$ Is Normal

In the general case an unknown β is a nuisance parameter in the sense of Section 28.2.5 and must be handled exactly as any other nuisance parameter is handled. To find the likelihood of an observed $\bar{x}$ for some particular value of ξ, we must successively take each possible value of $\tilde{\beta}$, use the method of Section 31.2.2 to compute the desired likelihood *given* that value of $\tilde{\beta}$, and then take a weighted average of all these "conditional" likelihoods using the probabilities of the corresponding values of $\tilde{\beta}$ as the weights. In one special but very important case, however, the distribution of $\tilde{x}$ can be found very much more easily. This case, which is the only one we shall study in this course, is defined by the following assumptions:

1. The distribution of $\tilde{\beta}$ is Normal and independent of ξ.
2. The distribution of $\tilde{\epsilon}$ is Normal and independent of both ξ and β.

The first of the two assumptions of independence means that the measuring process does not tend to have a greater systematic error when the true value being measured is large than when it is small, etc. The second independence assumption means that the erraticness of the measuring process does not tend to be greater when the mean measurement $\mu = \xi + \beta$ is large than when it is small, etc. We remind the student that in any real application the justification for these assumptions must be very carefully checked before the assumptions are made. The first one in particular is *not* true of many real measuring processes.

Provided that the stated assumptions *are* made, we may reason as follows. Our model of the sample mean asserts that

$$\tilde{x} = \xi + \tilde{\beta} + \tilde{\epsilon}.$$

Since the expectation of a sum of constants and random variables is equal to the sum of the individual expectations and since $E(\tilde{\epsilon}) = 0$,

$$E(\tilde{x}) = \xi + E(\tilde{\beta}).$$

Since $\tilde{\beta}$ and $\tilde{\epsilon}$ are assumed independent and since the variance of a sum of independent random variables is the sum of the individual variances,

$$\sigma^2(\tilde{x}) = \sigma^2(\tilde{\beta}) + \sigma^2(\tilde{\epsilon}).$$

Finally, since the sum of any number of constants and Normal random variables is Normal,

The distribution of $\tilde{x}$ is Normal.

Computation of Likelihoods. Suppose now that in some particular problem a Normal distribution *has* been assigned to $\tilde{\beta}$, that the sample size is large enough to permit us to treat the distribution of $\tilde{\epsilon}$ as Normal, and that $\tilde{\beta}$ and $\tilde{\epsilon}$ are independent of each other and of ξ. If in addition we have enough information on the individual sampling errors to treat the variance $\sigma^2(\tilde{\epsilon})$ as known, we can use the two formulas just above to compute the numerical values of $\sigma^2(\tilde{x})$ and of $E(\tilde{x})$ for any given ξ, and therefore the likelihood of any observed $\bar{x}$ given any particular ξ can be computed from the usual formulas

$$P(\bar{x}|\xi) = \frac{\delta\bar{x}}{\sigma(\tilde{x})} P'_N(u), \qquad u = \frac{\bar{x} - E(\tilde{x})}{\sigma(\tilde{x})}.$$

31.2.5   *The Posterior Distribution of $\tilde{\xi}$ When the Prior Distribution Is Normal and $\tilde{x}$ Is Normal with Known Variance*

In Chapter 30 we dealt with a very special class of problems in which costs could be said to depend directly on the mean μ of some population of potential sample measurements x because bias was assumed zero and therefore the real cost-determining quantity ξ was necessarily equal to the population mean μ. For this reason we were able to take $\tilde{\mu}$ rather than $\tilde{\xi}$ as the basic random variable of these problems, and in Section 30.3 we then saw that computation of the posterior distribution of $\tilde{\mu}$ could often be very greatly simplified by making use of the fact that if

1. The prior distribution of the basic random variable $\tilde{\mu}$ is Normal,
2. The sampling distribution of the statistic $\tilde{x}$ is Normal,
3. The variance of the statistic $\tilde{x}$ is known,

then the posterior distribution of $\tilde{\mu}$ is Normal with parameters given by the formulas

$$E_1(\tilde{\mu}) = \frac{I_0 E_0(\tilde{\mu}) + I_{\bar{x}}\bar{x}}{I_0 + I_{\bar{x}}}, \qquad I_1 = I_0 + I_{\bar{x}},$$

where

$$I_{\bar{x}} = \frac{1}{\sigma^2(\tilde{x})}, \qquad I_0 = \frac{1}{\sigma_0^2(\tilde{\mu})}, \qquad I_1 = \frac{1}{\sigma_1^2(\tilde{\mu})}.$$

Now this relation between the prior and posterior distributions of a basic random variable clearly does not depend on the name given to the variable, nor does it depend in any essential way on whether or not the physical counterpart of the variable happens to be the mean of some population or whether the statistic used to summarize the sample is the mean of the sample. The fact that μ was the mean of the population of potential measurements and that the sample was summarized by its mean $\bar{x}$ was really of importance because it *implied* the satisfaction of a fourth *essential* condition:

4. The expected value of the statistic used to summarize the sample is equal to the true value of the basic random variable.

We can assert in complete generality that:

No matter what physical quantity is represented by a basic random variable and no matter what statistic is used to summarize a sample, the same relation between the prior and posterior distributions will hold that held for $\tilde{\mu}$ provided that these four essential conditions are satisfied.

Suppose then that a Normal prior distribution is assigned to ξ in a problem of the kind we are *now* considering, that the sampling distribution of $\tilde{x}$ can be treated as Normal, and that $\sigma^2(\tilde{\beta})$ and $\sigma^2(\tilde{\epsilon})$ and thus $\sigma^2(\tilde{x})$ can be treated as known. The first three of the four essential conditions are then met; but unless $E(\tilde{\beta})$ is zero the expected value of $\tilde{x}$ will be, not ξ, but $\xi + E(\tilde{\beta})$, and it would appear that the last of the four essential conditions is *not* met.

If, however, we think of our statistic as being, not the sample mean $\tilde{x}$ itself, but the "corrected" sample mean

$$\tilde{x} - E(\tilde{\beta}) = \xi + [\tilde{\beta} - E(\tilde{\beta})] + \tilde{\epsilon},$$

we see at once that

$$E[\tilde{x} - E(\tilde{\beta})] = \xi + E(\tilde{\beta}) - E(\tilde{\beta}) = \xi,$$

$$\sigma^2[\tilde{x} - E(\tilde{\beta})] = \sigma^2(\tilde{x}) = \sigma^2(\tilde{\beta}) + \sigma^2(\tilde{\epsilon}).$$

In words, the expected value of the "corrected" sample mean *is* equal to the true value ξ of the basic random variable while the variance of this new statistic is the same as the variance of the ordinary sample mean and therefore is known if the variance of $\tilde{x}$ is known. It follows immediately that if

1. The prior distribution of ξ is Normal,
2. The distribution of $\tilde{x}$ is Normal,
3. The variance $\sigma^2(\tilde{x}) = \sigma^2(\tilde{\beta}) + \sigma^2(\tilde{\epsilon})$ is known,

then

The posterior distribution of ξ is Normal

and the parameters of this posterior distribution are given by

$$E_1(\xi) = \frac{I_0 \, E_0(\xi) + I_{\tilde{x}}[\bar{x} - E(\tilde{\beta})]}{I_0 + I_{\tilde{x}}} \qquad I_1 = I_0 + I_{\tilde{x}}$$

where

$$I_{\tilde{x}} = \frac{1}{\sigma^2(\tilde{x})} \qquad I_0 = \frac{1}{\sigma_0^2(\tilde{\xi})} \qquad I_1 = \frac{1}{\sigma_1^2(\tilde{\xi})}$$

Example. Let us reconsider the marketing example of Chapter 30 with the modification introduced in Section 31.2.3 of this chapter. As in Chapter 30, we assume that the prior distribution of the *true* mean sales per potential customer ξ is Normal with parameters $E_0(\xi) = 8$ and $\sigma_0(\xi) = 3$, that the sample consists of 100 observations and is summarized by $\bar{x} = 5$ and $s = 7$, and that we may treat the estimate $\sigma(\tilde{\epsilon}) = s = 7$ as a known true value. We modify the original problem only by assuming that the executive believes that the sampling process may be biased and assigns to the bias $\tilde{\beta}$ a Normal distribution with parameters $E(\tilde{\beta}) = +2$ and $\sigma(\tilde{\beta}) = 6$. We compute

$$\sigma^2(\tilde{x}) = \sigma^2(\tilde{\beta}) + \sigma^2(\tilde{\epsilon}) = 6^2 + .7^2 = 36.49,$$

$$I_{\tilde{x}} = \frac{1}{\sigma^2(\tilde{x})} = \frac{1}{36.49} = .027, \qquad I_0 = \frac{1}{\sigma_0^2(\xi)} = \frac{1}{3^2} = .111,$$

$$I_1 = .111 + .027 = .138, \qquad \sigma_1(\xi) = \frac{1}{\sqrt{.138}} = 2.70,$$

$$E_1(\xi) = \frac{(.111 \times 8) + [.027 \times (5 - 2)]}{.111 + .027} = 7.02.$$

31.2.6　*Ineffectuality of Large Samples When Bias Is Suspected*

Although the corrected sample mean indicates sales of 3 units per potential customer, the executive's *uncertainty* about the bias is so great that he attaches very little importance to this estimate. In his opinion, the corrected sample mean contains only .027 unit of information whereas his own subjective sales estimate $E_0(\xi) = 8$ contained .111 unit; his revised estimate $E_1(\xi) = 7.02$ is therefore much closer to his original estimate than it is to the indication of the sample. These results are in striking contrast to the results obtained in Section 30.3.1, and they illustrate an extremely important general principle:

> Increasing the size of a sample reduces only the uncertainty due to pure sampling error; it does absolutely nothing to reduce uncertainty due to suspected bias.

Even if all 20,000 potential customers had been sampled, so that $\sigma^2(\tilde{\epsilon}) = 0$, the executive would still set $\sigma^2(\tilde{x}) = \sigma^2(\tilde{\beta}) = 36$; and this is virtually as large as the value 36.49 which we obtained for a sample of 100.

31.2.7　*Posterior Dependence between $\tilde{\xi}$ and $\tilde{\beta}$*

Even though the *prior* distributions of ξ and $\tilde{\beta}$ are completely independent, the *posterior* distributions of ξ and $\tilde{\beta}$ will in general be *interdependent*. Although formal analysis of this point would involve multivariate probability theory beyond the scope of this course, it is easy to convince oneself that such dependence must exist by thinking of the state of affairs which will prevail after a very large sample has been taken.

Suppose, for example, that such a sample has yielded $\bar{x} = 10$. Because the sample is large, the pure sampling error is almost certainly very small and therefore we are convinced that the mean μ of the sampling process must be very close to 10. But since $\mu = \xi + \beta$ by definition, this implies that if $\xi = 7$ (say), then β must be very close to 3, and so forth. *As our knowledge of μ increases through sampling, ξ and $\tilde{\beta}$ become more and more interdependent even though they were completely independent before any sample was taken.*

This fact has one very important implication. We have seen on several occasions (e.g. Chapter 21, Problem 7) that if *two* samples are taken, we can obtain the final posterior distribution by first computing the distribution posterior to the *first* sample and then using this distribution as the *prior* distribution for the second sample. This procedure is always legitimate if correctly applied; but *if there is uncertainty about bias we cannot use the formulas at the bottom of page 472 for the second step in the calculation* because the validity of those formulas depends critically on the assumption that ξ and $\tilde{\beta}$ are independent. The distribution posterior to two samples *can* be obtained, however, by first "pooling" the two samples into a single sample with a single n and $\bar{x}$ and then applying the formulas on page 472 once and once only.

31.3 Measurement Bias in Samples from Two-valued Populations

It is more or less common knowledge that a process which generates measurements in the ordinary sense of the word may be biased in the sense discussed above, but many businessmen seem to believe that no such difficulty is likely to arise when "measurement" consists simply in reporting whether a sample item is a "success" or a "failure"—good or defective, user or nonuser of a certain product. Everyone realizes of course, that the "value" of such an item may be incorrectly reported, but it is commonly thought that these errors will average out in a large sample.

In actual fact, however, the direct contrary is true. *Measurement bias is even more likely to be present in samples from two-valued populations than in samples from many-valued populations,* and the reason is not hard to see. Let us use the following notation:

p: true fraction of successes in the population.
q: true fraction of failures in the population.
π_s: relative frequency with which the observer reports a failure as a success.
π_f: relative frequency with which the observer reports a success as a failure.

The long-run frequency P_r with which sample items will be *reported* as successes is the sum of the true successes reported as successes plus the true failures reported as successes:

$$P_r = p(1 - \pi_f) + q\pi_s = p + (q\pi_s - p\pi_f).$$

This long-run fraction P_r of *reported* successes corresponds to the long-run average μ of a set of measurements, the fraction p of *true* successes corresponds to the true value ξ of the quantity being measured, and the difference between these two fractions is the bias of the sampling procedure:

$$\beta = \mu - \xi = P_r - p = q\pi_s - p\pi_f.$$

The important thing to notice is that bias can be zero only if either

$$\pi_s = \pi_f = 0,$$

i.e. if there are *no errors of observation at all*, or if

$$\frac{\pi_s}{\pi_f} = \frac{p}{q},$$

i.e. if the two π's happen to be in *just such a ratio that they cancel each other's effects.*

In much consumer research great pains are taken to design the sampling procedure in such a way as to make π_f equal to π_s, but it is important to realize that even if this is successfully accomplished bias is *not* eliminated. If we use π to denote the assumed equal value of π_f and π_s, we may rewrite the expression for the expected fraction of reported successes as

$$P_r = p(1 - \pi) + q\pi = p(1 - \pi) + (1 - p)\pi$$
$$= p + 2\pi(.5 - p).$$

It is immediately apparent that

> Whatever the true value of p, the expected value of the fraction of *reported* successes will always be between the true fraction of successes and .5. The difference between p and q will always tend to be *under*stated.

31.4   Selection Bias

It was emphasized in Section 23.5.2 and reemphasized in Section 31.2.1 that our entire treatment of samples drawn from a population of *objects already in existence* (rather than being taken in the order that they are generated by a random process such as a machine tool or a measuring instrument) depends on the assumption that the sampling is *simple*, i.e. on the assumption that *every member of the population has an equal chance of being the next item drawn into the sample.* We have just seen that even when this condition is met, errors of measurement or reporting may create *measurement bias* and that when such bias is suspected the distribution of the sample mean is quite different from the distribution which applies when we are sure that no bias is present. We shall now see that failure to meet the condition of simple sampling may also be a source of bias and affect the distribution of the sample mean in this same way. This new kind of bias will be called *selection bias.*

As a typical situation where selection bias may be present, suppose that in order to reduce travel expense and save time the marketing-research department of our previous example had restricted its sample of 100 potential customers to firms located east of the Mississippi River, giving every such customer an equal chance of entering the sample but excluding all other potential customers. Common sense tells us immediately that this sampling procedure would be likely to result in a "biased sample" even though absolutely no errors were made in the measurement of potential sales to each of the sample members, and we shall now formalize this common-sense result and see how to deal with it.

31.4.1   Definition of Selection Bias

Let us again imagine each of the 20,000 potential customers as represented by a card on which two numbers are written, the first giving the *true value* of the quantity of the regular product which the customer would purchase when sold in the regular way and the second giving the potential *sample measurement* which would result if the firm were drawn into the sample and offered the hand-made product in the course of the sample survey. We again define

ξ: mean of the 20,000 true values,
μ: mean of the 20,000 potential sample measurements,

but we now also imagine that the cards representing customers located in the East have been segregated into a separate group and that the numbers on these cards have been averaged to compute

ξ_E: mean of the true values of the Eastern customers,
μ_E: mean of the potential sample measurements for the Eastern customers.

Since the sample is drawn in such a way that the Eastern customers all have an equal chance of entering the sample while the other customers have none, the expected value of an individual sample measurement is μ_E. As before we define the *pure sampling error* of an individual measurement as the difference between the actual value of that measurement and its expected value

$$\epsilon = x - \mu_E,$$

and we define the *total bias* as the difference between the expected value of an individual measurement and the true mean of the entire population

$$\beta = \mu_E - \xi.$$

This bias is due in part to the fact that the true mean of the selected Eastern subpopulation is not the same as the true mean of the entire population and in part to the fact that systematic error is present in measuring sales to even the selected subpopulation. Defining the *selection bias*

$$\beta_s = \xi_E - \xi$$

and the *measurement bias*

$$\beta_m = \mu_E - \xi_E$$

we see that the *total bias* as defined above can be cleanly separated into two parts

$$\beta = \beta_s + \beta_m.$$

31.4.2 *Interpretation of a Biased Sample*

No new theory whatever is required to make use of the information in a sample which is suspected of containing one or both of these two components of bias. The random variable $\tilde{x}$ will still be the sum of the constant true mean of the entire population plus two random variables, the total bias and the mean sampling error:

$$\tilde{x} = \xi + \tilde{\beta} + \tilde{\epsilon}.$$

The mean sampling error $\tilde{\epsilon}$ will be handled exactly as before: its mean is 0 by definition and its variance can be estimated from the internal evidence of the sample by first estimating the variance of an *individual* sampling error as

$$\sigma^2(\tilde{\epsilon}) = s^2 = \frac{1}{n-1} \Sigma(x - \bar{x})^2$$

and then computing

$$\sigma^2(\tilde{\bar{\epsilon}}) = \frac{1}{n} \sigma^2(\tilde{\epsilon}) \frac{N-n}{N-1},$$

where N is the size of the selected *subpopulation*. The probability distribution of the total bias may be directly assessed as before, or we may feel that we can make more effective use of our experience and judgment by assessing separate distributions of its two components and then combining these distributions to get the distribution of the total bias. If the distributions assigned to the two components are Normal with parameters $E(\tilde{\beta}_s)$, $\sigma(\tilde{\beta}_s)$, $E(\tilde{\beta}_m)$, and $\sigma(\tilde{\beta}_m)$, and if these two distributions are independent, the distribution of the total bias will be Normal with parameters

$$E(\tilde{\beta}) = E(\tilde{\beta}_s) + E(\tilde{\beta}_m),$$
$$\sigma^2(\tilde{\beta}) = \sigma^2(\tilde{\beta}_s) + \sigma^2(\tilde{\beta}_m).$$

The assumption of independence will usually be reasonable, since in most situations information that the selection bias had some particular value would have no effect on our opinions about the measurement bias and vice versa.

31.4.3 Bias and Sample Size

In Section 31.2.6 we used a hypothetical example to illustrate the implications of the fact that the variance of the mean of a sample in which bias is suspected is

$$\sigma^2(\tilde{x}) = \sigma^2(\tilde{\beta}) + \frac{1}{n}\sigma^2(\tilde{\epsilon})\frac{N-n}{N-1},$$

so that only the second term decreases as the sample size increases and the total can never be less than the fixed value of the first term. To emphasize the importance of this point by a real example we recall the most famous sampling fiasco in history, the presidential poll conducted by the *Literary Digest* in 1936. Over 2 million registered voters filled in and returned the straw ballots sent out by the *Digest*, so that there was less than one chance in 1 billion of a *sampling* error as large as $\frac{2}{10}$ of one percentage point,† and yet the poll was actually off by nearly 18 percentage points: it predicted that 54.5 per cent of the popular vote would go to Landon, who in fact received only 36.7 per cent.‡

Since sampling error cannot account for any appreciable part of the 18-point discrepancy, it is virtually all actual bias. A part of this total bias may be measurement bias due to the fact that not all people voted as they said they would vote; the implications of this possibility were discussed in Section 31.3. The larger part of the total bias, however, was almost certainly selection bias. The straw ballots were mailed to people whose names were selected from lists of owners of telephones and auto-

† Neglecting the finite-population correction, the standard deviation of the mean sampling error is $\sigma(\tilde{\epsilon}) = \sqrt{pq/n}$ and this quantity is largest when $p = .5$. The number of ballots returned was 2,376,523, and with a sample of this size the largest possible value of $\sigma(\tilde{\epsilon})$ is $\sqrt{.5 \times .5/2,376,523} = .000322$, or .0322 percentage point, so that an error of .2 percentage point is $.2/.0322 = 6.17$ times the standard deviation. The total area in the two tails of the Normal distribution below $u = -6.17$ and above $u = +6.17$ is .0000000007.

‡ Over 10 million ballots were sent out. Of the 2,376,523 ballots which were filled in and returned, 1,293,669 were for Landon, 972,897 for Roosevelt, and the remainder for other candidates. The actual vote was 16,679,583 for Landon and 27,476,673 for Roosevelt out of a total of 45,647,117.

mobiles, and the subpopulation which was *effectively* sampled was even more restricted than this: it consisted only of *those owners of telephones and automobiles who were willing to fill out and return a straw ballot.* The true mean of this subpopulation proved to be entirely different from the true mean of the population of all United States citizens who voted in 1936.

It is true that there was no evidence at the time this poll was planned which would have suggested that the bias would be as great as the 18 percentage points actually realized, but experience with previous polls *had* shown biases which would have led any sensible person to assign to $\tilde{\beta}$ a distribution with $\sigma(\tilde{\beta})$ equal to *at least* 1 percentage point. A sample of only 23,760 returned ballots, one one-hundredth the size actually used, would have given $\sigma(\tilde{\epsilon})$ a value of only $\frac{1}{3}$ percentage point, so that the standard deviation of $\tilde{x}$ would have been

$$\sigma(\tilde{x}) = \sqrt{\sigma^2(\tilde{\beta}) + \sigma^2(\tilde{\epsilon})} = \sqrt{1 + .11} = 1.05$$

percentage points. Using a sample 100 times this large reduced $\sigma(\tilde{\epsilon})$ from $\frac{1}{3}$ point to virtually zero, but it could not affect $\sigma(\tilde{\beta})$ and thus *on the most favorable assumption* could reduce $\sigma(\tilde{x})$ only from 1.05 points to 1 point. To collect and tabulate over 2 million additional ballots when this was the greatest gain that could be hoped for was obviously ridiculous before the fact and not just in the light of hindsight.

31.4.4   Avoidance of Selection Bias: "Probability Sampling"

As we have already said, sampling is *simple* only if the physical process by which the sample is drawn is such that every member of the entire population has an equal chance of entering the sample, i.e. such that if the process were applied over and over to the same population every member of that population would in fact be drawn with equal frequency in the long run. When sampling is simple, the expected *true value* of a sample item is necessarily equal to the mean of all the true values in the population and selection bias is necessarily zero. When sampling is *not* simple, it is only by pure accident that the expected true value of a sample item—the average true value of the items which would be drawn if the sampling were repeated over and over—will be equal to the mean of the true values in the entire population. Accordingly we are justified in treating selection bias as if it were *known* to be zero—i.e., in setting $\sigma(\tilde{\beta}_s) = 0$—only if all the available evidence indicates that sampling processes of the kind used in the problem at hand are in fact simple;†

---

† It is not actually necessary to give every member of the population an *equal* chance of being drawn: if every member has *some* chance of being drawn and if these chances are *known*, we can assure zero selection bias by using a properly weighted average of the sample items instead of a simple unweighted mean. The actual techniques involved are beyond the scope of this course.

and there is a good deal of evidence to show that processes which at first glance seem simple are in fact surprisingly far from simple.

It might seem, for example, that a simple sample of telephone subscribers in the city of Boston could be drawn by opening the Boston telephone directory "at random," putting a pencil on the page "at random," taking the name nearest the point of the pencil, and continuing in this way. A sample of parts in a tote tray is ordinarily selected by a similar procedure, the inspector being instructed simply to take the required number of parts "at random" with no formal mechanism for making the choice. Experience has shown, however, that in many cases such informal procedures do *not* give every member of the population an equal chance of entering the sample. The inspector may tend to avoid or to prefer pieces near the corner of the tote tray; the person opening the telephone book may tend to avoid or to prefer opening it very near the front cover. As we said before, such behavior does not *necessarily* create bias— the pieces near the corners of the tote tray *may* be of exactly the same average quality as the other pieces in the tray—but it keeps us from being *sure* that there is no bias and therefore forces us to assign a nonzero value to $\sigma(\tilde{\beta}_s)$.

The standard method of attempting to give every member of a population a really equal chance of entering the sample is the following.

1. Make a complete list of the entire population.
2. Assign a serial number to every member of the population.
3. Use a table of random numbers or a similar mechanism to draw a sample of the serial numbers.

Samples drawn by procedures of this sort are commonly known as "probability samples."

Even a procedure such as the one just described will often fail to achieve its object completely, however. Especially in surveys of human populations, there are three principal ways in which selection bias may still creep in:

1. The list of the population may be incomplete or inaccurate.
2. The interviewer may fail to find some of the members drawn into the sample (the problem of the "not-at-homes").
3. Some persons may refuse to be interviewed (the problem of "nonresponse").

A well-run sampling procedure can do much to eliminate bias due to causes such as these; but *no matter how hard we try, we can never be absolutely sure that no selection bias is present.*

31.4.5   *"Judgment Sampling"*

In many practical situations, our judgment may tell us that there is no need to go to the expense of giving every member of the population an equal chance of entering the sample.   If we are dealing with a reputable supplier, we may feel quite sure that he will fill a container with parts in the order in which they are produced and that an acceptance sample can be taken from the top of the container without incurring selection bias. If we wish to determine what fraction of housewives can tell the difference between brand A and brand B of instant coffee, we may believe that the taste buds of residents of Allston are no different from those of inhabitants of the United States as a whole, and we may therefore decide to take our sample from residents of Allston only.   We may decide to make a survey by mail on the assumption that that part of the population which is on our mailing list *and* which responds to the mailing will be roughly the same as the population as a whole.

Notice, however, that the word "judgment" in judgment sampling must not be neglected.   If we were trying to determine what fraction of all United States housewives *preferred* brand A to brand B of instant coffee, we should consider the fact that the regular coffees which have the largest sales in certain parts of the country are noticeably different in blend and roast from those which dominate the market in other parts of the country.   It would be very dubious, therefore, whether the fraction of Allston housewives preferring brand A is equal to the fraction preferring A in the country as a whole.   The *Literary Digest* poll referred to above is an example of a very poor judgment, namely that the part of the United States voting population which consisted of automobile and telephone owners willing to answer a poll by mail contained the same fraction of Landon supporters as the entire population of United States voters.

Validation.   To some extent the judgment on which we have relied in taking a judgment sample can be checked from the sample itself by a process known as *validation*.   It is very common practice to secure from members of the sample information on income, home-ownership, age, sex, education, and other social and economic characteristics and to compare the distribution of these characteristics in the sample with the known distributions of these characteristics in the population as a whole.   If these factors have about the same distribution in the sample as they do in the population as a whole, *and if* these factors are thought to be the principal causes of variation among people as regards the particular characteristic being measured by the sample, we will feel more confident that the results of the sample are unbiased.

Whenever possible, the sample should of course be validated for characteristics more specifically related to the characteristic being measured.   If, for example, we have used a judgment sample to measure the fraction of people able to distinguish between two brands of instant coffee, we could question each person in the sample concerning his coffee-drinking habits, previous usage of regular vs. instant coffee, etc., and check the distribution of these characteristics in the sample against available data on their distribution in the United States as a whole or in the region in which the two brands are marketed.   If then we found that the sample contained, say, an unduly high fraction of regular users of instant coffee, we might seriously question our initial assumption that a sample drawn in this way would be representative of the population as a whole in ability to distinguish between two brands of instant coffee.

31.4.6   The Economics of the Choice of a Sampling Method

The judgment on which a judgment sample is based—viz., that the mean of a selected part of the population is equal or nearly equal to the mean of the whole—may always turn out after the fact to have been wrong: the sample may actually have serious bias.   For this reason many people have argued that the *only* "correct" or "scientific" procedure is to use so-called "probability sampling" for all purposes.   The question is by no means this simple, however.   A probability sample will in general cost more than a judgment sample, and we must ask whether the reduction in the risk of selection bias as measured by $\sigma^2(\tilde{\beta}_s)$ is worth this extra expense.   Or we can look at the problem another way: for any *given expenditure* on sampling, we can in general take a larger sample if we select an easily accessible part of the population than if we take a probability sample from the whole population.   Because the sample size is larger, there will be less risk of pure *sampling error* with the judgment sample than with the probability sample, and this fact may more than offset the greater risk of *bias* which is incurred by taking a judgment sample.

Suppose, for example, that we wish to determine the fraction of people who can distinguish brand A of instant coffee from brand B and that we are fairly sure from previous experience that this fraction will not be less than 20 per cent or greater than 80 per cent.   Suppose further that we have a budget of $1000 for the sampling operation, that it would cost $5 per head to take a judgment sample, and that it would cost $20 per head to take a probability sample.   The sample sizes accordingly would be 200 for the judgment sample and 50 for the probability sample, so that the finite-population correction can be neglected in both cases. If then in fact $p = .20$ or $.80$, the variance $\sigma^2(\tilde{\epsilon}) = pq/n$ of the pure sampling error would be $.2 \times .8/200 = .0008$ for the judgment sample and $.2 \times .8/50 = .0032$ for the probability sample.   Since the pure sampling variance of the probability sample is thus $.0032 - .0008 = .0024$ greater than that of the judgment sample, the probability sample will be *worse* than the judgment sample unless $\sigma^2(\tilde{\beta}_s)$ for the judgment sample is at least $.0024$ greater than it is for the probability sample.†

† The use of $p = .20$ or $.80$ gives the smallest value to $\sigma^2(\tilde{\epsilon})$ for any n and therefore is most favorable to the probability sample. If $p = .50$, $\sigma^2(\tilde{\epsilon})$ is equal to $.5 \times .5/200 = .00125$ for the judgment sample and $.5 \times .5/50 = .00500$ for the probability sample; the difference is $.00375$ in favor of the judgment sample.

Suppose now that previous experience with surveys of this type leads us to assign some definite value to $E(\tilde{\beta}_s)$ under the judgment plan and convinces us that there is a 50-50 chance that the true value of $\tilde{\beta}_s$ will actually be within 3 percentage points of this most probable value. The reasoning of Section 31.2.3 then leads us to set

$$\sigma(\tilde{\beta}_s) = \frac{.03}{.67} = .045,$$

$$\sigma^2(\tilde{\beta}_s) = .045^2 = .0020;$$

and even if (contrary to the implications of the remark at the end of Section 31.4.4) we set $\sigma^2(\tilde{\beta}_s) = 0$ for the probability sample, the judgment sample is the more reliable of the two.

In other situations it will be possible to trade risk of selection bias against risk of measurement bias rather than against risk of pure sampling error: by using a judgment sample and accepting the resulting increase in $\sigma(\tilde{\beta}_s)$ we may be able to make a more than compensating decrease in $\sigma(\tilde{\beta}_m)$. This will be typically true in surveys where highly skilled interviewers can be used if the respondents are chosen within narrow geographical limits while much less skilled interviewers must be used if a nationwide probability sample is to be interviewed.

Complex Sample Designs. The entire discussion in this chapter is intended only to bring out certain basic principles involved in the interpretation and design of samples; it is in no sense even an introduction to the complex technical problems involved in the efficient design of large-scale sample surveys. These technical problems are far beyond the scope of this course, but one general point must nevertheless be mentioned. It is only when relatively small amounts are at stake in the ultimate decision and relatively little is to be spent on acquiring sample evidence as a basis for the decision that *any* of the simple designs which we have discussed will be appropriate. When large sums are at stake and large amounts are to be spent on acquiring evidence, the best sampling plan will almost always involve *partial* trade-offs of selection bias against pure sampling error, selection bias against measurement bias, and so forth. Thus it may be better to take a medium-sized simple sample in each of a small number of cities or "clusters" than it would be *either* to take a very large simple sample in a single city or a very small simple sample from the entire population of the United States. Similarly it may be better to rely primarily on unskilled interviewers who have been "calibrated" by comparison with a few skilled interviewers than to rely on either skilled or unskilled interviewers alone.

PROBLEMS

1. In a situation like that of Chapter 26, a *very large* number of measurements have been made on each of 20 batches of raw material, each batch being measured under constant conditions, and the true X content ξ of each batch has then been determined in the final product.   The results have been tabulated in the form of Table 31.2 and the 20 β's in the last column have been summarized by

$$\tfrac{1}{20}\Sigma\beta = +.17; \qquad \sqrt{\tfrac{1}{19}\Sigma(\beta - .17)^2} = .32.$$

The differences between each individual measurement and the mean of all the measurements made *on the same batch* have been computed for every batch and summarized by

$$\sqrt{\frac{1}{n_1 + n_2 + \cdots + n_{20}} \, [\Sigma(x - \mu_1)^2 + \Sigma(x - \mu_2)^2 + \cdots + \Sigma(x - \mu_{20})^2]} = .9.$$

A new batch is received, $n = 9$ measurements are made, and their average is computed as

$$\bar{x} = 2.08.$$

   a. Compute the likelihood of the observed sample mean given $\xi = 3.0$ and compare with the corresponding figure in Table 26.3.

   b. Compare the amount of information contained in the sample mean under the assumptions of the present problem with the amount of information contained in this same statistic under the original assumptions of Chapter 26.

   2. Assume that the prior distribution assigned to $\tilde{\xi}$ by the manufacturer of Chapter 26 is not the discrete distribution of Table 26.1 but a Normal distribution with parameters

$$E_0(\tilde{\xi}) = 2.725, \qquad \sigma_0(\tilde{\xi}) = .370.$$

(These are the actual values of the mean and variance of the original discrete distribution.)   Compute the posterior distribution of $\tilde{\xi}$

   a. Under all the conditions described in Problem 1 above.

   b. Under these same conditions except that all 20 recorded β's are 0.

   3. 70 per cent of the population prefer Smith's cornflakes and 30 per cent prefer Jones's but 20 per cent of either group will state a preference for whatever is in a box labeled X regardless of their true preferences and 20 per cent will similarly state a preference for Y.   Half of the respondents in a sample are given Smith's cornflakes in a box labeled X and Jones's in a box labeled Y; the codes are reversed for the other half of the respondents.   What is the expected fraction of the sample reporting a preference for Smith's cornflakes?

   4. Two extremely large samples of housewives have been taken to determine the fraction preferring Smith's cornflakes to Jones's.   In one sample Smith's were coded X and Jones's Y; in the other sample the codes were reversed.   The stated preferences were:

Contents	Label	Fraction of subsample preferring
Smith's	X	.76
Jones's	Y	.24
		1.00
Smith's	Y	.56
Jones's	X	.44
		1.00

Letting $\tilde{p}$ denote the fraction of all housewives who actually prefer Smith's product and treating sampling error as negligible because of the very large sample size, *a.* Discuss in common-sense terms the implications of the sample evidence concerning the true value of $\tilde{p}$.

b. Outline a procedure for assigning a formal posterior distribution to $\tilde{p}$ but do not make any actual computations.

5. A company located in Chicago wishes to measure readership of a new advertisement which it has just published in a magazine with national circulation, and management has authorized the marketing-research director to spend $2500 on the investigation. The director has made similar investigations on five previous occasions, on each of which a simple probability sample of the magazine's entire mailing list was used, but his experience on these five occasions has led him to think that he might do better this time by sampling only those readers who live in Chicago and are thus readily accessible. The results of the surveys of the readership of five earlier advertisements are shown in the table below. If it would cost $25 per head to take a nationwide sample in the new investigation or $5 per head to sample only Chicago

| | Readership, per cent | |
Advertisement	National	Chicago
1	12	14
2	17	20
3	15	14
4	21	18
5	18	20

readers, what should the company do?

6. Recompute the answer to Chapter 30, Problem 1*d*, bringing in the additional assumption that Mar-Pruf's management believes that the average potential customer is almost certain to say that he will buy more than he will actually buy. Management guesses that the most likely average amount of overstating is 20 gallons per year but would not bet more than even money that this best guess is actually within 10 gallons per year of the true figure.

CHAPTER 32

Comparison of Two Unknown Quantities; the Importance of Sample Design

In all the problems which we have studied so far, the costs which would result from any act depended on a *single* unknown quantity such as a fraction defective, a chemical content, or the consumption of a certain product. We shall now consider problems where the costs of the possible acts depend on the *difference* between *two* unknown quantities. This is perhaps the most common type of statistical problem encountered in business practice outside the field of quality control. It includes such problems as deciding whether or not a new package design will increase sales by enough to pay for the additional cost, since we are usually uncertain about what sales will be if we retain the old package as well as about what they will be if we change to the new. It includes problems of deciding whether a certain report will create an improvement or a deterioration in the attitude of employees, since we are usually uncertain about their present attitude as well as about the attitude which will exist if the report is circulated, and so forth.

32.1 A Problem and Its Analysis if No Sample Is Taken

A manufacturer of instant coffee is considering a more modern-looking design for the jar and label with which he packages his product. The proposed new jars and labels can be bought for the same price as the old and the only extra cost involved in the change would be about $20,000 for minor modifications in the jar-filling machines. The manufacturer believes that if the new package proves successful it will be successfully imitated by the rest of the industry after about 2 years; and since his margin net of freight averages $.11 per ounce, this means that the new package must increase his sales by $20,000/$.11 = 182,000 ounces within the 2-year period in order to break even. His sales have been running about 70 million ounces per year, so that an increase of this magnitude is readily conceivable; his real worry is whether a change to the new design might actually reduce his sales.

486

32.1.1   The Random Variables ξ_1 and ξ_2

The profit-determining random variables of this problem are (1) total sales during the next 2 years if the old package is retained and (2) total sales during the next 2 years if the new package is adopted, but instead of working directly with these variables we shall express them in terms of *mean sales per store per month*, i.e. total sales divided by the number of stores in the United States and by the number of months in the 2-year period. The manufacturer has a nearly complete list of all grocery stores in the United States, and we shall treat this list as if it were in fact complete and perfectly accurate. There are 400,000 stores on the list, so that if total sales over the 2 years should be 140 million ounces, say, mean sales per store per month would be

$$\frac{140,000,000}{400,000 \times 24} = 14.6 \text{ ounces},$$

and so forth.

The problem thus involves the basic random variables

ξ_1: mean sales per store per month if the *old* package is retained;
ξ_2: mean sales per store per month if the *new* package is adopted.

The true value of either ξ is the number which *would* be obtained by offering the package in question to *all United States stores for all 24 months* and dividing the resulting total sales by $400,000 \times 24 = 9,600,000$; only one of the true values can ever actually be known.

Conditional Profit in Terms of ξ_1 and ξ_2. If the manufacturer retains the *old* package his total sales during the 2-year period will be $9,600,000\xi_1$ and his total profit will be \$.11 times this quantity. To get the conditional total profit with the *new* package we treat ξ_2 in the same way and then subtract the \$20,000 cost of modifying the machinery. We thus have the conditional profits:

With the old package,   \$1,056,000 ξ_1,
With the new package,   \$1,056,000 ξ_2 − \$20,000.

32.1.2   Analysis in Terms of Relative Profit and Difference in Sales

Let us state the manufacturer's problem as one of choice between *acceptance* and *rejection* of the new package. It is obvious that the desirability of either act depends only on whether profit with the new package is *greater* or *less* than profit with the old package; it does *not* depend on the *absolute* amount of profit which will be made with *either* package. We can therefore simplify our problem by looking, not at the absolute profits of the two acts, but at their profits *relative to the profit which will be made if the old package is retained*. Subtracting conditional profit with the old package from conditional profit with the new we obtain the conditional *relative profit* of acceptance:

Conditional RP of acceptance = $1,056,000 ($\xi_2 - \xi_1$) − $20,000.

Since *rejecting* the new package is the same thing as retaining the old,

Conditional RP of rejection = $0.

The Random Variable $\tilde{\delta}$. These results make it clear that the economics of the problem depend only on the *difference* between ξ_2 and ξ_1 and not on the absolute value of either of these two random variables by itself. We can therefore further simplify our problem by defining a new random variable

$$\tilde{\delta} = \tilde{\xi}_2 - \tilde{\xi}_1 \qquad \textit{Definition of } \tilde{\delta}$$

and expressing the conditional relative profits in the form

Conditional RP of acceptance = $1,056,000 δ − $20,000,
Conditional RP of rejection = $0 δ + $0.

These conditional relative profits are graphed against δ in Figure 32.1, and we see immediately that

The economics of choice in our present problem are identical to the economics of choice in a two-action problem with linear costs which depend on a single random variable. It is only the name $\tilde{\delta}$ of the basic random variable which is different.†

Expected Relative Profit. Since the conditional relative profit of either act is a linear function of δ, the *expected* relative profit of either act is obtained by merely substituting $E(\tilde{\delta})$ for δ in the formula for the conditional relative profit; the proof is identical to that given in Section 30.4.1 for problems where the basic random variable was called $\tilde{\mu}$.

Cost of Uncertainty. The relative profits of acceptance and rejection are equal when $\tilde{\delta}$ has the *break-even* value δ_b determined by

$$\$1,056,000 \, \delta_b - \$20,000 = \$0,$$
$$\delta_b = \frac{\$20,000}{\$1,056,000} = .019.$$

Following exactly the same line of reasoning we used in Section 30.4.2 and

---

† We could have defined *relative* profits or costs in problems involving a single unknown just as well as in our present problem. The reason for not so doing was that in those problems the use of relative profit or cost would have been an unnecessary complication, whereas in problems involving the difference between two unknowns it is a very real simplification

arbitrarily calling acceptance act 1 we can define the *loss constant*

$$k_t = |k_1 - k_2| = |\$1{,}056{,}000 - \$0| = \$1{,}056{,}000$$

and obtain formulas for the *conditional value of perfect information* which are identical to those of Section 30.4.2 except that the symbol μ is replaced by δ. This means that the formulas for the *expected* value of perfect information or *cost of uncertainty* derived in Sections 30.4.3 and 30.4.4 can

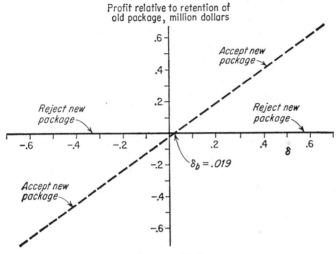

Profit relative to retention of old package, million dollars

Figure 32.1

also be applied to our present problem if μ is replaced by δ.   In particular: if the distribution of $\tilde{\delta}$ is Normal, then

$$\text{Cost of uncertainty} = k_t \sigma(\tilde{\delta}) G(D),$$

where

$$D = \frac{|\delta_b - E(\tilde{\delta})|}{\sigma(\tilde{\delta})}.$$

32.1.3   The Decision without Sampling

Since the economics of this new type of problem can be expressed in terms of a single basic random variable $\tilde{\delta}$, a decision without sampling is reached in exactly the same way that it is reached in a problem expressed in terms of a single $\tilde{\xi}$: the businessman must assign a probability distribution to the basic random variable and use it to evaluate the relevant expectations.   One of the real advantages in working with $\tilde{\delta}$ rather than with $\tilde{\xi}_1$ and $\tilde{\xi}_2$ is that it will almost certainly be easier for the businessman to express his judgments about the effect of the new package in the form of a probability distribution of $\tilde{\delta}$ than it would be to express them in the form of two interrelated distributions of $\tilde{\xi}_1$ and $\tilde{\xi}_2$.

The Probability Distribution. When asked for his marketing judgment concerning the possible effects of the new design, the manufacturer answers that his best guess is that it will increase sales by a modest amount, say 1 per cent of last year's volume or about 700,000 ounces per year. He goes on, however, to add that he has seen many cases where apparently unimportant changes in package design have led to rather remarkable gains and losses and that he thinks that there is really only an even chance that his best guess is within a million ounces of the true figure.

To work with these opinions we must express the manufacturer's figures in the same units in which we measure the quantity $\tilde{\delta}$, that is, in ounces per store per month. Dividing 700,000 ounces by the 400,000 stores on the list and by the 12 months in a year we find that the manufacturer's best guess is $\delta = .146$ ounce per store per month. Treating the 1 million ounces in the same way, we find that he believes that there is only an even chance that his best guess will be in error by less than .208 ounce per store per month. The way in which the manufacturer has stated his uncertainty about his best guess indicates that he would adopt a symmetric probability distribution if pressed; and if he agrees that a Normal distribution has about the right shape we can use the reasoning of Section 30.2.3 to show that

$$E_0(\tilde{\delta}) = .146,$$
$$\sigma_0(\tilde{\delta}) = \frac{.208}{.67} = .310.$$

The Better Decision and Its Expected Relative Profit. The expected relative profit of a decision to *reject* the new package is obviously $0, since by relative profit we mean the difference between the profit of a given act and profit with the old package. The expected relative profit of a decision to *accept* the new package is

$$\$1,056,000 \ E_0(\tilde{\delta}) - \$20,000 = (\$1,056,000 \times .146) - \$20,000$$
$$= \$134,000.$$

While this result tells the manufacturer absolutely nothing about the *absolute* profit he can "expect" to earn if he accepts, it tells him that if he accepts he can "expect" to earn $134,000 *more than if he rejects*. Acceptance is thus the better act under the probability distribution which the manufacturer's experience has led him to assign to the differential effect $\tilde{\delta}$ of the new package.

The Cost of Uncertainty. The manufacturer was not at all sure about the value of $\tilde{\delta}$, however, and therefore he should also look at the cost attached to his uncertainty. To find this we compute

$$D_0 = \frac{|\delta_b - E_0(\tilde{\delta})|}{\sigma_q(\delta)} = \frac{|.019 - .146|}{.310} = |-.41| = +.41,$$

use Table IV to find

$$G(.41) = .2270,$$

and finally compute the expected loss of the better decision as

$$k_t\sigma_0(\delta)G(D_0) = \$1,056,000 \times .310 \times .2270 = \$74,300.$$

This is the *cost of uncertainty if the manufacturer acts on the information now available*, and it represents a very sizable risk.

32.2　An Experiment with Independent Samples

Because of the risk involved in acting purely on the basis of judgment, the manufacturer decides to make a comparative store test and authorizes his marketing-research department to buy a certain amount of testing. It is beyond the scope of this course to find the best way—or even a tolerably good way—of conducting and analyzing this experiment; we shall nevertheless proceed to discuss two grossly inefficient ways since by so doing we can illustrate two very important general principles.

1. In all but the very simplest situations, the amount of information which can be obtained for a dollar of sampling expense varies to an almost incredible extent with the design of the survey or experiment which elicits the information.

2. Whatever the design may be, however, the information obtained from the sample will be used in a way which is basically identical to the way in which we have used sample information in earlier chapters.

32.2.1　The Experimental Design

Suppose first that *two separate samples* of 100 stores each are drawn from the manufacturer's list of all United States grocery stores in such a way that every name on the list has an equal chance of being drawn. If any store in either sample does not stock the manufacturer's product at present, this store is left without stock. Among the stores which *do* stock the product at present, those in the first sample continue to receive the old package while those in the second sample are supplied with the new package. At the beginning of the experiment each store's opening inventory of the product is recorded; the experiment is run for 1 month during which all deliveries of the product to each store are recorded; and at the end of the experiment closing inventory is counted and sales are computed for each store by subtracting closing inventory from the sum of opening inventory plus deliveries. In processing the data obtained from the experiment, the few stores which did not stock either product are *not* excluded: they are counted in their respective samples as having had 0 sales.

32.2.2   The Statistic $\tilde{d}$

Suppose now that when the data from the two samples have been analyzed they appear as follows:

Sample from first population (old package)	Sample from second population (new package)
$n_1 = 100$ store-months	$n_2 = 100$ store-months
$\bar{x}_1 = 14.27$ ounces	$\bar{x}_2 = 13.56$ ounces
$s_1 = 7.23$ ounces	$s_2 = 7.49$ ounces

Since it turned out so convenient to replace the two random variables $\tilde{\xi}_1$ and $\tilde{\xi}_2$ by a single random variable $\tilde{\delta} = \tilde{\xi}_2 - \tilde{\xi}_1$, it naturally occurs to us that we will profit by handling the two sample statistics $\bar{x}_1$ and $\bar{x}_2$ in a similar way, and we therefore define a new statistic

$$\tilde{d} = \tilde{x}_2 - \tilde{x}_1$$

whose observed value in this particular experiment was

$$d = \bar{x}_2 - \bar{x}_1 = 13.56 - 14.27 = -.71.$$

It can be shown that *we will obtain the same posterior distribution for $\tilde{\delta}$ by use of d that we would obtain by the separate use of the two statistics $\bar{x}_1$ and $\bar{x}_2$.* In common sense, it is the difference between the two sample means which supplies information on the difference between the two population means.

The Sampling Distribution of $\tilde{d}$.   In order to use this statistic $\tilde{d}$ we must know its sampling distribution given any possible value of the parameter δ, and to find this distribution we proceed exactly as we proceeded in Chapter 31 to find the distribution of the mean $\tilde{x}$ of a single sample.   The first step is to write out the formula for the composition of the d observed in any one particular experiment.   Using β_1 and β_2 to denote the *total biases* (cf. Section 31.4.2) of the sampling procedures by which $\bar{x}_1$ and $\bar{x}_2$ were respectively obtained and using $\bar{\epsilon}_1$ and $\bar{\epsilon}_2$ to denote the *pure sampling errors* contained in the observed $\bar{x}_1$ and $\bar{x}_2$, we have by Section 31.1.4

$$\begin{aligned} d = \bar{x}_2 - \bar{x}_1 &= \xi_2 + \beta_2 + \bar{\epsilon}_2 - \xi_1 - \beta_1 - \bar{\epsilon}_1 \\ &= (\xi_2 - \xi_1) + (\beta_2 - \beta_1) + \bar{\epsilon}_2 - \bar{\epsilon}_1. \end{aligned}$$

We have already agreed to denote the difference $(\xi_2 - \xi_1)$ by the symbol δ; let us now similarly define

$$\beta_d = \beta_2 - \beta_1.$$

β_d is the systematic error in the statistic d, i.e. the *mean* amount by which d would differ from δ if the whole sampling procedure were applied over and over and d were computed on each separate occasion.   We can now write for the composition of any observed d:

$d = \delta + \beta_d + \bar{\epsilon}_2 - \bar{\epsilon}_1.$

Having found the composition of any particular d, we are ready to study the distribution, given any specified δ, of the random variable

$\tilde{d} = \delta + \tilde{\beta}_d + \tilde{\bar{\epsilon}}_2 - \tilde{\bar{\epsilon}}_1.$

Since the expected value of any sum of constants and random variables is the sum of the (expected) values, and since $E(\tilde{\bar{\epsilon}}_1) = E(\tilde{\bar{\epsilon}}_2) = 0$ by definition (Section 31.2.1),

$$E(\tilde{d}) = \delta + E(\tilde{\beta}_d)$$

The two samples are taken in such a way that $\tilde{\bar{\epsilon}}$ and $\tilde{\bar{\epsilon}}_2$ are necessarily independent of each other, and there is also every reason to assume that they are independent of $\tilde{\beta}_d$—if we knew (say) that the first sample had happened to have a high pure *sampling error*, this information would not affect the probability distribution we assign to the *systematic error* of the whole sampling procedure, and so forth. Then since the variance of a sum of independent random variables is the sum of the variances,

$$\sigma^2(\tilde{d}) = \sigma^2(\tilde{\beta}_d) + \sigma^2(\tilde{\bar{\epsilon}}_1) + \sigma^2(\tilde{\bar{\epsilon}}_2)$$

The formulas for $E(\tilde{d})$ and $\sigma^2(\tilde{d})$ apply regardless of the *shapes* of the distribution of $\tilde{\beta}_d$, $\tilde{\bar{\epsilon}}_1$, and $\tilde{\bar{\epsilon}}_2$, but the *shape* of the distribution of $\tilde{d}$ does depend on the shapes of the distributions of these three random variables. *In our particular example*, each of the two pure sampling errors $\tilde{\bar{\epsilon}}_1$ and $\tilde{\bar{\epsilon}}_2$ is the sum of $n = 100$ individual sampling errors and therefore can be treated as approximately Normal regardless of the shape of the distribution of the individual errors. If we assume that the businessman's uncertainty about $\tilde{\beta}_d$ can also be described by a Normal distribution (cf. Section 31.2.3), then since the distribution of the sum of any number of independent Normal random variables is Normal

The distribution of $\tilde{d}$ is Normal.

All that remains is to assign the proper numerical values to the quantities $E(\tilde{\beta}_d)$, $\sigma(\tilde{\beta}_d)$, $\sigma(\tilde{\bar{\epsilon}}_1)$, and $\sigma(\tilde{\bar{\epsilon}}_2)$ in our example. As far as the latter two quantities are concerned, we know (Section 31.2.1) that the variance of the sampling error of an *individual* observation in either sample can be estimated by the statistic s as computed for that sample; and we also know that because each s rests on $f = n - 1 = 99$ degrees of freedom we can treat these estimates as if they were certainties. We thus have

$$\sigma(\tilde{\bar{\epsilon}}_1) = s_1 = 7.23; \qquad \sigma(\tilde{\bar{\epsilon}}_2) = s_2 = 7.49.$$

We can then compute the standard deviations of the sampling errors of the *sample means* in the usual way; neglecting the finite-population correction because the sampling ratio is only 100/400,000 we obtain (cf. Section 31.2.1)

$$\sigma(\tilde{\epsilon}_1) = \frac{\sigma(\bar{\epsilon}_1)}{\sqrt{n_1}} = \frac{7.23}{\sqrt{100}} = .723,$$

$$\sigma(\tilde{\epsilon}_2) = \frac{\sigma(\bar{\epsilon}_2)}{\sqrt{n_2}} = \frac{7.49}{\sqrt{100}} = .749.$$

As for the bias $\tilde{\beta}_d$, we are justified in our present example in treating it as virtually known to be virtually 0. This is *not* because the two samples are *individually* unbiased. On the contrary, each of the samples may contain very serious selection bias because of the fact that an experiment run in one particular month is taken as representing all the 24 months in which the marketer is interested. There may be important secular and seasonal variations in consumption of the marketer's product, and if there are it would be very dangerous to assume that total sales in the 24-month period would be proportional to sales in the experimental month. The marketer is interested, however, not in the *absolute* level of sales but in the *differential* effect of the new package; and it seems reasonable to assume that these secular and seasonal factors will *affect the two samples to very nearly the same degree.* This being so, the bias in the *difference* between $\bar{x}_2$ and $\bar{x}_1$ can reasonably be expected to be negligibly small.

Our conclusions can be summarized as follows. *The sampling distribution of the statistic $\tilde{d}$ in our example is Normal with parameters*

$$E(\tilde{d}) = \delta,$$
$$\sigma^2(\tilde{d}) = \sigma^2(\tilde{\epsilon}_1) + \sigma^2(\tilde{\epsilon}_2) = .723^2 + .749^2 = 1.084.$$

32.2.3   The Posterior Distribution and Expectations

Since the prior distribution of $\tilde{\delta}$ is Normal and the sampling distribution of $\tilde{d}$ can be treated as Normal with known variance, the posterior distribution of $\tilde{\delta}$ is Normal with parameters given by the formulas in Section 31.2.5 with δ substituted for ξ and d substituted for $\bar{x}$. Since we have already seen that

$$E_0(\tilde{\delta}) = +.146, \qquad \sigma_0(\tilde{\delta}) = .310,$$
$$d = -.71, \qquad \sigma^2(\tilde{d}) = 1.084,$$

we can now compute

$$\frac{1}{\sigma_1^2(\tilde{\delta})} = \frac{1}{.310^2} + \frac{1}{1.084} = 10.4 + .9 = 11.3,$$

$$E_1(\tilde{\delta}) = \frac{(.146 \times 10.4) + (-.710 \times .9)}{11.3} = +.078,$$

$$\sigma_1(\tilde{\delta}) = \frac{1}{\sqrt{11.3}} = .298.$$

The variance of the sampled populations and therefore of the statistic $\tilde{d}$ is so great that the manufacturer's experiment should have virtually no effect on the distribution he assigns to the basic random variable $\tilde{\delta}$. Although the statistic $\tilde{d}$ had the value $-.71$, the manufacturer should assess $E_1(\tilde{\delta}) = +.078$. His uncertainty about $\tilde{\delta}$ was originally measured by $\sigma_0(\tilde{\delta}) = .308$; his experiment has reduced this only to $\sigma_1(\tilde{\delta}) = .298$.

The Better Decision and Its Expected Relative Profit. The expected relative profit of acceptance under the posterior distribution is

$$\$1,056,000\ E_1(\tilde{\delta}) - \$20,000 = (\$1,056,000 \times .078) - \$20,000$$
$$= \$62,400.$$

Since this is positive, acceptance is the better decision.

The Cost of Uncertainty. To find the posterior cost of uncertainty we compute the value of D for the posterior distribution:

$$D_1 = \frac{|\delta_b - E_1(\tilde{\delta})|}{\sigma_1(\tilde{\delta})} = \frac{|.019 - .078|}{.298} = |-.20| = +.20,$$

use Table IV to find

$$G(.20) = .3069,$$

and compute

$$k_t\sigma_1(\tilde{\delta})G(D_1) = \$1,056,000 \times .298 \times .3069 = \$96,600.$$

The prior cost of uncertainty was only \$74,300: *the posterior cost of uncertainty is actually* \$22,300 *higher than the prior cost.* What the sample has done is simply to tell the manufacturer that he is in a very risky position; the variance of $\tilde{d}$ was so great that the sample has *not* been effective enough to tell him how to act with little risk.

32.3   Populations of Differences

Common sense has probably already told the student that the manufacturer could have used his 200 store-months of testing to much better advantage if he had tried both the old and the new package in every store used in the experiment. Under the design described above, it is quite possible that the new package will by pure chance be put predominantly in stores which sell little of the manufacturer's brand while the old is put in stores which sell much more; it is also quite possible that the reverse event will occur.† The large sampling variance computed for $\tilde{d}$ is due in very large part to the uncertainty which results from this possibility,

---

† It is irrelevant for our present purpose to know whether the store-to-store variation in demand for the brand is due to differences in size of store, in the customers' liking for coffee as such, or in their preference for the manufacturer's brand over other brands.

and we shall now consider an alternative design for the experiment which eliminates this source of uncertainty.

32.3.1 The Experimental Design

Let us now suppose that the experiment is run for 2 months instead of 1 but that only 100 stores are used instead of 200. During the first month of the experiment the stores are supplied with the old package, during the second month with the new. Audits are made at the end of both months, so that sales in the two packages are separately recorded for every store in the sample; stores not stocking the product are recorded as having 0 sales with both packages. In this way chance selection of the stores in which the two packages are tested can no longer favor either package over the other.

The first and most important thing for the student to observe is that we *cannot* proceed by computing mean sales per store-month for each package, taking d as the difference between these two observed sales rates, and applying the formulas for the distribution of $\tilde{d}$ given in Section 32.2.2 above. The formula for the expectation $E(\tilde{d})$ would still apply, but the formula

$$\sigma^2(\tilde{d}) = \sigma^2(\tilde{\beta}_d) + \sigma^2(\tilde{\epsilon}_1) + \sigma^2(\tilde{\epsilon}_2)$$

for the sampling variance of $\tilde{d}$ does *not* apply. Suppose, for example, that the "average store" in the sample happens to sell more of the manufacturer's brand than the average store in the United States. Then *both* $\tilde{\epsilon}_1$ and $\tilde{\epsilon}_2$ will tend to be above their zero expectations. If the average store in the sample happens to sell less than the national average, *both* $\tilde{\epsilon}_1$ and $\tilde{\epsilon}_2$ will tend to be negative. In other words, *a high value of $\tilde{\epsilon}_1$ will tend to be accompanied by a high value of $\tilde{\epsilon}_2$ or a low value by a low value, and therefore the variance of their difference is not equal to the sum of their individual variances.*†

32.3.2 Populations and Samples of Differences

In the present problem there is a very simple way of getting out of the difficulties occasioned by the interdependence of $\tilde{\epsilon}_1$ and $\tilde{\epsilon}_2$. Instead of considering the sample as being drawn from *two different populations*, each consisting of 400,000 *sales rates* with means ξ_1 and ξ_2, we may consider it as drawn from a *single population* consisting of 400,000 *differences between sales rates*. If some particular store would sell 20 ounces per month in the old package and the same store would sell 19 in the new, the "value" of this member of the population is $19 - 20 = -1$. The mean of this *population* is the mean of the store-by-store *differences* which would result from adoption of the new package, and we shall denote it by

† In technical language, the addition theorem for variances does not apply because $\tilde{\epsilon}_1$ and $\tilde{\epsilon}_2$ are *correlated:* cf. the footnote in Section 16.3.

ξ: mean of the differences in monthly sales by individual stores which will result from acceptance of the new package.

The *sample* then consists of 100 differences drawn from this population of differences: *for each individual store in the sample* we subtract sales in the old package from sales in the new and call the *difference* the value of this sample item.

If we take this point of view, then once the store-by-store differences have been computed we can throw away the actual sales figures and never look at them again.   Accordingly we shall suppose for the present that the results of the experiment are fully described by the following summary:

$n = 100$ paired store-months;
$\bar{x} = -.21$;
$s = 1.53$.

We repeat that each observation x is the *difference* between the two sales rates in a *single store*.   The statistic $\bar{x}$ is computed by averaging the 100 store-by-store x's which constitute the sample, and the statistic s is computed from these same differences.

32.3.3   The Posterior Distribution of $\tilde{\xi}$

Since in this problem the mean difference ξ is *economically* identical to the difference δ between the two means of our previous analysis, we assume that the manufacturer assigns to ξ the same prior distribution he assigned to δ, that is, a Normal distribution with parameters

$E_0(\tilde{\xi}) = +.146$,
$\sigma_0(\tilde{\xi}) = .310$.

We can then compute the parameters of the posterior distribution of $\tilde{\xi}$ by the usual formulas.   *Assuming that there is no bias*, applying large-sample theory, and neglecting the finite-population correction, we estimate

$$\sigma^2(\tilde{x}) = \sigma^2(\tilde{\epsilon}) = \frac{\sigma^2(\tilde{\epsilon})}{n} \doteq \frac{s^2}{n} = \frac{1.53^2}{100} = .0234$$

and compute

$$\frac{1}{\sigma_1^2(\tilde{\xi})} = \frac{1}{.310^2} + \frac{1}{.0234} = 10.4 + 42.7 = 53.1,$$

$$E_1(\tilde{\xi}) = \frac{(+.146 \times 10.4) + (-.21 \times 42.7)}{53.1} = -.140,$$

$$\sigma_1(\tilde{\xi}) = \frac{1}{\sqrt{53.1}} = .137.$$

The Better Decision and Its Expected Relative Profit.   Remembering that the mean difference ξ is economically identical to the difference δ

between the two mean sales rates, we can simply substitute ξ for δ in the expression given in Section 32.1.2 for the conditional relative profit of acceptance:

Conditional RP of acceptance $= \$1,056,000\ \xi\ -\ \$20,000.$

Since this is a linear function of ξ, the expected relative profit of accept-- ance is

$$\$1,056,000\ E_1(\xi)\ -\ \$20,000\ =\ \$1,056,000\ \times\ (-.140)\ -\ \$20,000$$
$$=\ -\$168,000.$$

The manufacturer can "expect" to be \$168,000 better off if he retains the *old* package.

The Cost of Uncertainty. To find the expected loss of the better decision, in this case rejection, we compute

$$D_1 = \frac{|\xi_b - E_1(\xi)|}{\sigma_1(\xi)} = \frac{|+.019 - (-.140)|}{.137} = \frac{.159}{.137} = 1.16,$$

look up

$$G(1.16) = .06086,$$

and compute

$$k_t\sigma_1(\xi)G(D_1) = \$1,056,000 \times .137 \times .06086 = \$8,800.$$

This is very substantially less than the \$74,300 prior cost of uncertainty computed in Section 32.1.3.

32.4   The Importance of Sample Design

32.4.1   Comparison of the Two Designs Already Discussed

In the first example analyzed above, the statistic d had the value $-.71$; in the second example the corresponding statistic $\bar{x}$ had the value $-.21$. The former was over three times as far below the break-even value $\delta_b = \xi_b = .019$ as the latter and yet:

1. The second experiment should logically lead the manufacturer to reverse his prior decision to accept whereas the former should not.

2. The second experiment reduced the cost of uncertainty from \$74,300 to \$8,800 whereas the former actually raised it to \$96,600.

These differences are due to the fact that the variance of the statistic $\bar{d}$ in the first design was much greater than the variance of the statistic $\bar{x}$ in the second: the respective values were 1.084 and .0234. These figures rest, of course, on values which were simply *assumed* for the population variances (more accurately, for their estimates s^2); but while we cannot hope to *prove* anything by a pair of examples we *can* show that the assumed values are *reasonable*.

The values assumed for $\sigma(\bar{\epsilon}_1)$ and $\sigma(\bar{\epsilon}_2)$ in the first design were respectively 7.23 and 7.49 ounces per store per month, and these values are almost certainly too low given the assumed mean monthly sales of $70,000,000/(12 \times 400,000) = 14.58$ ounces per store per month. It is a known fact that the frequency distribution of the total dollar volumes of all United States grocery stores is J-shaped—there are a great many extremely small stores, a fair number of medium-sized stores, and a very few extremely large stores. A frequency distribution of store-by-store sales of the manufacturer's brand would have a similar shape, and we can get a rough idea of the standard deviation of this distribution by using what we already know about the J-shaped exponential distribution. The standard deviation of any exponential distribution is equal to its mean, and we would therefore really expect the standard deviation of sales of the manufacturer's brand to be about 14 ounces per store per month. The standard deviations of the sample measurements x and therefore of the sampling errors ϵ should be very nearly equal to the standard deviations of the true sales rates, i.e. closer to 14 than to 7 ounces per store per month. *We have certainly not overstated the ineffectiveness of our first experimental design.*

As for the second design, we have almost certainly understated its effectiveness relative to the first. A very large part of the store-to-store variation in the differences measured in the second design is simply an indirect effect of store-to-store variation in demand for the manufacturer's brand as such. Suppose, for example, that the true effect of the new package is to lower sales by 10 per cent in all stores. Then a store which on the average would sell 20 ounces per month in the old package would sell 2 ounces less in the new; a store which would sell 80 ounces in the old package would sell 8 ounces less in the new; and the standard deviation of the whole population of *differences* sampled in the second design would be 10 per cent of the standard deviation of either of the two populations of *sales rates* sampled in the first design. In setting up our assumptions about the results of the second experiment we have provided more than generously for this kind of variation. Although we assumed that the mean difference due to the new package was of the order of 1 per cent of sales, we assumed that the standard deviation of the differences was over 20 per cent of the standard deviation of the sales rates: we assumed $\sigma(\bar{\epsilon}) = 1.53$ in the second design after assuming $\sigma(\bar{\epsilon}_1) = 7.23$ and $\sigma(\bar{\epsilon}_2) = 7.49$ in the first design.

It is true, of course, that the differences sampled in the second design vary from store to store for other reasons in addition to the one just discussed. "Chance" factors such as weather will have an effect on the difference as measured in each store, and this effect will vary from store to store. There may also be some variation from store to store in the true effect of the new package—customers may prefer it in some places and dislike it in others. It is virtually certain, however, that the variation due to all these causes put together is small compared to the variation due to variation in sales of the manufacturer's brand of coffee as such. The fact that some stores have total coffee sales 1000 times as large as others tends to make their "differences" 1000 times as great as others, and none of the other sources of variation is at all likely to have effects even approaching this magnitude. Since we have assumed a population variance that allows for this first source of variation many times over, we may safely conclude that *we have very substantially understated the superiority of the second design over the first.*

32.4.2   The Concept of Statistical Efficiency

What we have just shown is that the indecisiveness of the first design discussed above compared to the second was not due to chance or to arbitrary assumptions but to the fact that the second design was inherently more *efficient* than the first.   Regardless of the true value of the effect of the new package, the statistic $\bar{x}$ of the second design was bound to have less variance than the statistic $\tilde{d}$ of the first design; and this meant that the information $I_{\bar{x}} = 1/\sigma^2(\bar{x})$ obtained from the second design was bound to be greater than the information $I_d = 1/\sigma^2(\tilde{d})$ obtained from the first.

Now it is obvious that if we use a sufficiently large number of store-months of testing under the first design we could obtain as much information from that design as we did in fact obtain from 200 store-months of testing under the second design.   This suggests a way of actually quantifying the efficiency of the first design relative to the second.   If it would take 800 store-months of testing under the first design to get the same information which we got with 200 under the second, we can say that the first design is one-fourth as efficient as the second.   We would prefer, however, to be able to compare the two designs in general, without specifying a particular number of store-months under either design as a base, and to make this possible we define

n_t: total number of store-months used in an experiment.

This quantity had the value 200 in *both* the designs we have analyzed, even though the number of *stores* was only 100 under the second design.

In the first design, each of the two independent samples was of size $n = n_t/2$.   Substituting this value for n_1 and n_2 in the formula given in Section 32.2.2 for the variance of $\tilde{d}$ and assuming as before that $\sigma(\tilde{\beta}_d) = 0$ we can compute

$$\sigma^2(\tilde{d}) = 0 + \frac{7.23^2}{n_t/2} + \frac{7.49^2}{n_t/2} = \frac{217}{n_t},$$

$$I_d = \frac{1}{\sigma^2(\tilde{d})} = \frac{n_t}{217} \doteq .00461 n_t.$$

In the second design each sample item was a difference obtained by *two* store-months of testing and therefore the size of the sample of differences was $n_t/2$. Substituting this value for n in the formula given in Section 31.2.4 for the variance of $\bar{x}$ and assuming as before that $\sigma(\tilde{\beta}) = 0$ we obtain

$$\sigma^2(\bar{x}) = 0 + \frac{1.53^2}{n_t/2} = \frac{4.68}{n_t},$$

$$I_{\bar{x}} = \frac{1}{\sigma^2(\bar{x})} = \frac{n_t}{4.68} = .214n_t.$$

Thus we see that each store-month of testing under the first design produces only $.00461/.214 = .022$ as much information as each store-month of testing under the second design; we can say that the *statistical efficiency of the first design relative to the second is 2.2 per cent.* Or we can put the result the other way to and say that it will require $.214/.00461 = 46$ *times as many store-months of testing* to obtain any specified amount of information by use of the first design as it would by use of the second.

32.4.3 Still Better Designs

Although our object is only to point out the very great importance of good experimental design and not to show how to make a good design, it is important to emphasize that the second design discussed in this chapter is by no means the *best* design for a problem of the kind with which the manufacturer of coffee was faced. In actual fact, this design is far from being even reasonably good; and in order to warn the student not to assume that he is capable of designing an experiment simply because he has learned how to use the results, we shall now point out four glaring weaknesses in the second design. The first three of these weaknesses bear on the way in which the data were collected, the fourth on the way in which it was analyzed.

1. The fact that the old package was used in the first month in all stores while the new package was used in the second means that any seasonal change in coffee consumption between the two months is *confounded* with the effect of the package. It would obviously have been better to split the sample into two halves, assign the old package to one half and the new package to the other half in the first month, and reverse the assignments in the second month. Any seasonal effect would have been almost completely eliminated by such a *balanced design.*

2. About 20 per cent of the grocery stores in the United States do about 80 per cent of the total grocery business, and it is obvious that if we have good information on the effect of the new package in these stores we will be almost certain to come to the right decision. Even substantial percentage errors concerning the effect of the new package in the remain-

ing 80 per cent of the stores can do little harm.   Since the cost of a store-month of testing in a small store will be almost if not quite as much as the cost of a month in a large store, common sense tells us that most of the stores in a properly designed sample would be chosen among the 20 per cent which do most of the total business.   The sample should have been *stratified*.

3. It is obvious that two stores in a single city can be tested and audited much more cheaply than two stores in two different cities.   If 100 stores are drawn with equal probability from a list of all United States stores, it is certain that auditors will have to be sent to nearly 100 different cities.   By only slightly reducing the number of cities, it would be possible to include two or three stores per city for the same total expense and thus make another substantial reduction in the variance of $\bar{x}$.   The sample should have been *clustered*.

4. We have already suggested that the natural assumption in a situation like this one is that the true effect of the package is to increase or decrease sales in each store by roughly the same *percentage* and not by roughly the same *absolute amount*.   It is therefore clear that if we had looked at the population of the second design as a population of *ratios* rather than as a population of *differences*, the mean of the sample ratios would have had far less variance than the mean of the sample differences. If the data of the second design had been analyzed in terms of ratios rather than differences, the gain in efficiency would very probably have been at least as great as the gain made by going from the first design to the second.

PROBLEMS

1. Verify that the break-even value $\delta_b = .019$ agrees with the statement that adoption of the new package will be justified only if total sales in a 2-year period are thereby increased by at least 182,000 ounces.

2. At the end of the chapter four possible improvements in the second design were briefly described.   Only one of these, analysis of the data in terms of ratios rather than differences, makes any real difference in the way the sample results would be summarized and used in reaching a decision and computing expected loss.   Suppose then that the marketing-research department had employed a consulting statistician to design the experiment and process the data and that he had submitted the following report.

"The experiment consisted of drawing a stratified, clustered sample of 100 stores and testing each package in each store for one month.   The results can be summarized by a statistic $\bar{z}$ whose sampling distribution is approximately Normal with mean

$$E(\bar{z}) = \xi,$$

where ξ is the mean of the population of store-by-store *differences* in monthly sales with the two packages.   The observed value of this statistic was

$$z = -.21$$

and the data yield an estimate

$$\hat{\sigma}^2(\bar{z}) = .0155$$

of the variance of the distribution of $\bar{z}$."

    a. Compute the expected relative profit of accepting the new package.

    b. Select the better decision and compute the expected loss of this decision.

    c. How many store-months of testing under the second design of the text are needed to yield information equal to that provided by one store-month under this new design?

    d. What is the statistical efficiency of the second design relative to this new design?

    3. The reason why analysis of the *percentage changes* caused by the new package is a little more difficult than analysis of the *differences* is simply that the manufacturer's net gain cannot be calculated from the percentage change alone: it also depends on the base to which this percentage is applied, i.e. on sales if the old package is retained, and this base is also unknown. In general, however, uncertainty concerning the base will be of relatively little importance in comparison with uncertainty concerning the ratio, and a good approximate solution can be obtained by treating the base as known. Suppose therefore that the data of the second experiment had been considered as a sample of 100 *ratios*

$$r = \frac{\text{monthly sales in new package}}{\text{monthly sales in old package}}$$

from a population consisting of 400,000 such ratios. The ratio r would then be computed for each store in the sample to arrive at a mean ratio $\bar{r}$; suppose that the observed value of $\bar{r}$ was

$$\bar{r} = .985.$$

Suppose further that the variation of the individual ratios for the 100 stores in the sample had been measured by

$$s = \sqrt{\tfrac{1}{99}\Sigma(r - \bar{r})^2} = .153.$$

Finally, define

    ρ = mean of the *population* of 400,000 ratios.

    a. Assuming that sales with the old package would be 70 million ounces per year, express the conditional relative profit of acceptance and the cost of uncertainty in terms of ρ.

    b. Assign a Normal prior distribution to $\tilde{\rho}$ which is consistent with the manufacturer's opinions as given in Section 32.1.3.

    c. Find the posterior distribution of $\tilde{\rho}$.

    d. Compute the posterior expected relative profit of acceptance and cost of uncertainty.

    e. Recompute (*d*) as it would be if it were assumed that sales in the old package would be 80 million ounces rather than 70 million.

    4. In January, 1957, a number of American railroads were offering a special passenger tariff known as the "Family-Fare Plan." There were some variations in the details from road to road, but basically the tariff provided that if a husband bought a round trip at the regular rate, his wife could buy a round trip at half price and his children could buy their round trips at still lower prices. A single ticket was issued to cover the transportation of the entire family.

There was great controversy among passenger officers of the various roads concerning the effect of the Family-Fare Plan on revenue and profit, and the Grand Western Railroad was seriously considering its abandonment. A good deal of revenue was at stake: sales of Family-Plan tickets amounted to about $4 million per year on the Grand Western, and if the same passengers had been carried at full fare this figure would have been nearly doubled. While the general passenger agent of the Grand Western believed that 90 per cent of the passenger-miles sold under the special tariff would not have been sold at all under the normal tariff, the senior executives of the Grand Western knew that the general passenger agent of another railroad serving exactly the same major cities believed that about 90 per cent of the passenger-miles sold under the special tariff *could* have been sold at regular fares.

The president of the Grand Western, H. B. Jones, was particularly puzzled by the fact that both his own GPA and the GPA of the other road based their contradictory statements on the results of surveys carried out by having ticket agents ask purchasers of Family-Fare tickets whether or not they would have made the same trip if the special rates had not been in effect.   Jones was inclined to believe that the samples taken by the two men were too small to be reliable, and since there was no one among the road's personnel who was an expert in such matters he called in a representative of a marketing-research agency specializing in consumer surveys and laid the problem before him.   The agency representative answered that both the samples were so large that sampling error as such could not possibly account for more than 1 or 2 of the 80 percentage points of difference and went on to assert that the real difficulty was that reliable answers to a question like the one asked of the ticket buyers could not possibly be obtained through hurried interviews conducted by ticket clerks under unfavorable conditions.   Even if the Grand Western sample were extended to a 100 per cent count, there would in his opinion be no more real knowledge than there was before any data were collected.   He recommended that the railroad employ his agency to draw a small equal-probability sample of purchasers of Family-Fare tickets and have the persons in the sample interviewed in their homes by really skilled interviewers.

When asked about the cost of such a survey, the agency representative quoted a price of $1000 for general expenses plus $100 per family in the sample, explaining the high cost per head as due in part to the fees of the skilled interviewers and in part to the time and expense which would be incurred in securing interviews with people selected with equal probabilities among all persons who had traveled on Family-Fare tickets during the preceding year.   It seemed to Jones that this obviously implied that a sample large enough to give reliable results would be prohibitive in cost, but the agency representative argued that this was not necessarily true and that in any case a good deal of very useful information could be obtained by taking a very small pilot sample and analyzing its results.   Since the total amount of Grand Western revenue at stake was really substantial, Jones finally decided to contract with the marketing-research agency to interview a sample of 50 families at a cost of $6000.

Before taking the sample the agency examined the available data on the values of the individual Family-Fare tickets sold during the previous year and found that the large majority of the tickets were for short trips and actually accounted for only a small part of the total dollar sales; 80 per cent of the dollars came from individual sales of $150 and over.   The railroad and the agency quickly agreed that the sample should be drawn exclusively from families who had paid over $150 for their tickets, since it seemed very likely that the behavior of these families alone would determine whether the plan was or was not profitable over all.

The pilot sample was promptly drawn and interviewed with the results shown (in simplified form) in the table below.   The figure shown in the column headed "effect of cancellation" was calculated by subtracting the amount which the family

actually spent on its Family-Fare ticket *from* the amount it *would* have spent traveling
on the Grand Western if Family Fares had not been available.

Effect of cancellation	Number of families
−$200	10
− 100	12
0	7
+ 100	16
+ 200	5
	50

When these results were in Jones was still very unsure about what to do next.
It was easy to calculate that the effect of cancellation of the plan on families in the
sample would have been a reduction in revenue amounting to $600 in total or $12 per
family on the average.   Jones also knew that about 20,000 Family-Fare tickets had
been sold for amounts of $150 and over in the past year, so that *if* the $12 sample
figure held for the entire population, about $240,000 would be lost in one year by
abandoning the plan.   The road's passenger-train schedules and consists were such
that the reduction in passenger-miles traveled would have no effect on train costs, so
that this loss of revenue was an out-and-out loss of that much net income.

Jones believed that conditions were changing so rapidly that the entire question
would have to be reexamined next year and therefore that there was no sense in pro-
jecting profit or loss farther than a year in advance, but he was seriously disturbed
about basing his decision on a sample of only 50 families.

a. On the evidence of the pilot sample alone, what is the best course of action
and what risk is involved?

b. Express your own judgment concerning reactions to a Family-Fare plan in the
form of a prior distribution of the basic random variable and recompute your answers
to (*a*).

c. Recompute your answers to (*a*) making the additional assumption that Jones
believes that most people do not really know what they will do until they do it and
therefore would be willing to bet even money that the average dollar effect of cancellation as estimated by interviews would be at least $25 above or below the true effect
of actual cancellation even if 100 per cent of the customers were included in the
sample.

PART FOUR

The Value of Additional Information

CHAPTER 33

Evaluation of a Decision to Sample
and Then Act; Preposterior Analysis

33.1 Introduction to Part Four of the Course

The only acts which we have hitherto considered as "possible" in any situation have been acts which disposed of the problem at hand once and for all. We have decided to accept or to reject, to stock 3 units or to stock 4, but we have not yet considered the possibility of deciding to collect more evidence before reaching *any* final decision on acceptance or stock level. Even when we were studying the use of information obtained from samples, we asked only what final or terminal act should be chosen in the light of the sample evidence already at hand; we did not ask whether the taking of the sample had been sensible in the first place or whether perhaps *another* sample should be taken before any final or terminal decision was reached.

It is obvious, of course, that in many situations the best possible immediate decision *will* be a decision to collect more evidence—specifically, to take a sample (or another sample)—before deciding on a terminal act; and it is the analysis of such decisions which will occupy us in this part of the course. We already know *how* to choose between terminal acts; we shall learn how to decide *when* to make the choice. This latter problem is much the more interesting and important of the two, since the correct answer is much less often apparent to unaided common sense.

Terminal Acts and Terminal Decisions. Since we are now obliged to talk about decisions which lead ultimately to other decisions, we shall avoid a great deal of confusion if we agree on some new terminology and adhere to it carefully. Henceforth an act which puts a final end to a problem will always be called a *terminal act.* Thus acceptance or stocking 3 units is a terminal act; taking a sample of size 10 is *not* a terminal act. A choice among terminal acts will be called a *terminal decision;* a decision to sample now and act later is *not* a terminal decision.

Total Expected Cost of a Decision to Sample. A decision to sample rather than to take immediate terminal action clearly involves an irrevocable commitment to make another decision after the sample has been taken and interpreted, and therefore the *total* expected cost entailed by the *original* decision is the sum of the expected values of two separate kinds of cost:

1. The cost of taking and interpreting the sample;
2. The costs which will be entailed by the decision which must be made after the sample evidence is in.

Clearly a reasonable man will want to sample if and only if this *total* expected cost is less than the expected cost of immediate terminal action. We already know how to evaluate the expected cost of immediate terminal action, which is simply the expected cost of the best terminal act under the prior probability distribution. Computation of the total expected cost of decisions to sample and postpone terminal action will be the subject of Part Four of the course.

33.1.1   Single-sample vs. Sequential Decision Procedures

Although a decision to sample involves a commitment to make *some* second decision after the sample evidence is in, it is obvious that this second decision need not always be a *terminal* decision.   The information obtained from the sample may well be such that the rational course of action is to sample again before reaching a terminal decision; and this procedure may be repeated many times before a point is reached where still another sample would *not* be worth its cost and therefore a terminal decision is finally reached.   If the businessman is willing to proceed in this way, he is following what is known as a *sequential* decision procedure.

Under some circumstances, however, a sequential decision procedure is clearly undesirable or impossible.   The nature of the problem may be such that there is no time to take more than one sample before reaching a terminal decision; or the fixed cost involved in taking any sample at all may be so large (as in the case of a nationwide consumer survey) that it is clearly absurd even to consider taking repeated small samples rather than a single large sample.   If the businessman considers himself definitely committed to reaching a terminal decision after a single sample has been taken, he is following a *single-sample* decision procedure.

It is obvious that calculation of total expected cost will be much simpler for a single-sample decision procedure than for a sequential procedure.   The total expected cost of a decision to take a single sample and then act is simply the sum of the cost of sampling and the expected cost of terminal action after the sample has been taken.   The total expected cost of a decision to embark on a sequential procedure is the cost of the first sample plus *either* the expected cost of terminal action immediately after the sample has been taken *or* the total expected cost of another decision to proceed sequentially, whichever is less.   For this reason *we shall restrict our discussion in the next few chapters to single-sample procedures*.   After we have thoroughly understood the way in which the

total cost of such a procedure is computed and used, we shall then go on
to see how a series of such computations can be used to evaluate the total
expected cost of a sequential procedure.

33.1.2   The Assumption of Optimal Terminal Action

We have already pointed out that a reasonable man will decide to
sample only if the total expected cost of that decision is less than the
expected cost of the terminal act which is *best* in the light of the evidence
available without sampling.   It is equally clear that the cost of terminal
action which is entailed by a decision to sample and *then* choose a terminal
act should be evaluated on the assumption that the chosen act will be the
one which is *best* in the light of all the information available after the
sample evidence is in.   Strictly speaking, we should have defined the
total expected cost of a decision to sample and then act as the sum of the
cost of sampling plus the cost of *optimal* terminal action, but we shall
avoid repetition by simply stating once and for all that

> Whenever we speak of the cost of terminal action, we assume that
> the terminal act will be the one which is optimal in the light of the
> information available *at the time the act is actually chosen.*

33.2   Expected Terminal Cost of a Single-sample Procedure

Even though the cost of a single sample of known size is often an
expected cost rather than a cost certain, its evaluation is simple in most
practical business problems and we shall not spend time in this course on
the rather rare situations where the evaluation is difficult.   The only real

Table 33.1

p	$P_0(p)$	Conditional cost		Conditional loss	
		Accept	Reject	Accept	Reject
.01	.7	$ 2	$8	$ 0	$6
.05	.1	10	8	2	0
.15	.1	30	8	22	0
.25	.1	50	8	42	0
	1.0				

problem before us is therefore the evaluation of the expected cost of
terminal action or *expected terminal cost* entailed by a decision to sample
and then choose a terminal act: this cost must be evaluated *before* the
sample is taken although we cannot even know what terminal act will be
chosen until *after* the sample is taken.   The method by which this evaluation is carried out can best be explained by analyzing a simple example.

In Chapter 22 we assumed that a manufacturer had already taken a sample of size $n = 10$ to aid him in deciding between acceptance and rejection of a Bernoulli process, and we computed the *posterior* expected costs of these two terminal acts in the light of the *known sample outcome* $r = 0$. In the present chapter we shall continue to work with the arbitrarily chosen sample size $n = 10$, but we now place ourselves in the position of the manufacturer *before* the sample is taken and seek to evaluate the *prior* expected cost of taking *whichever act turns out to be optimal* in the light of the *as yet unknown* sample outcome. The data of the problem as given in Chapter 22 are summarized for the student's convenience in Table 33.1.

33.2.1   Conditional Terminal Cost

In Table 22.5 we showed that *after* the sample of 10 had been taken and the outcome $\tilde{r} = 0$ had been observed, the (posterior expected) costs of acceptance and rejection were respectively $3.83 and $8.00. Since we assume that the *optimal* terminal act will always be chosen, we can say that *the* posterior terminal cost given the information $\tilde{r} = 0$ was $3.83. From our present point of view, *before* the sample is taken, we can say that $3.83 *will be* the terminal cost *if* the outcome $\tilde{r} = 0$ is observed. From this point of view, the figure $3.83 is just another example of a *conditional* cost—conditional in this case on the sample outcome.

Table 33.2

r	$P_0(r)$	Optimal terminal act	Cost of optimal terminal action	
			Conditional	Expected
0	.718	Accept	$3.83	$2.74
1	.149	Reject	8.00	1.19
2	.066	Reject	8.00	.53
3	.039	Reject	8.00	.31
4	.019	Reject	8.00	.15
5	.007	Reject	8.00	.06
6	.002	Reject	8.00	.02
	1.000			$5.00

Now if we can compute the conditional cost of optimal terminal action or *conditional terminal cost* given the outcome $\tilde{r} = 0$, we can obviously compute this conditional cost for any other value of $\tilde{r}$. All that we have to do is use the method of Table 22.4 to compute the posterior distribution of $\tilde{p}$ for the new value of $\tilde{r}$, use this distribution to compute the posterior costs of acceptance and rejection by the method of Table 22.5, and select the lesser of these two costs as the conditional terminal cost given the value of $\tilde{r}$ in question. The results of such computations **for** every possible value of $\tilde{r}$ are shown in Table 33.2. Column 1 shows all the possible values of $\tilde{r}$ in the sample of $n = 10$ which we are using as an example, the act with the lesser posterior cost given each value of $\tilde{r}$ is shown in the third column, and the cost of this optimal act is shown in the fourth.

33.2.2   Prior Expected Terminal Cost

The method by which *expected* terminal cost can be evaluated before the sample is taken is now virtually self-evident: *we simply multiply the conditional cost given each possible value of $\tilde{r}$ by the probability of that value of $\tilde{r}$ as assessed before the sample is taken and add the products.*

Computation of the probability of any given value of $\tilde{r}$ before the sample is taken presents no new problem whatever. Since the parameter p is unknown, $P_0(r)$ must be computed as a marginal probability by the method of Section 12.3; but such a computation is a necessary step in the computation of the posterior distribution of $\tilde{p}$ for the given value of $\tilde{r}$. Thus the probability that $\tilde{r} = 0$ was computed as .718 in Table 22.4, and the probabilities shown in the second column of Table 33.2 for all other values of $\tilde{r}$ were obtained in the same way. The product of each conditional cost times the corresponding probability is shown in the last column of Table 33.2, and the $5 total of this column is the *prior* expected cost of taking whatever action is optimal in the light of all the evidence available *after* a sample of size 10 has been taken and inspected. More briefly, $5 is the *expected terminal cost of a single-sample procedure with $n = 10$.*

In terms of frequencies rather than probabilities: if the process is set up by the operator a very great number of times and the frequency distribution of setup quality corresponds to the probability distribution of Table 33.1, if from each setup a sample of 10 pieces is taken, and if the setup is then accepted or rejected according to the third column of Table 33.2, the sum of the costs incurred through accepting defective product plus the payments to the expert setup mechanic will average $5 per run.

33.3   Expected Terminal Loss of a Single-sample Procedure

We have seen throughout this course that it is almost always instructive to separate the expected cost of immediate terminal action into two parts:

1. The expected *cost of terminal action under certainty*, i.e. the cost we would "expect" to incur if we were to be given perfect information before actually choosing the terminal act;
2. The expected *opportunity loss* which arises because the terminal act must actually be chosen in the absence of perfect information and therefore may prove "wrong" after the cost-determining event has actually occurred.

The same separation can be made and is even more instructive when we are considering decisions to sample and then act, since by making the sample large enough we can (provided that no unknown bias is suspected) make the expected opportunity loss due to wrong terminal action as small as we please, whereas we can never reduce that part of expected terminal cost which would be present even if we had perfect information.

We have seen repeatedly that the expected loss of a specified terminal act can be computed in either of two ways:

1. By taking the expectation of the *conditional losses* of the act;
2. By taking the difference between the expected *cost* of the act and the expected cost of terminal action under certainty.

These same two alternatives are available for computing the prior expected value of the opportunity loss which will be incurred by taking whatever terminal act turns out to be optimal in the light of an as yet unknown sample outcome.

33.3.1 Computation Using Conditional Terminal Losses

In computing the expected terminal *cost* of a single-sample procedure with $n = 10$, we took as the conditional terminal cost for each value of $\tilde{r}$ the posterior expected cost of the terminal act which was optimal for that value of $\tilde{r}$; we then multiplied each of these conditional costs by the probability of the corresponding value of $\tilde{r}$ and added the products.

Table 33.3

r	$P_0(r)$	Optimal terminal act	Loss of optimal terminal action	
			Conditional	Expected
0	.718	Accept	$1.12	$ .80
1	.149	Reject	2.57	.38
2	.066	Reject	.27	.02
3	.039	Reject	.01	0
4	.019	Reject	0	0
5	.007	Reject	0	0
6	.002	Reject	0	0
	1.000			$1.20

Expected terminal *loss* can be computed in exactly the same way, using the posterior expected loss of the terminal act which is optimal for each value of $\tilde{r}$ as the conditional terminal loss for that value of $\tilde{r}$.

We saw in Table 22.9 that after no defective had been found in a sample of 10 the (posterior expected) losses of acceptance and rejection were respectively $1.12 and $5.29 and therefore that the terminal loss of the *optimal* act given the information $\tilde{r} = 0$ was $1.12. From our present point of view this is the *conditional* terminal loss *given* $\tilde{r} = 0$. Repetition of the calculations which produced this figure $1.12 in Chapter 22 gives the conditional losses for all other values of $\tilde{r}$ shown in the fourth column of Table 33.3; the first three columns of this table are identical to the corresponding columns of Table 33.2.

In the last column of Table 33.3 the expectation of these conditional losses is evaluated in the usual way, resulting in the figure $1.20 for the *prior* expected loss of optimal terminal action *after* taking a sample of 10. More briefly, this is the *expected terminal loss of a single-sample procedure with n = 10*.

33.3.2   Computation Using Expected Cost under Certainty

We saw in Table 22.10 that, in the light of the information available before any sample is taken, *expected terminal cost under certainty* is $3.80.   In Section 33.2.2 we saw that, in the light of this same information, *expected terminal cost with n = 10 is $5*.   It follows immediately that *expected terminal loss with n = 10* is $5.00 − $3.80 = $1.20, and this agrees of course with the result obtained just above by use of the conditional losses.

In terms of repeated trials: if the process is set up by the operator a great number of times and the frequency distribution of setup quality corresponds to the probability distribution of Table 33.1, if on each occasion a sample of size 10 is taken, and if the terminal decision on each occasion is optimal in the light of the total information available, costs will average $1.20 more per run than they would average if on each occasion we had *perfect* knowledge of the quality of the setup and acted accordingly.

33.4   Total Expected Cost or Loss of a Single-sample Procedure

We cannot of course judge the merits of a decision to sample and then act by looking only at the prior expected cost or loss of the terminal action which will ultimately be taken; we must also look at the cost of taking the sample.   Let us suppose that the only sampling cost in our example is the cost of the inspector's time, and let us suppose that the time required to draw any sample of reasonable size, maintain records, etc., will cost $.25, while the time required to inspect the pieces in the sample will cost $.02 per piece.   For the sample of size $n = 10$ which we have been using as an example we then have

Cost of sampling = $.25 + $.02 n = $.25 + ($.02 × 10) = $.45.

It is now a trivial problem to compute the *total* expected cost or loss of a decision to sample $n = 10$ *and* then to take optimal terminal action.   In Section 33.2 we saw that in our example the prior expected *cost* of optimal terminal action after taking a sample of 10 was $5 and in Section 33.3 we saw that the corresponding *loss* was $1.20.   We have just seen that the cost of sampling is $.45, and it follows that

Total expected cost = $5.00 + $.45 = $5.45,
Total expected loss = $1.20 + $.45 = $1.65.

Notice that the $.45 expenditure incurred by taking the sample of 10 pieces can be regarded as a *loss* just as well as it can be regarded as a *cost*, since our standard of reference for computing opportunity loss is always the cost of action with *free* perfect information.   If we were dealing with a problem involving a finite population and thus could actually obtain perfect information by taking a 100 per cent sample, the total expected loss of a decision to take a 100 per cent sample and then act optimally would be simply the cost of the sample.

33.4.1 Comparison with Immediate Terminal Action

We saw in Chapter 22 that if a terminal decision is to be made immediately, on the basis of the information available without sampling, then the better act is to reject at an expected *cost* of $8 (Table 22.3) or *loss* of $4.20 (Table 22.8).   A decision to take a sample of 10 and then take optimal terminal action is thus better than immediate terminal action by either of the differences

$8.00 − $5.45 = $2.55,
$4.20 − $1.65 = $2.55.

Observe, however, that this result obviously does *not* imply that taking a sample of size 10 is the *best possible* decision: some other sample size may lead to still lower cost or loss.

33.5 The Value vs. the Cost of Sampling

The comparison just made between the cost or loss of immediate terminal action and the total cost or loss of a decision to take a sample of size 10 and then act can also be expressed as a comparison between the $.45 cost of taking the sample and the amount by which the sample is "expected" to reduce the cost or loss of terminal action.   We have already seen that the cost and loss of *immediate* terminal action are respectively $8 and $4.20 and that the corresponding figures for terminal action *after sampling* are $5 and $1.20—notice that these latter figures do *not* include the cost of sampling.   We thus have

$8.00 − $5.00 = $3.00,
$4.20 − $1.20 = $3.00

as the *expected* reduction which a sample of size $n = 10$ will produce in *terminal* cost or loss.†

This expected reduction in terminal cost or loss can be considered the *expected value of the information to be obtained from the sample.* The *net gain* which we "expect" to make by sampling $n = 10$ before choosing a terminal act is this amount less the \$.45 cost of obtaining the information or

$$\$3.00 - \$.45 = \$2.55.$$

33.6   Summary and Generalization

Although the analysis of a decision to sample and then take optimal terminal action has been explained in terms of a specific example,

The method of analysis described above can be used to compute total expected profit, cost, or loss in any single-sample decision problem whatever.

To make this point clear we shall now summarize the method in completely general terms, without reference to the specific details of *any* particular decision problem.

The steps by which the total expected *cost* of any single-sample decision procedure can be computed are the following:

1. List every possible outcome of the sample and compute the *marginal probability* of each by the method of Section 12.3.
2. For each possible sample outcome, compute the posterior expected costs of all possible acts by one of the methods described in Part Three of the course and select the least of these as the *conditional terminal cost* for that sample outcome.
3. Multiply the conditional terminal cost for each sample outcome by the probability of that sample outcome and add the products to obtain the prior *expected terminal cost.*
4. Add the cost of sampling to obtain the *total expected cost* of the decision to sample and then take optimal terminal action.

To compute total expected *profit,* the same outline applies with two obvious minor changes: the conditional terminal profit for a given sample outcome is the *greatest* of the posterior expected profits for that outcome rather than the least, and total expected profit is obtained by *subtracting* the cost of sampling from expected terminal profit. Total expected *loss* can be found either (1) by following exactly the same outline as given for cost, the word "loss" being everywhere substituted for "cost," or (2) by adding the cost of sampling to the difference between the expected

† Remember that this is an *expected* reduction; as we have already seen (e.g. in Section 32.2.3), the sample information *may* actually *increase* expected cost or loss.

terminal cost or profit of the decision procedure and the expected cost or profit under certainty.

Interdependent Decisions. We have seen in Section 24.1 that in some situations the conditional costs of certain acts cannot be computed without knowledge of how *future* decisions will be made. This is true, for example, when a decision to reject means scrapping a lot of product and the costs which will be incurred in replacing the scrapped product cannot be computed without knowing how future lots will be accepted or rejected. In the language we are now using, a decision to reject in such a situation is *not a terminal decision*—it does not dispose of the problem once and for all. The method of analysis which we have studied in this chapter is therefore *not applicable to such problems;* a suitable method will be developed in Chapter 36.

33.6.1   Optimal Sample Size

Since we know how to compute total expected profit, cost, or loss for any sample size n in any single-sample decision problem, we know in principle how to find the *best* sample size in any such problem: we simply compute cost, profit, or loss for a large number of values of n and select the one with the greatest profit or the least cost or loss. It may seem that this is impossible even in principle because the number of possible n's is infinite, but this is not so. We have emphasized repeatedly that the expected value of *perfect* information is measured by the expected loss of the best immediate terminal act. Since the expected value of the information to be obtained by sampling can never be greater than the expected value of perfect information, it will never pay to take a sample so large that the cost of sampling is greater than the loss of the best immediate terminal act; and we therefore have only a finite number of n's to consider.†

When sampling is expensive relative to the loss of immediate terminal action, the largest admissible n will be fairly small and it will be quite feasible to evaluate total profit, cost, or loss for every admissible n by actually using a trial-and-error procedure of this sort. In most problems, however, this procedure would be extremely laborious and in subsequent chapters we shall therefore seek short cuts which take advantage of special features of the particular problem at hand. These short cuts will be of three kinds:

† In our example the expected loss of immediate terminal action is \$4.20 and the cost of sampling is \$.25 + \$.02 n. Since

$$\$.25 + (\$.02 \times 197.5) = \$4.20$$

we see at once that the optimal sample size is below 197.5. Computation of a few trial sample sizes will restrict the range of admissible n's still further. Thus we have seen that with $n = 10$ expected terminal loss in our example is only \$1.20, and since a sample of $n = 70$ would cost $(70 - 10) \times \$.02 = \$1.20$ more than a sample of 10, we already know that the optimal sample size is below 70.

1. We may be able to find shorter methods for computing total cost or loss for given n.

2. We may be able to prove that under certain conditions an n which is better than $n - 1$ and better than $n + 1$ is the best of all n's.

3. We may be able to find mathematical formulas which will give us either the best value of n or a good approximation to it very quickly.

33.6.2   The Cost of Uncertainty

We have repeatedly emphasized that the *cost of uncertainty* is the irreducible expected loss of the *best possible* decision under uncertainty. As long as we were dealing with situations where (further) sampling was impossible and the only acts under consideration were terminal acts, the cost of uncertainty was simply the expected loss of the best terminal act. As soon as (further) sampling is possible, this is no longer true: the cost of uncertainty is the total expected loss of the *best possible decision procedure*. If sequential decision procedures are not admissible in a given situation, the cost of uncertainty will be the total expected loss of the best possible single-sample procedure, i.e. of a single-sample procedure using a sample of optimal size (immediate terminal action being considered a single-sample procedure with $n = 0$). If sequential procedures *are* admissible, the best such procedure must be evaluated and compared with the best single-sample procedure before we can know the true cost of uncertainty.

PROBLEMS

1. Verify all entries in the line for $r = 1$ in Table 33.2 and in the same line in Table 33.3 and prove that rejection is in fact the better act for $r = 1$.

2. In the situation of the example in the text but with a sample of size $n = 3$ rather than 10, assuming that the cost of sampling is $.25 + $.02 n:

   a. Given the marginal probabilities $P(\tilde{r} = 2) = .021$ and $P(\tilde{r} = 3) = .002$, complete the computation of the marginal distribution of $\tilde{r}$.

   b. Given that the *conditional* terminal cost for $r = $ either 2 or 3 is $8, compute the *expected* cost of terminal action after sampling $n = 3$.

   c. Using the result of (*b*) and the fact that the prior expected cost of action under certainty is $3.80, compute the expected loss of terminal action after sampling $n = 3$.

   d. Given that the *conditional* terminal losses given $r = 2$ and 3 are respectively $.06 and $.00, check your answer to *c* by taking the expectation of all possible conditional terminal losses.

   e. Find the expected value of the information in a sample of $n = 3$, the expected net gain of taking a sample of this size, and expected total cost and loss with a sample of this size.

3. Given that the *best* sample size for the example of the text is $n = 27$ and that the expected terminal cost of a decision to take a sample of this size and then take optimal terminal action is $4.22, compute:

   a. The expected value of the information in the sample.

   b. The expected net gain from sampling.

   c. The cost of uncertainty.

   d. The expected terminal loss.

CHAPTER 34

Two-action Problems with Linear Costs:
Expected Loss and the Prior Distribution
of the Posterior Mean

In Part Three of the course we repeatedly made use of the fact that when
the conditional cost of a particular terminal act is a *linear* function of the
value of the basic random variable, the expected cost of that act under
any probability distribution is the same as if the basic random variable
were known with certainty to have a value equal to the mean of its distribution. At that time we used this relation to simplify the computation of posterior expected costs *after* a sample had been taken and a particular outcome had been observed; but it can be used equally well
before the sample is taken to calculate what the posterior expected
costs *will* be *if* any given sample outcome is observed, i.e. to simplify
computation of conditional terminal cost for each possible sample outcome. In the present chapter we shall first illustrate the method using
the same example which we used in Chapter 33, and we shall then proceed
to show how the method leads to an extremely simple and convenient
formula for the expected value of sample information when the prior
and sampling distributions are Normal.

34.1   Computation of Conditional Terminal Cost by Use of $E_1(\tilde{p})$

In Figure 22.1 we saw that the conditional costs of the two possible
terminal acts in the example discussed in the last chapter are both linear
functions of the value of the basic random variable $\tilde{p}$—they graph as
straight lines when plotted against p. Specifically, the formulas for the
two lines were

Conditional cost of acceptance = \$200 p,
Conditional cost of rejection = \$8.

Because of this linearity we could write immediately

Posterior expected cost of acceptance = \$200 $E_1(\tilde{p})$,
Posterior expected cost of rejection = \$8.

34.1.1   Conditional Terminal Cost

We also saw in Table 22.6 that after the outcome $\tilde{r} = 0$ had been observed in a sample of $n = 10$ the value of $E_1(\tilde{p})$ was .01916 and therefore the posterior cost of acceptance was $200 \times .01916 = \$3.83$. Since the conditional terminal cost for any value of $\tilde{r}$ is by definition the posterior cost of the *optimal* act given that value of $\tilde{r}$ and since $\$3.83 < \$8.00$, this tells us immediately that $3.83 is the conditional terminal cost given $\tilde{r} = 0$.

The value of $E_1(\tilde{p})$ given the next higher value $\tilde{r} = 1$ is computed in Table 34.1, where the first five columns correspond to Table 22.4 and the last column corresponds to Table 22.6. In this case we observe that $200 \times .08134 = \$16.27$ is *greater* than $8; we conclude that the optimal terminal act given $\tilde{r} = 1$ is rejection and that the conditional terminal cost is $8.

Table 34.1

p	$P_0(p)$	$P_b(r\|p)$	$P(r,p)$	$P_1(p\|r)$	$p\,P_1(p)$
.01	.7	.0914	.06398	.429	.00429
.05	.1	.3151	.03151	.212	.01060
.15	.1	.3474	.03474	.233	.03495
.25	.1	.1877	.01877	.126	.03150
	1.0		.14900	1.000	.08134 = $E_1(\tilde{p})$

34.1.2   Prior Expected Terminal Cost

In Table 34.2 we list all possible values of $\tilde{r}$ and opposite each one its probability, the corresponding value of $E_1(\tilde{p})$, and the conditional terminal cost as determined by the method just described. Notice that the *marginal* probabilities of the various values of $\tilde{r}$ are brought out automatically in the computation of $E_1(\tilde{p})$—the probability that $\tilde{r} = 1$ appears as the total .149 of the fourth column in Table 34.1. The prior expected terminal cost is then computed in the last column of Table 34.2 in the usual manner, by multiplying each of the conditional costs by the corresponding probability and adding the products; the results agree of course with Table 33.2.

34.1.3   Behavior of $E_1(\tilde{p})$ as r Increases

One very minor advantage of the present method of analysis over the general method used in the previous chapter lies in the fact that it permits us to shorten the computation of expected terminal cost by observing what happens to $E_1(\tilde{p})$ as r increases.

Rejection will be the optimal act and $8 will be the conditional terminal cost whenever $200\,E_1(\tilde{p})$ is greater than $8, i.e. whenever $E_1(\tilde{p})$

is above the break-even value (cf. Section 22.4.3)

$$p_b = \frac{\$8}{\$200} = .04.$$

Looking again at Table 34.2 we can see that each successive value of $E_1(\tilde{p})$ is larger than the previous value; and if we stop to think for a moment we see that it is obvious that each increase in the number of

Table 34.2

| r | $P_0(r)$ | $E_1(\tilde{p})$ | Terminal cost | |
			Conditional	Expected
0	.718	.01916	$3.83	$2.74
1	.149	.08134	8.00	1.19
2	.066	.17514	8.00	.53
3	.039	.21099	8.00	.31
4	.019	.22752	8.00	.15
5	.007	.23714	8.00	.06
6	.002	.24282	8.00	.02
7	.000	.24608	8.00	.00
8	.000	.24787	8.00	.00
9	.000	.24896	8.00	.00
10	.000	.25000	8.00	.00
	1.000			$5.00

defectives in the sample *must* increase the expected value which it is rational to assign to the process fraction defective. Thus we did not really need to compute all the values of $P(r)$ and $E_1(\tilde{p})$ shown in Table 34.2. As soon as we found that $E_1(\tilde{p})$ was greater than .04 for $\tilde{r} = 1$, we could have concluded that the conditional terminal cost was $8 for

Table 34.3

| Sample outcome | Probability | Terminal cost | |
		Conditional	Expected
$r = 0$, $E_1(\tilde{p}) < .04$	.718	$3.83	$2.74
$r > 0$, $E_1(\tilde{p}) > .04$	.282	8.00	2.26
	1.000		$5.00

this value of $\tilde{r}$ *and all higher values;* and since we already knew that $P(\tilde{r} = 0) = .718$, we could have computed $P(\tilde{r} \geq 1) = 1 - .718 = .282$. Prior expected terminal cost could then have been computed as in Table 34.3.

34.2 $E_1(\tilde{p})$ Considered as a Statistic; the Prior Distribution of the Posterior Mean

When we first introduced the notion of a statistic in Section 25.4, we emphasized that while a statistic is by definition a random variable whose value *depends on the sample outcome*, it is *not* necessarily computed *exclusively* from the values of the sample observations.   Thus we have called $u = [r - E(\tilde{r})]/\sigma(\tilde{r})$ a statistic even though its value depends on the parameters $E(\tilde{r})$ and $\sigma(\tilde{r})$ as well as on the sample outcome r; and in exactly the same way we can consider $E_1(\tilde{p})$ a statistic: it is a random variable whose value depends on the sample outcome.   *The sample is summarized just as well by the statistic* $E_1(\tilde{p})$ *as it is by the statistic* r; *since* r *is sufficient, so is* $E_1(\tilde{p})$.

In order to compute prior expected terminal cost we have hitherto considered each possible sample outcome as summarized by the statistic r, computed the conditional terminal cost for each value of $\tilde{r}$, multiplied each conditional cost by the probability of the corresponding value of $\tilde{r}$, and added the products.   We can describe this operation equally well if we everywhere substitute $E_1(p)$ for r: we can regard the *conditional costs* in Table 34.2 as conditional on $E_1(\tilde{p})$ rather than on r, and we can regard the *probabilities* in that table as the prior probabilities of the various possible $E_1(\tilde{p})$ rather than as the prior probabilities of the various possible r.   Looked at in this way, the second and third columns of Table 34.2 give us the prior distribution of the mean of the posterior distribution of the basic random variable, or more briefly, the *prior distribution of the posterior mean.*

Notation.   When the posterior mean is regarded as a random variable, our standard system of notation calls for the symbol $\tilde{E}_1(\tilde{p})$; the probability that the posterior mean is greater than .04 would be written $P[\tilde{E}_1(\tilde{p}) > .04]$.   This notation is so clumsy that we shall abridge it by defining

$\tilde{E}_1$: the mean of the posterior distribution of any random variable when this mean is itself regarded as a random variable whose value depends on an as yet unknown sample outcome.

34.2.1   Use of the Distribution of $\tilde{E}_1$ to Compute Expected Terminal Cost

Although the interpretation of Table 34.2 as showing the distribution of $\tilde{E}_1$ rather than the distribution of $\tilde{r}$ makes no change in the actual arithmetic by which expected terminal cost with $n = 10$ is computed, it can give us greater insight into the meaning of this computation by showing how closely it resembles the computation of expected terminal cost under certainty.   To bring this out we shall first give a graphic representation of the computation of expected terminal cost under certainty and then show that exactly the same representation can be used for the computation of expected terminal cost under a single-sample procedure.

Terminal Cost under Certainty. If we refer back once more to the graphs of the two conditional costs in Figure 22.1, we see immediately that when we are told the true value of $\tilde{p}$ we will select the act whose cost line is *lower* at that value of $\tilde{p}$. Figure 34.1 reproduces Figure 22.1 except that the parts of the cost lines which represent costs that would

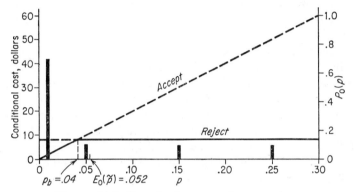

Figure 34.1. Terminal cost under certainty.

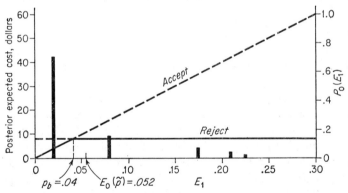

Figure 34.2. Terminal cost under a single-sample procedure.

not be incurred under certainty have been dashed. *Conditional cost under certainty is represented by the broken line formed by the solid parts of the accept and reject lines in Figure* 34.1.

To compute *prior expected* terminal cost under certainty we simply read the solid conditional cost line in Figure 34.1 at each possible value of $\tilde{p}$, multiply each conditional cost by the prior probability of that value of $\tilde{p}$, and add the products. A graph of the prior distribution of $\tilde{p}$ has been superimposed upon the graph of conditional cost in Figure 34.1, and the computation of expected cost can be thought of as proceeding by multiplying the height of each bar by the height of the solid cost line at the mid-point of the bar and adding the products. Probabilities are represented by heights rather than areas in this figure in order to make their numerical values easier to read.

Terminal Cost under a Single-sample Procedure. Since the posterior expected costs of the two possible acts given any sample outcome E_1 are the same as if $\tilde{p}$ were known with certainty to have the value E_1, we may relabel the vertical axis of Figure 22.1 as "posterior expected cost" if at the same time we relabel the horizontal axis as E_1; and since we will choose the optimal act after sampling just as we would under certainty, the lower of the two lines at any E_1 shows the conditional terminal cost. Accordingly the graph of conditional terminal cost under a single-sample procedure shown by the solid cost line in Figure 34.2 is identical to the graph of conditional terminal cost under certainty shown in Figure 34.1.

To compute *prior expected* terminal cost with $n = 10$, we superimpose on the cost lines in Figure 34.2 a graph of the prior distribution of $\tilde{E}_1$ for $n = 10$ which was given numerically in Table 34.2. The calculations of Table 34.2 then correspond to multiplying the height of each bar in Figure 34.2 by the height of the solid cost line at the middle of the bar and adding the products.

34.2.2   Use of the Distribution of $\tilde{E}_1$ to Compute the Expected Value of Sample Information

The prior distribution of the posterior mean $\tilde{E}_1$ can also be used to make a direct computation of the *expected value of the information to be obtained from a sample*, and in general this will prove to be the most efficient and clearest way of analyzing two-action problems with linear costs. Since there is a very close analogy between this computation and the computation of the *expected value of perfect information*, we shall give a graphic representation of this latter computation before giving a similar representation of the computation of the value of sample information.

Expected Value of Perfect Information. It was shown in Table 22.6 that $E_0(\tilde{p}) = .052$ in our example; and since the break-even value $p_b = .04$ (cf. Section 22.4.3), we know at once that rejection is the better act under the prior distribution of $\tilde{p}$: the cost line for rejection is lower than the cost line for acceptance at $p = .052$ in Figure 34.1. If then we are given perfect information that $\tilde{p}$ has any value *above* the break-even value p_b, this information will be valueless: rejection will still be the better act and the information will have no effect. If, however, we receive perfect information that $\tilde{p}$ has a value *below* p_b, we will reverse our choice of act and save the difference in cost; this difference is the *conditional* value of perfect information.

The only possible value of $\tilde{p}$ below p_b is $p = .01$, as can be seen from Figure 34.1, and the difference between the heights of the two cost lines at this point is the

Conditional VPI = \$8 − (\$200 × .01) = \$6.

The prior probability that $\tilde{p}$ has this value is

$P_0(\tilde{p} = .01) = .7,$

and therefore the *expected* value of perfect information is

Expected VPI = \$6 × .7 = \$4.20

in agreement with Table 22.8.

Expected Value of Sample Information.   We now proceed to compute the expected value of the information in a sample of size 10 in exactly this same way except that we use Figure 34.2 and the prior distribution of $\tilde{E}_1$ rather than Figure 34.1 and the prior distribution of $\tilde{p}$.   If $\tilde{E}_1$ has a value *greater* than p_b, we will choose the same act after sampling that we would have chosen without sampling and the sample information will have been valueless.   If, however, $\tilde{E}_1$ has a value *less* than p_b, we will reverse our choice and "expect" to save the difference between the heights of the two cost lines at that value of $\tilde{E}_1$.   The only possible value of $\tilde{E}_1$ below p_b is $E_1 = .01916$ and the difference between the heights of the two cost lines at this point is the

Conditional VSI = \$8 − (\$200 × .01916) = \$4.17.

The prior probability that $\tilde{E}_1$ will have this value is

$P_0(\tilde{E}_1 = .01916) = .718,$

and therefore the expected value of the information to be obtained from a sample of size 10 is

Expected VSI = \$4.17 × .718 = \$3.00

in agreement with Section 33.5.   We remind the student that the expected *net gain* from taking the sample is this amount less the cost of sampling.

34.3   The Distribution of $\tilde{E}_1$ When the Prior and Sampling Distributions Are Normal and the Sampling Variance Is Known

When the prior distribution of the basic random variable is given in numerical form, the distribution of the posterior mean $\tilde{E}_1$ must always be obtained by numerical methods as in the example we have just discussed.   When on the contrary the prior distribution is specified by an algebraic formula, we can often find a formula for the distribution of $\tilde{E}_1$ and thus greatly simplify the calculation of the expected value of the information in a sample.   In this course we shall give formulas of this sort only for the case where the prior and sampling distributions are both Normal and the variance of the sampling distribution is known.

More specifically, we shall deal only with situations of the kind described in Sections 31.1 and 31.2. We assume throughout the rest of this chapter that any sample mean $\bar{x}$ can be regarded as the sum of the *true value* ξ of the quantity being measured, the *bias* β of the measuring or sampling process, and the mean *pure sampling error* $\bar{\epsilon}$,

$$\bar{x} = \xi + \beta + \bar{\epsilon};$$

and we assume that when these quantities are considered as random variables the following conditions are met:

1. The prior distribution of $\tilde{\xi}$ is Normal.
2. The distribution of $\tilde{\beta}$ is Normal and independent of $\tilde{\xi}$ except possibly for the effect of a pilot sample.
3. The distribution of $\tilde{\bar{\epsilon}}$ is Normal and independent of both $\tilde{\xi}$ and $\tilde{\beta}$.
4. The variance $\sigma^2(\tilde{\epsilon})$ of an individual pure sampling error is known.
5. The variance $\sigma^2(\tilde{\bar{\epsilon}})$ of the mean pure sampling error can be written $(1/n)\sigma^2(\tilde{\epsilon})$: either the population of potential ϵ's is infinite or the finite-population correction is negligible.

On these assumptions it can be shown that

The distribution of $\tilde{E}_1$ is Normal

as we might expect; and even without these assumptions it can be shown that in almost *any* problem *the mean of the distribution of $\tilde{E}_1$ is equal to the mean of the prior distribution of $\tilde{\xi}$ itself:*

$$\mathrm{E}(\tilde{E}_1) = \mathrm{E}_0(\tilde{\xi}) \qquad \textit{No restrictions}$$

Before the sample is taken we think that the posterior mean $\tilde{E}_1$ *may* be *either* greater or less than the prior mean E_0, but because we have no way of telling which kind of change will occur the *expected* value of $\tilde{E}_1$ is *equal* to E_0.

The *variance* of $\tilde{E}_1$, unlike the mean, *does* depend critically on our assumptions, and we shall have to consider two quite different cases: (1) $\tilde{\beta}$ *independent* of $\tilde{\xi}$ and (2) $\tilde{\beta}$ *dependent* on $\tilde{\xi}$ through the effect of a pilot sample. The situation where bias is *known* can be considered a special case of *either* of these two more general cases.

34.3.1 *Variance of $\tilde{E}_1$ When No Pilot Sample Has Been Taken*

When the bias of the measuring or sampling process has a distribution which is *independent* of the distribution of the basic random variable, the variance of the $\tilde{E}_1$ to be obtained from a sample of size n can be found by first calculating the quantities

$$\sigma^2_\infty(\tilde{E}_1) = \sigma^2_0(\xi) \frac{\sigma^2_0(\xi)}{\sigma^2_0(\xi) + \sigma^2(\tilde{\beta})}$$

$$\sigma^{*2}_\epsilon = \sigma^2(\bar{\epsilon}) \left[\frac{\sigma^2_0(\xi)}{\sigma^2_0(\xi) + \sigma^2(\tilde{\beta})} \right]^2$$

$\tilde{\beta}$ and ξ *independent; no pilot*

and then applying the formula

$$\sigma^2(\tilde{E}_1) = \sigma^2_\infty(\tilde{E}_1) \frac{\sigma^2_\infty(\tilde{E}_1)}{\sigma^2_\infty(\tilde{E}_1) + (1/n)\sigma^{*2}_\epsilon}$$

To get some intuitive feeling for the common sense of these formulas, we first observe that when the bias β is *known*, i.e. when $\sigma(\tilde{\beta}) = 0$, the formulas reduce to

$$\sigma^2_\infty(\tilde{E}_1) = \sigma^2_0(\xi), \qquad \sigma^{*2}_\epsilon = \sigma^2(\bar{\epsilon}),$$

$$\sigma^2(\tilde{E}_1) = \sigma^2_0(\xi) \frac{\sigma^2_0(\xi)}{\sigma^2_0(\xi) + (1/n)\sigma^2(\bar{\epsilon})}.$$

β *known*

If we take no sample at all, $n = 0$, then $\sigma(\tilde{E}_1) = 0$: the "posterior" mean is *certain* to be equal to the prior mean because the posterior distribution of ξ *is* the prior distribution when no new evidence has been obtained. If on the contrary the sample is so large that there is *no* sampling error, $n = \infty$, then the variance of $\tilde{E}_1$ is equal to the variance of ξ itself: if we visualize the sampling operation as being carried out repeatedly, the sample will give us perfect information on the value of ξ on each individual occasion and therefore $\tilde{E}_1$ will have a frequency distribution identical to that of ξ itself.

Next returning to our original set of formulas, applying when there *is* uncertainty about bias, we first remark that in this case just as in the previous one $\sigma(\tilde{E}_1) = 0$ if $n = 0$: the "posterior" mean is certain to be equal to the prior mean if no sample is taken. The existence of uncertainty about bias does change the results for nonzero sample sizes, however. Because of his uncertainty about β, a businessman would not have complete confidence in the results of even an infinitely large sample; therefore his prior expectation of ξ would have an effect on his posterior expectation even in the face of the evidence obtained from such a sample; and therefore the distribution of the $\tilde{E}_1$ which might be obtained from such a sample is "pulled in" toward $E_0(\xi)$. It is still true that the *mean* of the distribution of $\tilde{E}_1$ is $E_0(\xi)$, but the *variance* of the distribution is reduced from $\sigma_0^2(\xi)$ to a fraction of this amount, the fraction becoming smaller as the ratio of $\sigma(\tilde{\beta})$ to $\sigma_0(\xi)$ becomes larger. Finally, observe that because the "adjusted sampling variance" σ_ϵ^{*2} is only a fraction of $\sigma^2(\tilde{\epsilon})$, any given ratio $\sigma^2(\tilde{E}_1)/\sigma_\infty^2(\tilde{E}_1)$ can be obtained with a smaller sample size n when there is uncertainty about bias than when there is no such uncertainty. Essentially this is another reflection of a fact already pointed out in Section 31.2.6: uncertainty about bias means that sampling suffers from the law of diminishing returns sooner and more severely than it would otherwise and *in this respect* has an effect similar to the effect of a reduction in pure sampling variance.

34.3.2　Variance of $\tilde{E}_1$ after a Pilot Sample Has Been Taken

In a great many practical problems a terminal decision is not made immediately upon learning the results of the very first sample to be taken. In particular, it is a very common and very sound practice to begin the investigation of the facts bearing on an important decision by taking a small *pilot sample,* the exact size of which is determined by convenience rather than by exact economic analysis. If such a pilot sample is taken, its outcome *may* be so decisive that no further sampling is necessary; but it may also be that calculation of the expected loss of terminal action at this point shows that substantial risk is involved, and the businessman will then want to make a careful economic analysis in order to decide whether a *second* sample should be taken and if so how large it should be.

If there is no uncertainty about bias, no special problems are involved in such analysis. The distribution of ξ posterior to the pilot sample becomes the prior distribution in regard to the proposed new sample, and if we let $E_0(\xi)$ and $\sigma_0(\xi)$ denote the parameters of this *"revised prior"* distribution, the mean of the distribution of the $\tilde{E}_1$ which will result from any *new* sample is equal to $E_0(\xi)$ and its variance is given immediately by the formulas in Section 34.3.1.

If on the contrary there *is* uncertainty about bias, then we *do* have a special problem: the formulas in Section 34.3.1 do not apply because *the random variables ξ and $\tilde{\beta}$ are no longer independent after the pilot sample has been taken* (cf. Section 31.2.7). The *mean* of the distribution of $\tilde{E}_1$ is still equal to the mean of the *revised* prior distribution of ξ; but to obtain the *variance* of $\tilde{E}_1$ we must go all the way back to the *original* prior distributions of ξ and $\tilde{\beta}$ which applied *before* the pilot made ξ and $\tilde{\beta}$ interdependent. Defining

$\sigma_{00}^2(\xi)$, $\sigma_{00}^2(\tilde{\beta})$: the variances of the *original* distributions of ξ and $\tilde{\beta}$, as assessed *before* the pilot sample was taken,

we first compute the variance of $\tilde{E}_1$ for an infinite sample and the "adjusted sampling variance" as they were *before* the pilot sample was taken,

$$\sigma_\infty'^2 = \sigma_{00}^2(\xi) \frac{\sigma_{00}^2(\xi)}{\sigma_{00}^2(\xi) + \sigma_{00}^2(\tilde{\beta})}$$

$$\sigma_\epsilon^{*2} = \sigma^2(\tilde{\epsilon}) \left[\frac{\sigma_{00}^2(\xi)}{\sigma_{00}^2(\xi) + \sigma_{00}^2(\tilde{\beta})}\right]^2$$

Then defining

n_0: the size of the *pilot* sample,

we have for the variance of the $\tilde{E}_1$ to be obtained from an infinite *new* sample

$$\sigma_\infty^2(\tilde{E}_1) = \sigma_\infty'^2 \frac{(1/n_0)\sigma_\epsilon^{*2}}{\sigma_\infty'^2 + (1/n_0)\sigma_\epsilon^{*2}} \qquad Posterior\ to\ pilot$$

and from this we can compute the variance of the $\tilde{E}_1$ to be obtained from a new sample of finite size n:

$$\sigma^2(\tilde{E}_1) = \sigma_\infty^2(\tilde{E}_1) \frac{\sigma_\infty^2(\tilde{E}_1)}{\sigma_\infty^2(\tilde{E}_1) + (1/n)\sigma_\epsilon^{*2}}$$

Notice that this final formula for $\sigma^2(\tilde{E}_1)$ is identical to the corresponding formula in Section 34.3.1 and that the formula for $\sigma_\infty^2(\tilde{E}_1)$ reduces to the corresponding formula in Section 34.3.1 when $n_0 = 0$, i.e. when no pilot sample has been taken.

"Informationless" Original Distributions. A very important special case of the general problem treated in this section arises when the *original* distribution of ξ is "informationless," i.e. when $\sigma_{00}(\xi) = \infty$. The formulas given above reduce in this case to

$$\sigma_\infty^2(\tilde{E}_1) = \frac{1}{n_0}\sigma^2(\tilde{\epsilon}), \qquad \sigma_\epsilon^{*2} = \sigma^2(\tilde{\epsilon}), \qquad \sigma_{00}(\xi) = \infty$$

$$\sigma^2(\tilde{E}_1) = \frac{1}{n_0}\sigma^2(\tilde{\epsilon})\frac{n}{n_0 + n}, \qquad Pilot\ of\ size\ n_0$$

and we see that

> When the evidence of the pilot sample constitutes our *only* information about ξ, uncertainty about bias is irrelevant to the distribution of $\tilde{E}_1$.

The essential effect of bias is to reduce the weight given to the sample evidence *relative* to the prior evidence; *if there is no prior evidence, then we must rely completely on the sample evidence however shaky we may hold this evidence to be.*

34.3.3   Example

In Section 32.3 we studied a marketing problem in which a sample of 100 observations drawn from a population of 400,000 differences had shown that

$$\sigma^2(\bar{\epsilon}) \doteq 1.53^2 = 2.34;$$

the Normal prior distribution of the mean difference $\tilde{\xi}$ had had mean $+.146$ and standard deviation .310; and on the assumption that the sampling process was unbiased the sample evidence had led to a Normal posterior distribution with mean $-.140$ and standard deviation .137. The expected loss of terminal action under this posterior distribution was \$8800; and we now suppose that because this is a fairly substantial risk the marketer in question is thinking of taking 50 more observations before reaching a terminal decision and therefore wishes to determine the distribution of the $\tilde{E}_1$ which might result from this proposed sample.

The distribution of $\tilde{E}_1$ is Normal because the problem satisfies the conditions listed at the beginning of Section 34.3, and its mean is equal to the mean of the *revised* prior distribution (posterior to the pilot):

$$E(\tilde{E}_1) = -.140.$$

Its variance can be found in either of two ways.

1. Because a pilot sample has been taken, we can use the formulas of Section 34.3.2.   We have

$$\sigma_{00}^2(\tilde{\xi}) = .310^2 = .0961, \qquad \sigma_{00}^2(\tilde{\beta}) = 0, \qquad n_0 = 100,$$

$$\sigma_{\infty}'^2 = .0961 \, \frac{.0961}{.0961 + 0} = .0961,$$

$$\sigma_{\epsilon}^{*2} = 2.34 \left(\frac{.0961}{.0961 + 0} \right)^2 = 2.34,$$

$$\sigma_{\infty}^2(\tilde{E}_1) = .0961 \, \frac{\frac{1}{100} \times 2.34}{.0961 + \frac{1}{100} \times 2.34} = .0188,$$

$$\sigma^2(\tilde{E}_1) = .0188 \, \frac{.0188}{.0188 + \frac{1}{50} \times 2.34} = .00539.$$

2. Because there is no uncertainty about bias, we can apply the formulas of Section 34.3.1 directly to the variance

$$\sigma_0^2(\tilde{\xi}) = .137^2 = .0188$$

of the *revised* prior distribution.

$$\sigma_\infty^2(\tilde{E}_1) = .0188 \frac{.0188}{.0188 + 0} = .0188,$$

$$\sigma_\epsilon^{*2} = 2.34 \left(\frac{.0188}{.0188 + 0}\right)^2 = 2.34,$$

$$\sigma^2(E_1) = .0188 \frac{.0188}{.0188 + \frac{1}{50} \times 2.34} = .00539$$

as before.

34.4   Evaluation of a Single-sample Procedure When the Distribution of $\tilde{E}_1$ Is Normal

In Figure 34.3 we show the same two-action problem with completely general linear costs and Normal prior distribution of ξ which we depicted in Figure 30.4a.   The narrower Normal distribution shown in this figure and not in Figure 30.4a represents the prior distribution of the posterior mean $\tilde{E}_1$ for some arbitrarily chosen sample size.

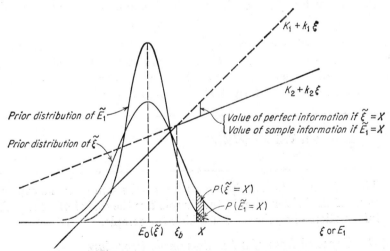

Figure 34.3. Value of perfect or sample information.

34.4.1   Expected Loss of Immediate Terminal Action

We start by reviewing the way in which we compute the expected loss of *immediate* terminal action without sampling.   This is the same thing as the expected value of *perfect* information to be received before any sample is taken, and we already know that if we define the *terminal loss constant*

$$k_t = |k_1 - k_2|$$

this value is given by the formulas

$$\text{Expected VPI} = k_t \sigma_0(\xi) G(D_0), \qquad D_0 = \frac{|\xi_b - \text{E}_0(\xi)|}{\sigma_0(\xi)}.$$

When we derived this result in Section 30.4 we had not yet introduced methods for dealing with bias and we therefore treated the cost-determining random variable as if it were necessarily equal to the long-run average μ of the sample observations. The student should now review the derivation and observe that every argument holds without change when ξ is substituted for $\tilde{\mu}$.

34.4.2   Expected Value of Sample Information; Net Gain of Sampling

We next take up the problem of computing the expected value of the information to be obtained from the sample which gives the distribution of $\tilde{E}_1$ shown in Figure 34.3. In Section 34.2.2 above we examined a particular numerical example and saw that

> The *expected value of sample information* is computed from the distribution of the posterior mean in exactly the same way that the expected value of perfect information is computed from the distribution of the basic random variable itself.

If the student will now again read Section 30.4, this time everywhere substituting $\tilde{E}_1$ for $\tilde{\mu}$, he will see that what was true in this particular example is true in complete generality for *any* distribution of $\tilde{E}_1$. It follows that when $\tilde{E}_1$ is Normal with mean $\text{E}(\tilde{E}_1) = \text{E}_0(\xi)$

$$\text{Expected VSI} = k_t \sigma(\tilde{E}_1) G(D_E) \qquad D_E = \frac{|\xi_b - \text{E}_0(\xi)|}{\sigma(\tilde{E}_1)}$$

The *net gain* to be expected from taking the sample is the expected *value* of the information in the sample *less* the *cost* of obtaining that information—i.e., the cost of taking the sample.

34.4.3   Expected Loss of a Single-sample Procedure

Sample information is valuable because it reduces the expected loss of terminal action. The expected *terminal* loss of a single-sample procedure is therefore equal to the expected loss of *immediate* terminal action *less* the expected value of the sample information:

$$\text{Expected terminal loss} = k_t[\sigma_0(\xi) G(D_0) - \sigma(\tilde{E}_1) G(D_E)].$$

The *total* expected loss of the procedure is its terminal loss *plus* the cost of sampling. Alternatively, it is the expected loss of *immediate* terminal action *less* the *net gain* of sampling.

34.4.4   Expected Profit or Cost of a Single-sample Procedure

The expected profit or cost of a single-sample procedure is usually much less interesting than the expected loss, but it is easy to find when it is required.   To do so, we simply *subtract* the *net gain* of sampling from the expected *cost* of the optimal immediate act or *add* the net gain to the expected *profit* of the optimal immediate act.

34.4.5   Example

We are now ready to compute the value of an additional sample in the marketing problem of Section 32.3.   In our original discussion of the problem we saw that

$$k_t = \$1,056,000, \qquad \xi_b = +.019;$$

and in Section 34.3.3 of the present chapter we saw that the distribution of the $\tilde{E}_1$ to be obtained from an additional 50 observations would be Normal with parameters

$$E(\tilde{E}_1) = -.140; \qquad \sigma(\tilde{E}_1) = \sqrt{.00539} = .0734.$$

We now compute

$$D_E = \frac{|.019 - (-.140)|}{.0733} = \frac{.159}{.0733} = 2.17,$$

use Table IV to find

$$G(2.17) = .00532,$$

and compute

Expected VSI $= \$1,056,000 \times .0733 \times .00532 = \$412.$

A sample of 50 observations will pay for itself only if the cost of taking the 50 observations is less than \$412.

The *expected terminal loss* of a decision to sample $n = 50$ is the terminal loss of action without sampling less the reduction in loss which the sample information is expected to produce, or \$8800 − \$412 = \$8388. Expected *total* loss is this amount plus the cost of sampling.

The reason why the value of the information in a sample of 50 is so small compared with the value of perfect information is easily seen from Figure 34.4, which is an enlargement of a part of Figure 32.1 on which the prior distributions of ξ and $\tilde{E}_1$ of our present example are superimposed.   Because $E_0(\xi)$ is *below* ξ_b, the better act without sampling is to reject and additional information will be valuable only if it tells us that

$\tilde{\xi}$ or $\tilde{E}_1$ is *greater* than ξ_b and thus reverses the original choice of terminal act.   Because the tail of the prior distribution of $\tilde{\xi}$ which lies above ξ_b is fairly large, there is a good chance that perfect information would in fact reverse the choice of act and therefore the expected value of perfect information is substantial.   In contrast, the distribution of $\tilde{E}_1$ given by a sample of only 50 observations is so narrow that it has an almost negligible tail above ξ_b; consequently there is an almost negligible chance that a

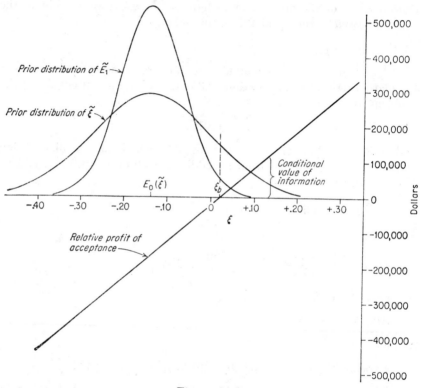

Figure 34.4

sample of this size will yield really valuable information and the expected value of the information is very small.

PROBLEMS

1. In the situation of Chapter 33, Problem 2, $E_1(\tilde{p}|r = 2) = .21310$ and $E_1(\tilde{p}|r = 3) = .23120$.

   a. What is the prior distribution of the random variable $\tilde{E}_1$?

   b. What terminal act is optimal for each possible value of $\tilde{E}_1$?

   c. By use of each possible value of $\tilde{E}_1$ compute the conditional terminal cost for that outcome.

   d. By use of your answers to (*a*) and (*c*) compute the prior expected terminal cost.

2. Discuss in general terms the effect of (*a*) expected bias and (*b*) uncertainty concerning bias on the expected value of the information to be gained from a sample of any given size.

3. In the situation of Chapter 30, Problem 1, compute the expected value of the information to be gained from another 100 observations

a. If management is willing to assume that the sampling procedure is unbiased and starts from the posterior distribution which you computed in answer to Chapter 30, Problem 1*d*.

b. If management holds the views about bias described in Chapter 31, Problem 6, and starts from the posterior distribution which you computed in answer to that problem.

4. In the situation of Chapter 32, Problem 4, compute the expected value of the information to be gained from another 100 interviews

a. On the assumptions of part *a* of the original problem.

b. On the assumptions of part *c* of the original problem.

CHAPTER 35

Two-action Problems with Linear Costs: Optimal Sample Size

We saw in Chapter 33 that in any decision problem whatever the total expected loss of a single-sample decision procedure with a sample of any given size can always be evaluated by numerical methods and the optimal sample size can always be found by evaluating a sufficiently large number of different sample sizes. It was pointed out at that time, however, that in certain kinds of problems these laborious numerical methods are not needed, and in Chapter 34 we derived a simple formula for total expected loss in two-action problems with linear costs, Normal prior and sampling distributions, and known sampling variance. We shall now see that in this same class of problems there is no need to evaluate total loss with a large number of sample sizes in order to find the optimal sample size; the desired result can be quickly found by a single, direct calculation.

35.1 Basic Assumptions

The reasoning of the present chapter will be based on the assumptions about the distributions of $\tilde{\xi}$, $\tilde{\beta}$, and $\tilde{\epsilon}$ which were summarized in Section 34.5.2. Since the great majority of practical problems involve either an infinite population or a finite population which is extremely large relative to any reasonable sample size, we shall assume that $\tilde{\epsilon}$ has variance

$$\sigma^2(\tilde{\epsilon}) = \frac{1}{n}\,\sigma^2(\tilde{\epsilon});$$

i.e., we assume that *the finite-population correction is negligible if it is present at all.*

35.1.1 Cost of Sampling

As regards the cost of sampling, we shall assume that it is a *linear function of the sample size*, i.e. that it is given by a formula of the type

Cost of sampling $= K_s + k_s n.$

The term K_s represents the *fixed costs* of setup, administration, analysis, reporting, etc., which will be incurred if any sample is taken at all but whose amounts do not depend on the sample size.   The term $k_s n$ gives the *variable cost* of sampling on the assumption that the incremental cost k_s of each additional sample item is the same.

35.2   Behavior of the Net Gain of Sampling as n Increases

35.2.1   *Value of the Information in an Infinite Sample*

We can obtain a base point for consideration of optimal sample size by computing the expected value of the information in an *infinitely large* sample.   This will of course depend on the variance of the $\tilde{E}_1$ which might be obtained from such a sample, and as we saw in Section 34.3, the way in which this variance is to be computed depends critically on the independence or interdependence of the distributions of $\tilde{\xi}$ and $\tilde{\beta}$.   If these distributions are independent, $\sigma^2_\infty(\tilde{E}_1)$ is to be computed by use of the formulas in Section 34.3.1; if they were originally independent but have become interdependent because a pilot sample has been taken, we must proceed as in Section 34.3.2 by first computing σ'^2_∞ as it was *before* the pilot sample was taken and then using this result to compute the value of $\sigma^2_\infty(\tilde{E}_1)$ *after* the pilot sample.   But in either case we define

$$D_\infty = \frac{|\xi_b - \mathrm{E}_0(\tilde{\xi})|}{\sigma_\infty(\tilde{E}_1)} \qquad \textit{No restrictions}$$

and then inserting these limiting values $\sigma_\infty(\tilde{E}_1)$ and D_∞ in place of $\sigma(\tilde{E}_1)$ and D_E in the formula for the expected value of sample information given in Section 34.4.2 we obtain the

Maximum $\mathrm{EVSI} = k_t \sigma_\infty(\tilde{E}_1) G(D_\infty)$.

This value is an upper bound on the amount which it is reasonable to spend for sampling, since the value of any finite sample will necessarily be less than the value of an infinite sample and no reasonable man will pay more for a sample than the information it contains is worth.

Minimum Terminal Loss.   It is worth remarking that if $\sigma(\tilde{\beta}) = 0$, then $\sigma_\infty(\tilde{E}_1) = \sigma_0(\tilde{\xi})$, $D_\infty = D_0$, and the expected value of an infinite sample is equal to the expected value of *perfect* information: when there is no uncertainty about bias, an infinitely large sample will in fact give us perfect information on the value of $\tilde{\xi}$.   Since the expected value of perfect information is the same thing as the expected loss of immediate terminal action, and since the expected terminal loss of a single-sample procedure is this amount reduced by the value of the sample information, we see that *expected terminal loss approaches* 0 *as the sample size approaches*

∞ *provided that there is no uncertainty about bias.* If, however, uncertainty about bias exists, i.e. if $\sigma(\tilde{\beta}) > 0$, the value of the information in a sample can never equal the value of perfect information because $\sigma(\tilde{E}_1)$ can never equal $\sigma_0(\tilde{\xi})$; and therefore terminal loss can never be reduced below some minimum which depends on the magnitude of $\sigma(\tilde{\beta})$.

35.2.2   Net Gain of Sampling

The *net* gain to be expected from any sample is the expected value of the information it will contain less the cost of obtaining this information:

Expected net gain $= k_t \sigma(\tilde{E}_1) G(D_E) - K_s - k_s n.$

The optimal sample size n^* will be the value of n which yields the greatest possible expected net gain.

Before we can find a procedure for determining the exact value of n^* in any given problem we must examine the general way in which expected net gain varies with n. This can be investigated by the aid of the calculus,† and we shall now examine the conclusions reached by such an investigation and show why they are plausible even though we cannot examine the justification for these conclusions in full detail.

35.2.3   The Essential Parameters of the Decision Problem

It is obvious that the way in which net gain varies with sample size in any problem will depend in some way or another on the values of all the eight parameters which define the problem: the break-even value ξ_b, the loss constants k_t, k_s, and K_s, the mean of the prior distribution $E_0(\tilde{\xi})$, and the standard deviations $\sigma_0(\tilde{\xi})$, $\sigma(\tilde{\beta})$, and $\sigma(\tilde{\epsilon})$. If we had to consider the effect of each of these eight parameters separately, our task would be hopelessly complex; but fortunately it can be shown that the *general nature* of the behavior of net gain depends only on the value of the fixed sampling cost K_s and the values of two *combinations* of the other seven parameters: the one which we called D_∞ in Section 35.2.1 and

$$Z = \frac{\sigma_\infty(\tilde{E}_1)}{\sigma_\epsilon^*} \sqrt[3]{\frac{k_t \sigma_\epsilon^*}{k_s}}$$

where $\sigma_\infty(\tilde{E}_1)$ and σ_ϵ^* are to be computed from the formulas in Section 34.3.1 if the distributions of $\tilde{\xi}$ and $\tilde{\beta}$ are independent, or from the formulas in Section 34.3.2 if these distributions were originally independent but have become interdependent because a pilot sample has already been taken.

---

† Specifically, by examining the first and second derivatives of net gain with respect to n.

We are now ready to examine the behavior of net gain with n as determined by D_∞, Z, and K_s. We shall proceed by first describing the behavior for the case $K_s = 0$; we shall then see that it is extremely easy to modify this description to allow for the effect of a nonzero K_s.

35.2.4   Behavior of Net Gain When $K_s = 0$ and $D_\infty = 0$

D_∞ has the value 0 when the mean $E_0(\xi)$ of the prior distribution is equal to the break-even value ξ_b. Half the prior probability is on one side of ξ_b, half on the other; if either of the two terminal acts is chosen *without* sampling, there is an even chance that this act will be the wrong one. In such a situation even a very small sample will substantially increase the probability of choosing the right act, and accordingly the expected value of the sample information at first increases very rapidly as n increases from 0. This initial rate at which value increases with n is always greater than the rate at which the variable sampling cost $k_s n$ increases, and therefore net gain = value minus cost always starts by *increasing* with n, as shown in Figure 35.1. The value of the information has a definite maximum, however, and therefore increases more and more slowly as n becomes greater, whereas the cost continues indefinitely to increase in strict proportion to n. The result is that there is some value of n beyond which cost increases faster than value, and at this point the *net* gain stops rising and starts to fall. The highest point on the net-gain curve marks the optimum value of n.

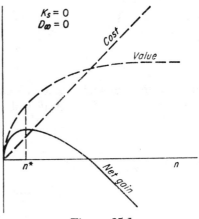

Figure 35.1

35.2.5   Behavior of Net Gain When $K_s = 0$ and $D_\infty > 0$

When $D_\infty > 0$ the prior distribution definitely favors one of the two terminal acts and it is very improbable that a really small sample will affect the decision. $E_0(\xi)$ is some distance to one side or the other of ξ_b, and if the standard deviation of $\tilde{E}_1$ is very small, as it is when n is very small, there is virtually zero probability that sampling will actually reverse the choice of terminal act by yielding an E_1 on the opposite side of ξ_b from $E_0(\xi)$. Accordingly the expected value of sample information starts by increasing very slowly with n. As n becomes large enough for the sample to have a real chance of affecting the decision, the value increases more rapidly; but as the value approaches the value of an infinite sample its rate of increase again becomes small and approaches 0.

Since the variable cost of sampling increases steadily with n from the very beginning, it is not obvious that there will be *any* value of n for which

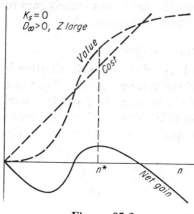

the expected value of the sample is greater than its cost. Whether or not there is such a value can be shown to depend on the relative magnitudes of D_∞ and Z. *If Z is larger than a certain critical value which depends on D_∞*, the net gain will behave as shown in Figure 35.2, first becoming negative, then rising to some maximum positive value at the optimal value of n, and then falling off to become more and more negative. *If Z is smaller than this critical value*, net gain will behave in one of the ways depicted in Figures 35.3a and

Figure 35.2

b: there may or may not be a peak in the net-gain curve; but even if there is, the top of the peak will represent a *negative* net gain and the

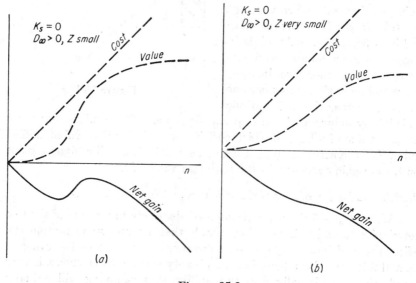

Figure 35.3

best sample size will be no sample at all. The critical value of Z is graphed as a function of D_∞ in Figure 35.4.†

---

† The figure has a scale showing $P_N(\hat{u} > D_\infty)$ as well as D_∞ itself; this extra scale has no meaning in our present problem but will be of interest in Part Five of the course.

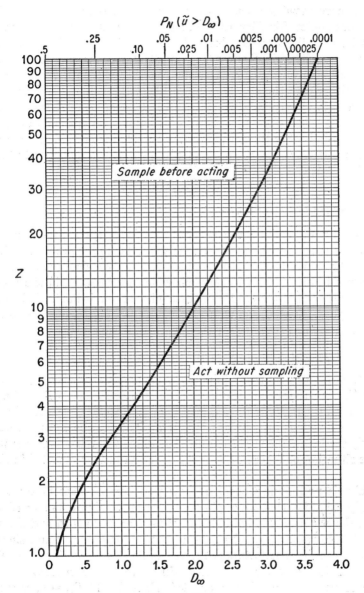

Figure 35.4

35.2.6   The Effect of Nonzero K_s

It is now easy to see the effect of a fixed element of sampling cost. Every point on the line showing sampling *cost* in any of the graphs we have just examined will be raised by the amount K_s, the *value* of the sample information will be totally unaffected, and therefore every point on the curve showing *net gain* will be lowered by the amount K_s. In the situations depicted in Figures 35.3a and b no sample is worth its cost even when $K_s = 0$; the same conclusion holds a fortiori when $K_s > 0$. In the situations depicted in Figures 35.1 and 35.2, moving the net-gain curve downward may or may not carry the peak below 0 on the vertical scale, but in either case the change will not affect the value of n at which the peak occurs. If the peak remains over 0 after being lowered by the amount K_s, this lowering has no effect whatever on optimal sample size; it merely diminishes the net gain to be expected from taking a sample of this size. If, however, the peak goes below 0, it will be better to take no sample at all.

35.3   Optimal Sample Size

Having determined the general way in which expected net gain behaves with sample size n, we are ready to take up the problem of finding the exact value of the optimal sample size n^*. We shall follow the same procedure in discussing this problem which we followed in the previous section: we shall first consider the case where there is no fixed element in sampling cost, $K_s = 0$, and we shall then see how our conclusions can very easily be modified to allow for the presence of such a cost.

35.3.1   *Optimal Sample Size When $K_s = 0$*

The first step in determining optimal sample size when $K_s = 0$ is to determine whether or not there is *any* sample size which will yield a positive net gain. If $D_\infty = 0$, so that Figure 35.1 applies, we know immediately that such a sample size exists; if $D_\infty > 0$, the question can be quickly settled by the use of Figure 35.4, which will tell us whether we are in the situation of Figure 35.2 or one of the situations depicted in Figure 35.3.

If this preliminary check reveals that sample sizes better than 0 actually exist, i.e. that we are in the situation of Figure 35.1 or 35.2 and not in the situation of Figure 35.3, our next problem is to find the value n^* which corresponds to the peak of the net-gain curve; and since the curve is necessarily flat at its peak, we can do this by finding an algebraic expression for the *slope* of the net-gain curve and then looking for the value or values of n which make this slope 0. If $D_\infty = 0$, there will always be one and only one such n, corresponding to the single peak in Figure 35.1. If $D_\infty > 0$ and Figure 35.4 tells us that we are in the situation of Figure 35.2, there will be two n's which give zero slope, the smaller one corresponding to the bottom of the dip in the net-gain curve and the larger one to the top of the peak. Since the formula for the slope of the net-gain curve is not a simple one and it requires a good deal of computation to find the n which makes the slope 0 for given Z and D_∞, we do not give the formula itself but instead present Chart II, from which the value of n^* can be determined much more easily. This chart shows, not the optimal sample size n^* itself, but the optimal value of the ratio

$$h = \frac{n}{(\sqrt[3]{k_t \sigma_\epsilon^* / k_s})^2}.$$

The results shown in Figure 35.4 have been taken into account in constructing Chart II, so that it is not actually necessary to consult Figure 35.4 when $D_\infty > 0$ in order to determine whether an optimal nonzero sample size exists: if the Z of the problem at hand is to the left of the end of the line for the D_∞ of that problem, there is no sample size which will even pay for its variable cost.†

Approximation for Large Z. If we examine the shapes of the curves in Chart II we get the impression that every one of the curves tends to become a straight line as Z increases, and it can be proved that this is true. As Z increases, the optimal h for any D_∞ is given more and more accurately by the approximate formula

$$h \doteq \sqrt{\frac{1}{2Z}} \, P'_N(D_\infty),$$

which plots as a straight line on the kind of grid used for Chart II. This formula can be used to find optimal sample size for values of Z greater than 80, the largest value shown on the chart.‡

35.3.2   Optimal Sample Size When $K_s > 0$

If there is a fixed element of sampling cost K_s as well as a variable element $k_s n$, we will a fortiori act *without* sampling whenever Figure 35.4 or Chart II tells us to do so. If, however, the figure or the chart tells us that we *should* sample, this proves only that the savings expected from a sample of size n^* will cover the *variable* sampling cost $k_s n^*$. We also know, however, that if there *is* any nonzero sample size which will yield a positive net gain, the best such sample size is still n^* as given by Chart II: it was pointed out in Section 35.2.6 above that the effect of adding K_s to the cost of sampling is simply to lower every point on the net-gain curve by the same amount and that the peak in the curve still occurs at the same value of n as it does when $K_s = 0$. Consequently we have only

---

† It is this fact which accounts for the abrupt cutoffs in the curves of Chart II. If the curves were extended smoothly to the left, they would give the locations of negative peaks like the one in Figure 35.3a.

‡ As can be seen from the way in which each curve approaches its asymptote, the approximate formula always *overstates* the optimal sample size. The accuracy of the approximation for given D_∞ improves as Z increases; for given Z it becomes worse as D_∞ increases. At $Z = 80$ the approximation is excellent for D_∞ as large as 3, in which case the error is only about 10 per cent.

to determine whether the sample size n^* given by Chart II can be expected to produce savings greater than $K_s + k_s n^*$, and this question is quickly settled by evaluating the savings from the formula

$$\text{Expected VSI} = k_t \sigma(\tilde{E}_1) G(D_E).$$

35.3.3 Example

Suppose that we must choose between act 1 and act 2 in the following situation. The conditional costs of the two acts are

Cost of act 1 = \$1,000,000,
Cost of act 2 = \$2,000,000 − \$250,000 ξ.

The prior distribution assigned to ξ is Normal with parameters

$$E_0(\xi) = 8, \qquad \sigma_0(\xi) = 5.$$

The cost of sampling will be

$$K_s + k_s n = \$1000 + \$9\,n.$$

The standard deviation of the pure sampling error of a single observation is known to be

$$\sigma(\tilde{\epsilon}) = 10;$$

the bias of the sampling procedure is uncertain and is assigned a Normal distribution with parameters

$$E(\tilde{\beta}) = 3, \qquad \sigma(\tilde{\beta}) = 2.$$

We first determine the break-even value and terminal loss constant:

$$\$1,000,000 = \$2,000,000 - \$250,000\ \xi_b;$$
$$\xi_b = \frac{\$1,000,000}{\$250,000} = 4;$$
$$k_t = |0 - (-\$250,000)| = \$250,000.$$

We then compute

$$\sigma_\epsilon^* = \sigma(\tilde{\epsilon})\,\frac{\sigma_0^2(\xi)}{\sigma_0^2(\xi) + \sigma^2(\tilde{\beta})} = 10\left(\frac{5^2}{5^2 + 2^2}\right) = 10 \times .862 = 8.62,$$

$$\sigma_\infty(\tilde{E}_1) = \sigma_0(\xi)\sqrt{\frac{\sigma_0^2(\xi)}{\sigma_0^2(\xi) + \sigma^2(\tilde{\beta})}} = 5\sqrt{.862} = 4.64,$$

$$D_\infty = \frac{|\xi_b - E_0(\xi)|}{\sigma_\infty(\tilde{E}_1)} = \frac{|4 - 8|}{4.64} = .86,$$

$$Z = \frac{\sigma_\infty(\tilde{E}_1)}{\sigma_\epsilon^*}\sqrt[3]{\frac{k_t \sigma_\epsilon^*}{k_s}} = \frac{4.64}{8.62}\sqrt[3]{\frac{\$250,000 \times 8.62}{\$9}}$$

$$= .538 \times 62.1 = 33.4.$$

Above $Z = 33.4$ on Chart II we read $h = .065$ for $D_\infty = .8$ and $h = .059$ for $D_\infty = 1.0$. Interpolating for $D_\infty = .86$ we get

$$h = .063$$

and compute

$$n^* = h \left(\sqrt[3]{\frac{k_t \sigma_\epsilon^*}{k_s}} \right)^2 = .063 \times 62.1^2 = 243.$$

This result proves (1) that if any sample should be taken at all, then 243 is the optimum sample size, and (2) that the savings due to sampling will more than cover the variable sampling cost $k_s n^* = \$9 \times 243 = \$2187$. We do not yet know, however, that the savings will cover the *total* sampling cost $K_s + k_s n^* = \$1000 + \$2187 = \$3187$. To answer this question we must find the actual expected *value* of the information to be gained from $n^* = 243$ observations and this depends on $\sigma(\tilde{E}_1)$ and D_E, not on $\sigma_\infty(\tilde{E}_1)$ and D_∞. We therefore compute

$$\sigma(\tilde{E}_1) = \sigma_\infty(\tilde{E}_1) \sqrt{\frac{\sigma_\infty^2(\tilde{E}_1)}{\sigma_\infty^2(\tilde{E}_1) + (1/n^*)\sigma_\epsilon^{*2}}}$$

$$= 4.64 \sqrt{\frac{4.64^2}{4.64^2 + \frac{1}{243} \times 8.62^2}} = 4.61,$$

$$G(D_E) = G(.87) = .1061,$$

$$\text{Expected VSI} = k_t \sigma(\tilde{E}_1) G(D_E)$$
$$= \$250,000 \times 4.61 \times .1061 = \$122,000.$$

The sample does pay for itself and handsomely; rounding the sampling cost to the nearest \$1000 we have

$$\text{Expected net gain} = \$122,000 - \$3,000 = \$119,000.$$

Our problem is now completely solved, but out of curiosity we may look at the total expected loss of the optimal single-sample procedure. To find the expected loss of immediate terminal action without sampling we compute

$$D_0 = \frac{|\xi_b - E_0(\xi)|}{\sigma_0(\xi)} = \frac{|4 - 8|}{5} = .80,$$

$$G(D_0) = G(.80) = .1202,$$

$$\text{Expected VPI} = k_t \sigma_0(\xi) G(D_0) = \$250,000 \times 5 \times .1202 = \$150,000.$$

Subtracting from this the expected net gain of sampling we have

$$\text{Expected total loss} = \$150,000 - \$119,000 = \$31,000.$$

The reason why the expected loss remains as heavy as it does despite the use of an optimal decision procedure is simply that nothing can be done to reduce uncertainty about sampling bias. Even if sampling cost nothing and an infinite sample were taken, the value of the sample information would be only

$$\text{Maximum EVSI} = k_t \sigma_\infty(\tilde{E}_1)G(D_\infty) = \$250{,}000 \times 4.64 \times G(.86)$$
$$= \$125{,}000$$

and the expected loss would still be $\$150{,}000 - \$125{,}000 = \$25{,}000$.

35.4 Effect of Nonoptimal Sample Size

Some interesting general results concerning the unnecessary loss which results from taking a sample of nonoptimal size can be given for the special case where there is no uncertainty about bias and no fixed

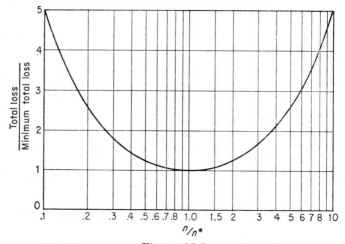

Figure 35.5

element K_s in sampling cost and where the optimum sample size is not zero.   In this case it can be shown that *the ratio*

$$\frac{\text{Total expected loss with sample of arbitrary size } n}{\text{Total expected loss with sample of optimal size } n^*}$$

is less than

$$\frac{1}{2}\left(\frac{n}{n^*} + \frac{n^*}{n}\right)$$

for all D_∞ and Z.

This limiting value is graphed in Figure 35.5, and it is immediately apparent that a *moderate* error in sample size is of no *practical importance whatever*—a sample which is 10 per cent above or below optimum cannot increase total expected loss by as much as $\frac{6}{10}$ of 1 per cent; a sample which is 20 per cent above or below optimum cannot increase total expected loss by more than 2.5 per cent. What is more, even these very low maximum effects are actually approached only when Z is very large; for values of Z which occur in common practice the effect of nonoptimal sample size is very substantially less than the limit given by Figure 35.5. Observe on the other hand that *substantial* departures from optimal sample size may have *really serious effects:* a sample which is half or twice what it ought to be may increase total expected loss by as much as 25 per cent, and total expected loss may be more than doubled if the sample is a fourth or four times the optimal size.

35.5   Optimum Sample Size When the Assumptions of This Chapter Are Violated

The only two-action problems for which it is possible to devise a really simple method of determining optimal sample size are those in which all the assumptions underlying the results of this chapter are met and which can therefore be solved by the methods derived in this chapter. Violation of any of these assumptions usually means that the only absolutely sure way of finding the exact optimal sample size is actually to evaluate total expected loss for each of a large number of different sizes. Our assumption that the terminal and sampling costs are linear is very close to exact in the great majority of the two-action problems which arise in practical business situations, and when bias is suspected a Normal distribution will usually describe the businessman's beliefs at least as well as any other, but it is often necessary to decide on a sample size in situations where our assumptions about the distributions of $\tilde{\xi}$ and $\tilde{\epsilon}$ are seriously violated in one or more of the following respects:

1. The prior distribution of $\tilde{\xi}$ is not Normal;
2. The sampling distribution of $\tilde{\epsilon}$ is not Normal;
3. The variance of $\tilde{\epsilon}$ is not known.

Even if we do have to resort to numerical evaluation of a number of different sample sizes in such situations, it would help a great deal to have some indication of the general range of n's within which the optimum probably lies; and it naturally occurs to us that we may be able to obtain such an indication by applying the methods of this chapter even though we cannot hope that they will yield the *exact* optimum. We shall now test this idea by trying it out on the problem which we discussed in Chapter 33; we shall see that the conditions of that problem violate the assumptions of the present chapter in all three of the ways listed above and that every one of the violations is severe.

The basic random variable of the problem we are about to analyze is the long-run fraction of defectives which will be generated by a Bernoulli process. We saw in Section 31.3 that this long-run fraction p of *true* defectives corresponds to ξ while the long-run fraction P_r of *reported* defectives corresponds to μ; the two quantities are not necessarily equal, and the difference $P_r - p$ is the bias β of the sampling process. We shall here assume, however, as we did in our earlier discussions of this same example, that the inspector will not select good pieces in preference to defectives or vice versa and that he will report all good pieces as good pieces and all defectives as defectives. This assumption not only determines the distribution of $\tilde{\beta}$, leading us to set

$$E(\tilde{\beta}) = 0, \qquad \sigma(\tilde{\beta}) = 0;$$

it also affects the distribution of the pure sampling error $\tilde{\epsilon}$ of a single sample observation. An individual observation $\tilde{x}$ in a problem of this sort will have the value 1 if the piece is *reported* defective or the value 0 if the piece is *reported* good; and the pure sampling error of such an observation is the difference $\tilde{\epsilon} = \tilde{x} - P_r$ between the individual observation and the long-run average of all *observations*. The variance of this error is therefore $\sigma^2(\tilde{\epsilon}) = P_r(1 - P_r)$; but because we have assumed that $P_r = p$, we can replace this formula by

$$\sigma^2(\tilde{\epsilon}) = p(1 - p) = pq.$$

We are now ready to examine the three ways in which this problem violates the assumptions on which the results of the present chapter were based.

1. The prior distribution of the basic random variable is not a symmetric, continuous Normal distribution but an extremely skew, discrete distribution which asserts that the only possible values of the variable are .01, .05, .15, and .25 and which assigns $\frac{7}{10}$ of the total prior probability to the smallest of these four values.

2. The sampling distribution is binomial and the Normal approximation to the binomial is very poor for the value $P_r = p = .01$ which has $\frac{7}{10}$ of the total prior probability.

3. The variance of the sampling error of a single observation $\tilde{\epsilon}$ is not only unknown but unknowable: it is equal to $P_r(1 - P_r) = pq$ and therefore its value may be as low as $.01 \times .99 = .0099$ or as high as $.25 \times .75 = .1875$.

In order to obtain an approximately optimal sample size for this problem we shall proceed as follows. We shall compute the mean and variance of the actual discrete prior distribution of $\tilde{p}$ and then act as if these were the mean and variance of a Normal prior distribution. We shall pay no attention at all to the non-Normality of the sampling distribution of $\tilde{\epsilon}$, and we shall treat the variance of an individual error $\tilde{\epsilon}$ as if it were known to have the value which it would in fact have if $\tilde{p}$ had the value $E_0(\tilde{p})$. There is no proof that this procedure is the best one possible, and it might be argued in particular that we should compute $\sigma^2(\tilde{\epsilon})$ for each possible value of $\tilde{p}$ and then take a weighted average with the prior probabilities as the weights. The one indisputable advantage of our procedure is its simplicity.

The mean of the prior distribution of $\tilde{p}$ for this problem was shown in Table 22.6 to be

$E_0(\tilde{p}) = .052.$

In Table 35.1 the variance of this distribution is computed as

$\sigma_0^2(\tilde{p}) = .006115.$

Table 35.1

p	$P_0(p)$	$p - E_0(\tilde{p})$	$[p - E_0(\tilde{p})]^2$	$[p - E_0(\tilde{p})]^2 P_0(p)$
.01	.7	$-.042$	.001764	.001235
.05	.1	$-.002$	.000004	.000000
.15	.1	$+.098$	.009604	.000960
.25	.1	$+.198$	.039204	.003920
	1.0			.006115

If $\tilde{p}$ actually had the value $E_0(\tilde{p}) = .052$, the variance of an individual pure sampling error would be

$\sigma^2(\tilde{\epsilon}) = .052 \times .948 = .0493$

and we treat the problem as if $\tilde{\epsilon}$ would have this variance *regardless* of the true value of $\tilde{p}$.

It was shown in our original discussion of this problem that

$p_b = .04, \qquad k_t = \$200,$
$K_s + k_s n = \$.25 + \$.02\, n,$

and we now have all the data required to apply Chart II. Because $\sigma(\tilde{\beta}) = 0,$

$$\sigma_\epsilon^* = \sigma(\tilde{\epsilon}) = \sqrt{.0493} = .222,$$
$$\sigma_\infty(\tilde{E}_1) = \sigma_0(\tilde{p}) = \sqrt{.006115} = .0782.$$

We then compute

$$D_\infty = \frac{|p_b - E_0(\tilde{p})|}{\sigma_\infty(\tilde{E}_1)} = \frac{|.04 - .052|}{.0782} = .15,$$

$$Z = \frac{\sigma_\infty(\tilde{E}_1)}{\sigma_\epsilon^*} \sqrt[3]{\frac{k_t \sigma_\epsilon^*}{k_s}} = \frac{.0782}{.222} \sqrt[3]{\frac{\$200 \times .222}{\$.02}} = .352 \times 13.05 = 4.59.$$

Above $Z = 4.59$ in Chart II we read $h = .170$ for $D_\infty = .1$ and $h = .172$ for $D_\infty' = .2$. Interpolating for $D_\infty = .15$ we obtain

$$h = .171$$

and we compute

$$n^* = .171 \times 13.05^2 = 29.$$

The Accuracy of the Approximation. The *exact* optimal sample size for this problem can be determined by using the numerical methods of Chapter 33 or the first part of Chapter 34 to compute the *exact* net gain from sampling for a large number of different n's; the curve labeled

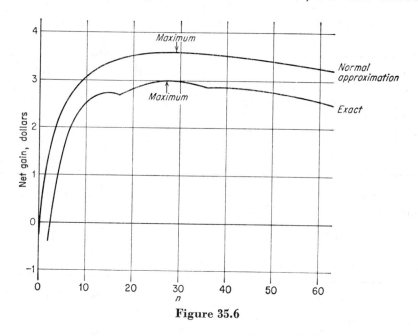

Figure 35.6

"exact" in Figure 35.6 summarizes the results of such computations. The exact optimum is $n = 27$, which yields a true net gain of \$2.99; the approximation $n = 29$ obtained by use of the Normal approximation has a true net gain of \$2.98, or only \$.01 or $\frac{1}{3}$ of 1 per cent less than the maximum attainable by exact calculations.

We have already emphasized that the conditions of this example constitute really extreme violations of the assumptions on which the results of this chapter were based. We took $\sigma^2(\bar{\epsilon})$ as known to have the value .0493 when it could have any value from .0099 to .1875 and when there was actually probability .7 that it would have the very low value .0099. The difference between the true prior distribution and a Normal distribution with the same mean and variance is shown graphically in Figure

35.7; notice that this Normal distribution actually assigns substantial probability to negative values of $\tilde{p}$. It seems likely, therefore, that *moderate* violations of the assumptions underlying the results of the present chapter are very unlikely to have any serious effect on the optimality of the sample size obtained by the use of these results; and extensive investigations of other quite different numerical examples have uniformly corroborated this conclusion.

It must be emphasized, however, that the Normal approximation to the actual value of the net gain is *not* very good. The curve labeled "Normal approximation" in Figure 35.6 shows this approximation as a

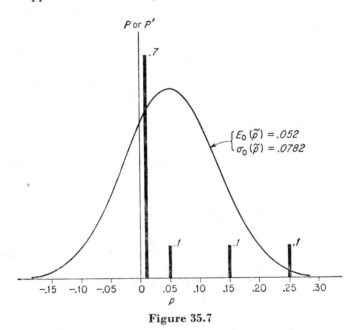

Figure 35.7

function of n, and we observe that the approximate *value* is *substantially different* from the true value even though the *peak of the curve* of approximate value occurs at *very nearly the same n* as the peak of the curve of true value. This result is also typical, and if we think back to the implications of the difference between Figures 35.2 and 35.3*a* we reach the following conclusions concerning the use of the Normal approximation to determine optimal sample size:

> When the Normal approximation leads to a *nonzero* sample size, we can usually feel quite sure that for all practical purposes this is the *best nonzero* sample size; but the Normal approximation (1) may tell us to sample when we should not sample at all or (2) may tell us not to sample when we should take a sample of substantial size.

The first of these dangers is easy to guard against; all that we have to do is compute the *exact* expected net gain with a sample of the size yielded by the Normal approximation. If the gain is positive, it will rarely be worth the trouble to try to improve on the sample size; if the gain is negative, it will almost always be true that there is no sample size which will yield a positive net gain. The second danger is a source of more trouble: when the Normal approximation tells us *not* to sample, we must compute the exact expected net gain for enough different sample sizes to learn the general shape of the *true* net-gain curve and thus either convince ourselves that there is in fact no n for which the gain is positive or else by trial and error actually find the n which yields the greatest positive net gain.

PROBLEMS

1. In the situation of Chapter 30, Problem 1, assuming that sampling costs $25 per customer and that management is convinced that the sampling procedure is unbiased and starts from the posterior distribution which you computed in answer to part d of that problem, compute:

a. The optimal size for a second sample to be taken before a decision is finally reached.

b. Expected total loss under a single-sample decision procedure using a sample of optimal size.

2. Same as Problem 1 but assume that management holds the views about bias described in Chapter 31, Problem 6, and starts from the posterior distribution which you computed in answer to that problem.

3. Same as above for the situation and sampling cost of Chapter 32, Problem 4*a*.

4. Same as above for the situation of Chapter 32, Problem 4*c*.

5. In the situation of Chapter 24, Problem 5, find an approximation to the optimal sample size for a single-sample decision procedure by treating the prior distribution of $\tilde{p}$ as if it were Normal and the variance of a sampling error as if it were known.

CHAPTER 36

Interdependent Two-action Problems
under a Stationary Distribution†

In the last three chapters we have developed methods for finding optimal single-sample procedures for choice between two acts both of which are definitely *terminal*, i.e. where the choice of either act disposes of the problem at hand once and for all. We now turn to situations where at least one of the acts which may be chosen after sampling does *not* put an end to the problem at hand but leaves it to be solved by a future decision or sequence of decisions, with the result that *the conditional or expected cost of the act in question depends on the way in which these future decisions will be made.* In the general case the solution of such interdependent decision problems requires extremely heavy computation, but we shall see in this chapter that in certain rather common circumstances the optimal decision procedure can be found with surprising ease.

36.1   Statement of an Example

We saw in Chapter 24 that two-action problems become interdependent whenever the choice between the acts will or may affect not only the *costs* which will be immediately incurred but also the *quantity of product or service* which will be obtained. We now return to the first of the two examples which we discussed at that time (Section 24.1.1).

A part is manufactured by a Bernoulli process in lots which contain 2500 pieces for actual use in assembly plus however many pieces are required for sampling inspection. Production is by a sequence of batch processes costing a total of $30 per batch for labor, power, etc., plus $.03 per piece for materials. Each defective sent to the assembly department occasions an excess cost of $3.75; and although defectives can be reliably identified by inspection, this inspection is destructive and therefore a lot *cannot* be screened: it must be accepted or scrapped. Inspection costs $.062 per piece inspected, and adding the cost of manufacturing the sample pieces we have

Cost of sampling = $.092 n.

† The results of this chapter are not required in any following chapter.

The manufacturer is about to produce one lot of parts, and on the basis of his past experience he assigns the distribution shown in Table 36.1 to the $\tilde{p}$ of the process during this run.

Table 36.1
Prior Distribution and Expectation of $\tilde{p}$

p	$P_0(p)$	$p\ P_0(p)$
.01	.60	.0060
.03	.20	.0060
.05	.10	.0050
.07	.07	.0049
.09	.03	.0027
	1.00	.0246 $= E_0(\tilde{p})$

Computation of the *cost of accepting* the lot which is about to be produced presents no difficulties. The conditional expected number of defectives in the part of the lot which will be sent to the assembly department is $2500p$, the conditional cost due to these defectives is $\$3.75 \times 2500p = \$9375\ p$, and since this is a linear function of p we see immediately that the unconditional

Expected cost of acceptance $= \$9375\ E(\tilde{p})$.

If the decision is made without sampling, $E(\tilde{p})$ will be the mean of the prior distribution of $\tilde{p}$; if the decision is made after sampling, $E(\tilde{p})$ will be the mean of the posterior distribution.

It is the *cost of rejecting* the lot which gives trouble. The assembly requirement which led to scheduling this present lot must be filled. If the present lot is rejected and scrapped, another must be manufactured; if this second lot is rejected, still another must be manufactured; and so on until a lot is finally accepted and the requirement is filled.

36.2 The Assumption of Stationarity and the Criterion of Average Cost per Accepted Lot

Even without formal analysis it is clear that the best way of deciding whether to accept or reject any *future* batch of product will depend on the prior distribution which the manufacturer assigns to $\tilde{p}$ *just before the batch in question is produced*, exactly as the best way of reaching a decision concerning the present lot depends on the distribution assigned to $\tilde{p}$ just before the present run is made. If on any particular occasion the manufacturer feels certain that $\tilde{p}$ will have some definite value, there will obviously be no sense in sampling that run; either its output should be accepted without question or the run should not be made at all. If the manufacturer is convinced that $\tilde{p}$ will have either a very high or a very low value, he will need only a very small sample to tell him whether to accept or reject; and so forth. It follows immediately that *if the prior distribution which the manufacturer assigns to p̃ changes over time, the optimal decision procedure to apply to each successive lot will change over time.*

Even if the manufacturer could now predict the distribution which it will be reasonable to assign to p̃ just before each future run is made, it would obviously be extremely difficult to determine the optimal decision procedure for every future run and then compute the expected cost of rejecting the present run. If, as is far more likely, the manufacturer *cannot* now predict what distribution it will be reasonable to assign to p̃ just before each future run is made (and this is the truly general case), the problem is even more complex. It is literally *impossible* to determine *now* what procedure *will be* optimal for each future run, and computation of the cost of rejecting the present run will involve assigning a probability to every possible combination of future probability distributions.

36.2.1 The Assumption of Stationarity

Conceptually we can solve even this horribly complex problem by the method of "backward induction" which we shall study in Chapter 38, but the computational burden would usually be prohibitive even with the aid of high-speed computers. We shall therefore restrict our study to situations where it is legitimate to assume that

> The prior distribution which it will be reasonable to assign to p̃ just before making any future run will be *exactly the same* as the distribution which it is reasonable to assign to the p̃ of the present run.

Although this assumption is formally very strong and can never be justified in a *literal* sense, it is *practically* justified in many real business situations. All that is really required is that the prior distribution should be *very unlikely* to change *very much* during the *next few* future runs, and this will be true when the following conditions are met.

1. The businessman has no reason to think that there will be any appreciable change in the near future in the way in which the value of the basic random variable *actually varies* from one occasion to the next.

When the basic random variable is the parameter of a Bernoulli process and its value depends on the quality of the setup, this first condition will be satisfied if the businessman has no reason to think that the person making the setup will become noticeably more or less skillful during the next several setups. When the basic random variable is the X content of a batch of raw material, the condition will be satisfied if the businessman has no reason to think that the factors responsible for batch-to-batch variation in X content will change materially during the production of the next several batches of material.

2. The businessman's present *beliefs* about the way in which the value of the basic random variable varies from one occasion to the next rest on so much already acquired experience that it is virtually impossible for the additional experience acquired on the next few occasions to modify them appreciably.

If condition 1 is satisfied and if in addition the businessman knows exactly how many defectives were produced on each of the last 50 production runs, the distribution he now assigns to $\tilde{p}$ before making a run is unlikely to be much affected by the fraction defective which he observes in the next few runs. If condition 1 is satisfied and if in addition the true X content of the last 50 batches of raw material has been accurately determined, the distribution which the businessman now assigns to the $\tilde{\xi}$ of an untested new batch is unlikely to be much affected by the quality of the next few batches.

36.2.2   Average Cost per Accepted Lot

The assumption of stationarity is of crucial importance in problems of the kind we are now studying because it implies that *the decision procedure which is optimal for choice between acceptance and rejection of the* present *lot is also optimal for any* future *lot and vice versa*. The costs which will be *immediately* incurred as a result of acceptance or rejection are identical for all lots even without the assumption of stationarity; with this assumption added, *all* the circumstances surrounding the decision are identical for all lots and therefore the same decision procedure must be optimal for every lot. This means that we are no longer obliged to find a different best way of making each of a large number of future decisions before we compute the expected cost of rejecting the present lot and thus complete the data we need to find the best way of making the present decision. Instead:

Given the assumption of stationarity, we can make a *direct* evaluation of any proposed decision procedure by computing the *average cost per accepted lot* which will result from applying this procedure to *all* lots, present and future; and we can then look systematically for the procedure which minimizes this average cost.

This way of looking at our present problem has a certain superficial resemblance to the way in which we sometimes talked about the evaluation of decision procedures for *independent* two-action problems, where we actually computed the *expected* cost of applying a given procedure to an *individual* decision but visualized the meaning of this expected cost by assuming in effect that the distribution of the basic random variable was stationary and that the expected cost represented the *average* cost per lot of applying the procedure in question to a *large number* of lots. It is therefore very important to realize that there are *two absolutely essential differences between our present problem and problems in which the successive decisions are independent.*

1. When successive decisions are independent, the assumption of stationarity and the interpretation of an expected cost as an average cost per lot is merely a way of visualizing the meaning of an expectation; in our present problem, we are really working with true long-run averages and the validity of our results depends on the validity of the assumption of stationarity.

2. When both terminal acts will yield the same amount of usable product or service, we can visualize the problem as one of minimizing average cost *per decision* (e.g., per lot purchased or per lot manufactured), but when the choice between the two acts affects yield as well as cost, we must minimize average cost *per unit of yield* (in our example, per *accepted* lot).

36.3   Computation of Average Cost per Accepted Lot

A single-sample decision procedure or *sampling plan* is fully defined by (1) the sample size n and (2) a rule stating which sample outcomes should lead to acceptance and which to rejection.   If the same prior distribution is assigned to $\tilde{p}$ before each lot is sampled and if the size of the sample is the same on every occasion, it is obvious without proof that we will want to *reject* all lots in which the number of defectives r is *greater than* some specified limit c and to *accept* all lots in which r is *equal to or less than c.*   In actual practice the inspector would be given a rule of exactly this form, i.e. he would be told the size of sample to take and the value of the *acceptance number c.*

We know, however, that the information in any sample can be summarized by the mean of the posterior distribution of $\tilde{p}$ just as well as it can be summarized by the number of defectives r, and it will be easier to compute the costs which will be incurred under any given sampling plan if we do think of the sample as summarized by $E_1(\tilde{p})$ rather than by r. We shall therefore think of our problem in terms of finding the best sample size n and *critical value* p_c to use in a rule of the form

Take a sample of size n, compute $E_1(\tilde{p})$, and *reject* the lot if $E_1(\tilde{p})$ is *greater* than some critical value p_c, *accept* if $E_1(\tilde{p})$ is *equal to or less than* p_c.

As the first step toward finding the best values of n and p_c we shall now see how to compute average total cost per accepted lot under a plan with any *given* values of n and p_c, taking $n = 20$ and $p_c = .035$ as an example.   The method we shall use for this purpose is basically the same method of preposterior analysis in terms of $\tilde{E}_1$ which we used in Sections 34.1 and 34.2: looking at the problem *before* any particular lot is sampled, we list all the values of $\tilde{E}_1$ which *may* result from the sample, compute the posterior expected cost corresponding to each E_1, and then take the proper weighted average of these costs.

36.3.1   The Prior Distribution of the Posterior Mean

To compute the *prior* distribution of the *posterior* mean $\tilde{E}_1$ for the sample size $n = 20$ which we are using as an example we proceed exactly as in Section 34.1.1: for each possible sample outcome r, we compute the prior probability of that outcome, the posterior distribution of $\tilde{p}$ given that outcome, and the mean of that posterior distribution.   The calculations for the outcome $r = 0$ are shown in Table 36.2 by way of review.

Table 36.2
Computation of the Posterior Distribution Given $n = 20$, $r = 0$

p	Prior $P_0(p)$	Likelihood $P_b(\tilde{r} = 0 \vert p)$	Joint $P(\tilde{r} = 0, p)$	Posterior $P_1(p \vert r = 0)$	Expectation $p\,P_1(p)$
.01	.60	.8197	.4907	.750	.00750
.03	.20	.5348	.1070	.163	.00489
.05	.10	.3585	.0358	.055	.00275
.07	.07	.2342	.0164	.025	.00175
.09	.03	.1516	.0045	.007	.00063
	1.00		.6544	1.000	.01752

Table 36.3
Prior Distribution of $\tilde{E}_1$ for $n = 20$

r	E_1	$P(E_1)$
0	.0175	.654
1	.0313	.240
2	.0489	.074
3	.0612	.023
Over 3	Over .0612	.009
		1.000

The total of the products $p\,P_1(p)$ in the last column shows that *if* the sample outcome is $r = 0$, *then* $\tilde{E}_1$ will have the value .01752; and the total of the joint probabilities shows that the prior probability that $\tilde{E}_1$ *will* have this value is .6544.   Repeating these calculations for the outcomes $r = 1$, 2, etc., we obtain the *prior distribution* of the *posterior* mean which is shown with all numbers rounded to three significant figures in Table 36.3.

36.3.2   *Average Cost per Lot Manufactured*

The next step toward our ultimate objective of finding average cost *per accepted lot* under the plan ($n = 20$, $p_c = .035$) is to compute average cost *per lot manufactured* under this plan, and to do this we must first look at the *conditional* costs which may arise as a result of manufacturing any *one* lot and applying to it the plan in question.

1. *Direct manufacturing cost.*   The cost of manufacturing the 2500 pieces intended for use in assembly amounts to

$$\$30 + (\$.03 \times 2500) = \$105 \text{ certain,}$$

regardless of the sampling plan applied to the lot after it has been manufactured.   The cost of the additional pieces provided for destructive inspection is included in

2. *Sampling cost.*   This depends on the size of the sample which will be taken from the lot but not on the critical value p_c; for the sample size $n = 20$ we are now considering it is $\$.092 \times 20 = \$2$ to the nearest dollar.

3. *The cost to which the defectives in the lot will give rise in the assembly department if the lot is accepted.*   The *prior* expected value of this cost depends on both n and p_c; we shall now see how to compute it by first computing the *conditional* cost for every possible sample outcome and then taking the expectation of these conditional costs.

We observe first of all that, because $p_c = .035$ in the sampling plan which we are evaluating, the lot will be *rejected* if the sample yields an E_1 above .035 and therefore the defectives in the lot cannot give rise to any cost in the assembly department; the *conditional* cost of defectives *given* $\tilde{E}_1 > .035$ is *zero*.   If on the contrary $\tilde{E}_1 \leq .035$, the lot will be *accepted* and the defectives it contains will give rise to a cost.   By Table 36.3 there are two possible values of $\tilde{E}_1$ which lead to acceptance: $E_1 = .0175$ and $E_1 = .0313$.   We have already seen that when a lot *is* accepted, the expected cost due to defectives is $\$9375 \, E(\tilde{p})$.   Consequently *if* $\tilde{E}_1 = .0175$ after a particular run has been made and a sample has been inspected, the conditional expected cost of accepting the defectives generated on that run is $\$9375 \times .0175$; *if* $\tilde{E}_1 = .0313$, the conditional cost is $\$9375 \times .0313$.

Having determined the posterior or conditional cost of defectives for every possible E_1 under the plan ($n = 20$, $p_c = .035$), we are now ready to compute the prior or *unconditional* expected cost of defectives under that procedure.   This is done in Table 36.4 in the usual way, by multiplying each conditional cost by the probability of the E_1 which gives rise to that cost and adding the products.   We remind the student once more that if the $\$178$ cost of defectives computed in Table 36.4 is interpreted as an average rather than an expectation, it is the average cost *per lot manufactured* and *not* the average cost per lot *accepted*.

Table 36.4
Cost of Defectives per Lot Manufactured
Sample $n = 20$; accept if $\tilde{E}_1 < .035$

E_1	$P(E_1)$	Cost of defectives	
		Conditional	Expected
.0175	.654	\$9375 × .0175	\$9375 (.0175 × .654)
.0313	.240	\$9375 × .0313	\$9375 (.0313 × .240)
.0489+	.106	0	0
	1.000		\$9375 × .0190 = \$178

Adding the expected cost of defectives which we have just computed to the \$105 manufacturing cost and \$2 sampling cost which will be incurred as a result of producing any one lot, we obtain the *total*

Average cost per lot manufactured = \$105 + \$2 + \$178 = \$285.

36.3.3   Average Cost per Accepted Lot

If on the average only half of all lots are accepted under a given decision procedure, then on the average two lots will have to be manufactured to get one accepted lot and the cost per lot accepted will be twice the cost per lot manufactured. If two-thirds of all lots are accepted, three-halves of a lot will have to be manufactured to get one accepted lot; and in general,

$$\text{Cost per accepted lot} = \frac{\text{cost per lot manufactured}}{\text{probability of acceptance}}$$

In our example, we see immediately from Table 36.3 that there is probability $.654 + .240 = .894$ that $\tilde{E}_1$ will have a value less than or equal to .035, and under a plan which accepts only if $\tilde{E}_1 \leq .035$ this means that a fraction .894 of all lots manufactured will be accepted. It follows that under this plan

$$\text{Average cost per accepted lot} = \frac{\$285}{.894} = \$319.$$

36.3.4   A General Formula for Average Cost per Accepted Lot

The calculations by which we have just evaluated the total cost per accepted lot under the sampling plan ($n = 20$, $p_c = .035$) can be neatly summarized by a formula if we look back to see what really happened in the last column of Table 36.4. Each product within parentheses in that column is of the form $E_1 P(E_1)$, and the column contains such a product for every possible E_1 in the interval from $-\infty$ to the "critical value" $p_c = .035$ specified by the sampling plan. The sum .0190 of these products is therefore the partial expectation $\mathrm{E}_{-\infty}^{.035}(\tilde{E}_1)$, and since the probability .894 that a lot will be accepted is simply $\mathrm{P}(\tilde{E}_1 \leq .035)$, we can write

$$\text{Average cost per accepted lot} = \frac{\$105 + \$2 + \$9375\ \mathrm{E}_{-\infty}^{.035}(\tilde{E}_1)}{\mathrm{P}(\tilde{E}_1 \leq .035)}.$$

More generally, for *any* sample size n and *any* "critical value" p_c distinguishing between values of $\tilde{E}_1$ which will lead to acceptance and values which will lead to rejection, we have

$$\text{Average cost per accepted lot} = \frac{\$105 + \$.092\ n + \$9375\ \mathrm{E}_{-\infty}^{p_c}(\tilde{E}_1)}{\mathrm{P}(\tilde{E}_1 \leq p_c)}$$

36.3.5   The Definition of Total Cost

We now explicitly call attention to the fact that the actual *definition* of "cost" which we have used in this problem is different from the definition used in problems with independent decisions. When all possible acts have the same yield, we need pay no attention to the cost of *manufacturing* because the manufacturing cost per unit of yield is not affected by the terminal act or by the sampling plan used to select a terminal act. In the example discussed in Chapters 22 and 33, every lot manufactured yielded 500 pieces for use in assembly whether or not the process was "rejected" (readjusted) before the lot was produced: readjustment affected only the cost due to defectives. In problems of the present kind, on the contrary,

> The sampling plan affects manufacturing cost *per unit of yield* and therefore manufacturing cost must be included in computing average cost per unit of yield.

36.4   Selection of the Optimal Sampling Plan

Now that we know how to compute the average cost per accepted lot which will result from applying any given sampling plan to all lots, we could proceed to determine the optimal sampling plan by simply computing average cost per accepted lot for a sufficiently large number of n, p_c combinations. The computations would be very laborious, however, and we shall now see that it will usually be better to attack the problem indirectly rather than head-on.

The indirect approach consists in solving a number of artificial problems in each of which we assume that the manufacturer will be required to make his decisions concerning all *future* lots in a way which is *arbitrarily specified* but that he is free to make his decision concerning the *present* lot in any way he pleases and wishes to use an *optimal* plan for this purpose. The solution of an artificial problem of this kind helps us toward the solution of our real problem because, as can be proved:

1. If and only if the plan specified for all future lots is in fact the *optimal* plan for use with *all* lots, this same plan will turn out to be the optimal plan for a decision concerning the *present* lot.
2. If the plan specified for all future lots is *not* the optimal plan for all lots, then the plan which is *optimal* for the *present* lot will be a *better* plan for use with *all* lots.

This suggests that we can find the optimal plan for our real problem by *successive approximations,* using the present-lot optimal plan which emerges from one artificial problem as the arbitrarily specified future-lot plan for the next artificial problem until we reach a stage where both plans are the same; and it can be proved that we will in fact always arrive at the true optimal plan by following a procedure of this sort.

Although this indirect procedure requires us to solve several artificial problems instead of just one real problem, it nevertheless reduces computations very substantially because an approximate solution to each of the artificial problems can be found very easily.   Our assumed knowledge of the way in which all *future* decisions will be made enables us to assign a definite cost to rejection of the *present* lot; and this means that these artificial problems are perfectly ordinary two-action problems for which approximately optimal sample sizes can be determined by the method developed in Chapter 35.   We shall now proceed to use the indirect procedure to find the optimal sampling plan for the example we have been discussing throughout this chapter.

36.4.1   The First Artificial Problem

We are free to start our series of successive approximations in any way that we please.   We could assume that the manufacturer will be required to apply the sampling plan ($n = 100$, $p_c = .5$) to all future lots, or that he will be required to accept (or even to reject) all future lots without sampling.   For no particular reason we choose to start by assuming that *all future lots will be accepted without sampling,* and our first artificial problem is to find the procedure which will be optimal for reaching a decision concerning the *present* lot *given* this assumption about all future lots.

The Conditional Costs.   Computation of the conditional cost of *acceptance* gave us no difficulty even in the real problem: acceptance will yield the pieces required for assembly at the perfectly definite

Conditional cost of acceptance = $\$9375\,p$.

The difficulty in the real problem was with *rejection*, since we did not know exactly how the required pieces would be obtained if the present lot were rejected and therefore we did not know what rejection could be expected to cost. In the present artificial problem, however, the expected value of this cost is just as definite as the expected cost of acceptance. Since every lot manufactured will be accepted, the manufacturing cost will be $105 per accepted lot and the cost of defectives per accepted lot will be $9375 $E_0(\tilde{p})$ = $9375 × .0246 = $231, making a total of $336 per accepted lot. If the present lot is rejected this is what the manufacturer can "expect" to spend in replacing it; and therefore the

"Conditional" cost of rejection = $336.

The word "conditional" is put in quotation marks because the cost of rejection does not actually depend on the p of the present run.

Our artificial problem is thus a perfectly ordinary two-action problem with linear costs, and the nature of these costs can be summarized in the usual way by computing the *loss constant*

$$k_t = |k_1 - k_2| = |\$9375 - \$0| = \$9375$$

and the *break-even value* of $\tilde{p}$ which makes the costs of the two terminal acts equal:

$$\$9375\, p_b = \$336; \qquad p_b = \frac{\$336}{\$9375} = .0358.$$

Notice that the $105 which will be spent in *manufacturing* the present lot was omitted from *both* the conditional costs because it will be spent whether this lot is accepted or rejected (cf. Section 36.3.5). We could equally well have *included* this cost in *both* the conditional costs; if we had done so, we would have obtained exactly the same values for k_t and p_b.

Solution of the Problem by the Normal Approximation. We now proceed to find an approximate solution to our first artificial problem by the method of Normal approximation described in Section 35.5. In effect, we replace the true discrete prior distribution of Table 36.1 by a Normal prior distribution with the same mean and variance, assume that the distribution of the mean pure sampling error $\tilde{\epsilon}$ is Normal rather than binomial, and treat the variance of an individual error $\tilde{\epsilon}$ as if it were known to have the value which it would actually have if $\tilde{p}$ had the value $E_0(\tilde{p})$. We already know (Table 36.1) that the mean of the prior distribution is

$$E_0(\tilde{p}) = .0246,$$

and in Table 36.5 we compute the variance of this distribution as

$$\sigma_0^2(\tilde{p}) = .000470.$$

Table 36.5
Variance of the Prior Distribution of $\tilde{p}$

p	$P_0(p)$	$p - E_0(\tilde{p})$	$[p - E_0(\tilde{p})]^2$	$[p - E_0(\tilde{p})]^2\, P_0(p)$
.01	.60	$-.0146$	.000213	.000128
.03	.20	$+.0054$	.000029	.000006
.05	.10	$+.0254$	.000645	.000064
.07	.07	$+.0454$	.002061	.000144
.09	.03	$+.0654$	.004277	.000128
	$\overline{1.00}$			$\overline{.000470}$

The sampling error will be treated as if its variance were known to be

$$\sigma_0^2(\tilde{\epsilon}) = E_0(\tilde{p})[1 - E_0(\tilde{p})] = .0246 \times .9754 = .0240.$$

We continue to assume as we did in computing Tables 36.2 and 36.3 that there is *no uncertainty about sampling bias*, $\sigma(\tilde{\beta}) = 0$, so that

$$\sigma_\epsilon^* = \sigma(\tilde{\epsilon}) = \sqrt{.0240} = .155,$$
$$\sigma_\infty(\tilde{E}_1) = \sigma_0(\tilde{p}) = \sqrt{.000470} = .0217.$$

We now compute

$$D_\infty = \frac{|p_b - E_0(\tilde{p})|}{\sigma_\infty(\tilde{E}_1)} = \frac{|.0358 - .0246|}{.0217} = .52,$$

$$Z = \frac{\sigma_\infty(\tilde{E}_1)}{\sigma_\epsilon^*} \sqrt[3]{\frac{k_t \sigma_\epsilon^*}{k_s}} = \frac{.0217}{.155} \sqrt[3]{\frac{9375 \times .155}{.092}} = .140 \times 25.1 = 3.51.$$

Above $Z = 3.51$ in Chart II we read $h = .167$ for $D_\infty = .4$ and $h = .150$ for $D_\infty = .6$. Interpolating for $D_\infty = .52$, we obtain

$$h = .157$$

and compute

$$n^* = h \left(\sqrt[3]{\frac{k_t \sigma_\epsilon^*}{k_s}} \right)^2 = .157 \times 25.1^2 = 99.$$

Except for possible error due to the use of the Normal approximation, we have shown that *if* all *future* lots were to be accepted without sampling, *then* the best single-sample decision procedure to use in disposing of the *present* lot would be to test a sample of 99 pieces, use the results of this test to compute $E_1(\tilde{p})$ for the run on which the lot was manufactured, and then reject the lot if $E_1(\tilde{p})$ is above the break-even value $p_b = .0358$, accept if $E_1(\tilde{p}) \leq p_b$.

36.4.2   The Second Artificial Problem

Average Cost under the First Approximation.   We also know that the plan which has just been shown to be optimal for the present lot under the assumptions of the first artificial problem is a better plan for application to all future lots than the plan which was part of those assumptions. We therefore define our second artificial problem by assuming that all *future* lots *will* be disposed of according to the plan "sample $n = 99$, reject if $E_1(\tilde{p}) > .0358$"; and the first step toward the solution of this problem is to compute the resulting average cost per accepted lot. Observe that we take the *break-even value* p_b computed for the *first* artificial problem as the *critical value* p_c of the *second* artificial problem.

To get the exact value of this average cost we would have to compute the exact distribution of $\tilde{E}_1$ for $n = 99$ in the same way that we computed this distribution for $n = 20$ in Section 36.3.1; but since our whole procedure depends on the validity of the Normal approximation to the distribution of $\tilde{E}_1$, we shall use that approximation for our present calculation as well as for determining the optimal sample size in each artificial problem.

What we need are the values of $P(\tilde{E}_1 \le p_c)$ and $E_{-\infty}^{p_c}(\tilde{E}_1)$ to use in the formula for average cost given in Section 36.3.4. Remembering from Section 34.3.2 that

$$E(\tilde{E}_1) = E_0(\tilde{p}),$$

we can put the critical value p_c in standard measure by defining

$$u_c = \frac{p_c - E_0(\tilde{p})}{\tilde{\sigma}(\tilde{E}_1)} \qquad \textit{Definition of } u_c$$

Observe carefully that although the p_c of the present problem has the same value as the p_b of the previous problem, the u_c of the present problem differs from the D_∞ of the previous problem in two respects: there are no absolute-value signs around the numerator, and the denominator is not $\sigma_\infty(\tilde{E}_1)$, which is independent of the sample size, but $\sigma(\tilde{E}_1)$, which depends on the sample size. From the definition of u_c and the continuity of the Normal distribution

$$P(\tilde{E}_1 \le p_c) = P_N(\tilde{u} < u_c)$$

and by using the formula given in Section 18.2.3 for the partial expectation of a Normal variable and again substituting $E_0(\tilde{p})$ for $E(\tilde{E}_1)$ we obtain

$$E_{-\infty}^{p_c}(\tilde{E}_1) = E_0(\tilde{p})\, P_N(\tilde{u} < u_c) - \sigma(\tilde{E}_1)\, P_N'(u_c)$$

To apply these formulas to the sampling plan ($n = 99$, $p_c = .0358$) we compute

$$\sigma(\tilde{E}_1) = \sigma_0(\tilde{\xi}) \sqrt{\frac{\sigma_0^2(\tilde{\xi})}{\sigma_0^2(\tilde{\xi}) + \sigma^2(\tilde{\beta}) + (1/n)\sigma^2(\tilde{\epsilon})}}$$

$$= .0217 \sqrt{\frac{.000470}{.000470 + 0 + \frac{1}{99} \times .0240}} = .0176,$$

$$u_c = \frac{.0358 - .0246}{.0176} = +.64,$$

$$P(\tilde{E}_1 \leq .0358) = P_N(\tilde{u} < +.64) = 1 - .2611 = .7389,$$

$$P'_N(+.64) = .3251,$$

$$E_{-\infty}^{p_c}(\tilde{E}_1) = (.0246 \times .7389) - (.0176 \times .3251) = .0125.$$

We then substitute these values in the formula given in Section 36.3.4 to obtain

Average cost per accepted lot

$$= \frac{\$105 + (\$.092 \times 99) + (\$9375 \times .0125)}{.7389} = \$313.$$

Second Approximation to Optimal Sample Size. We now proceed exactly as we did in solving our first artificial problem. The new break-even value for a decision concerning the *present* lot is

$$p_b = \frac{\$313}{\$9375} = .0334.$$

The values of σ_ϵ^*, $\sigma_\infty(\tilde{E}_1)$, and $\sqrt[3]{k_t \sigma_\epsilon^*/k_s}$ are exactly the same as in the first approximation, and therefore

$$Z = .140 \times 25.1 = 3.51$$

also has the same value as in the first approximation; but because the value of p_b has changed we must recompute

$$D_\infty = \frac{|p_b - E_0(\tilde{p})|}{\sigma_\infty(\tilde{E}_1)} = \frac{|.0334 - .0246|}{.0217} = .41.$$

Above $Z = 3.51$ in Chart II we read .167 for $D_\infty = .4$ and .150 for $D_\infty = .6$. Interpolating for $D_\infty = .41$ we obtain

$$h = .166$$

and compute

$$n^* = .166 \times 25.1^2 = 105.$$

If the sampling plan ($n = 99$, $p_c = .0358$) were to be applied to *all future* lots, *then* the best sampling plan to apply to the *present* lot would be ($n = 105$, $p_c = .0334$).

36.4.3   The Third Artificial Problem

Average Cost under the Second Approximation. We next compute the average total cost per accepted lot which will result from applying this revised plan ($n = 105$, $p_c = .0334$) to all future lots.

$$\sigma(\tilde{E}_1) = .0217 \sqrt{\frac{.000470}{.000470 + \frac{1}{105} \times .240}} = .0178;$$

$$u_c = \frac{.0334 - .0246}{.0178} = +.49;$$

$$P(\tilde{E}_1 \le .0334) = P_N(\tilde{u} < +.49) = 1 - .3121 = .6879;$$

$$P_N'(+.49) = .3538;$$

$$E^{p_c}_{-\infty}(\tilde{E}_1) = (.0246 \times .6879) - (.0178 \times .3538) = .0106;$$

Average cost per accepted lot

$$= \frac{\$105 + (\$.092 \times 105) + (\$9375 \times .0106)}{.6879} = \$311.$$

Third Approximation to Optimal Sample Size. The new break-even value is

$$p_b = \frac{\$311}{\$9375} = .0332,$$

leading to

$$D_\infty = \frac{|.0332 - .0246|}{.0217} = .40.$$

The value of Z is again unchanged at 3.51, and from Chart II we read

$$h = .167$$

leading to

$$n^* = .167 \times 25.1^2 = 105.$$

36.4.4   The Exact Solution of the Real Problem

Because the third artificial problem has yielded the same sample size $n^* = 105$ which we obtained from the second artificial problem, we know that this is the true optimal sample size for the Normalized version of the real problem; and because the $p_b = .0332$ of the third problem is so close to the $p_b = .0334$ of the second problem we can also feel sure that for all practical purposes $p_c = .0332$ is the optimal critical value for the Normalized version of the real problem. All that remains is to see whether the use of the Normal approximation has resulted in any material error.

To do this we first compute the *exact* distribution of $\tilde{E}_1$ for $n = 105$ by the method of Section 36.3.1 and find that $p_c = .0332$ corresponds to an acceptance number $c = 3$. We then use the exact distribution of $\tilde{E}_1$

to compute average cost per accepted lot with values of p_c corresponding to acceptance numbers 2, 3, and 4, find that the cost is higher for $c = 2$ and 4 than it is for $c = 3$, and thus prove that $c = 3$ is in fact optimal *given* $n = 105$ and that the plan ($n = 105$, $c = 3$) leads to an exact average cost of \$295.56 per expected lot. We then repeat this procedure for $n = 104$ and 106, find that $c = 3$ is optimal for these sample sizes as well as for $n = 105$, and show that when used with $c = 3$ they result in average costs per accepted lot which are respectively \$.01 and \$.02 higher than the \$295.56 which is obtained with $n = 105$.

Thus in this particular example the Normal approximation led us to the *exact optimal size;* but what is much more important is the evidence just given to show that *the curve of total cost against sample size is so flat in the neighborhood of the true optimal sample size that moderate errors in sample size will occasion no appreciable excess cost.*

We must also observe, however, that the Normal approximation does *not* give a very good approximation to the actual cost which will result from the use of any given sampling plan. Under the optimal plan ($n = 105$, $p_c = .0332$) the Normal approximation leads to virtually the same \$311 per accepted lot that we computed in Section 36.4.3 for the plan ($n = 105$, $p_c = .0334$), and this cost differs materially from the \$295.56 obtained by use of the exact distribution of $\tilde{E}_1$. The general conclusion to be reached from this and many similar examples is of exactly the same nature as the corresponding conclusion in Section 35.5:

> When the Normal approximation leads to a *nonzero* sample size, we can usually feel sure that for all practical purposes this is the *best nonzero* sample size; the only real danger with the Normal approximation is (1) that it may tell us to sample when we should not sample at all and (2) that it may tell us not to sample when we should take a sample of substantial size.

As we saw in Section 35.5, it is easy to guard against the first danger because we have only to compute a single exact expected cost; in our example we have already seen that the \$295.56 exact cost of ($n = 105$, $p_c = .0332$) is less than the \$336 cost of accepting all lots. It is only when the Normal approximation tells us *not* to sample that we are forced to make fairly heavy computations in order to sketch out the general nature of the curve showing exact average cost as a function of n.

36.5   Opportunity Loss

To evaluate opportunity loss in problems of the kind we are now studying we must express it in exactly the same way that we express cost, as an *average per unit of yield.* It is extremely difficult to compute a *conditional* loss of this sort, since to specify the "condition" we must specify the value which $\tilde{p}$ will have on each of an infinitely long sequence of runs; but it is easy to compute the *expected* loss per unit of yield by first computing expected cost per unit of yield under certainty.

36.5.1 Average Cost per Accepted Lot under Certainty

In our particular example, it is obvious without proof that if we were to be given free perfect information on the true value of $\tilde{p}$ just after the present *and all future* runs were made, we would accept any lot if the p of the run on which it was made was equal to or less than some critical value p_c, reject if it was greater than p_c; the rule is identical to the rule under uncertainty except that $\tilde{E}_1$ is replaced by $\tilde{p}$. Again, exactly the same logic which led to the formula at the end of Section 36.3.4 for average cost under a sampling plan leads to the formula for the

$$\text{Average cost per accepted lot} = \frac{\$105 + \$9375\ \mathrm{E}^{p_c}_{-\infty}(\tilde{p})}{\mathrm{P}(\tilde{p} \leq p_c)}$$

of using an *arbitrarily chosen* p_c under certainty.

The *optimal* value for p_c under certainty can be found by successive approximations in a way which resembles the way in which we found the optimal p_c under uncertainty but is simpler because we do not have to determine an optimal n at the same time.

First Approximation. We start as in Section 36.4.1 by assuming that all future lots will be accepted without sampling, leading to a cost of \$336 per future lot and a break-even value $p_b = \$336/\$9375 = .0358$ for the present lot. Because there is no sample size to compute, this completes the first-approximation decision plan.

Second Approximation. We start by computing the average cost per accepted lot which will result from applying the plan ($p_c = .0358$) to all future lots. Taking our data from Table 36.1 we compute

$$\mathrm{P}(\tilde{p} \leq .0358) = .60 + .20 = .80,$$
$$\mathrm{E}^{.0358}_{-\infty}(\tilde{p}) = (.01 \times .60) + (.03 \times .20) = .0120.$$

Substituting these values in the formula for cost under certainty we obtain

Average cost per accepted lot
$$= \frac{\$105 + (\$9375 \times .0120)}{.80} = \frac{\$218}{.80} = \$272.$$

Assuming now that this *will* be the average cost of future lots, we obtain as the new break-even value for the *present* lot

$$p_b = \frac{\$272}{\$9375} = .0290.$$

Third Approximation. We find the cost of using the plan ($p_c =$ .0290) on all future lots by computing

$$P(\tilde{p} \le .0290) = .60,$$
$$E_{-\infty}^{.0290}(\tilde{p}) = .01 \times .60 = .0060,$$

Average cost per accepted lot

$$= \frac{\$105 + (\$9375 \times .0060)}{.60} = \frac{\$161}{.60} = \$268.$$

This result leads to a new break-even value for the *present* lot

$$p_b = \frac{\$268}{\$9375} = .0286.$$

We now observe that if we were to compute another approximation starting with $p_c = .0286$ we would get exactly the same values for $P(\tilde{p} \le p_c)$ and $E_{-\infty}^{p_c}(\tilde{p})$ that we got with $p_c = .0290$ and would thus be led back to $p_b = .0286$. We conclude that *under certainty the optimal value of p_c would be .0286 and the average cost per accepted lot would be $268.*

36.5.2   Expected Opportunity Loss per Accepted Lot

We have already seen that the average cost per accepted lot which results from the use of the optimal plan ($n = 105$, $p_c = .0332$) under uncertainty is $296 to the nearest dollar. Subtracting the corresponding cost under certainty we have for this optimal plan

Expected loss per accepted lot $= \$296 - \$268 = \$28.$

Unless some other *type* of decision procedure such as sequential sampling can be made to give lower cost than the optimal single-sample procedure, this is the *cost of uncertainty per accepted lot.*

PROBLEMS

1. The Allied Electromechanical Corporation manufactures electronic computers and leases them on terms which provide that all maintenance shall be performed by Allied at no cost to the lessee. Each computer uses a number of type AT-17-GG vacuum tubes; these tubes are purchased by Allied at a price of $2 each in lots containing 1000 tubes for actual use (either as original equipment or for replacement) plus however many tubes are required for sampling inspection.

Failure of any one of these tubes causes malfunctioning of the computer in which the failure occurs, and on the average it takes 2 hours before an Allied engineer can arrive on the scene, locate the source of trouble, and replace the tube. The out-of-pocket cost of such trouble-shooting amounts to about $20, but what is much more serious is the customer's dissatisfaction because the computer is useless while the trouble is being repaired; Allied's management feels that $200 is a conservative estimate of the good-will cost of each failure. Records kept by Allied over the last year show that there is a good deal of lot-to-lot variability in the mean life of the tubes in one lot; the distribution is roughly Normal with mean 4500 hours and standard deviation 1500 hours. This standard deviation is so large that Allied believes that it may be desirable to scrap the worst lots and sacrifice the purchase price rather than install the tubes in computers.

Allied has developed a very reliable method of measuring the service life of a tube without actually putting it in service in a computer; but because the tubes must remain on test until they fail the test is quite expensive, costing about $10 per tube tested. The test is really an accelerated test and is not necessarily run until every tube in the sample has failed, but it yields an "estimate" or statistic which has the same probability distribution as the mean of a sample of tubes used under regular service conditions. This distribution is roughly Normal with a mean equal to the true mean life of the tubes in the lot from which the sample is taken and with variance $(1/n)\sigma^2(\tilde{\epsilon})$; Allied's experiments have shown that $\sigma(\tilde{\epsilon}) = 4500$ hours approximately.

a. Show that a reasonable single-sample decision procedure for Allied's problem will consist of a rule telling the inspector to take a sample of a certain size, compute the statistic which plays the role of $\tilde{x}$, and then scrap the lot if $\tilde{x}$ is *less* than some critical value $\tilde{x}_c$.

b. Using ξ to denote the true mean life of the tubes in a lot, show that this rule is equivalent to a rule calling for the scrapping of the lot if $E_1(\tilde{\xi})$ is less than some critical value ξ_c.

c. Show that the prior distribution of $\tilde{E}_1$ is Normal with parameters

$$E(\tilde{E}_1) = 4500,$$

$$\sigma(\tilde{E}_1) = 1500 \sqrt{\frac{1500^2}{1500^2 + (1/n)4500^2}} = 1500 \sqrt{\frac{225}{225 + 2025/n}},$$

and that if

$$u_c = \frac{\xi_c - 4500}{\sigma(\tilde{E}_1)}$$

then

$$E_{\xi_c}^\infty(\tilde{E}_1) = 4500\, P_N(\tilde{u} > u_c) + \sigma(\tilde{E}_1)\, P_N'(u_c).$$

d. Show that under any given sampling plan (n, ξ_c) the *average cost per lot purchased* will be the sum of

Cost of purchase $= \$2\,(1000 + n)$,
Cost of inspection $= \$10\,n$,
Cost of replacement $= \$220 \times 1000\, P(\tilde{E}_1 > \xi_c)$.

e. Show that the average *number of tube-hours of service* obtained from one purchased lot will be

Hours of service $= 1000\, E_{\xi_c}^\infty(\tilde{E}_1)$.

f. Using these results, show that the *average cost per tube-hour of service* will be

$$H = \frac{\$12\,n + \$2000 + \$220{,}000\, P(\tilde{E}_1 > \xi_c)}{1000\, E_{\xi_c}^\infty(\tilde{E}_1)}.$$

g. Show that if tube-hours of service obtained from all *future* lots cost $\$H$ each on the average, then the decision concerning the *present* lot is an ordinary two-action problem with linear costs:

Acceptance: $220,000
Rejection: $1000 $H\xi$
Sampling: $12 n

What has happened to the purchase cost and why?

h. Show that for the present-lot problem defined in (*g*)

$$\xi_b = \frac{\$220}{H},$$
$$k_t = \$1000\, H,$$
$$k_s = \$12.$$

i. The calculations leading to the determination of the true optimal plan for the real problem are summarized in Table 36.6. Starting from the result $H = \$.04025$ of the first approximation, verify all the entries in the line describing the second approximation.

Table 36.6

Approximation number	Plan	Cost per tube-hour
0	Accept all lots	\$.04933
1	$n = 98,\ \xi_c = 4460$	.04025
2	$n = 78,\ \xi_c = 5466$	.03673
3	$n = 61,\ \xi_c = 5990$	.03564
4	$n = 55,\ \xi_c = 6173$	.03551
5	$n = 55,\ \xi_c = 6195$	.03551

2. In the problem discussed in Section 24.1.2, assume that the distribution of $\tilde{p}$ given in Table 24.2 can be treated as stationary, that the cost of inspecting one piece is \$.03, and that each production run will consist of 500 pieces *in addition* to any pieces manufactured for inspection before the run is begun.

a. Show that in this problem the \$.45 *direct* cost of manufacturing a *good* piece is irrelevant, so that in defining the costs to be minimized this cost may always be excluded.

b. Show that under any given sampling plan (n, p_c), the *average cost per production run* (exclusive of the direct cost of good pieces) will be the sum of

Cost of sampling $= \$.03\, n + \$.29\, n\, E_0(\tilde{p})$,
Cost of acceptance $= \$.29 \times 500\, E^{pe}_{-\infty}(\tilde{E}_1)$,
Cost of rejection $= [\$35.00 + (\$.29 \times 500 \times .1)]\, P(\tilde{E}_1 > p_c)$.

c. Show that the *average number of good pieces* obtained from one production run will be

$$n[1 - E_0(\tilde{p})] + 500[P(\tilde{E}_1 \leq p_c) - E^{pe}_{-\infty}(\tilde{E}_1)] + 500 \times .9\, P(\tilde{E}_1 > p_c).$$

d. Using these results and substituting the numerical value of $E_0(\tilde{p})$ show that the *average cost per good piece will be* (exclusive of the actual manufacturing cost of the good piece)

$$G = \frac{\$.1141\, n + \$145\, E^{pe}_{-\infty}(\tilde{E}_1) + \$49.5\, P(\tilde{E}_1 > p_c)}{.71n + 500[1 - .1\, P(\tilde{E}_1 > p_c) - E^{pe}_{-\infty}(\tilde{E}_1)]}.$$

e. Show that if an arbitrarily specified plan which yields an average cost of $\$G$ per good piece is to be applied to all *future* runs, then the decision concerning the *present* run is an ordinary two-action problem with linear costs:

Acceptance: $\$(.29 + G)\, 500p$
Rejection: $\$35 + \$(.29 + G)\, 500 \times .1$
Sampling: $\$.03\, n + \$.29\, n\, E_0(\tilde{p}) - \$n\, [1 - E_0(\tilde{p})]G$

Discuss the reason for the difference between the cost of sampling in this present-run problem and the cost of sampling per production run.

f. Again substituting the numerical value of $E_0(\tilde{p})$ show that for the present-run decision

$$p_b = \frac{\$49.50 + \$50.00\,G}{\$500\,(.29 + G)} = \frac{.099 + .1G}{.29 + G},$$
$$k_t = \$500\,(.29 + G),$$
$$k_s = \$(.1141 - .71G).$$

g. Show that if all runs are *rejected (readjusted) without sampling*, the average cost per good piece will be \$.1100 (exclusive of the direct manufacturing cost of the good pieces).

h. Starting from the assumption that all future lots will be rejected without sampling, use the Normal approximation to show that a first approximation to the optimal plan is $(n = 32, p_c = .275)$ and that under this plan cost as computed by the Normal approximation will average \$.1028 per good piece.

i. Show that the second approximation to the optimal plan is $(n = 30, p_c = .278)$ and that under this plan cost as computed by the Normal approximation will average \$.1028 per good piece.

Exact calculations show that when $n = 30$, the critical value p_c corresponds to an acceptance number $c = 7$. The exact costs per good piece under plans in the neighborhood of $(n = 30, c = 7)$ are shown in Table 36.7, where it appears that $(n = 30, c = 7)$ is in fact the exact optimal plan.

Table 36.7
Exact Cost per Good Piece

c	n		
	29	30	31
6	.10175	.10191	.10212
7	.10165	.10159	.10161
8	.10250	.10216	.10191

Many-action Problems with Proportional Losses; General-purpose Estimation

In Chapters 34 and 35 we studied the computation of expected loss and the determination of optimal sample size in the very important class of business problems in which a choice must be made between just *two possible terminal acts* and the conditional *cost* of either act is a *linear* function of the basic random variable. In the present chapter we shall study another very important class of problems, in which:

1. The terminal act can be described by a number which may have *any value within a certain interval*, e.g. quantity stocked, size of scrap allowance, amount of a certain reagent used in a chemical process.
2. The conditional *loss* is *proportional* to the difference between the value of the basic random variable and the number which describes the terminal act.

37.1 Basic Assumptions

As an example of a many-action problem with proportional losses, suppose as we did so often in Parts One and Two of this course that an item is stocked periodically and spoils if it is not sold before the end of the period in which it is stocked. If stock exceeds demand, there will be a loss proportional to the size of the overage; if demand exceeds stock, there will be a loss proportional to the size of the underage. Suppose further that there is a known population of potential customers of size

N: total number of potential customers in the population

and that it is possible to sample this population and determine more or less accurately how many units will be demanded by each person drawn into the sample.

In our earlier discussions of problems of this type we have taken total demand as the basic random variable, but this variable is very awkward when sampling enters the picture and therefore we shall now take as our basic random variable

$\tilde{\xi}$: the mean demand *per potential customer.*

Even if a 100 per cent sample is taken, the mean μ of the quantities which the customers *say* they will buy may not be equal to the mean ξ of the quantities which they will *actually* buy when the merchandise is really offered for sale. The difference $\beta = \mu - \xi$ is the bias of the sampling process, while the difference between an individual observation x and the mean μ of the (potential) 100 per cent sample is the pure sampling error ϵ of the observation.

As we did in Chapters 34 and 35, we shall assume throughout the present chapter that

1. The individual pure sampling errors $\tilde{\epsilon}$ are independent except possibly for the effect of a finite population, and their variance $\sigma^2(\tilde{\epsilon})$ is known.
2. The mean $\tilde{\epsilon}$ can be treated as Normally distributed.
3. The prior distribution of $\tilde{\xi}$ is Normal and independent of $\tilde{\epsilon}$.
4. The cost of sampling is a linear function of the sample size, $K_s + k_s n$.

In deriving a formula for *total expected loss* we shall allow both for possible uncertainty about bias and for possible finiteness of the population just as we did in Chapter 34; our formula will provide for uncertainty about bias on the assumption that the distribution of $\tilde{\beta}$ is Normal, and it will hold whether or not it is necessary to make a finite-population correction in computing $\sigma^2(\tilde{\epsilon})$.

In discussing *optimal sample size,* on the other hand, our treatment will differ somewhat from our treatment of the two-action problem in Chapter 35. Our real purpose in studying optimal sample size is not to train statisticians who will actually compute sample sizes but to give the student of business some understanding of the general way in which optimal sample size depends on the various circumstances or "parameters" of a practical decision problem. In problems of the kind we are now studying it is possible to obtain clear and simple results concerning optimal sample size only if we assume *either* (1) that the finite-population correction is negligible *or* (2) that there is no uncertainty about bias. In Chapter 35 we made the first of these two assumptions and thus obtained results which gave some understanding of the way in which uncertainty about bias affects optimal sample size. In the present chapter we shall make the second assumption in order to show the very peculiar way in which finiteness of the population may affect optimal sample size.

37.2   The Optimal Terminal Act and Its Expected Loss

Whether or not a sample is taken, the terminal decision in our problem will be made under a Normal probability distribution: as we said in the previous section, we are assuming that the prior distribution is

Normal and that the sampling distribution is Normal with known variance, and this means that the posterior distribution will be Normal if a sample is taken. We have already discussed the methods by which the optimal terminal act (stock level) can be selected and its expected loss evaluated when the conditional losses are of the type we are now discussing and the probability distribution is Normal (Chapter 18); we shall review the results here merely in order to reexpress them in terms of the mean demand ξ rather than the total demand $\tilde{z}$ which we used as the basic random variable in this earlier discussion. Because the formulas which we shall review apply under *any* Normal distribution, we shall write $E(\tilde{\xi})$ and $\sigma(\tilde{\xi})$ without subscripts to indicate whether they refer to a "prior" or "posterior" assessment of the distribution.

37.2.1 Description of the Terminal Act and the Conditional Losses

In our previous analyses of problems of this general type we have always described the terminal act by the value of Q, the total quantity stocked. This was the natural and convenient way to proceed when we were using the total demand $\tilde{z}$ as the basic random variable of the problem, but now that we are using the mean demand per customer $\tilde{\xi}$ as the basic random variable it will be more convenient to describe the terminal act by

$q = Q/N$: quantity stocked *per customer.*

For the same reason we shall no longer describe the conditional losses by the constants k_o and k_u which measure the loss for each unit by which total stock is over or under total demand. Instead, we shall describe them by new constants which measure the loss for each unit by which stock *per customer* is over or under demand *per customer,* defining

κ_o: loss for each unit by which the act q is over the value ξ,
κ_u: loss for each unit by which the act q is under the value ξ.

Since $z = N\xi$ and $Q = Nq$, the difference between Q and z will be N times the difference between q and ξ and therefore a unit difference between q and ξ will cause N times the loss caused by a unit difference between Q and z. This means that in inventory problems of this sort we are using as an example,

$\kappa_o = Nk_o, \qquad \kappa_u = Nk_u.$

Suppose, for example, that $k_o = \$3$ and that there are $N = 1000$ potential customers so that κ_o as given by this formula has the value $\$3000$. If we stock $Q = 40$ units, this amounts to $q = .040$ unit per customer; and if there is actually a demand for a total of 30 units, this amounts to $\xi = .030$ unit per customer. The *overage per customer* is thus .010 unit, and if we multiply this by $\kappa_o = \$3000$ we get the same $\$30$

loss that we would have got by multiplying the *total overage* of 10 units by $k_o = \$3$.

37.2.2   The Optimal Terminal Act and Its Expected Loss

Formulas for the optimal terminal act and for its expected loss can be taken directly from the discussion in Sections 18.2.2 and 18.2.3. Although the example which was used to illustrate that discussion involved an act called Q and a basic random variable called $\tilde{z}$, the argument itself in no way depended on this particular illustration; it depended *only* on the facts (1) that the conditional losses were proportional to the difference between the act and the value of the basic random variable and (2) that the basic random variable had been assigned a Normal probability distribution. Even if our present problem did not involve inventories at all, we would be entitled to use those formulas provided that these two essential conditions were met; all that we have to do is to substitute for the symbols there used the corresponding symbols of the new problem. In our present problem the substitution is q^* for Q^*, $\tilde{\xi}$ for $\tilde{z}$, κ_o for k_o, and κ_u for k_u.

Proceeding in this way we first find from Section 18.2.2 that if we use q^* to denote the *best* quantity to stock per customer and

$$u^* = \frac{q^* - \mathrm{E}(\tilde{\xi})}{\sigma(\tilde{\xi})}$$

to denote the corresponding value of the unit random variable $\tilde{u}$, then q^* and u^* must be values such that

$$\mathrm{P}(\tilde{\xi} < q^*) = \mathrm{P}_N(\tilde{u} < u^*) = \frac{\kappa_u}{\kappa_u + \kappa_o} \qquad \text{\textit{Definition of } } q^* \text{ \textit{and} } u^*$$

We find the best amount to stock per customer by first using Table III to find the value u^* which satisfies this condition and then computing

$$q^* = \mathrm{E}(\tilde{\xi}) + u^*\sigma(\tilde{\xi})$$

The expected loss of the optimal terminal act q^* under the given probability distribution is then found in Section 18.2.3:

$$\text{Expected loss of optimal terminal act} = (\kappa_u + \kappa_o)\,\mathrm{P}'_N(u^*)\sigma(\tilde{\xi})$$

Before proceeding further the student should work through Problem 1 at the end of this chapter to make sure that he understands the meaning and use of these formulas.

37.3 Total Expected Loss of a Single-sample Decision Procedure

37.3.1 Prior Expected Loss of Optimal Terminal Action after Sampling

As we have already said, the formulas given above can be used either (1) to select the optimal *immediate* terminal act and to compute its expected loss under the *prior* distribution or (2) to select the terminal act which is optimal after a sample has *actually been taken* and to compute its expected loss under the *posterior* distribution which has resulted from that sample. In the former case we substitute the values of $E_0(\xi)$ and $\sigma_0(\xi)$ for $E(\xi)$ and $\sigma(\xi)$ in the formulas; in the latter case we substitute the values of $E_1(\xi)$ and $\sigma_1(\xi)$.

When we set out to evaluate a single-sample decision procedure, however, we need still a different expected terminal loss: we need the *prior* expected value of the loss due to optimal terminal action in the light of an *as yet unknown* sample outcome. In the two-action problems which we studied in Chapters 33 through 36, both the act and its posterior expected loss depended on the sample outcome; and this meant that in order to obtain the *prior* expected value of the loss which would be incurred through optimal action *after* sampling we had to compute the posterior expected loss for *every possible sample outcome*, multiply each of these conditional terminal losses by the prior probability of the outcome in question, and add the products.

In our present problem the task is fortunately very much simpler. Although the optimal *act* after sampling depends on both $E_1(\xi)$ and $\sigma_1(\xi)$, *the posterior expected loss depends only on $\sigma_1(\xi)$ and the value of $\sigma_1(\xi)$ is known before the sample is taken.* As we saw in Section 34.5.2, it is computed by simply substituting the known variance of the sample mean

$$\sigma^2(\tilde{x}) = \sigma^2(\tilde{\beta}) + \frac{1}{n}\sigma^2(\tilde{\epsilon})\frac{N-n}{N-1}$$

in the formula

$$I_1 = I_0 + I_{\tilde{x}}$$

to obtain

$$\frac{1}{\sigma_1^2(\xi)} = \frac{1}{\sigma_0^2(\xi)} + \frac{1}{\sigma^2(\tilde{\beta}) + (1/n)\sigma^2(\tilde{\epsilon})(N-n)/(N-1)}.$$

37.3.2 Total Expected Loss

We now turn to the problem of evaluating the *total* expected loss of a decision to sample and then act, i.e. the sum of the prior expected value of the posterior terminal loss plus the cost (loss) of sampling. As we have already said, we shall assume that the cost of sampling will be composed of two parts, a fixed element which will be incurred if any sample is taken at all and a variable part which is proportional to the size of the sample:

Cost of sampling $= K_s + k_s n$.

Adding this to the expected terminal loss derived in the previous section we have

$$\text{Total expected loss} = K_s + k_s n + (\kappa_u + \kappa_o)\, \mathrm{P}'_N(u^*)\sigma_1(\xi)$$

To find total expected loss for any given sample size n we first compute $\sigma_1(\xi)$ for this value of n by means of the formula at the end of Section 37.3.1 and we then substitute the values of n and $\sigma_1(\xi)$ in the formula for the total expected loss.

37.4 Behavior of Total Loss As n Increases

The optimal sample size in any particular problem can always be found by evaluating total expected loss for a sufficiently large number of different n's and selecting the n^* which minimizes the loss. Since the formula for the loss allows for both uncertainty about bias and finiteness of the population, the n^* obtained in this way would be a true optimum. We shall now proceed, however, to make a systematic investigation of the way in which the data of the problem affect the optimal sample size, and in order to do this

> We shall assume in the remainder of this chapter that there is *no uncertainty about bias*: $\sigma(\tilde{\beta}) = 0$.†

As we did in Section 35.2, we shall begin our investigation by examining the general economic effect of increasing n, although in the present case it will be more convenient to look at terminal loss and total loss rather than at the value of sample information and the net gain from sampling. Again as in Section 35.2, we shall proceed by first assuming that there is no fixed element in sampling cost, $K_s = 0$, and then showing that it is easy to modify our conclusions to allow for the effect of a nonzero K_s.

37.4.1 *The Essential Parameters and the Sampling Ratio*

Once more as in Section 35.2, our task would be hopelessly complex if we tried to look at the effect of each individual parameter on the behavior of loss with increasing n and we therefore work instead with the really

† *Known* bias is never a problem: cf. Section 31.2.2.

essential *combinations* of parameters. As in the two-action problem, these turn out to be only two in number in addition to K_s:

$$A^3 = \frac{1}{N^3}\left[\frac{\sigma(\tilde{\epsilon})(\kappa_u + \kappa_o)\, P'_N(u^*)}{2k_s}\right]^2$$

$$B = \frac{\sigma^2(\tilde{\epsilon})}{N\sigma_0^2(\tilde{\xi})}$$

Essential parameters when $\sigma(\tilde{\beta}) = 0$

It will also be more convenient to work in terms of

$$\frac{n}{N}: \text{the sampling ratio}$$

rather than in terms of n itself.

37.4.2   Behavior of Total Loss When $K_s = 0$

In Figure 37.1 all possible pairs of values for A and B are divided into four groups designated by the numerals I through IV, and in Figure

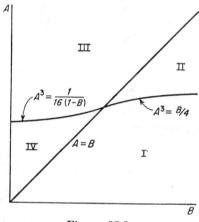

Figure 37.1

37.2 the sum of terminal loss plus *variable* sampling cost $k_s n$ is graphed as a function of n/N for each group.† From the sketches we see that in region I the best decision is to act *without sampling* while in regions II and III the best decision is to take a *complete count* or 100 per cent sample; *it is only in region IV that it pays to sample in the ordinary sense of the word.*

† What is actually graphed is the ratio

$$\frac{\text{Terminal loss plus variable sampling cost}}{\text{Cost of a 100\% sample}}$$

and the dashed horizontal line represents a ratio of 1.

37.4.3   Behavior of Total Loss When $K_s > 0$

The effect of a fixed element of sampling cost on Figure 37.2 is obvious: except for the point at $n/N = 0$, every point on every curve is raised by the *same* amount K_s.†

The implications are also obvious. In Region I, where sampling is disadvantageous even when $K_s = 0$, sampling is certain to be still more disadvantageous when $K_s > 0$. In Regions II and III, where a 100 per cent sample should be taken when $K_s = 0$, a 100 per cent sample will still be better than any smaller *nonzero* sample when $K_s > 0$ but this additional sampling cost may make it better not to sample at all. In Region IV, where a sample of less than 100 per cent should be taken

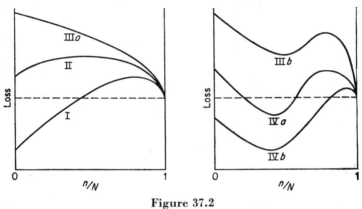

Figure 37.2

when $K_s = 0$, the bottom of the dip in the loss curve will still occur at the same value of n when $K_s > 0$ and this value of n will still be the best *nonzero* sample size, but it may be better not to sample at all than to incur the cost K_s.

37.5   Optimal Sample Size

As in Section 35.3 we shall first show how to determine the optimal sample size n^* when there is no fixed element in sampling cost and then show how to check and if necessary modify this sample size to allow for a nonzero K_s.

37.5.1   Optimal Sample Size When $K_s = 0$

We first decide whether we should take no sample at all ($n/N = 0$), take a complete count ($n/N = 1$), or use some value of n/N between 0 and 1. For this purpose we refer to Chart VI, which is the same as Figure 37.1 except that it is drawn to scale and shows in addition the optimal value of n/N for certain A, B pairs in region IV.

† In Section 35.2.6 we saw that the effect of K_s on curves of *net gain* was to *lower* every point except the point at $n = 0$ by the same amount.

If Chart VI shows that a sample should be taken rather than a complete count or no sample at all, *then* the value of n/N which minimizes the sum of action cost plus variable sampling cost is the smaller† of the two values which satisfy the equation

$$\frac{n}{N} = \frac{A}{\sqrt[3]{1 - n/N}} - B\left(1 - \frac{n}{N}\right).$$

A first approximation to the optimum value of n/N can be obtained by interpolation between the n/N lines on the chart. For values of n/N above .3, say, the value obtained in this way will have a reasonably small relative error and can be taken as the solution of the problem. For lower values of n/N a better approximate solution is given by

$$\frac{n^*}{N} \doteq \frac{A - B}{1 - B - A/3}$$

The value given by this formula is always too low, but it is more than accurate enough for most practical purposes. When $A < .3$ and $B = 0$, the error is less than 2 per cent of the true optimum; when $A < .3$ and $B < .1$ the error is less than 3 per cent.‡

37.5.2 Optimal Sample Size When $K_s > 0$

When there is a fixed element in sampling cost in a problem of the kind we are now studying, we handle it in exactly the same way that we handle it in a two-action problem (Section 35.3.2). Since the effect of K_s is to raise every point on a total-loss curve except the point at $n/N = 0$ by the same amount, we know:

1. If it does *not* pay to sample when $K_s = 0$, it will not pay when $K_s > 0$;
2. If it *does* pay to sample when $K_s = 0$, then the optimal sample size for $K_s = 0$ is the best *nonzero* sample size for $K_s > 0$ but this size must be checked to see if it is still better than $n/N = 0$.

37.5.3 Example

An item costs $1, sells for $3, and spoils if it is not sold on the day on which it is stocked. The retailer has 1000 potential customers; he

† The two values of n/N which satisfy this equation correspond to the two points where the total-loss curve for region IV is flat; the larger value gives *maximum* total loss.

‡ If more accurate values are required, they may be obtained by successive approximations. Substitute the value given by the approximate formula in the right side of the *exact* formula and thus compute a new trial value. Substitute this value in the right side to get a new trial value, and so forth. The problem is solved when two successive "trial values" are equal to the desired number of decimal places.

"expects" that they will demand 5 units each on the average but he assigns a "standard error" of 2 units to this forecast. The population can be sampled at a cost of \$1.50 per individual in the sample plus a fixed cost of \$100 for administration, analysis, etc. The retailer is convinced that the sampling process is unbiased and knows that the standard deviation of the population of individual demands† is 4 units. We thus have

$$
\begin{aligned}
N &= 1000, & \kappa_o &= N k_o = N\,\$1 = \$1000, \\
\mathrm{E}_0(\tilde\xi) &= 5, & \kappa_u &= N k_u = N(\$3 - \$1) = \$2000, \\
\sigma_0(\tilde\xi) &= 2, & k_s &= \$1.50, \\
\sigma(\tilde\epsilon) &= 4, & K_s &= \$100.
\end{aligned}
$$

We first compute the "critical fractile"

$$
\frac{\kappa_u}{\kappa_u + \kappa_o} = \frac{\$2000}{\$2000 + \$1000} = .67.
$$

From Table III we find that

$$
\mathrm{P}_N(\tilde u > .44) = .33, \qquad \text{i.e.} \qquad \mathrm{P}_N(\tilde u < .44) = .67,
$$

so that

$$
u^* = .44;
$$

and from Table II we then find that

$$
\mathrm{P}'_N(u^*) = .362.
$$

We then compute

$$
A^3 = \frac{1}{1000^3}\left(\frac{4 \times \$3000 \times .362}{2 \times \$1.50}\right)^2 = .002097,
$$
$$
A = \sqrt[3]{.002097} = .1280,
$$
$$
B = \frac{4^2}{1000 \times 2^2} = .0040.
$$

We consult Chart VI, observe that a sample should be taken and that the optimum sampling ratio will be between .10 and .15, and then obtain a better value for n/N by using the approximation formula

$$
\frac{n^*}{N} \doteq \frac{.1280 - .0040}{1 - .0040 - .0427} = .130.
$$

From this we compute the actual sample size

$$
n^* = .130N = .130 \times 1000 = 130.
$$

---

† Since we are assuming no measurement or selection bias, the population of individual true demands is identical to the population of potential sample observations x.

So far we know only that $n^* = 130$ is the best sample size other than 0 and that the saving in terminal loss to be expected from such a sample will more than pay for the *variable* sampling cost $k_s n^*$. We must check to see whether it will also cover the fixed cost $K_s = \$100$, and to do this we must actually evaluate total expected loss with $n = 130$ and with $n = 0$. To find total loss with $n = 0$ we simply substitute $\sigma_0(\xi) = 2$ in the formula for expected terminal loss:

Expected terminal loss $= (\$2000 + \$1000) \times .362 \times 2 = \$2172$.

To find the expected loss of terminal action after taking a sample of $n = 130$ we first compute

$$\sigma^2(\tilde{x}) = \sigma^2(\tilde{\beta}) + \frac{1}{n}\sigma^2(\tilde{\epsilon})\frac{N - n}{N - 1} = 0 + \left(\frac{1}{130} \times 4^2 \times \frac{870}{999}\right) = .1072,$$

$$\frac{1}{\sigma_1^2(\xi)} = \frac{1}{\sigma_0^2(\xi)} + \frac{1}{\sigma^2(\tilde{x})} = \frac{1}{2^2} + \frac{1}{.1072} = 9.58,$$

$$\sigma_1(\xi) = \frac{1}{\sqrt{9.58}} = .323.$$

We then have

Expected terminal loss $= \$3000 \times .362 \times .323 = \$351$,
Cost of sampling $= \$100 + (\$1.50 \times 130) = \$295$,
Total expected loss $= \$351 + \$295 = \$646$.

This total is well below the loss of immediate terminal action and the sample should be taken. An expenditure of \$295 on sampling can be expected to reduce terminal loss by $\$2172 - \$351 = \$1821$ for a net gain of \$1526.

37.6   The Effect of Uncertainty Concerning $\sigma(\tilde{\epsilon})$

In deriving the procedure for determining optimal sample size which has just been described, we assumed that the standard deviation of the pure sampling error $\tilde{\epsilon}$ of any individual sample observation is known with certainty *before* the sample is taken. We shall now see, however, that under certain conditions we can treat the *expected* value of $\sigma(\tilde{\epsilon})$ *as if it* were the true value and still be sure that the resulting sample size will be either exactly or virtually optimal provided only that the size of this sample is such that $\sigma(\tilde{\epsilon})$ *will* be known with (virtual) certainty *after* the sample has been taken.

The conditions under which it is legitimate to disregard uncertainty about $\sigma(\tilde{\epsilon})$ can easily be discovered by looking at the procedure by which we could always take full and exact account of this uncertainty in determining optimal sample size. Uncertainty about $\sigma(\tilde{\epsilon})$ affects the determination of the *optimal* n because for any *given* n the value of $\sigma_1(\xi)$ depends on $\sigma(\tilde{\epsilon})$ and therefore the

$$\text{Total expected loss} = K_s + k_s n + (\kappa_u + \kappa_o) \, \mathrm{P}'_N(u^*)\sigma_1(\xi)$$

depends on $\sigma(\tilde{\epsilon})$. This difficulty can always be resolved, however, by the standard device of assigning a probability distribution to $\sigma(\tilde{\epsilon})$. For any given n, the unconditional total loss can then be found by evaluating the conditional total loss for every possible value of $\sigma(\tilde{\epsilon})$ and taking a weighted average of these conditional losses using the probabilities of the corresponding values of $\sigma(\tilde{\epsilon})$ as the weights; and the true optimal n can be found by computing total loss in this way for a sufficiently large number of n's, graphing loss as a function of n, and looking for the n which corresponds to the lowest point on the loss curve.

Suppose now that we try to short-cut the computation of the total loss for given n by simply inserting the expected or average value of $\sigma(\tilde{\epsilon})$ in the formula for total loss instead of inserting every possible value of $\sigma(\tilde{\epsilon})$ and then averaging the resulting losses. *If* this short-cut method of computing total loss would give exact or nearly exact results for values of n in the neighborhood of the true optimal n, *then* a graph of total loss as computed by the short-cut method would have its lowest point at or near the true optimal n. Selecting a sample size by treating the expected value of $\sigma(\tilde{\epsilon})$ as if it were the true value and then using Chart VI or the formula in Section 37.5.1 is nothing but a convenient way of finding the n which corresponds to the lowest point on a graph of total loss as computed by the short-cut method; and it follows that a sample size determined by this procedure will be exactly or virtually optimal if the short-cut computation of total loss gives exactly or virtually correct results in the neighborhood of the *true* optimal n.

We shall therefore now examine the conditions under which the short-cut method of computing total loss for given n gives exact or nearly exact results, and to do so we start by replacing $\sigma_1(\xi)$ in the formula for total loss by its definition. When $\sigma(\tilde{\beta}) = 0$, as we assume throughout our discussion of optimal sample size in this chapter, the definition of $\sigma_1(\xi)$ given in Section 37.3.1 above can be written in the form

$$\sigma_1(\xi) = \sigma(\tilde{\tilde{\epsilon}}) \sqrt{\frac{1}{1 + \sigma^2(\tilde{\tilde{\epsilon}})/\sigma_0^2(\xi)}},$$

where

$$\sigma(\tilde{\tilde{\epsilon}}) = \sigma(\tilde{\epsilon}) \sqrt{\frac{1}{n} \frac{N-n}{N-1}}.$$

The formula for the total expected loss can then be written

$$\text{Total expected loss} = C + D\sigma(\tilde{\epsilon}) \sqrt{\frac{1}{1 + \sigma^2(\tilde{\tilde{\epsilon}})/\sigma_0^2(\xi)}},$$

where C and D are constants which do not depend on $\sigma(\tilde{\epsilon})$.

37.6.1   Zero Prior Information on ξ

When prior information on ξ is negligible and the person responsible for the decision sets $\sigma_0(\xi) = \infty$ (cf. Section 30.3.3), the square-root factor in the formula for the total loss has the value 1 regardless of the value of $\sigma(\bar{\epsilon})$ and the formula reduces to

Total expected loss $= C + D\sigma(\bar{\epsilon})$.

This is a *linear* function of $\sigma(\bar{\epsilon})$ and therefore its *exact* expected value can be obtained by simply inserting the expected value of $\sigma(\bar{\epsilon})$ in the formula. It follows immediately that

> If prior information on ξ is negligible, then regardless of the extent of our uncertainty about the true value of $\sigma(\bar{\epsilon})$ we can obtain the *exact* optimal sample size by treating the expected value of $\sigma(\bar{\epsilon})$ as if it were the true value.

37.6.2   Nonzero Prior Information on ξ

When the prior information is not negligible, i.e. when $\sigma_0(\xi)$ is not infinite, the value of the square-root factor in the formula for the total expected loss depends on $\sigma(\bar{\epsilon})$. This means that the formula as a whole is *not* a linear function of $\sigma(\bar{\epsilon})$ and therefore that the loss obtained by inserting the expected value of $\sigma(\bar{\epsilon})$ in the formula will *not* be exactly equal to the weighted average of the losses obtained by inserting every possible value of $\sigma(\bar{\epsilon})$.

Suppose, however, that the values of $\sigma_0(\xi)$ and of the true optimal n^* are such that the ratio

$$\frac{\sigma^2(\bar{\epsilon})}{\sigma_0^2(\xi)} = \frac{\sigma^2(\bar{\epsilon})}{\sigma_0^2(\xi)} \frac{N - n^*}{n^*(N - 1)}$$

is very small for all values of $\sigma(\bar{\epsilon})$ which seem at all likely. Then for any n in the neighborhood of the true n^* the square-root factor will have a value very close to 1 for all likely values of $\sigma(\bar{\epsilon})$; and this means that if we *did* compute the conditional loss for all possible values of $\sigma(\bar{\epsilon})$ it would be only the factor $\sigma(\bar{\epsilon})$ *outside* the square-root sign which would make these values differ appreciably one from the other. In other words, the total loss for any n in the neighborhood of the true n^* is *virtually* a linear function of $\sigma(\bar{\epsilon})$, and therefore we would get an *almost* exact value for the total loss by simply inserting the expected value of $\sigma(\bar{\epsilon})$ in the formula. It follows that a graph of total loss computed by this short-cut method would have its lowest point at an n very close to the true n^*, and it is this nearly optimal n which we will obtain if we apply the method of Section 37.5.1 treating the expected value of $\sigma(\bar{\epsilon})$ as if it were the true value.

In a real problem we of course do not know in advance whether the true n^* is large enough to make this procedure valid, but its validity is easy to check after an approximately optimal n has been tentatively determined by its use.   To make this check we first choose two extreme values of $\sigma(\tilde{\epsilon})$, one so small that we are virtually sure that it is below the true value and one so large that we are virtually sure that it is above the true value, and then evaluate the square-root factor for these two extreme values.   *If the ratio of the smaller to the larger value of the square root is much closer to 1 than the ratio of the smaller to the larger value of $\sigma(\tilde{\epsilon})$ itself, we may feel sure that our sample size is very close to the true optimal size.*

Example.   In the example previously analyzed, suppose that the merchant had not said that he *knew* the value of $\sigma(\tilde{\epsilon})$ to be 4 but had said that this was the value he "expected" $\sigma(\tilde{\epsilon})$ to have; all that he felt really sure of was that $\sigma(\tilde{\epsilon})$ was between 0 and 8.   The optimal sample size for $\sigma(\tilde{\epsilon})$ *known* to have the value 4 has already been calculated as $n = 130$; we now proceed to check the validity of this figure in the face of the actual uncertainty concerning $\sigma(\tilde{\epsilon})$.   We first compute $\sigma^2(\tilde{\epsilon})$ for $n = 130$ and for $\sigma(\tilde{\epsilon}) = 0$ and $\sigma(\tilde{\epsilon}) = 8$:

$$\sigma(\tilde{\epsilon}) = 0: \qquad \sigma^2(\tilde{\epsilon}) = 0;$$
$$\sigma(\tilde{\epsilon}) = 8: \qquad \sigma^2(\tilde{\epsilon}) = \frac{8^2}{130}\frac{870}{999} = .428.$$

Remembering that $\sigma_0^2(\xi) = 4$, we then compute the square-root factor for these two values of $\sigma(\tilde{\epsilon})$:

$$\sigma(\tilde{\epsilon}) = 0: \qquad \sqrt{\frac{1}{1 + 0/4}} = 1.00;$$
$$\sigma(\tilde{\epsilon}) = 8: \qquad \sqrt{\frac{1}{1 + .428/4}} = \sqrt{.903} = .95.$$

The square-root factor varies only in the ratio .95 to 1.00 while $\sigma(\tilde{\epsilon})$ itself varies in the ratio 0 to 8.   We may feel absolutely sure that the excess loss which the merchant can expect to suffer by using $n = 130$ instead of a truly optimal sample is totally negligible compared with the cost of the computations which would be required to determine this truly optimal sample.

37.7   General-purpose Estimation

In a great many situations a businessman wants additional information on the value of some unknown quantity, not because he is on the point of choosing among a number of definite, well-defined terminal acts whose costs depend on this quantity, but simply to guide his thinking in some general problem area.   To give a single example, a soap manufacturer who is thinking about developing and marketing a new detergent designed especially for use in automatic dishwashers may want to get some idea of the number of homes equipped with automatic dishwashers long before his thinking reaches the stage where he is ready even to specify his possible terminal acts, let alone to say exactly how the profitability of each act depends on the number in question.

Until the businessman has completely specified his terminal acts and their conditional costs, he will think primarily if not exclusively in terms of an *estimate* of the quantity in which he is interested rather than in terms of a *probability distribution* of this quantity. He will make rough calculations in which he treats the estimated number of homes equipped with dishwashers as if this estimate were a true value even though he knows that the estimate is almost certainly in error by some amount and that before making any *final* decision he may have to take formal account of his uncertainty about the true number. In such situations there is obviously no "objective" way of computing the amount by which a sample of any given size can be expected to reduce terminal loss and therefore there is no "objective" way of assigning a value to the information which will be obtained from the sample. The cost of sampling is still perfectly real, however, and a reasonable man will still want to approach the problem of sample size by thinking about value received for money spent.

In such situations the businessman will usually feel that the larger the error in the estimate, the greater the harm this error can be "expected" to do; and often (although by no means always) he will be even more specific and say that he "expects" the harm to be roughly *proportional* to the size of the error, at least up to a certain point. He may, for example, feel that he would be willing to spend $1000 to learn the true number of homes equipped with dishwashers if he knew that his present best estimate of that number was in error by ±50,000 but that he would not be willing to spend more than $500 to learn the true number if he were sure that his present estimate was in error by only ±25,000.

In those situations where the businessman does feel that the loss which will result from an erroneous estimate can be "expected" to be roughly proportional to the size of the error, the amount which it is reasonable *for him* to spend on sampling can be determined by the methods developed in this chapter. The businessman has an *immediate* decision problem of choosing one estimate among all possible estimates of an unknown quantity. Each possible estimate is a possible *terminal act;* and since the businessman has said that the conditional loss of this act will be proportional to the difference between the act and the true value of the basic random variable, he has a *many-action problem with proportional losses.* Provided that the problem also satisfies the assumptions of this chapter concerning the distributions of the basic random variable and the statistic which summarizes the sample, the optimal sample size can be found by the method described in Section 37.5.

Although the two loss constants κ_u and κ_o are not *necessarily* equal in a problem of general-purpose estimation, they will in fact be equal in the great majority of practical cases—the businessman will feel that over-estimating the true value by a certain amount is neither more nor less serious than underestimating it by the same amount. When this is true, the optimal terminal act or "best estimate" will be the *median* of the posterior distribution of the quantity being estimated. If this posterior distribution is Normal, its median will be equal to its mean; and if prior information is negligible in comparison with the information in the sample, then the best estimate will be simply the observed value $\bar{x}$ of the sample mean.

PROBLEMS

1. A product costs $3.015, sells for $10, and spoils if it is not sold on the day on which it is stocked. There are 2000 individuals who are potential customers for the product; a Normal distribution with parameters $E(\tilde{\xi}) = 10$, $\sigma(\tilde{\xi}) = 2$ is assigned to the average number of units which will be demanded per person in the population, i.e. to the mean of the 2000 individual demands. Show that:

    a. The best terminal act is $q^* = 11.04$ units per customer.

    b. The best actual number of units to stock is 22,080.

    c. The expected loss of this act is $13,940.

2. In the situation of Chapter 23, Problem 10, suppose that Mr. Smith believes that the most probable value for the proportion of potential customers who will actually order a skillet is .06 but thinks that there is only an even chance that this "best guess" is within $\pm.02$ of the true proportion. Mr. Smith is convinced that a person would respond to a sample mailing if and only if he would respond to a regular mailing.

    a. Assuming that Mr. Smith would accept a Normal prior distribution of $\tilde{p}$, compute the values of the parameters of this distribution (cf. Section 30.2.3).

    b. Compute $\sigma(\tilde{\varepsilon})$ for $p = .01$ to .11 inclusive by steps of .01 (11 values in all), and by taking a weighted average of these conditional values show that the expected value of $\sigma(\tilde{\varepsilon})$ is approximately .231.

    c. Find an approximately optimal sample size for Mr. Smith's problem.

    d. Check the validity of your treatment of $\sigma(\tilde{\varepsilon})$ in part *c* by the method described in Section 37.6.2.

    e. Evaluate the net gain to be expected from taking a sample of the size you recommend.

    f. What is Smith's expected profit without sampling? If he takes a sample of optimal size?

    g. Suppose that a sample of $n = 600$ is taken and that $r = 36$ of these customers buy. How many skillets should Smith buy on contract? (HINT: First compute the best stock as if the 36 orders received from the sample mailing were to be filled with skillets bought on contract; then correct this answer to take account of the actual facts of the situation.)

    h. Compare your answer to (*c*) with the answer you would have obtained if you had roughly estimated the expected value of $\sigma(\tilde{\varepsilon})$ by the method of Section 35.5 rather than by carrying out part *b* of this problem.

CHAPTER 38

Sequential Decision Procedures

Our discussion of decisions to sample and postpone terminal action has been based thus far on the assumption that, for one reason or another, *at most one* sample will be taken. Given this assumption, the terminal act which would be optimal for each possible sample outcome could be selected by the methods of Part Three of the course and the prior expected value of the loss which would result from the decision made *after* sampling could then be evaluated by simply multiplying the terminal loss corresponding to each possible outcome by the probability of that outcome and adding the products. We now take up the more difficult problem which arises when the alternatives among which a choice must be made after a sample has been taken include not only all the possible *terminal* acts but also the decision to *sample and postpone terminal action again.* When we try to evaluate the cost or loss of this last decision given any particular outcome of the original sample we seem to become involved in an infinite regress, since the new decision to sample can be looked on as the beginning of a new sequential procedure and we are already unable to compute the loss of the original procedure on which we embarked before the original sample was taken. We shall see, however, that the regress is not really infinite; it *has* an end, and once we have found the end the entire problem can be solved by methods with which we are already familiar.

Statement of an Example. The principles by which we can find an optimal sequential decision procedure and compute its total expected cost, profit, or loss will be explained by analysis of the following simple example. A Bernoulli process has been set up for a production run in such a way that the process-average fraction defective is not known with certainty; but if the process is readjusted at extra cost, the process average can be brought down to a known, low figure. Each defective produced by the process entails a certain cost, and the problem is to decide whether to accept the process and risk a large cost due to defective product or to reject the process and incur the cost of readjustment. It is possible to take a sample before making the final decision on acceptance or rejection, but sampling is quite expensive, costing $6 per item inspected. Since it is possible at no extra cost per item to manufacture the sample pieces one at a time, it seems very likely that it will be more economical to follow an *item-by-item sequential procedure*, deciding after each piece has been inspected whether to reject the process (readjust), accept the process (proceed with the production run), or make and inspect another sample piece.

Quite obviously the computations which we shall have to make in order to evaluate a sequential decision procedure will be more complex than the calculations which would be required to evaluate a single-sample procedure. In order to keep from becoming lost in a maze of figures, we shall assume that the sampling procedure is known to be unbiased and we shall use highly unrealistic values for the cost of rejection and for the

Table 38.1
Prior Distribution; Payoff and Loss Tables

p	$P_0(p)$	Conditional cost		Conditional loss	
		Accept	Reject	Accept	Reject
.05	.2	$ 100	$1000	$ 0	$900
.50	.7	1000	1000	0	0
.95	.1	1900	1000	900	0
	1.0				

probability distribution assigned to $\tilde{p}$ before the sampling starts; but except for complexity our results will be typical of those which would be obtained with more realistic data. The prior distribution of $\tilde{p}$ and the conditional costs and losses are shown in Table 38.1.

38.1 Decision Procedures as Games against Chance

The sequence of decisions and events which ultimately leads to a terminal decision under a sequential decision procedure can usefully be visualized as a series of moves in a game between two players: a "Person" and "Chance." The Person has the first move in the game. In our present example he has a choice among three possible moves: Accept, Reject, and Sample (make and inspect *one* sample piece). If he chooses Accept or Reject, the game is over, but if he chooses Sample, the game goes on and Chance has the next move. Chance has two possible moves, good and defective—i.e., Chance may "decide" to make the sample piece either good or defective. After Chance has moved (after the sample piece has been inspected), the next move is again up to the Person, who again chooses among Accept, Reject, and Sample. As before, Accept or Reject ends the game while Sample gives another move to Chance, who then chooses between good and defective.

The alternation of *personal moves* and *chance moves* continues in this way until the game ends.   It is only the Person who can end the game; if he so desires (and has enough money to pay for the sampling) he can make the game go on forever.   A complete history of any one "play" of such a game consists of a list of all the moves actually made by both players in the order in which they were made.   If we use A, R, and S to denote the three possible personal moves (accept, reject, and sample) and g and d to denote the two possible chance moves (good and defective), the history of a particular play of the game might be $SgSdR$: the Person samples twice, observing gd in that order, and then ends the game by rejecting.

38.1.1   The Game Tree

If a game of this sort is arbitrarily limited to a finite number of moves—if the Person is *obliged* either to accept or reject after *not more than* a certain number of sample observations have been made—we can

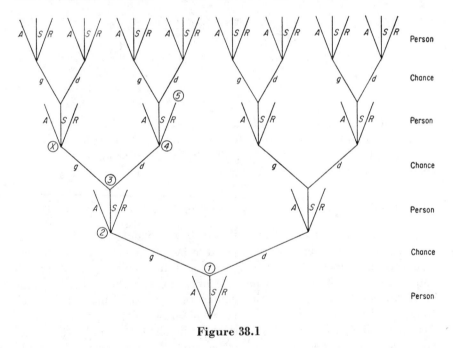

Figure 38.1

represent all the possible plays of the game by a diagram like the one in Figure 38.1.   Such a diagram is known as a *game tree*.   The game starts from the bottom of the tree, where the Person may go up the A or R branch (accept or reject), thus ending the game, or up the S branch (sample).   If he goes up the S branch, he arrives at the *position* in the tree marked by the circled 1.   Chance then chooses between the g

branch and the d branch (makes the sample piece good or defective); if the g branch is chosen (if the sample piece is good), the Person arrives at the position marked 2 on the tree. The Person then moves again, and if he again chooses to sample he arrives at position 3. If Chance's next move is d, the Person arrives at 4; if the Person then decides to reject, he goes up the R branch and ends the game at 5: no further branches emanate from this position. The whole history of this particular play of the game has been $SgSdR$.

38.1.2 Limitation of the Game Tree by Expected Terminal Loss

Our primary interest is in games or decision procedures in which there is no arbitrary limit on the number of moves, i.e. on the number of times that the Person can sample and thus go up an S branch on the game tree. In such cases the complete game tree extends infinitely far upward, but even in this case we can usually show by some very simple reasoning that there are only finitely many branches which represent *rational* moves by the Person. *Every* possible play of the game ultimately reaches a point where it is easy to see that taking an additional sample observation is irrational.

Table 38.2
Posterior Distribution of $\tilde{p}$ Given Sample Outcome gg

p	Prior $P_0(p)$	Likelihood $P(gg\|p) = q^2$	Joint $P(gg,p)$	Posterior $P_1(p\|gg)$
.05	.2	.9025	.18050	.5074
.50	.7	.2500	.17500	.4919
.95	.1	.0025	.00025	.0007
	1.0		.35575	1.0000

Suppose, for example, that after the moves SgS have been made, putting the Person at position 3 in Figure 38.1, Chance moves g instead of d and puts the Person at position X rather than position 4. In ordinary language, the Person has now taken a total of two observations and has observed the sample outcome gg. Given this information, we know perfectly well how to compute the (posterior) expected losses of the two possible terminal acts even though we do not yet know how to compute the total expected loss of another decision to sample. We first compute in Table 38.2 the posterior distribution which it is rational to assign to $\tilde{p}$ in the light of this sample outcome, taking the prior distribution from Table 38.1 and computing the likelihood of the sample as $qq = q^2$.† We then compute the expected *losses* of acceptance and rejection in Table

† We could equally well have used binomial tables to find likelihoods for the statistic $r = 2$ in a sample of $n = 2$; cf. Section 25.4.

38.3, taking the probabilities from Table 38.2 and the conditional losses from Table 38.1.

The results of Table 38.3 show us at once that *if* the Person decides to end the game when he is in position X, he should end it by accepting rather than rejecting—the loss of acceptance given the sample *gg* is only $.60 whereas the loss of rejection is $456.70. These losses imply more than this, however. No matter how many observations the Person takes, he can never reduce his expected terminal loss below 0; and since he can terminate now for a loss of only $.60 while a single additional observation will cost him $6, he should obviously accept *now* and end the game.

In Figure 38.2 we show a game tree for our example which includes all personal moves that are not *obviously* irrational in the sense in which an S move at X in Figure 38.1 would be obviously irrational. To construct such a tree we start from the bottom, with the Person's first move,

Table 38.3
Expected Terminal Losses Given Sample Outcome *gg*

p	$P_1(p)$	Loss of acceptance		Loss of rejection	
		Conditional	Expected	Conditional	Expected
.05	.5074	$ 0	$0	$900	$456.70
.50	.4919	0	0	0	0
.95	.0007	900	.60	0	0
	1.0000		$ .60		$456.70

and compute the expected losses (under the prior distribution) of the two possible terminal acts either of which will end the game at that point. These losses, $90 for acceptance and $180 for rejection, are entered at the tops of the corresponding branches of the tree. At this point it is already obvious that *if* the game is to be ended at this point, it should be ended by acceptance; and therefore we bar off the lowest R branch by a double horizontal line.

It is *not* clear, however, that immediate acceptance is better than sampling, since the loss of acceptance is $90 while the cost of an observation is only $6, and we must therefore construct a second level of the tree. From the top of the original S branch we draw two branches to represent the two possible chance moves and we mark the ends of these branches *g* and *d*. Emanating from each of these two positions we then draw three branches corresponding to the three possible personal moves and we proceed to compute the expected losses of the two *terminal* moves A and R at each of the two positions. At position *g* we first compute the posterior distribution of $\tilde{p}$ given the sample outcome *g* just as in Table

38.2 except that the likelihood of this outcome is q rather than q^2, and we then use this posterior distribution as in Table 38.3 to find that the posterior losses are \$8.30 for acceptance and \$313.70 for rejection. For position d, with likelihoods p rather than q, the same procedure gives a loss of \$187.90 for acceptance and \$19.80 for rejection.

At both position g and position d we can now bar off the terminal act with the greater loss, but in neither case can we go on to say that the better of the two terminal acts is definitely better than taking another observation at a cost of \$6 and consequently we go on to construct another level of the tree. We now have two pairs of chance moves to

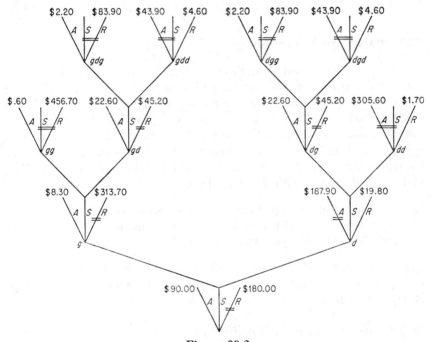

Figure 38.2

draw, one pair leading to positions gg and gd, the other pair to positions dg and dd—the label on each position shows the results of all observations up to that point in the order in which they occurred. At each of these four positions we now draw the three branches for the three personal moves and compute the expected losses for the moves A and R. Reading across Figure 38.2 from left to right the losses calculated at this stage are \$.60, \$456.70, \$22.60, \$45.20, \$22.60, \$45.20, \$305.60, and \$1.70.†

† It is no coincidence that the figures \$22.60 and \$45.20 appear twice. The posterior distribution and therefore the posterior losses are necessarily identical for the sample outcomes gd and dg, since in sampling from a Bernoulli process either outcome can be represented by the total number of observations $n = 2$ and the sufficient statistic $r = 1$.

This time we can actually say that termination is optimal at two of the four positions and bar off the S branch as well as the branch corresponding to the more costly of the two terminal acts. We have already discussed position gg, and similar reasoning holds for position dd. At positions gd and dg, on the contrary, all that we can do is bar off the less good of the terminal acts; we must go on to construct still another level of the tree starting from the S branches at these two positions.

The ensuing loss calculations lead to the figures shown at the very top of the tree in Figure 38.2, and now we find that in every single case one or the other of the two terminal acts has a loss less than the cost of a single additional observation.† The construction of the tree is complete.

38.2   Backward Induction

So far we have used no methods of analysis that we have not used in the earlier chapters of this part of the course—the game tree is simply a systematic way of laying out the results of our computations. These methods leave us with a number of unsolved problems, however: we do not yet know whether sampling or terminal action is better at positions g, d, gd, and dg in Figure 38.2. To solve these problems we now introduce the one really new idea in this chapter, the method of *backward induction*, and even this idea is basically very simple:

> By starting at the top of the game tree and *working back*, we can use the known losses at higher levels to determine both the best moves and the associated losses at lower levels.

In order to illustrate the method without becoming lost in all the notation of Figure 38.2, that part of the tree which branches out from position gd is reproduced in Figure 38.3.

38.2.1   Evaluation of the Position gd

We first proceed to determine the best move for the Person to take if he gets into position gd and the total expected loss associated with this best move.

1. Because we already know that if the Person gets into position gdg he should accept at a loss of $2.20, we can say that $2.20 is *the* loss *of this position*—more explicitly it is the *posterior expected loss of* optimal *action given the sample outcome gdg*. Similarly $4.60 is the loss of the position gdd. This way of looking at the problem is represented by writing $2.20 directly beside the position gdg and $4.60 beside the position gdd in Figure 38.3.

---

† Notice that the losses for positions gdg and dgg are identical, as are those for positions gdd and dgd.

2. If the Person is already in position *gd*, at the bottom of Figure 38.3, and decides to sample, these two losses of $2.20 and $4.60 correspond to the *conditional terminal losses* which we discussed in Chapter 33: *if* the result of the sample which he is about to take is *g*, his (expected) loss will be $2.20, while *if* the result of the sample is *d*, his loss will be $4.60. We can therefore get the *expected loss of proceeding optimally after sampling*

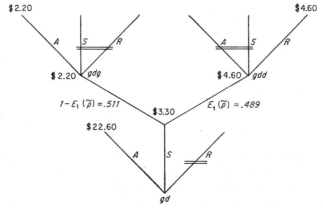

Figure 38.3

in exactly the same way that we did in Chapter 33: we multiply the conditional loss for each sample outcome by the probability of that outcome and add the products. Notice, however, that since the person is already in position *gd*, we do *not* want the probability of the outcome *gdg* as it would be calculated at the *outset* of the decision procedure: what we want is the probability of a *single* defective or good piece as evaluated *after gd has already been observed.*

Table 38.4
Posterior Distribution and $E_1(\tilde{p})$ Given Sample Outcome *gd*

p	Prior $P_0(p)$	Likelihood $P(gd\|p) = pq$	Joint $P(gd,p)$	Posterior $P_1(p\|gd)$	Expectation $p\,P_1(p)$
.05	.2	.0475	.00950	.0502	.003
.50	.7	.2500	.17500	.9247	.462
.95	.1	.0475	.00475	.0251	.024
	1.0		.18925	1.0000	.489 $= E_1(\tilde{p})$

We already know from Section 12.3.2 that when $\tilde{p}$ is unknown the (marginal) probability of a success (defective) on a *single* trial is equal to the expected value of $\tilde{p}$ and therefore we obtain the probabilities we require by simply computing the mean of the posterior distribution of $\tilde{p}$ given the previous sample outcome *gd*. This is done in Table 38.4, which shows that *for a person in position gd* the probability that the next sample piece will be defective is .489; the probability that the piece will be good is therefore $1 - .489 = .511$. The expected loss due to action after sampling is then evaluated as \$3.30 in Table 38.5 and this loss is entered at the *top* of the S branch in Figure 38.3 to show that it is the expected value of the loss which will be incurred *after* sampling.

Table 38.5

Sample outcome	Probability	Terminal loss	
		Conditional	Expected
g	.511	\$2.20	\$1.10
d	.489	\$4.60	\$2.20
	1.000		\$3.30

3. We can now determine the best move for a person who has reached position gd. Rejection has already been barred off as clearly inferior to acceptance; all that remains to be done is to compare the loss of acceptance with the *total* expected loss of a decision to sample at gd and then proceed optimally. The cost of proceeding optimally after sampling has just been evaluated at \$3.30; the cost of taking the observation is \$6; the total expected loss of a decision to sample and then proceed optimally is therefore \$9.30. Since the loss of acceptance in position gd is \$22.60, sampling is the best of all possible decisions in this position.

Thus we have determined that *if* the Person gets into position gd, his optimal move is to sample; and we have also determined that the total expected loss of *making this optimal move and continuing to move optimally thereafter* is \$9.30. We are now entitled to bar off the A branch at gd as well as the R branch and to write the loss \$9.30 beside the position gd just as we wrote the losses \$2.20 and \$4.60 beside the positions gdg and gdd when we started out on our backward induction. These entries will be actually made in Figure 38.4.

38.2.2 The Complete Sequential Procedure and Its Total Expected Loss

Quite obviously the method of backward induction just illustrated for a single step can be used to select the best move and compute its expected loss for any position in any sequential decision problem whatever. We start at the highest level of the tree and use the losses applying there to select the best act (terminal or other) for each position in the next lower level and thus to assign a loss to each such position. We then take these results to work down to the next lower level, and so forth. The work is carried out for our example in Figure 38.4, which starts by being identical to Figure 38.2 except that all the branches which were barred off in Figure 38.2 have been completely omitted in Figure 38.4 in order to avoid confusion.

The first step in the procedure is to compute the means of the posterior distributions for every position at which a choice still has to be made. As we have already seen, the mean for each position gives the probability that a sample item drawn at that position will be a defective and 1 minus the mean gives the probability that the piece will be good. All these probabilities have been entered in Figure 38.4 beside the chance

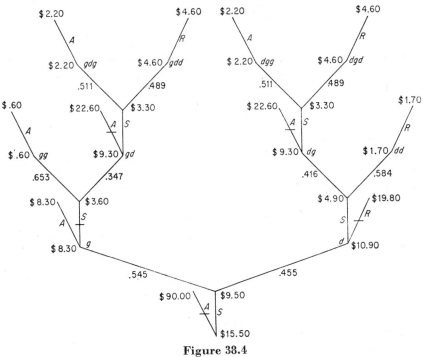

Figure 38.4

moves to which they refer—the .511 and .489 beside the moves leading to *gdg* and *gdd* respectively were calculated in Table 38.4.

After the probabilities are entered we are ready to work backward down the tree. We have already explained the calculations leading to the value $3.30 entered at the *top* of the *S* branch for position *gd* and to the selection of *S* as the best move at this position. Correspondingly the *A* branch at *gd* has been barred in Figure 38.4 and the value $3.30 + $6.00 = $9.30 has been assigned to the position *gd* itself. Identical calculations lead to the same figures and to the same best move at position *dg*.

Analysis of the second highest level of the tree is thus complete and we now take up the next lower level, starting with the position *g* at the left. In this position the expected loss of proceeding optimally after sampling is (.653 × $.60) + (.347 × $9.30) = $3.60, so that the *total* expected loss of sampling and then proceeding optimally is $3.60 + $6.00 = $9.60. The cost of acceptance at *g* is only $8.30, however, and we therefore decide that *a person reaching position g should* not *sample but should end the game by accepting.* Accordingly we bar off the *S* branch and write down $8.30 as the expected loss of position *g*. On the other side of the tree at the same level, position *d*, we find that the expected loss of proceeding optimally after sampling is

$$(.416 \times \$9.30) + (.584 \times \$1.70) = \$4.90,$$

so that the total expected loss of sampling and then proceeding optimally is $4.90 + $6.00 = $10.90. Since this is *less* than the $19.80 loss of the best terminal act at *d* (rejection), we bar off the *R* branch and enter $10.90 as the loss of the position itself.

Finally we come to the lowest level of the tree, where we find that the total expected loss of sampling and then proceeding optimally is $15.50 and far better than immediate acceptance at a loss of $90. It follows that in our example $15.50 is the *total expected loss of a decision to follow an optimal sequential decision procedure as evaluated before any of the steps in the procedure have been taken.*

38.2.3   Expected Sampling Cost and Expected Terminal Loss

The figure $15.50 just obtained for the total expected loss of the optimal sequential procedure can easily be broken down into its two components, expected terminal loss and expected sampling cost. The expected sampling cost is computed as $9.80 in Table 38.6; the logic

Table 38.6
Expected Sampling Cost

Sample item number	Probability	Cost	Expectation
1	1.000	$6	$6.00
2	1.000 × .455 = .455	$6	$2.70
3	1.000 × .455 × .416 = .189	$6	$1.10
			$9.80

of the calculation will be self-explanatory if the student traces the probabilities in the table back to Figure 38.4.   From this result we can obtain

$$\text{Expected terminal loss} = \$15.50 - \$9.80 = \$5.70,$$
$$\text{Expected sample size} = \frac{\$9.80}{\$6.00} = 1.6.$$

38.3 Incomplete Game Trees

The essence of the procedure described above for finding an optimal sequential procedure was to proceed in two steps: (1) construct the game tree level by level until every branch reached a fork where the loss of optimal terminal action was less than the cost of another observation, (2) come back down the tree using backward induction to decide what to do at the lower levels. In many situations it will not be possible to carry out this procedure completely—the tree which would result from step 1 is simply too large to be constructed and analyzed, even with the aid of high-speed computers.

Even though the complete game tree cannot be constructed and analyzed, it will usually be possible to come very close to the optimal sequential procedure by taking advantage of the fact that the probability of reaching any particular branch on a very high level is extremely small. If most of the lower branches have been terminated by the argument used in step 1 and there are only a relatively few forks left "open" on the highest level which has actually been reached, we may come very close to an optimal solution by simply making a good guess at the loss associated with each top-level "open" position† and then applying backward induction to work back down the tree. The validity of the results can be checked by proceeding a few levels higher and performing the same computations over again; if we get the same choices for all the lower positions that we got before, our solution is almost certainly optimal or very close to optimal.

In some circumstances even this approximate procedure may be impossible to apply because of the volume of computations required, and unfortunately the problem of finding optimal or near-optimal sequential procedures in such circumstances is an almost totally untouched subject for research. The only case which has been solved is the case of prior distributions which assign nonzero probabilities to just two values of the basic random variable, and this case occurs so rarely in practice that we shall not study it in this course.

38.4 Comparison of Sequential with Single-sample Procedures

The advantage of a sequential over a single-sample decision procedure can be seen in a qualitative way by simply examining Figure 38.4. If we use a single-sample procedure with $n = 1$, everything is fine provided that the sample outcome is g; but if the outcome is d, we will lose

---

† We can always use the methods described in Chapters 33 to 35 to evaluate the total expected loss of using an optimal *single-sample* procedure at one of these "open" positions, and we shall see in a moment that the loss of an optimal *sequential* procedure cannot be greater than this.

$8.90 by rejecting at a loss of $19.80 instead of taking another observation and then proceeding optimally at a loss of $10.90. If we take a fixed sample of size $n = 2$, the second item will be totally wasted if the first item is good; it is only if the first item is defective that this second observation serves any useful purpose. Similarly the third item in a sample of size $n = 3$ will be totally useless if the first two items are either both good or both defective. These observations imply that *the total expected loss of the optimal sequential procedure is less than the total expected loss of any possible single-sample procedure* in the situation of our example, and the same thing will be true in many decision problems.

It is important to emphasize, however, that there are many situations in which a sequential procedure is *not* superior to a single-sample procedure.

1. The whole advantage of proceeding sequentially comes from the freedom to continue sampling in "positions" where termination involves large risks and to stop sampling when a position is reached where termination involves little risk. Consequently a sequential procedure has no advantage at all in problems like the one studied in Chapter 37, where the posterior expected loss of optimal terminal action is exactly the same for all possible sample outcomes even though the choice of the optimal act depends on the sample outcome.†

2. If it is cheaper to take and analyze a sample of several items at one time than to take the same number of observations one at a time, a single-sample procedure may be more economical than a sequential procedure even though the latter does have higher "statistical efficiency"— i.e., has a lower expected terminal loss for given expected sample size. We have often assumed that the cost of a sample can be written $K_s + k_s n$. This implies that the cost of each sequential observation is $K_s + k_s$, and if K_s is not negligible compared to k_s a true item-by-item sequential procedure will almost certainly be undesirable. In such situations the best solution is often to proceed by taking the sample observations in *groups* and deciding after each *group* has been analyzed whether to take terminal action or to continue sampling, but the study of such procedures is beyond the scope of this course.

PROBLEMS

1. Using only data which can be read from Figure 38.4 and calculating no probabilities, compute the total expected loss of a *single-sample* decision procedure with $n = 1$.

2. If a person at position d in Figure 38.4 is allowed to take *at most one* more

---

† Sequential procedures *would* be useful in problems like those discussed in Section 37.6, since in this case the posterior expected value of $\sigma_1(\tilde{\xi})$ and therefore the posterior terminal loss depend on the sample evidence concerning the true value of $\sigma(\tilde{\epsilon})$.

observation, what is the expected value of the information to be gained from this observation?

3. Same as Problem 2 for a person in position g.

4. By using your answers to Problems 2 and 3, compute the expected value of the information to be gained from a second observation as assessed before the *first* observation is taken, and by combining this answer with your answer to Problem 1 compute the total expected loss of a single-sample decision procedure with $n = 2$.

5. In the example discussed in this chapter, the prior distribution of $\tilde{E}_1$ for a sample of $n = 3$ as evaluated before any sample observations have been taken is given in the table below. Assuming that the conditional cost of acceptance is $2000\,p$, compute the total expected cost and loss of a single-sample decision procedure with $n = 3$.

E_1	$P(E_1)$
.202	.259
.459	.291
.520	.277
.722	.173
	1.000

PART FIVE

Objectivist Statistics: Tests of Significance and Confidence Intervals

CHAPTER 39

The Classical Theory of Testing Hypotheses

39.1 Introduction to Part Five of the Course

The essence of the approach which we have taken to the problem of decision under uncertainty is the view that in the last analysis any person responsible for a decision must decide how much weight he wishes to attach to the consequences which his acts will have given each event which may occur. We have said that in assigning such weights a reasonable man should pay very careful attention to the available information bearing on the relative frequencies with which each event *would* occur in a large number of trials "like" the one about to be made, but we have insisted that a weight *must* be assigned no matter how slight the information on frequency may be and regardless of the fact that some other reasonable man might assign different weights to the same events. We have called these weights "probabilities" both because this is exactly the sense in which the word probability is used in everyday English and because we could show that logically consistent weights obey the rules which define the branch of mathematics known as the theory of probability.

It is only within the last few years that it has become fairly generally realized that subjective weights of this sort *can* be treated by a systematic theory, and even today there is substantial disagreement whether they *should* be so treated. Except in the very rare cases where the "prior" probabilities of cost-determining events or values of a basic random variable correspond to long-run frequencies which can be regarded as known with certainty, many statisticians still flatly refuse to use Bayes' theorem to compute posterior probabilities or posterior expected costs and losses.

For some time it was believed that prior probabilities were *unnecessary* and that a meaningful probability distribution which rested on the sample evidence *alone* could be assigned to a basic random variable after a sample had been taken, but this view was ultimately rejected by the great majority of statisticians as being simply without any logical foundations whatever. A new school of thought then grew up which (1) *identified* probability with long-run frequency and (2) held that no long-run frequencies should be computed unless they were *known with certainty*. Since in the great majority of practical problems involving samples the only long-run frequency distributions which are known with certainty are the *conditional* distributions of sample statistics *given* specified values of the parameters of the population from which the sample is drawn, this school developed procedures for reaching decisions under uncertainty by looking only at these conditional distributions. Thus in a problem involving the unknown process average p of a Bernoulli process, no probabilities would be assigned to the various possible values of p itself either before or after the sample was taken; the decision would be reached by considering only the probability or long-run frequency distribution of the statistic $\tilde{r}$ *given* specified values of the parameter p.

At least in the United States, the theory of these procedures for reaching decisions by looking only at *known, conditional* frequencies is now "classical" in the literal sense of the word: it is expounded in virtually every course on statistics and is adhered to by the great majority of practicing statisticians. The next three chapters will therefore be devoted to an examination of this classical theory in a simple but completely typical application: to problems in which a choice must ultimately be made between just two terminal acts.

39.2 Tests of Hypotheses and Statistical Decision Rules

In the first quarter of the twentieth century statisticians viewed their task as one of establishing the truth or falsity of statements or "hypotheses" rather than as one of showing how to choose among acts. The really great achievement of the theory which is now classical was to recognize that the establishment of ultimate truth is not an achievable goal for mere human endeavor and that the real problem of statistics is to aid in choice among acts under uncertainty, but the language of "hypotheses" remains as a historical residue.

If a person is being examined to determine whether or not he should be treated for tuberculosis, the problem is said in classical language to be one of choosing one or the other of the two hypotheses "has TB" and "does not have TB." If the test is intended to show not only whether the person should be treated at all but if so whether he should be treated by method A or by method B, the problem is said to be one of choosing among three hypotheses: "does not have TB," "has TB of the type best treated by method A," and "has TB of the type best treated by method B." The student should observe that there is definitely a one-to-one correspondence between hypotheses and acts even though the acts may not be fully described or named explicitly.

39.2.1 Null and Alternate Hypotheses

One special but very common type of problem is that in which a choice must be made between *just two* hypotheses, and in such problems the procedure by which the choice is made is commonly called a "test" *of* one of the hypotheses *against* the other.   The hypothesis which is "tested" is usually called the "null" hypothesis while the other is called the "alternate" hypothesis, and the choice is said to be between *accept-ance* and *rejection* of the *null* hypothesis rather than between acceptance of one hypothesis and acceptance of the other.   *Rejection* of the null hypothesis when it is actually true is said to be an *error of the first kind* or of type I; *acceptance* of the null hypothesis when it is actually false is said to be an *error of the second kind* or of type II.

This asymmetric usage is due to the belief widely held among statis-ticians that in almost all two-action problems which require statistical analysis one of the two hypotheses will be of such a nature that the con-sequence of rejecting it when true is much more serious than the conse-quence of accepting it when false—in other words, the truth of one of the two hypotheses is to be given a very strong benefit of any doubt which may exist, and attention is to be focused on this fact by calling this favored hypothesis the "tested" or the "null" hypothesis.†   As an example, consider the problem of deciding whether or not a certain batch of some drug contains impurities which make it poisonous.   The two hypotheses are "the drug is poisonous" and "the drug is not poisonous," and the former is called the null hypothesis because rejecting this hypoth-esis when it is true will lead to deaths whereas acceptance of this hypoth-esis when it is false leads merely to needless scrapping of the batch and the loss of a certain amount of money.   In situations where erroneous rejection of one hypothesis is neither more nor less serious than erroneous rejection of the other, either one may be called the null hypothesis.

Machine-setup Example.   In Chapters 22 and 33 we studied the problem faced by a manufacturer who must decide whether to proceed with a production run using the setup made by the regular operator of the machine or to have the setup checked and if need be readjusted by an expert setup mechanic at extra cost.   The manufacturer believes that the machine as set up by the operator will behave as a Bernoulli process with some unknown fraction defective p, and it was shown in Section 22.4.3 that if p had a value greater than $p_b = .04$ it would pay to readjust the setup while if p had a value less than .04 it would pay to leave the setup alone.   In Section 22.5.1 we saw that the loss due to failure to readjust when needed may be as high as \$42 whereas the loss due to needless readjustment will be only \$6, and accordingly the *null hypothesis* is "$p \geq .04$ and therefore the setup needs readjustment"; rejection of this hypothesis when true is an error of the first kind.‡

---

† The actual name "null" given to the favored hypothesis cannot be explained in terms of this rule; it is another historical residue and is explained in Section 41.4.2.

‡ Since the two acts are equally costly when $p = .04$ exactly, it is obviously immaterial whether we write the two hypotheses as $p \geq .04$ vs. $p < .04$ or as $p > .04$ vs. $p \leq .04$.

Packaging Example. In Chapter 32 we studied the problem faced by a marketer who must decide whether or not to adopt a new package for his product. Letting ξ denote the true increase in mean sales per store per month which the new package would in fact produce, we saw that the new package would just pay for the cost of the necessary modifications in the packaging machinery if ξ had the value $\xi_b = +.019$; if the new package was chosen when in fact ξ was less than ξ_b, the manufacturer would suffer a loss of $\$1,056,000(\xi_b - \xi)$, while if the opposite choice was made when ξ was in fact greater than ξ_b the loss would be $\$1,056,000(\xi - \xi_b)$. It is impossible to say which of these losses might be greater and thus really to single out the error of the first kind, so that we are free in principle to select either $\xi \leq \xi_b$ or $\xi \geq \xi_b$ as the null hypothesis. In such situations statisticians seem usually to pick as the null hypothesis the hypothesis which favors the *status quo*, and we shall follow their example by treating " $\xi \leq \xi_b$ and therefore the old package should be retained" as the null hypothesis; rejection of this hypothesis when in fact $\xi \leq \xi_b$ will therefore be an error of the first kind.

39.2.2   Statistical Hypotheses

We have already said that the only probability distributions which may be considered under the classical approach to the problem of decision under uncertainty are distributions which correspond to (conditionally) *known* long-run frequency distributions of sample observations or of statistics summarizing these observations, and this requirement affects the very way in which a decision problem must be stated even before it determines the way in which it must be solved.

Thus in the packaging example the hypotheses which accurately express the economics of the decision problem are $\xi > \xi_b$ (in which case adoption of the new package will be profitable) and $\xi \leq \xi_b$ (in which case adoption of the new package will not be profitable). Suppose, however (as we did in Section 32.3), that the marketer takes a sample of the store-by-store sales increases created by the new package and wishes to use the mean $\bar{x}$ of these increases as the basis for his choice between the hypotheses in question. Unless he is *absolutely sure* that his sampling procedure is unbiased (or knows by exactly how much it is biased), he cannot say that he *knows* the long-run frequency distribution of $\bar{x}$ given any particular ξ. The mean of this long-run frequency distribution is $\mu = \xi + \beta$, where β is the bias of the sampling procedure, and if β is not known with certainty then the long-run frequency distribution of $\bar{x}$ is not known with certainty even when ξ is given.

In Parts Three and Four of the course we dealt with this problem by assigning a subjective distribution to $\tilde{\beta}$ and saying that the probability distribution of $\bar{x}$ was Normal with parameters $E(\bar{x}) = \xi + E(\tilde{\beta})$ and $\sigma^2(\bar{x}) = \sigma^2(\tilde{\beta}) + \sigma^2(\tilde{\epsilon})$, but this probability distribution does not correspond to any *known* long-run frequency distribution and is therefore inadmissible under the classical theory. The decision maker *must* state his problem in terms such that conditional long-run frequencies are *known*, and in our present example this means that he must *restate his decision problem in terms of μ rather than ξ*. If his best guess is that the sampling procedure is unbiased, he will presumably take as his two hypotheses $μ \leq +.019$ and $μ > +.019$; if his best guess is that the sampling procedure is biased by some amount $β^*$ he will presumably take as his two hypotheses $μ \leq +.019 + β^*$ and $μ > +.019 + β^*$; but in neither case can he under the classical theory make any *formal* allowance for *uncertainty* about the amount of bias which may be present.

In classical language, a hypothesis concerning a parameter of a long-run frequency distribution ($μ$ in the packaging example) is known as a *statistical hypothesis* and is sharply distinguished from a *primary hypothesis* concerning the quantity in which the decision maker is really interested ($ξ$ in the packaging example). What we have said in the previous paragraphs amounts to this:

> The classical theory deals only with the testing of statistical hypotheses. If the businessman wishes to make allowance for the fact that a "primary" hypothesis in which he is really interested may be false even though the corresponding "statistical" hypothesis is true, he must make this allowance by the use of unaided judgment—the problem is not a statistical problem.

In the discussion of classical procedures which follows, we shall assume that the marketer *does* believe that the statistical hypotheses which correspond most closely to his primary hypotheses are:

> Null: the long-run frequency distribution of $\tilde{x}$ is Normal with mean $μ \leq +.019$;
> Alternate: the long-run frequency distribution of $\tilde{x}$ is Normal with mean $μ > +.019$.

Exactly the same kind of problem arises in the machine-setup example. The *statistical* hypotheses in this case must concern the long-run frequency P_r with which pieces will be *reported* as defective by the inspector (cf. Section 31.3) and not the long-run frequency p with which the process as set up by the operator would generate pieces which would actually prove defective in assembly. Again we shall simplify our subsequent discussion by assuming that the manufacturer is convinced that $P_r = p$ and therefore is willing to take as his two statistical hypotheses:

> Null: the long-run frequency distribution of the number $\tilde{r}$ of pieces reported defective in the sample is binomial with $p \geq .04$;

Alternate: the long-run frequency distribution of $\tilde{r}$ is binomial with $p < .04$.

39.2.3   Statistical Decision Rules

Having seen how a two-action problem is defined in classical theory, we are ready to look at the procedure by which the choice is to be made between rejection and acceptance of the null hypothesis. In outline, the advice of the classical school is this:

> Whether the decision is of a repetitive kind, as in the setup example, or of a more or less unique kind, as in the packaging example, the businessman should view his problem as one of choosing a *decision rule* which *could* be applied to an infinite number of decision problems like the one he currently faces and which specifies (1) the size of the sample which is to be taken and (2) exactly which act (accept or reject) should be taken given any and every possible sample outcome or value of the test statistic. To decide which of two possible rules of this kind is better or which of many possible rules is best he should look at the frequency with which each rule under consideration would lead to wrong decisions given *any and every possible value* of the parameter being tested.

Suppose for example that the manufacturer with the setup problem wishes to evaluate the following decision rule:

> Take a sample of 75 pieces from each new setup and reject the null hypothesis that $p \geq .04$ if and only if the number of defectives in the sample does not exceed three.

In order to examine the conditional frequencies with which errors of both kinds will occur under this rule given any and all possible values of p we first observe that:

1. If in fact $p \geq .04$, the null hypothesis is *true* and *rejection* of this hypothesis will be an error (of the first kind). Since the hypothesis *will* be rejected if $r \leq 3$, the conditional probability given any p greater than or equal to .04 that the rule will lead to this error is $P_b(\tilde{r} \leq 3 | n = 75, p)$.

2. If in fact $p < .04$, the null hypothesis is *false* and *acceptance* of this hypothesis will be an error (of the second kind). Since the hypothesis *will* be accepted if $r > 3$, the conditional probability given any p less than .04 that the rule will lead to this error is $P_b(\tilde{r} > 3 | n = 75, p)$.

Since there are infinitely many possible values of p—remember that the businessman is not really *sure* that the setup will have *exactly* one of the four values .01, .05, .15, and .25 which we have considered in earlier discussions of this problem—the only way of really looking at the conditional probabilities of a wrong decision given *all possible* values of p is to graph them.   The curve (or pair of curves) shown in Figure 39.1 is such a graph for the rule we have taken as an example.   The left branch of the curve shows that there is 0 probability under this rule of concluding that $p \geq .04$ when in fact $p = 0$ (we *cannot* get more than three defectives in the sample if the process generates none at all) but that as p increases this probability increases until it has the value .35 when p is just under .04. The right branch of the curve shows that there is 0 probability of concluding that $p < .04$ when in fact $p = 1$ (we *must* get more than three defectives in the sample if the process generates 100 per cent defectives) but

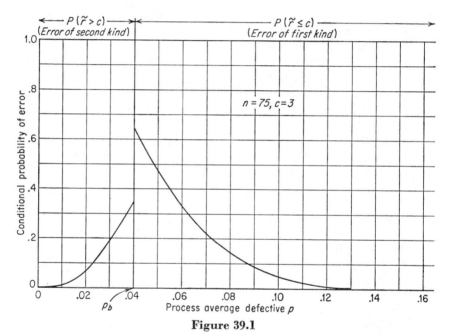

Figure 39.1

that as p decreases this probability increases until it has the value .65 when $p = .04$ exactly.

The remainder of this chapter will be devoted to a discussion of the ways in which statisticians of the classical school select a particular rule among all possible rules by looking at curves of this kind.   The discussion will be divided into two parts:

1. Choice of a rule when the sample size is predetermined and the only problem is to decide which act should follow each possible sample outcome.

2. Choice of a rule when the person responsible for the decision is free to take a sample of any size he pleases as well as to specify which terminal act should follow each possible sample outcome.

39.3   Choice of a Decision Rule When Sample Size Is Predetermined

39.3.1   Choice of a Rule before the Sample Is Taken

Suppose that for some reason the manufacturer faced with the setup problem has definitely decided to take a sample of size $n = 75$ but that he has not yet decided which values of the test statistic $\tilde{r}$ should lead to acceptance of the null hypothesis that $p \geq .04$ and which to rejection.

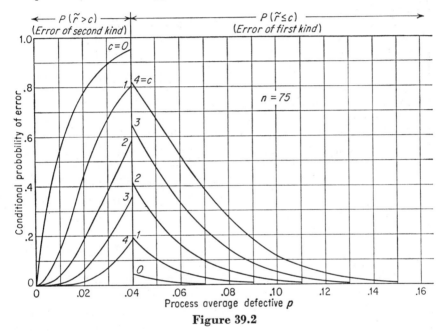

Figure 39.2

It is clear that the only decision rules which he will consider will be of the general form

Sample $n = 75$ and reject the null hypothesis that $p \geq .04$ if and only if $\tilde{r}$ *does not exceed* some predetermined number c,

since it would obviously be foolish to act on the assumption that p is high when r is low and vice versa.

The only problem is thus to choose a definite value for the "critical number" c; and as we have said, this is to be done by drawing a curve like the one in Figure 39.1 for each of a variety of values of c and deciding which of these curves gives the most desirable "mix" of conditional probabilities of error. Figure 39.2 shows the conditional probabilities of both kinds of errors for values of c from 0 to 4, and inspection of these curves immediately shows that

As the critical value c increases, the probability of an error of the *first* kind *increases* for all p which make the null hypothesis true and thus make an error of the first kind possible; but at the same time the probability of an error of the *second* kind *decreases* for all p which make the null hypothesis false and thus make an error of the second kind possible.

The manufacturer's problem is thus simply to *decide how far it pays to increase the risks of one kind of error in order to reduce the risks of the other kind of error.*

Limitation of Maximum Probability of an Error of the First Kind. In the pure theory of classical statistics, the manufacturer's problem as stated just above is "not a statistical problem" at all; it is a problem to be solved by *direct* application of unaided business judgment. If, however, we look at the examples given by statisticians to show how a reasonable man might actually make this choice, most of them suggest that he should reason as follows. Since the consequence of an error of the first kind (failure to readjust the setup when readjustment is needed) may be a loss of as much as $42 while the consequence of the opposite error cannot be more than $6, a rule should be chosen under which the conditional probability of an error of the *first* kind is less than $\frac{1}{2}$ for *all* values of p which make the null hypothesis true ($p \geq .04$) even though this means that the risk of an error of the *second* kind will necessarily be greater than $\frac{1}{2}$ for *some* values of p.

The *maximum tolerable* conditional probability of an error of the *first* kind is generally denoted by α (alpha), and while classical *theory* says absolutely nothing on the subject of the proper numerical value of α in any kind of problem, the *examples* given in classical discussions seem to suggest that it should almost never be greater than .1. Many statistical tables which are needed to test hypotheses of a more complex kind than those treated in this course are in fact drawn up in such a way that the largest value of α for which the test can be conducted is .1 or even .05. Looking back at Figure 39.2, we see that if the risk of an error of the first kind is to be limited to .1 in the present problem, only one decision rule is possible. With the sample size fixed at 75, the critical value c must be set at 0 because if we reject the null hypothesis when there is even a single defective in the sample the conditional probability of an error of the first kind will be .19 for *some* values of p which make the null hypothesis true. If, however, the manufacturer should decide to tolerate an α as high as .2, then he would choose the rule (75,1) because this rule gives less risk of errors of the second kind than the rule (75,0); if he decides to let α go as high as .5 (and this is often recommended in the literature on quality control even though it is almost never recommended in the literature on "testing hypotheses"), he would choose (75,2) and reduce his risk of errors of the second kind still further.

By examining the implications of Figure 39.2 a little more closely we can see that *if* a person simply wants to find the rule which (1) gives the lowest possible conditional probabilities of errors of the second kind (2) subject to the overriding requirement that *no* conditional probability of an error of the first kind shall exceed some number α, *then* there is no need to draw curves like those in Figure 39.2 at all. The curves show that under any given rule (any given value of c) the conditional probability of an error of the first kind is greatest when p has the *borderline value* .04 which marks the boundary between truth and falsity of the null hypothesis, and we did not actually have to draw the curves in order to know this because we know that the conditional probability of *low* values of r,

$$P_b(\tilde{r} \leq c | n = 75, p),$$

will decrease as p increases. We also know without drawing the curves that all conditional probabilities of errors of the first kind increase as c increases while all probabilities of errors of the second kind

$$P_b(\tilde{r} > c | n = 75, p)$$

decrease as c increases. It follows that the manufacturer can find the c which meets his objectives by simply finding the *largest* c for which

$$P_b(\tilde{r} \leq c | n = 75, p = .04)$$

does not exceed α.

39.3.2   Tests of Significance

If the person responsible for a decision has decided to act in accordance with the rule which reduces the conditional probabilities of errors of the second kind as far as they can be reduced without letting *any* conditional probability of an error of the first kind exceed some chosen number α, he does not really need to find the c of his chosen rule at all. Suppose for example that he has set $\alpha = .2$, taken a sample of 75 pieces, and observed three defectives. If he simply computes the probability given the "borderline" value $p = .04$ of getting a result *at least as unfavorable to the null hypothesis* as the one he actually observed,

$$P_b(\tilde{r} \leq 3 | n = 75, p = .04) = .65,$$

the fact that .65 is greater than the permissible α tells him immediately that the decision rule which would satisfy his requirements must have a c *smaller* than the observed $r = 3$, and he therefore knows immediately that the null hypothesis is to be *accepted*. If he had found only one defective and computed

$$P_b(\tilde{r} \leq 1 | n = 75, p = .04) = .19,$$

the fact that .19 is *less* than the permissible α would have told him immediately that the c of the desired rule was equal to or greater than the observed $r = 1$ and he could immediately have *rejected* the null hypothesis.

The argument can be followed graphically by looking at the conditional distribution of $\tilde{r}$ given $p = .04$ which is shown as Figure 39.3.

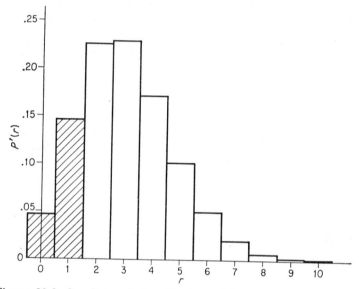

Figure 39.3. Conditional distribution of $\tilde{r}$ given $p = .04$ ($n = 75$).

The shaded tail of this distribution represents the maximum conditional probability of an error of the first kind under the rule (75,1),

$$P_b(\tilde{r} \le 1 | n = 75, p = .04) = .19,$$

and it is obvious that if c were increased from 1 to 2 this area would exceed the permissible $\alpha = .2$. It is also obvious from the figure that

1. If the r actually observed in a sample does not exceed $c = 1$, then $P_b(\tilde{r} \le r | n = 75, p = .04)$ cannot exceed α;
2. If the r actually observed in the sample does exceed c, then $P_b(\tilde{r} \le r | n = 75, p = .04)$ will exceed α.

The conditional probability *given the borderline value of the parameter* that pure chance will yield a sample statistic *at least as unfavorable to the null hypothesis as the one actually observed* is called the *statistical significance* of the observed statistic. Computing this probability and comparing it with a required maximum α is called *testing the significance* of the statistic at level α.

39.3.3 Choice of a Rule after a Sample Has Already Been Taken

The practice of formally selecting a decision rule before any sample is taken is standard in the field of quality control but much less common outside that field. In marketing research, for example, a statistician is much more likely to be asked what conclusions may legitimately be drawn from a sample which has already been taken than he is to be asked what conclusions should be drawn *if* a proposed sample yields such and such a result. We have seen that under a Bayes approach such problems can be solved by the methods of Part Three of this course with many fewer computations than are required to find a complete decision rule by the methods of Part Four, but under the classical approach there is absolutely no difference between the two kinds of problems.

If a terminal act must definitely be chosen after just one sample has been taken, then even though the actual decision rule is not selected until *after* the sample is taken, the selection should be made just as it would have been made *before* the sample was taken: by choosing a rule which gives a satisfactory balance between the conditional probabilities of errors of the first and second kind.

Suppose for example that the marketer faced with a packaging problem has already taken a sample of size $n = 100$ and that this sample has yielded statistics

$$\bar{x} = +.157,$$

$$s = \sqrt{\frac{1}{100 - 1} \Sigma(x - \bar{x})^2} = 1.25;$$

and suppose that the marketer wishes to make an immediate choice between the old and the new package without taking any further sample observations. Because his terminal decision is to be based on a sample of size $n = 100$, the marketer is interested only in decision rules based on samples of size $n = 100$; and since the null hypothesis in this problem asserts that μ is *not above* a specified value $\mu_b = .019$, it will clearly be logical to reject it provided that the sample mean $\bar{x}$ is *above* some duly chosen "critical value" which we shall call $\bar{x}_c$. In other words, the only decision rules which need be considered are those of the general form

Sample $n = 100$ and reject the null hypothesis that $\mu \le .019$ if and only if $\bar{x} > \bar{x}_c$.

Under such a rule the conditional probability of an error of the first kind for any μ which makes the null hypothesis true ($\mu \le .019$) is $P(\bar{x} > \bar{x}_c | \mu)$; the probability of an error of the second kind for any μ which makes the null hypothesis false ($\mu > .019$) is $P(\bar{x} \le \bar{x}_c | \mu)$. Because the estimate s is based on 99 degrees of freedom, we may treat the standard deviation of the individual members of the population of all possible sample observations as if it were known to have the value

$$\sigma = s = 1.25,$$

and the standard deviation of the long-run frequency distribution of $\tilde{x}$ *about the mean μ of this population of potential sample observations*† is therefore

$$\sigma(\tilde{x}) = \frac{\sigma}{\sqrt{n}} = \frac{1.25}{\sqrt{100}} = .125.$$

Given this standard deviation we can compute the required conditional probabilities by using the Normal approximation in the usual way. For any μ we first compute

$$u_c = \frac{\bar{x}_c - \mu}{\sigma(\tilde{x})} = \frac{\bar{x}_c - \mu}{.125}$$

and then use Table III to find

$$P(\tilde{x} > \bar{x}_c|\mu) \doteq P_N(\tilde{u} > u_c)$$

or

$$P(\tilde{x} \leq \bar{x}_c|\mu) \doteq P_N(\tilde{u} < u_c).$$

In Figure 39.4 graphs of these conditional probabilities are shown for several values of $\bar{x}_c$ and we can observe, for example, that under the rule with $\bar{x}_c = .225$ the conditional probability of an error of the first kind rises from almost nothing for $\mu < -.1$ to .05 at $\mu = \mu_b$ while the conditional probability of an error of the second kind falls from .95 at $\mu = \mu_b$ to almost nothing for $\mu > +.6$.

Selection of a Decision Rule by Specification of α. Once again the *theory* of classical statistics stops short as soon as a set of curves like this has been drawn. Traditional *practice*, on the other hand, would usually set a limit α on the conditional probability of an error of the first kind and select a rule to suit. Three of the rules depicted in the figure have actually been chosen to correspond to the values customarily assigned to α; by inspecting the lowest three *left*-hand branches the student can see that each $\bar{x}_c$ yields an α as follows:

$$\bar{x}_c = .309: \alpha = .01;$$
$$\bar{x}_c = .225: \alpha = .05;$$
$$\bar{x}_c = .180: \alpha = .1.$$

The fourth rule represents a choice of $\bar{x}_c$ which as we have already said is rarely suggested in the literature on testing hypotheses but which the

† Cf. Section 39.2.2 above; the classical theory does not discuss the distribution of $\tilde{x}$ about the "true value" ξ.

student may want to consider. With $\bar{x}_c = .019$, α has the value .5 and the greatest conditional probability of an error of the first kind is exactly *equal* to the greatest conditional probability of an error of the second kind.

Having duly decided which of these rules he prefers, the marketer can decide what to do on the basis of the $\bar{x} = +.157$ observed in the sample which has actually been taken. If $+.157$ is greater than the $\bar{x}_c$ of the chosen rule, he should reject the null hypothesis and adopt the new package; if $+.157$ is less than $\bar{x}_c$, he should retain his present package.

Decision by Test of Significance. If the marketer is willing to put a limit α on the maximum conditional probability of an error of the first

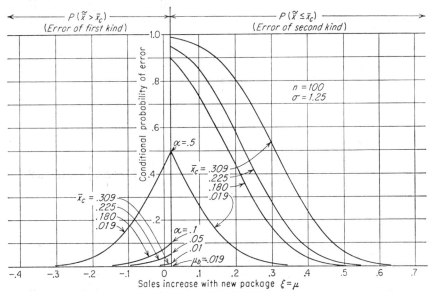

Figure 39.4

kind and then act in accordance with the rule which minimizes the conditional probabilities of errors of the second kind subject to this overriding requirement, he can (as in our earlier example) decide what to do on the basis of his observed sample without bothering to construct any curves like those in Figure 39.4.

In Figure 39.5 we show the conditional distribution of $\tilde{\bar{x}}$ given the borderline value $\mu = .019$, and since the null hypothesis that μ is *less than or equal to* .019 will be rejected for *high* values of $\tilde{\bar{x}}$, the maximum conditional probability of an error of the first kind will be equal to the area of the tail of this distribution to the *right* of $\bar{x}_c$. To find a rule which has any required α, the marketer chooses $\bar{x}_c$ so that this tail area is equal to α; if for example he sets $\alpha = .05$, he must choose $\bar{x}_c = +.225$ as shown in the figure.   Looking at the figure we see that

1. If the $\bar{x}$ actually observed in a sample exceeds $\bar{x}_c$, then clearly $P(\tilde{\bar{x}} > \bar{x}|\mu = .019)$ will be less than α.
2. If the $\bar{x}$ actually observed in a sample is less than $\bar{x}_c$, then clearly $P(\tilde{\bar{x}} > \bar{x}|\mu = .019)$ will be greater than α.

It follows that instead of computing the $\bar{x}_c$ which yields the required α and comparing the observed $\bar{x}$ with this critical value, the marketer needs only to compute the *statistical significance* of the observed $\bar{x}$,

$$P(\tilde{\bar{x}} > \bar{x}|\mu = .019),$$

compare this directly with α, and then reject the null hypothesis if the significance is numerically smaller than α, accept if it is greater than α.

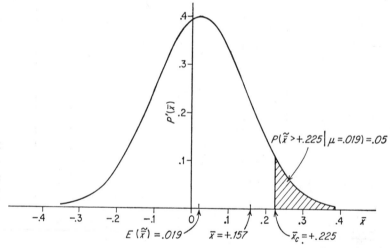

Figure 39.5. Conditional distribution of $\tilde{\bar{x}}$ given $\mu = +.019$ ($\sigma = 1.25$, $n = 100$).

The statistical significance of the $\bar{x} = +.157$ actually observed by the marketer is

$$P(\tilde{\bar{x}} > +.157|\mu = +.019) = P_N\left(\tilde{u} > \frac{.157 - .019}{.125}\right) = .14;$$

if he has actually chosen $\alpha = .05$, this means that he should *accept* the null hypothesis.

Observe that once again (and always) the statistical significance of an observed statistic is the conditional probability, given the *borderline* value of the parameter being tested, that pure chance would yield a statistic *at least as unfavorable to the null hypothesis* as the one actually observed.

39.4   Determination of Sample Size

In the previous section we studied the problem of choosing a statistical decision rule when the size of the sample was predetermined, either because a terminal decision had to be made immediately on the basis of whatever sample evidence was already at hand or for some other reason. We now turn to the problem of choosing a decision rule when the person responsible for the decision is free to specify the sample size as well as the values of the test statistic which will lead to rejection or acceptance of the null hypothesis or the "level of significance" α at which the test is to be conducted. In discussing this problem we shall assume that

1. *No* sample has as yet been taken;
2. It is possible to take one sample but *only one* before making a definite choice between the two terminal acts or hypotheses.

In classical theory this larger problem is to be solved by exactly the same methods which are used when the sample size is predetermined. The general form of the decision rule applicable to any given pair of null and alternate hypotheses will be identical to the form which would be proper if the sample size were predetermined, and as before the choice is to be made by taking a number of possible rules and looking at the conditional probabilities of both kinds of errors under these rules. The only difference will be that the person responsible for the decision must now consider and compare rules with a number of different values of n instead of being able to restrict his attention to rules with a single value of n.

It is clear, however, that although no new principles are involved, the practical difficulties are vastly greater because the fact that n is not predetermined means that the number of possible rules among which a choice must be made is infinitely greater than before. The *classical theory* gives no advice at all on how to cope with this problem practically, but the *traditional practice* seems to be to cut the problem down to practical size by *first deciding on* α (the maximum risk of an error of the first kind which is to be tolerated) and then looking at rules with various n's all of which satisfy this requirement.

To illustrate the procedure we show in Figure 39.6 the conditional probabilities of error in our packaging example under rules all of which have the traditional value $\alpha = .05$ but each of which has a different sample size as indicated in the figure. As we would expect, we find that as the sample size increases the conditional probabilities of errors of *both* kinds decrease for *all* values of μ except the borderline value μ_b. Sampling costs money, however—store testing of the kind used in this example would cost at least \$30 per sample observation—and the businessman must keep this in mind before he decides how far to go in reducing the risks of loss due to a wrong decision. The classical theory leaves this

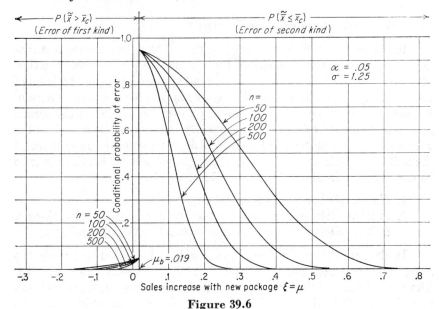

Figure 39.6

problem to the businessman's unaided judgment just as it leaves to his unaided judgment the problem of deciding how far to increase the risks of errors of one kind in order to reduce the risks of errors of the other kind.

PROBLEMS

1. Compute and graph curves showing the conditional probabilities of wrong decisions for the following decision rules.

a. In the setup example: sample $n = 50$, reject if the number of defectives in the sample does not exceed $c = 2$.

b. In the packaging example: sample $n = 25$, reject if $\bar{x} > +.200$.

2. In the literature on hypothesis testing, decision rules are usually described by *performance characteristics* or *power curves* which show the conditional probability of *rejecting the null hypothesis* for every value of the parameter being tested rather than by curves which show the probability of making *whatever decision is wrong* for every value of the parameter. Sketch performance characteristics for the two rules of Problem 1 and explain exactly how they must be read in order to obtain from them the probabilities of the two kinds of errors.

3. Suppose that in the packaging example we had chosen $\mu > .019$ as the null hypothesis and made $\mu \leq .019$ the alternate.

a. Draw the performance characteristic of the rule: sample $n = 25$, reject if $\bar{x} \leq +.200$.

b. Is or is not this rule the same in effect as the rule of Problem 1*b*?

c. If a sample of 25 is actually taken and yields $\bar{x} = +.040$, what is the statistical significance of this statistic (1) under the null hypothesis $\mu \leq .019$? (2) Under the null hypothesis $\mu > .019$?

d. If a decision must be reached without further sampling, which package do *you* think the marketer should choose?

4. Suppose that a sample of 10 pieces has already been taken in the setup problem and that a terminal decision must be reached without further sampling.

  a. Can *any* decision rule be found which satisfies the requirement $\alpha = .05$? $\alpha = .25$? $\alpha = .50$? What is the lowest α requirement which *can* be met by any available rule?

  b. Draw a curve showing the conditional probabilities of the two kinds of errors under the rule which does meet the lowest α requirement.

  c. Suppose that no defective has been found in the sample of 10 on which the decision is to be based. What is the statistical significance of this result?

  d. In the circumstances of part *c*, do *you* think the manufacturer should accept or reject the null hypothesis that $p \geq .04$?

  5. In the literature on quality control, a *sampling plan* is a decision rule of the form:

Take a sample of size n from the process (or lot); accept the process (or lot) if and only if the number r of defectives in the sample does not exceed c.

Such rules are usually described by *operating characteristics* which show for every value of p the conditional probability of *accepting* the *process* (or lot). State the rule of Problem 4*b* in this language, draw its operating characteristic, and explain exactly how it must be read in order to obtain the same information which can be obtained from your original curve.

CHAPTER 40

Evaluation of Statistical Decision Rules
in Terms of Expected Loss

40.1 Description of Decision Rules in Terms of Conditional Expected Terminal Loss

One of the reasons why we feel so helpless when asked to choose a decision rule by looking at curves like those shown in Figures 39.2, 39.4, and 39.6 is that these curves do not give anything like an adequate representation of even the conditional risks to which the businessman is exposed given a particular value of p or μ. If the penalty for making an error of the first kind were some *fixed amount* and the penalty for an error of the second kind were another *fixed amount*, then curves showing the conditional probabilities of errors of the two kinds would be directly relevant to a comparison of decision rules. In problems of the kind we are studying, however, the loss which will result from an error of either kind depends on the value of the unknown parameter p or μ in such a way that *an error of either kind is more serious the farther the true value of p or μ is from the break-even value p_b or μ_b.* The curves of Figures 39.2, 39.4, and 39.6 show that the *conditional probability* of an error of either kind will be greatest if p or μ has a value very near the break-even value; but if the parameter *is* near the break-even value, then choice of the wrong act will cost the businessman virtually nothing. They show relatively small conditional probabilities of error for values of p and μ well away from the break-even value, but if the parameter *is* quite far from the break-even value a wrong decision will entail a very severe loss.

This means that the true measure of the risk to which a given decision rule will expose the manufacturer if p or μ has any given value is not the conditional *probability* that the rule will lead to a wrong decision if p or μ has that value but the *expected value of the loss* to which the rule may lead if p or μ has that value. By computing and graphing these *conditional terminal losses* we can get a much more useful picture of the way in which a rule will operate given all possible values of the parameter than we can get by looking at conditional probabilities of error.

40.1.1 Machine-setup Example

To see how the conditional expected terminal loss of a particular decision rule is computed for any given value of p, let us take the rule ($n = 75$, $c = 1$) as an example and compute this loss for the two values $p = .01$ and $p = .05$. The student should remember that in so doing we are again assuming that the parameter p of the sampling distribution of $\tilde{r}$ is identical to the cost-determining process average of the machine—i.e., we are assuming that the sampling is *unbiased*.

$p = .01$. It was shown in our original discussion of this problem (Table 22.7) that if the manufacturer *accepts* the null hypothesis that $p \geq .04$ and readjusts the setup when $p = .01$, he will suffer a terminal loss of $200(.04 - .01) = \$6$; if he *rejects* the null hypothesis and refuses to readjust the setup, he has made the right decision and suffered no terminal loss. Looking at Figure 39.2 we can see that there is probability .173 that the rule (75,1) will lead to the *wrong* decision if $p = .01$; the probability that it will lead to the *right* decision is accordingly $1 - .173 = .827$. We can then compute the expected value of the terminal loss to be $1.04 as shown in Table 40.1; this is the *conditional* terminal loss of the rule (75,1) *given* $p = .01$.

Table 40.1
Conditional Expected Terminal Loss of Rule (75,1) Given $p = .01$

Sample outcome	Resulting decision	Probability	Terminal loss	
			Conditional	Expected
$r \leq 1$	Reject	.827	$0	$0
$r > 1$	Accept	.173	6	1.04
		1.000		$1.04

Table 40.2
Conditional Expected Terminal Loss of Rule (75,1) Given $p = .05$

Sample outcome	Resulting decision	Probability	Terminal loss	
			Conditional	Expected
$r \leq 1$	Reject	.106	$2	$ .21
$r > 1$	Accept	.894	0	0
		1.000		$ .21

$p = .05$. In this case the manufacturer will suffer no terminal loss if he accepts the null hypothesis that $p \geq .04$ and readjusts the setup but will suffer a loss of $200(.05 - .04) = \$2$ if he accepts. The probability that the rule (75,1) will lead to the *wrong* decision can be read as .106 from Figure 39.2 and the probability that it will lead to the *right* decision is correspondingly .894. The *conditional* expected terminal loss of the rule *given* $p = .05$ is then shown in Table 40.2 to be $.21.

A complete description of *any* decision rule in terms of conditional expected terminal loss can be obtained by carrying out computations of this sort for a number of values of p and then plotting them and fairing in a curve. Curves of this sort are shown in Figure 40.1 for the rules with $n = 75$ and values of c from 0 through 4 which were originally described in Figure 39.2.

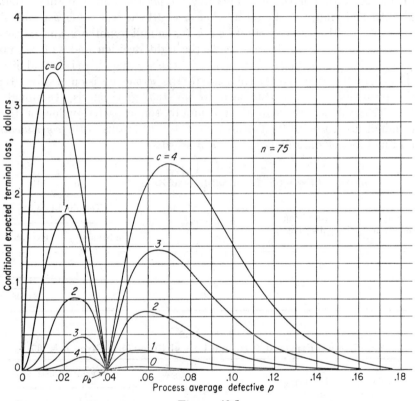

Figure 40.1

40.1.2 Packaging Example

It was shown in our original discussion of this problem that if the manufacturer chooses the new package when in fact its true effect is to increase sales by an amount ξ which is *less* than $\xi_b = +.019$ he will suffer a terminal loss of

$$\$20,000 - \$1,056,000\,\xi = \$1,056,000(.019 - \xi);$$

if he chooses the old package when in fact $\xi > +.019$ he will suffer a terminal loss of

$$\$1,056,000\ \xi - \$20,000 = \$1,056,000(\xi - .019).$$

If we again assume that the mean μ of all possible sample observations is exactly equal to the true effect ξ of the new package, we can use these formulas to compute conditional expected terminal loss under any given rule for any given value of μ. Let us take the rule ($n = 100$, $\bar{x}_c = +.180$) and the values $\mu = -.050$ and $\mu = +.100$ as examples.

$\mu = -.050$. The first loss formula tells us that if the manufacturer chooses the new package (rejects the null hypothesis) when $\mu = -.050$, he will suffer a terminal loss of

$$\$1,056,000[.019 - (-.050)] = \$72,900;$$

if he makes the opposite decision, he suffers no loss. From Figure 39.4 we can read that the probability that the rule $(100, +.180)$ will lead to the wrong decision *if $\mu = -.050$* is .033, and we can then compute the conditional expected terminal loss to be \$2410 as shown in Table 40.3.

Table 40.3
Conditional Expected Terminal Loss of Rule $(100, +.180)$ Given $\mu = -.050$

Sample outcome	Resulting decision	Probability	Terminal loss	
			Conditional	Expected
$\bar{x} \leq +.180$	Accept	.967	\$ 0	\$ 0
$\bar{x} > +.180$	Reject	.033	72,900	2410
		1.000		\$2410

Table 40.4
Conditional Expected Terminal Loss of Rule $(100, +.180)$ Given $\mu = +.100$

Sample outcome	Resulting decision	Probability	Terminal loss	
			Conditional	Expected
$\bar{x} \leq .180$	Accept	.739	\$85,500	\$63,200
$\bar{x} > .180$	Reject	.261	0	0
		1.000		\$63,200

$\mu = +.100$. The second loss formula tells us that if $\mu = +.100$ acceptance of the null hypothesis followed by retention of the old package will cause a terminal loss of

$1,056,000(+.100 - .019) = \$85,500,$

and the probability that the rule $(100,+.180)$ will lead to this decision can be read as .739 from Figure 39.4. The conditional expected terminal loss under this rule given $\mu = +.100$ is therefore $63,200 as shown in Table 40.4.

In Figure 40.2 conditional expected terminal losses given all possible values of μ are shown for all the decision rules originally described in Figure 39.4.

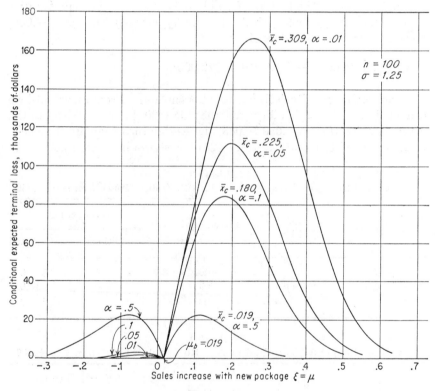

Figure 40.2

40.1.3 Immediate Implications of the Curves of Conditional Terminal Loss

Mere inspection of the curves of conditional terminal loss shown in Figures 40.1 and 40.2 immediately brings out the serious extent to which we can be misled by looking only at the worst conceivable consequence of either act or the greatest conditional probability of an error of either kind. If p or μ is extremely far away from the break-even value, almost *any* reasonable decision rule will give so small a probability of making a wrong decision that the expected value of the resulting loss is negligible. If on the other hand p or μ is extremely close to the break-even value, the loss entailed by a wrong decision will be so small that the probability of making a wrong decision is of no interest whatever. *It is the intermediate values of p and μ which give rise to really serious risks.*

Figures 40.1 and 40.2 also show clearly why we should *not* single out one of the two hypotheses as the null hypothesis and then choose a decision rule by requiring that the conditional probability of erroneously rejecting this hypothesis should not exceed some number α of the order of .01 or .05 even though this means that the conditional probability of erroneously accepting this hypothesis will be well over $\frac{1}{2}$ for some values of p or μ. In the setup example, choosing even the unusually high value .1 for α led to the selection of the rule (75,0); looking at Figure 40.1 we see that this makes the conditional expected loss very high if the null hypothesis is false ($p < .04$) and disproportionately low when the null hypothesis is true. Similarly the rules in Figure 40.2 with $\bar{x}_c = .309$, .225, and .180 reduce the conditional expected losses for $\mu \leq .019$ (null hypothesis true) to extremely low values at the cost of running extremely high risks when the null hypothesis is false. We can conclude that, in these two examples,

> Mere consideration of the possible consequences of errors gives no justification whatever for asymmetric treatment of the two hypotheses. Unless some *other* considerations are brought to bear, the sensible thing to do is simply to act in common-sense agreement with the sample evidence: if $\bar{x} > \mu_b$, act as if $\mu > \mu_b$; if the sample fraction defective r/n is greater than p_b, act as if $p > p_b$; and so forth. Tests of significance at traditional levels such as .05 are much worse than useless in selecting a terminal act—they lead to absurd and dangerous results.

What is more, *these two examples are typical of the vast majority of two-action problems encountered in business because in almost all practical two-action problems the loss which will result from an error of either kind increases with the "magnitude" of the error*—i.e. with the difference between the actual value of the cost or profit-determining parameter and the break-even value of that parameter. It is true that our two examples are of a special (though very common) kind in that the loss due a wrong decision will be strictly *proportional* to the magnitude $|p - p_b|$ or $|\mu - \mu_b|$ of the error; but even in problems where this is *not* true the curve of conditional expected loss under a decision rule will have the same general two-humped shape as those in Figures 40.1 and 40.2 if the loss which will actually result from an error increases in *any* reasonable way with the magnitude of the error. *The classical theory of testing hypotheses is really adapted only to problems where there is just one possible consequence of an error of the first kind and just one possible consequence of an error of the second kind;* and such problems are hard to invent and much harder to find in real business life.

40.2   Unconditional Expected Terminal Loss; Optimal Decision Rules When Sample Size Is Predetermined

We have said that *unless* some considerations other than the possible consequences of wrong decisions are brought into the picture, the best terminal act should usually be chosen by simply acting on the sample "estimate" ($\bar{x}$ or r/n) of the cost-determining parameter (μ or p). To see how such other considerations may enter, let us first of all observe that selection of a particular decision rule is an *act under uncertainty* in exactly the same sense that stocking 28 units or making a scrap allowance of 77 pieces is an act under uncertainty. The cost, profit, or loss of any such act depends on some unpredictable "event," and the event which will determine the (expected) cost, profit, or loss resulting from selection of a particular decision rule is the process average p which the operator actually achieves by his setup or the increase in sales ξ which would actually be effected by the new package. In other words, a graph like Figure 40.1 or 40.2 is really a form of *loss table* and the implications of this loss table are identical to those of all the other loss tables we have studied in this course. Each curve on the graph describes one possible act and corresponds to one column of the loss table, and in deciding which curve of conditional expected loss represents the best decision rule the business-man will want to consider how much *weight* he wants to give to each point on each curve.

40.2.1   Machine-setup Example

In terms of the setup example: if the manufacturer thinks that the operator is very likely to produce setups with p in the general vicinity of .01 to .02, he will think that the rule (75,0) is about the worst of all the rules shown in Figure 40.1 because it has very high conditional losses for these values of p and he may decide to use the rule (75,4) because it has very low conditional losses for these values of p. If on the contrary he thinks that the operator is very likely to produce setups with p in the general vicinity of .06 to .08, he will think that (75,4) is the worst of all the rules and that (75,0) may be the best. What is more, he will reason in this way *whether or not* he thinks he "really knows" the exact long-run frequencies with which the operator would produce setups with each possible p—even if his frequency data were extremely scanty, no sensible businessman would choose the same curve if the setup had been made by a skilled operator with 10 years' experience that he would choose if the setup had been made by a recently promoted sweeper with a bad hangover.

Let us therefore evaluate the five decision rules depicted in Figure 40.1 using the weights which we have previously used in discussing this example. The evaluation of the rules (75,0) and (75,4) is shown in Table 40.5, the weights or "prior probabilities" being taken from

Table 40.5
Computation of Unconditional Expected Terminal Loss

Event p	Probability $P_0(p)$	Loss of act (75,0)		Loss of act (75,4)	
		Conditional	Expected	Conditional	Expected
.01	.7	$3.17	$2.22	$ .01	$ .01
.05	.1	.04	0	1.35	.14
.15	.1	0	0	.17	.02
.25	.1	0	0	0	0
	1.0		$2.22		$ .17

Table 40.6
Unconditional Expected Terminal Losses

Act	Loss
75, 0	$2.22
75, 1	.74
75, 2	.22
75, 3	.13
75, 4	.17

Table 22.2 and the conditional expected terminal losses being read from Figure 40.1. The *unconditional* expected terminal losses found by evaluating all five rules in this way are summarized in Table 40.6, where we see that the best rule is (75,3). *Because the manufacturer attaches so much weight to the way in which the rule will perform if $p = .01$ and so little to what will happen if p has high values, the best rule is one which has quite low conditional losses for p below the break-even value even though this entails fairly high conditional losses for p above the break-even value.*

Observe that the loss of the rule (75,0) is *very* substantially higher than that of any of the other rules, and remember that setting up the null hypothesis $p \geq .04$ and testing it at either of the conventional levels .05 or .1 amounts to adopting the rule (75,0). The straight nonstatistical, common-sense procedure of comparing the sample fraction defective with the break-even value .04 would give much better results. Since $2/75 < .04$, $3/75 = .04$ exactly, and $4/75 > .04$, this procedure would amount to choosing either the rule (75,2) or the rule (75,3), and the latter rule is in fact optimal.

Finally, let us observe that the rule which the manufacturer has chosen in this way will always lead to exactly the same terminal act that the manufacturer would have chosen if he had analyzed the problem by the method used in our original discussion of this example in Chapter 22. Remembering that we are assuming for the moment that the sample size $n = 75$ is predetermined and that the manufacturer's only problem is to decide what terminal act to choose for each possible sample outcome, let us take the outcome $r = 1$ as an example and apply the method of Chapter 22 to choose the proper terminal act. In the first five columns of Table 40.7 the posterior distribution of $\tilde{p}$ is computed following the model of Table 22.4, and in the remainder of Table 40.7 the posterior losses of the two acts are computed following the model of Table 22.9.

Table 40.7

p	$P_0(p)$	$P_b(\tilde{r} = 1\mid p)$	$P(\tilde{r} = 1, p)$	$P_1(p)$	Loss if null hypothesis is accepted		Loss if null hypothesis is rejected	
					Conditional	Expected	Conditional	Expected
.01	.7	.3565	.2496	.967	$6	$5.80	$ 0	$0
.05	.1	.0843	.0084	.033	0	0	2	.07
.15	.1	.0001	.0000	.000	0	0	22	.00
.25	.1	.0000	.0000	.000	0	0	42	.00
	1.0		.2580	1.000		$5.80		$ .07

Because the expected loss of rejecting the null hypothesis is less than the expected loss of accepting it, the null hypothesis should be rejected—and when $r = 1$ this is exactly what should be done under the optimal "decision rule" (75,3).

Because the optimal rule (75,3) tells the manufacturer what to do for *all possible* sample outcomes rather than just *one particular* sample outcome, selection of this rule is actually equivalent to the method used in Section 33.3.1 to analyze a decision to take a sample of specified size and then act optimally *whatever* value of $\tilde{r}$ is observed in the sample. One method has technical advantages in one situation, the other in another, but what is really important is to realize that

No matter whether we formally compute posterior probabilities and posterior losses or set up decision rules and look at their possible consequences, a *reasonable* choice among possible acts under uncertainty can be made *only* if we first decide how much weight we wish to attach to each of the possible values of the cost-determining parameter or basic random variable.

40.2.2   Packaging Example

While the statistical form of the setup problem which we have just discussed is perfectly typical of the great majority of two-action problems to which tests of significance are commonly applied, the circumstances surrounding the problem are atypical in that the manufacturer had some fairly solid prior information on the value of the parameter p. The packaging example, however, is completely typical in every respect—the prior information is of the vaguest sort and two reasonable men who had examined the two packages might disagree totally on the odds at which they were willing to bet that the new package would increase sales by any given amount, i.e. on the weights they assigned to the various possible values of $\mu = \xi$.

If, however, we remember that when we use these weights to compute the unconditional expected loss of a decision rule we are simply computing the weighted-average height of the corresponding curve in Figure 40.2, we can see immediately that virtually *all* the weight would have to be attached to values of μ *below* the break-even value .019 to justify use of a decision rule based on any of the values conventionally chosen for α—i.e. to justify testing the significance of the observed $\bar{x}$ at any of the conventional levels. We may well ask why any reasonable businessman who felt virtually *certain* that the new package was no good would ever have spent money testing it in the first place.

If on the other hand the businessman feels that all values of μ in a fairly wide region around .019 are more or less equally likely, then regardless of *exactly* how he distributes his weights it is perfectly clear from Figure 40.2 that the curve for $\alpha = .5$ is going to have a much lower weighted-average height than any of the other curves in the figure. If in addition we observe that as α departs from .5 the height of the higher hump increases much more rapidly than the height of the lower hump decreases, we can see that under any halfway reasonable distribution of weights the best decision rule is going to correspond to an α which is nearly if not exactly equal to .5. Remembering that a rule with $\alpha = .5$ says simply that if $\bar{x} > .019$ we should act as if $\mu > .019$ and that if $\bar{x} \leq .019$ we should act as if $\mu \leq .019$, we see that tests of significance are completely unnecessary in this problem if they are made at level .5 and definitely harmful if they are made at any level which is substantially different from .5.

The point can be made even clearer if we actually compute the average heights of the curves in Figure 40.2. This can easily be done numerically for *any* distribution of weights by taking the weights for 10 or 20 evenly spaced values of μ, multiplying the height of the loss curve at each μ by the weight of that μ, adding the products, and dividing by the sum of the weights; but when the distribution of the weights can be described by a Normal curve the weighted average can be obtained still more easily by formula. Letting $E_0(\tilde{\mu})$ and $\sigma_0(\tilde{\mu})$ denote the mean and standard deviation of the Normal distribution of weights, we first compute the quantities

$$\sigma(\tilde{E}_1) = \sigma_0(\tilde{\mu}) \sqrt{\frac{\sigma_0^2(\tilde{\mu})}{\sigma_0^2(\tilde{\mu}) + \sigma^2(\bar{x})}},$$

$$D_0 = \frac{|\mu_b - E_0(\tilde{\mu})|}{\sigma_0(\tilde{\mu})}, \qquad\qquad D_E = \frac{|\mu_b - E_0(\tilde{\mu})|}{\sigma(\tilde{E}_1)},$$

$$I_0 = \frac{1}{\sigma_0^2(\tilde{\mu})}, \qquad\qquad I_{\bar{x}} = \frac{1}{\sigma^2(\bar{x})},$$

$$E_c = \frac{I_0 E_0(\tilde{\mu}) + I_{\bar{x}} \bar{x}_c}{I_0 + I_{\bar{x}}}, \qquad\qquad \Delta = \frac{E_c - E_0(\tilde{\mu})}{\sigma(\tilde{E}_1)}.$$

The average height of any loss curve—i.e., the *unconditional* expected terminal loss of any decision rule $(n, \bar{x}_c)$—is then given by

$$\begin{array}{ll} k_t\sigma_0(\tilde{\mu})G(D_0) - k_t\sigma(\tilde{E}_1)[\mathrm{P}'_N(\Delta) - D_E \, \mathrm{P}_N(\tilde{u} > \Delta)] & \textit{if } E_0(\tilde{\mu}) < \mu_b, \\ k_t\sigma_0(\tilde{\mu})G(D_0) - k_t\sigma(\tilde{E}_1)[\mathrm{P}'_N(\Delta) - D_E \, \mathrm{P}_N(\tilde{u} < \Delta)] & \textit{if } E_0(\tilde{\mu}) > \mu_b, \end{array}$$

where k_t is the terminal loss constant (Section 30.4.2) which in our example has the value \$1,056,000. Notice that on the assumption that $\mu = \xi$, the first term in both formulas is the *expected loss of optimal terminal action without sampling* (cf. Section 34.4.1). The second term, then, is the *reduction* in terminal loss which a decision rule with arbitrary n and $\bar{x}_c$ can be "expected" to produce; it is the expected value of the sample information *as used under the given decision rule.*

As an example, let us compute the weighted-average or unconditional expected terminal loss of the rule $(100, +.309)$—the expected terminal loss of testing at the .01 level—on the assumption that the marketer assigns to the possible values of $\mu = \xi$ the Normal distribution of weights with mean and standard deviation

$$E_0(\tilde{\mu}) = +.146, \qquad\qquad \sigma_0(\tilde{\mu}) = .310,$$

which we assumed in our original discussion of this example (Section 32.1.3). We first compute

$$\sigma(\tilde{E}_1) = .310 \sqrt{\frac{.310^2}{.310^2 + 1.25^2/100}} = .287,$$

$$D_0 = \frac{|.019 - .146|}{.310} = +.41, \qquad\qquad D_E = \frac{|.019 - .146|}{.287} = +.44,$$

$$I_0 = \frac{1}{.310^2} = 10.4, \qquad\qquad I_{\bar{x}} = \frac{100}{1.25^2} = 64.0,$$

$$E_c = \frac{10.4 \times .146 + 64.0 \times .309}{10.4 + 64.0} = +.286,$$

$$\Delta = \frac{+.286 - .146}{.287} = +.49.$$

Because $E_0(\tilde{\mu}) = +.146$ is greater than $\mu_b = +.019$ we then use the second formula for the unconditional expected terminal loss and compute

$$G(.41) = .2270,$$
$$P'_N(+.49) = .3538, \qquad P_N(\tilde{u} < +.49) = .6879,$$
$$k_t.310 \times .2270 - k_t.287(.3538 - .44 \times .6879)$$
$$= \$1,056,000 \times .0704 - \$1,056,000 \times .0147$$
$$= \$74,300 - \$15,500 = \$58,800.$$

The student will observe that the average or *unconditional* expected terminal loss of this rule is very substantially greater than the *greatest conditional* terminal loss of the rule with $\alpha = .5$, which is shown by Figure 40.2 to be about \$23,000. The average or *unconditional* expected terminal loss of that rule is only \$8700, or less than a sixth of the loss under the rule with $\alpha = .01$.

The Optimal $\bar{x}_c$. The *best* value for $\bar{x}_c$ under any given Normal distribution of weights—the value of $\bar{x}_c$ which gives the *lowest possible* average or unconditional loss—can be shown by the calculus to be

$$\bar{x}_c^* = \frac{(I_{\bar{x}} + I_0)\mu_b - I_0\, E_0(\tilde{\mu})}{I_{\bar{x}}}.$$

When this algebraic expression is substituted in the formula for E_c, we find that E_c becomes equal to μ_b; and since E_c is simply the mean of the posterior distribution of $\tilde{\mu}$ *given* $\bar{x} = \bar{x}_c$ we see that adopting a "statistical decision rule" with optimal $\bar{x}_c$ is exactly equivalent to deciding to choose the new package if $E_1(\tilde{\mu}) > \mu_b$, the old if $E_1(\tilde{\mu}) < \mu_b$. On the assumption that $\mu = \xi$, this result is identical to the result of our original discussion of this example, where we found that the new package should be chosen if $E_1(\xi) > \xi_b$, the old package if $E_1(\xi) < \xi_b$.

If we go on to substitute μ_b for E_c in the formula for Δ, the absolute value of Δ becomes equal to D_E and *both* loss formulas reduce to

$$k_t\sigma_0(\tilde{\mu})G(D_0) - k_t\sigma(\tilde{E}_1)G(D_E).$$

If μ is assumed equal to ξ, this result is identical to the formula derived in Part Four of the course for the expected terminal loss of a decision to *take a sample of size n and then choose whatever terminal act is optimal under the distribution of ξ as revised to take account of the information obtained from the sample* (cf. Section 34.4.3). In our example the best value of $\bar{x}_c$ is

$$\bar{x}_c^* = \frac{74.4 \times .019 - 10.4 \times .146}{64.0} = -.002;$$

and the corresponding unconditional expected loss is found by computing

$$G(D_E) = G(+.44) = .2169,$$
$$k_t.310 \times .2270 - k_t.287 \times .2169$$
$$= \$1,056,000 \times .0704 - \$1,056,000 \times .0623$$
$$= \$74,300 - \$65,800 = \$8,500.$$

Out of curiosity we can find the α of the optimal rule $(100, -.002)$ by computing

$$P(\bar{x} > -.002 | \mu = .019) = P_N\left(\bar{u} > \frac{.002 - .019}{.125}\right) = .57.$$

Because the manufacturer believes that the "prior" evidence actually favors the alternate *hypothesis* $\mu > .019$, *he should "test" the* "null" *hypothesis at a level even higher than .5.* Actually, however, the gain obtained by testing at the strictly optimal .57 level rather than at the common-sense .5 level is only $\$8700 - \$8500 = \$200$ and is inconsequential in comparison with the gain of $\$57,600 - \$8,700 = \$48,900$ obtained by testing at the .5 level rather than at the conventional .01 level. The same sort of thing will be true, furthermore, whenever the conditional costs of the various possible terminal acts are linear (so that the posterior expected cost of any act depends only on the posterior mean and not on the whole posterior distribution) and the prior information I_0 is slight in comparison with the sample information $I_{\bar{x}}$ (so that the posterior mean is nearly if not exactly equal to the sample mean $\bar{x}$).

Whenever (1) the conditional costs of the possible terminal acts are linear functions of the basic random variable and (2) virtually all the available information on the value of this random variable is summarized by the mean of a sample, common sense is really all that is needed to choose the best terminal act.

The conditional costs of the terminal act *are* nearly if not exactly linear in the great majority of the two-action problems encountered in practical business life, and in all such problems the theory of probability should be reserved for the two situations in which it is really needed:

1. When the sample evidence may be contrary to some really substantial prior evidence and the two must be carefully weighed against each other before choosing a terminal act;

2. When it is necessary to determine the proper size for a sample or to decide whether a sample or another sample should be taken before *any* terminal act is chosen.

40.3   Expected Total Loss and Optimal Sample Size

40.3.1   Conditional Expected Total Loss

Although curves which show conditional expected *terminal* loss make it easy to see the implications of a number of decision rules all of which involve the same sample size, they are not really adequate for comparison of rules with different sample sizes because they give no explicit recognition to the greater cost of a larger sample. What the businessman really wants to consider in such problems is the expected value of the *sum* of the terminal loss and the sampling cost to which each decision rule exposes him for any given value of the parameter under test. This sum will be referred to as the *conditional expected total loss* of a given rule since (as we saw in Section 33.4) money spent on sampling can be regarded as a loss just as accurately as it can be regarded as a cost.

To explain the construction and use of curves of conditional expected *total* loss we return to our packaging example, but because we have already seen that "testing" at a traditional level such as .05 is illogical in such a problem we shall not work with the rules originally depicted in Figure 39.6. Instead, we shall consider a number of "common-sense" rules all of which have $\bar{x}_c = \mu_b$ (i.e. which test at the .5 level). Curves of conditional probabilities of error for rules of this sort with a number of different sample sizes n are shown in Figure 40.3.

We already know how to compute the conditional expected *terminal* loss for any given μ under any such rule, so that to obtain the conditional expected *total* loss all that we have to do is add on the cost of sampling for that μ. In some situations the sampling cost or loss will actually depend on the value of μ, but in our present example it is independent of μ and depends only on n; we assume that it is given by the formula

Sampling cost = $\$30\, n$.

This means that a loss characteristic showing conditional expected *total* loss under any rule can be obtained by computing the conditional expected *terminal* loss for each μ in exactly the same way that we did in Section 40.1.2 and then simply adding on the $\$30\, n$ cost of sampling. Curves computed in this way are shown in Figure 40.4 for all the rules originally depicted in Figure 40.3.

40.3.2   Unconditional Expected Total Loss

There is only one *obvious* conclusion which can be drawn by mere inspection of the curves in Figure 40.4: the curve which describes the rule $(500, +.019)$ is higher for *all* values of $\mu = \xi$ than the curve for the rule $(347, +.019)$, and therefore the rule $(500, +.019)$ can be immediately eliminated as a contender.   With this sole exception, however, comparison of any two curves in the figure shows that

> The larger sample is necessarily worse than the smaller one for very low and very high values of $\mu = \xi$ (where even the smaller sample is almost sure to lead to a correct decision) and for values of μ near the break-even value (where it does not make much difference which terminal act is chosen); the larger sample is better than the smaller for values of μ which are far enough from μ_b to make a wrong decision result in a fairly serious loss and which are nevertheless close enough to μ_b to make it likely that a small sample will lead to the wrong decision.

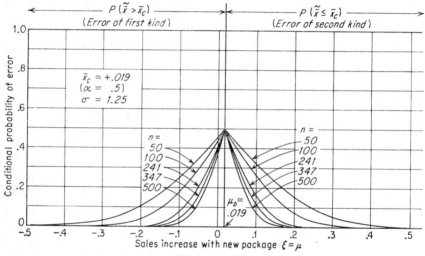

Figure 40.3

Once we have made this observation, it is clear that the only rational way of choosing among the curves of total loss in Figure 40.4 is to consider the *average* height of each of the curves, just as this was the only rational way of choosing among the curves of terminal loss in Figures 40.1 and 40.2.   This time, however, the businessman must really use careful judgment in choosing the weights which he wants to use in computing these averages.   When sample size was predetermined and choice of a decision rule meant simply choice of $\bar{x}_c$, we could argue as we did in Section 40.2.2 that *any* fairly broad distribution of weights would lead to just about the same result because terminal loss was virtually 0 outside the interval $\mu = -.3$ to $\mu = +.6$ for *all* rules (cf. Figure 40.2) and therefore any distribution which assigned roughly equal weights within this interval would lead to ranking the curves in the same order.   In our present problem, on the contrary, *the width of the prior distribution of $\tilde{\mu}$ is*

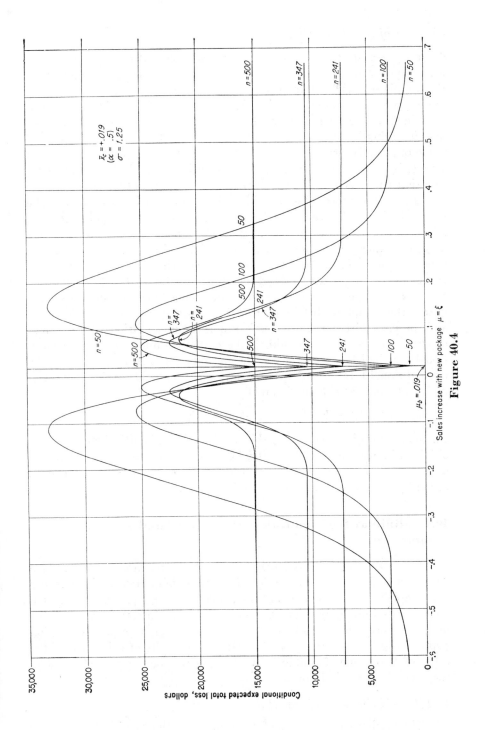

$\bar{x}_c = +.019$
$(\alpha = .5)$
$\sigma = 1.25$

$\mu_b = .019$

Sales increase with new package $\mu = \xi$

Conditional expected total loss, dollars

Figure 40.4

t'x really crucial factor in choosing the sample size. If most of the weight
is placed on values of μ in the middle range of those shown in Figure 40.4,
the sample size will be large because a large sample is needed to give adequate protection against terminal loss. If most of the weight is placed
on values of μ below and above those shown in Figure 40.4, the businessman is saying in effect that while he has no good idea at all of the *exact*
value of μ, he is virtually sure that it is so far from μ_b that a very small
sample is almost certain to lead to the right terminal decision and therefore that the cost of a large sample will almost certainly be wasted.

As for the procedures by which the average heights of curves like
those in Figure 40.4 can actually be computed, only one point need be
added to the discussion in Section 40.2.2. When sampling cost depends
only on n and not on μ, the average height of a curve of conditional
expected total loss will be simply the average height of the corresponding
curve of conditional expected terminal loss plus the fixed cost of sampling.
When this is true and when in addition the conditional terminal *costs* are
linear, the sampling distribution of $\tilde{x}$ is Normal with known variance,
and the prior distribution of $\tilde{\mu}$ is Normal, the unconditional total loss of
any rule can be found by adding the cost of sampling to the unconditional terminal loss as given by the formulas in Section 40.2.2 and the
unconditional total loss of a rule *in which $\bar{x}_c$ is optimal for the given n* can
be found from the simpler formula

$$k_t \sigma_0(\tilde{\mu})G(D_0) - k_t \sigma(\tilde{E}_1)G(D_E) + K_s + k_s n.$$

On the assumption that $\mu = \xi$ this latter result is identical to the result
obtained in Section 34.4.3; and it follows that the sample size which produces the decision rule with the lowest unconditional total loss can be
found by the method described in Chapter 35.

40.4 Minimax Decision Rules; Maximum Admissible Sample Size

Because sample size *is* sensitive to both the mean and the standard
deviation of the distribution assigned to the basic random variable before
the sample is taken, the person responsible for assigning this distribution
may well feel unhappy about his responsibility. In some situations the
mental agony which really careful assessment of a prior distribution
requires can be avoided by showing that the results of using one or the
other of two "rule-of-thumb" sample sizes will be completely satisfactory even if not strictly optimal.

40.4.1 Minimax Decision Rules

The minimax decision rule for a problem with any given set of costs
is defined as the decision rule under which the *worst conditional* expected

total loss is less than under any other rule.†   It can be proved that in problems where

1. The conditional terminal costs are linear functions of μ,
2. The cost of sampling is a linear function of n,
3. The sampling distribution of $\bar{x}$ is Normal with variance σ^2/n,
4. The value of σ^2 is known,

the minimax rule is to set $\bar{x}_c = \mu_b$ and take a sample of size

$$n_{\text{minimax}} \doteq .1933 \sqrt[3]{\left(\frac{k_t \sigma}{k_s}\right)^2}.$$

In our packaging example

$$n_{\text{minimax}} \doteq .1933 \sqrt[3]{\left(\$1,056,000 \times \frac{1.25}{\$30}\right)^2} = .1933 \times 1246 = 241.$$

Referring back to Figure 40.4 and looking only at the *peaks* of each curve the student can see that the height of the peaks decreases as n increases from 50 to 241 but then increases as n increases further. That $\bar{x}_c$ must be set equal to μ_b in a minimax rule is obvious, since moving $\bar{x}_c$ away from the break-even value with sample size held fixed lowers one peak of the curve but raises the other (cf. Figure 40.2) and therefore increases the *worst* conditional terminal loss without reducing the sampling cost.

    The minimax decision rule will actually be optimal if the businessman assigns probability $\frac{1}{2}$ to each of the two values

$$\mu \doteq \mu_b \pm 1.710 \sqrt[3]{\frac{k_s \sigma^2}{k_t}}$$

and 0 probability to all other values of μ,‡ and under this prior distribu-

---

† More accurately, this is the definition of the minimax-loss or minimax-regret decision rule. A minimax-cost rule can also be defined as the rule under which the worst conditional *cost* is minimized, but such rules often result in nonsensical conclusions and are of no practical interest. In our machine-setup example, the minimax-cost principle says that because the cost of readjustment is sure to be \$8 while the cost of defectives *can* be as high as \$50 if the machine is not readjusted, it *should* be readjusted even if the manufacturer has taken a sample of a million pieces without finding a single defective.

‡ In our example, the two points are

$$\mu = \mu_b + 1.710 \sqrt[3]{\$30 \times \frac{1.25^2}{\$1,056,000}} = \mu_t + 1.710 \times .0354$$
$$= +.019 + .061 = +.080,$$
$$\mu = +.019 - .061 = -.042,$$

and these are the locations of the two peaks of the curve for $n = 241$ in Figure 40.4.

tion the weighted average height of the loss curve or unconditional total loss will be equal to the height of the curve at its peak.   This height can be found from the formula

$$\text{Minimax total loss} \doteq .580 \sqrt[3]{(k_t\sigma)^2 k_s}$$

without actually drawing the entire loss curve; in our example

$$\text{Minimax total loss} \doteq .580 \sqrt[3]{(\$1,056,000 \times 1.25)^2 \times \$30}$$
$$= .580 \times \$37,400 = \$21,700.$$

Actually, of course, we are not interested in the prior distribution under which the minimax rule is strictly optimal or in the unconditional loss under this distribution.   What we are really interested in is the fact that the average height of a curve cannot be greater than the highest single point on the curve, which means that the unconditional loss of the minimax rule cannot exceed the value given by the last formula under *any conceivable* prior distribution.   This means that in problems where (1) the minimax rule is easy to find and (2) *the minimax loss is very small*, it may not be worth the effort required to improve on the minimax rule.

40.4.2   Maximum Admissible Sample Size

The *maximum admissible* sample size is the largest sample size which is optimal for *any conceivable* prior distribution given the costs or losses of the particular problem at hand.   In two-action problems with the four characteristics listed in Section 40.4.1 it can be proved that a prior distribution which assigns probability $\frac{1}{2}$ to each of the two values

$$\mu = \mu_b \pm \sqrt[3]{4e} \sqrt{\pi} \sqrt[3]{\frac{k_s\sigma^2}{k_t}}$$
$$\doteq \mu_b \pm 2.681 \sqrt[3]{\frac{k_s\sigma^2}{k_t}}$$

leads to a larger optimal sample size than any other prior distribution and that this sample size is

$$n_{\max} = \sqrt[3]{\frac{1}{2\pi e^2}} \sqrt[3]{\left(\frac{k_t\sigma}{k_s}\right)^2} \doteq .2782 \sqrt[3]{\left(\frac{k_t\sigma}{k_s}\right)^2}.$$

In our packaging example,

$$n_{\max} = .2782 \times 1246 = 347$$

and the two values of μ which must receive equal probability if this sample size is to be really optimal are

$$\mu = \mu_b + 2.681 \times .0354$$
$$= +.019 + .095 = +.114,$$
$$\mu = +.019 - .095 = -.076.$$

Looking at Figure 40.4 the student can see that these two points are near the centers of the two very narrow intervals within which a sample size of 347 does lead to lower conditional total loss than even the minimax sample size 241.

We are of course not really interested in the prior distribution for which this maximum admissible sample size is actually optimal. What is interesting is simply the fact that if we take a sample of this size we can feel *absolutely sure* that our sample is *large enough;* and in some situations it may turn out that the cost of such a sample is so low that it is not worth the trouble of deciding just how much smaller the sample really ought to be. This is scarcely true in our example, however, since a sample of size 347 will cost $30 \times 347 = \$10,400$ and it is certainly worth considerable effort to see whether this expenditure could be substantially reduced.

PROBLEMS

1. Draw curves of conditional expected terminal loss for the decision rules of Chapter 39, Problems 1*a* and *b*.

2. Use the method of Table 40.5 to compute the unconditional expected terminal loss of the rules $(10,0)$ and $(10,1)$ for the setup problem and compare your results with Table 33.3 of Section 33.3.1.

3. Draw a curve of conditional probability of error and a curve of conditional expected terminal loss for the decision rule $(100, -.002)$ applied to the packaging example.

4. Verify the assertion in Section 40.2.2 that the unconditional terminal loss of testing at the .5 level in the packaging example is $8700.

CHAPTER 41

Tests of Significance as Sequential Decision Procedures

In the last two chapters we have described and evaluated the use of tests of significance in situations where a choice between two terminal acts *must* be made after just one sample has been taken. We shall now examine the way in which these tests are used when it is *not* necessary to reach a terminal decision immediately and therefore the first question to answer after a sample has been taken is not which terminal act is better but whether another sample should be taken before definitely deciding on *either* of the terminal acts.

41.1 The Classical Theory

The classical approach to the problem of deciding whether or not to postpone terminal action after a sample has already been taken is identical in spirit to the classical approach to the problem of actually choosing a terminal act after a sample has already been taken. In both cases the choice is to be made by selecting a decision rule before even looking at the sample evidence which is actually at hand and then using this evidence according to the chosen rule.

The only classical decision rules which we have studied thus far, and the only ones which are related to tests of significance, are strictly *single-sample* decision procedures in the sense of Section 33.1.1: they specify the size of the sample and the terminal act to be taken for each possible outcome; they do *not* allow explicitly for postponement of terminal action. If our present problem is to be handled within the framework of this theory, the *only* way that it can be handled is by placing ourselves in the position in which we were *before* the present sample was actually taken and deciding what rule *should have been* chosen to give adequate control of errors of both kinds for all values of the parameter being tested. *After* this has been decided, we can proceed as follows.

1. If the sample actually taken is *smaller* than the sample called for by the chosen decision rule, terminal action should be postponed until the sample has been built up to the required size by taking additional observations.

2. If the sample actually taken is *at least equal in size* to the sample called for by the chosen rule, a terminal act should be chosen immediately in the way described in Section 39.3.3.

It is only in case 2 that a test of significance is justified in the classical theory, which treats testing the significance of an observed $\bar{x}$ at level α as simply an alternative computational device for comparing this $\bar{x}$ with the $\bar{x}_c$ of a decision rule which limits the maximum conditional probability of an error of the first kind to the specified α. It cannot be too strongly emphasized that

> In the classical theory, a test of significance is *not* a procedure for deciding whether or not to postpone terminal action; it is a procedure for choosing between terminal acts.

Now it is clearly a great nuisance to have to go through the procedure of determining what sample size is adequate for a terminal decision before being allowed to test the significance of a sample which is already at hand. It would be much nicer if we could compute the significance of the observed sample *first*, reject the null hypothesis if this significance is better (numerically smaller) than the required α, and be obliged to worry about errors of the second kind (accepting a false null hypothesis) only if the significance of the sample does not permit us to reject the null hypothesis immediately. *Such a procedure is strictly illegitimate in classical theory, however, because it completely fails to fulfill the objective of ensuring that no conditional probability of an error of the first kind exceeds the specified α.*

The reason can easily be seen by returning to the packaging example discussed in the last two chapters and supposing that μ in fact has the break-even value $+.019$ so that the null hypothesis is in fact true. If a first sample is taken and tested at any specified α, there will be probability α that this *first* test will result in erroneous rejection of the null hypothesis; and if failure to reject on the first test is followed by another sample and another test rather than by immediate acceptance of the null hypothesis, then obviously there will be an additional risk that this second test will result in erroneous rejection of the null hypothesis and the *total* risk of an error of the first kind will be greater than α.

41.2   The Traditional Practice

Tests of significance were used long before the currently classical theory of such tests was developed, and the original purpose of these tests was entirely different from their purpose according to the classical theory. This original purpose *was* to decide whether or not the sample evidence already at hand was or was not adequate to reject some null hypothesis,

and the alternative to rejection of the null hypothesis was *not* acceptance
of the null hypothesis—it was "suspension of judgment." Since "suspension of judgment" means identically the same thing as deciding to
collect more information before reaching *any* terminal decision, this
amounts to saying that tests of significance were originally conceived of as
sequential rather than single-sample decision procedures; and

> Although tests of significance are today almost always *justified* in
> terms of the classical theory of *single-sample* decision rules, they are
> actually *used* far more often as *sequential* decision rules.

An experimenter who has obtained data which support some interesting
hypothesis may withhold publication because the data are not "statistically significant," but he will rarely conclude from this fact that he must
now and forever discard this hypothesis from his mind as the classical
theory would require him to do.   On the contrary, he will continue to
regard his hypothesis as probable though "not proved," and if he can
obtain the required funds he will almost certainly go on to conduct
another experiment to obtain additional evidence in its support.

How this additional evidence is to be used seems to be a matter of
dispute among statisticians.   Common sense would seem to say that any
decision should be reached by looking at *all* the evidence which is available when the decision is made; and this would seem to imply very clearly
that if a test of significance is to be made after a second sample has been
taken, this test should be applied, not to the second sample by itself, but to
the pooled sample formed by combining all the observations made to
date.   This was in fact the generally accepted practice before the classical
theory of tests of significance became prevalent, but some statisticians
who adhere to the classical theory hold that the second sample should be
tested separately.   Actually of course *neither* procedure is legitimate in
terms of the classical theory because, as we saw at the end of the previous
section, the conditional probabilities of wrong decisions and particularly
the maximum conditional probability of an error of the first kind are
unknown and uncontrolled under *both* procedures.

If it were impossible to compute the true conditional probabilities
of wrong decisions under a sequential decision procedure, the use of tests
of significance as sequential procedures might be defended as a device for
securing at least order-of-magnitude control of these conditional probabilities.   In fact, however, it is perfectly possible to compute the exact
conditional probabilities of wrong decisions under any sequential decision
rule and thus to describe the performance of sequential rules by curves
of exactly the same kind that we used in Figures 39.1, 39.2, 39.4, 39.6,
and 40.3 to describe the performance of single-sample rules.   Suppose,
for example, that the marketer of the example discussed in the last two
chapters proposes to proceed as follows:

Take a sample of size $n_1 = 100$ and definitely accept the new package if the mean of this sample $\bar{x}_1 \geq +.200$ or definitely reject it if $\bar{x}_1 \leq -.200$. If, however, $-.200 < \bar{x}_1 < +.200$, take a second sample of size $n_2 = 100$ and accept the new package if the mean of this second sample $\bar{x}_2 > +.019$, reject it if $\bar{x}_2 \leq +.019$.

The conditional probability given any specified μ that this rule will lead to rejection of the new package is the *sum* of (1) the probability that the new package will be rejected on the basis of the *first* sample, plus (2) the joint probability that the first sample will lead to taking a second sample *and* this second sample will lead to rejection of the new package:

$$P(\bar{x} \leq -2.00|\mu) + P(-.200 < \bar{x}_1 < +.200|\mu) \times P(\bar{x}_2 \leq +.019|\mu).$$

The results of computations of this kind or their equivalent are actually used in selecting decision rules or "sampling plans" for use in quality control. In other areas, however—and particularly in "scientific" work where the consequence of a wrong decision will presumably be much more serious than the consequence of erroneous acceptance or rejection of a single lot of nuts and bolts—tests of significance continue to be used as the standard procedure for deciding whether or not judgment should be suspended and more evidence collected before a terminal decision is reached despite the fact that this means that the conditional probabilities of wrong terminal acts are completely unknown.

41.3 The Common Sense of Tests of Significance

It would seem quite justified to conclude that very few practicing statisticians really believe that decisions should be reached by looking at the conditional probabilities of wrong terminal decisions under various decision rules, and anyone who has ever actually tried to choose a decision rule by looking at such conditional probabilities may well sympathize with this attitude. The use which is actually made of tests of significance must be explained in some other way, and we suggest that the explanation is this:

Most *users* of tests of significance are intuitively interpreting statistical significance in a way which accords perfectly with Bayesian theory but not at all with the classical theory by which they formally justify their procedures.

A person responsible for a decision does not care about the *conditional* probabilities of making the wrong decision given each and every possible value of the basic random variable, but he may be very much interested in the *unconditional probability that the best terminal decision that he can make in the light of the evidence currently available will turn out to be wrong after the event.* If *this* probability is very small, he will want to make an immediate terminal decision; if it is large, he will want to collect more information before making any terminal decision; and we shall now see that *under certain conditions* this probability or a very good approximation to it is given by the "statistical significance" of a sample.

41.3.1 *Statistical Significance and Posterior Probability When the Sampling Distribution Is Normal*

If before taking any sample the marketer of our packaging example assigns to the basic random variable $\tilde{\mu}$ a Normal probability distribution with mean $E_0(\tilde{\mu})$ and "information" $I_0 = 1/\sigma_0^2(\tilde{\mu})$, then after the sample has been taken and $\bar{x}$ computed he is logically obliged (Section 30.3) to replace his original distribution of $\tilde{\mu}$ by a new Normal distribution with mean and information

$$E_1(\tilde{\mu}) = \frac{I_0\, E_0(\tilde{\mu}) + I_{\bar{x}}\bar{x}}{I_0 + I_{\bar{x}}},$$
$$I_1 = I_0 + I_{\bar{x}}.$$

If, however, he feels that his prior information I_0 is negligible in comparison with the information $I_{\bar{x}}$ provided by the sample—i.e., if the variance of his prior distribution is very large compared with the sampling variance of $\bar{x}$—then (Section 30.3.3) he will make no appreciable error by treating I_0 as if it were flatly 0 and assigning to $\tilde{\mu}$ a Normal distribution with mean and information

$$E_1(\tilde{\mu}) = \bar{x},$$
$$I_1 = I_{\bar{x}},$$

i.e. *with mean equal to the observed $\bar{x}$ and standard deviation equal to the standard deviation of $\bar{x}$.*

In Figure 41.1 we show two distributions which are conceptually entirely different: the upper one is the *conditional distribution of the statistic $\bar{x}$ given $\tilde{\mu} = \mu_b$*; the lower one is the *posterior distribution of the basic random variable $\tilde{\mu}$ given the observed statistic $\bar{x}$*. In the upper distribution the shaded tail represents $P(\bar{x} \geq \bar{x}|\mu_b)$, the *statistical significance* of the observed $\bar{x}$ as defined in Section 39.3.3. In the lower distribution the shaded tail represents $P(\tilde{\mu} < \mu_b)$, the *posterior probability of error* if we act on the assumption that $\tilde{\mu} > \mu_b$ in accordance with the available evidence. Since both distributions have the same standard deviation and since all Normal distributions are symmetric, we see that

> When prior information on the basic random variable is negligible in comparison with the information obtained from a Normally distributed sample mean, the unconditional posterior probability that

μ is *not* on the same side of μ_b as $\bar{x}$ is *numerically equal* to the statistical significance of the observed sample mean.

Let us work out these probabilities numerically using the data assumed in our discussion of this example in Chapters 39 and 40:

$$\mu_b = +.019, \qquad \bar{x} = +.157, \qquad \sigma(\bar{x}) = .125.$$

To find the *statistical significance* of the observed $\bar{x}$ we compute

$$\frac{\bar{x} - \mu_b}{\sigma(\bar{x})} = \frac{+.157 - .019}{.125} = +1.10,$$

$$P(\bar{\bar{x}} > \bar{x} | \tilde{\mu} = \mu_b) = P_N(\tilde{u} > +1.10) = .14.$$

To find the *posterior probability* that $\tilde{\mu}$ is below μ_b we compute

$$\frac{\mu_b - E_1(\tilde{\mu})}{\sigma_1(\tilde{\mu})} = \frac{\mu_b - \bar{x}}{\sigma(\bar{x})} = \frac{+.019 - .157}{.125} = -1.10,$$

$$P(\tilde{\mu} < \mu_b) = P_N(\tilde{u} < -1.10) = .14.$$

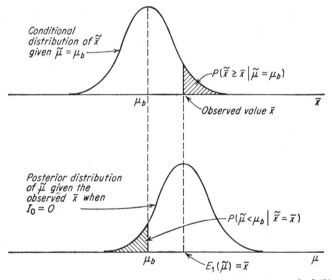

Figure 41.1. Statistical significance and posterior probability.

Observe that these computations have no relevance whatever to the problem of deciding which terminal act is better given the existing information—because the sample evidence favors the new package and prior evidence is negligible, it is *obvious* that the new package should be chosen if a definite choice is to be made at all. What the computations *do* show that is of real interest is that *if* the new package is definitely chosen now, there is probability roughly .14 that this decision will be proved wrong after the event, and therefore it *may* pay to collect more information before definitely choosing *either* package.

To see how large an error has been made in these computations by neglecting the marketer's prior information, which was represented by a Normal distribution with mean and standard deviation

$$E_0(\tilde{\mu}) = +.146, \qquad \sigma_0(\tilde{\mu}) = .310,$$

we compute

$$I_1 = I_0 + I_{\bar{x}} = \frac{1}{.310^2} + \frac{1}{.125^2} = 10.4 + 64.0 = 74.4,$$

$$\sigma_1(\tilde{\mu}) = \frac{1}{\sqrt{74.4}} = .116,$$

$$E_1(\tilde{\mu}) = \frac{10.4 \times .146 + 64.0 \times .157}{74.4} = .155,$$

$$\frac{\mu_b - E_1(\tilde{\mu})}{\sigma_1(\tilde{\mu})} = \frac{.019 - .155}{.116} = -1.17,$$

$$P(\tilde{\mu} < \mu_b) = P_N(\tilde{u} < -1.17) = .12.$$

Consideration of the prior evidence thus makes the marketer a little less uncertain about the rightness of adopting the new package, but the difference is small. The marketer still has some reason to think that it might be better to collect more evidence before reaching *any* terminal decision.

"Symmetric" Tests of Significance. Suppose next that instead of yielding a sample mean $\bar{x} = +.157$ which was $.157 - .019 = .138$ unit *above* the break-even value, the marketer's sample had yielded a mean $\bar{x} = -.119$ which was $-.119 - .019 = -.138$ unit *below* the break-even value. If the marketer considers his prior information to be negligible in comparison with the sample information, then it is completely obvious (1) that the better immediate choice would be the *old* package and (2) that the marketer's uncertainty about the correctness of this choice should be exactly the same as in the original example. In other words, the probability that the better act under uncertainty will actually be the wrong act is now

$$P(\tilde{\mu} > \mu_b | \bar{x} = -.138),$$

and if prior information is discarded this posterior probability will be numerically equal to the conditional probability

$$P(\tilde{\bar{x}} < -.138 | \mu = \mu_b) = .14.$$

This conditional probability is the statistical significance of the observed sample mean against the hypothesis that μ is *greater* than μ_b rather than the original null hypothesis that μ is *less* than μ_b, and it is thus quite clear that we should *not* select one of the two hypotheses as the "null" hypothesis and then compute the statistical significance of the sample evidence against this arbitrarily selected null hypothesis however the sample comes out. In common sense,

> Statistical significance is a more or less accurate measure of our uncertainty about the correctness of *whichever hypothesis seems more likely to be true,* and statistical significance should be computed so that it *does* measure this uncertainty.

In problems of the kind we are now studying, i.e. in problems where what we want to know is whether some quantity is above or below a break-even value, this means that the two hypotheses must be treated *symmetrically—neither* one should be singled out as a "null" hypothesis. The probability that the terminal act which *looks* better in the light of the sample information is *actually* wrong is always given by

$$P_N(\tilde{u} > D_1),$$

where D_1 is the standardized *absolute* difference between μ_b and $E_1(\tilde{\mu})$:

$$D_1 = \frac{|\mu_b - E_1(\tilde{\mu})|}{\sigma_1(\tilde{\mu})}.$$

The statistical significance of the sample should similarly be defined by looking at the standardized *absolute* difference between the observed $\bar{x}$ and μ_b,

$$|u| = \frac{|\bar{x} - \mu_b|}{\sigma(\bar{x})},$$

and computing the conditional probability

$$P_N(\tilde{u} > |u|).$$

41.3.2   Other Sampling Distributions

A general discussion of the relation between posterior probability and statistical significance in situations where the test statistic is *not* Normally distributed is beyond the scope of this course, but the fact that the two will be *nearly* equal when prior information is slight relative to sample information can be illustrated rather than proved by looking at the case where the basic random variable is the parameter $\tilde{p}$ of a Bernoulli process and therefore the test statistic $\tilde{r}$ has a binomial distribution.

In this case $\tilde{p}$ must have a value between 0 and 1 inclusive, and a person who feels that he knew virtually nothing about the value of $\tilde{p}$ before the sample was taken *may* decide to adopt a prior distribution which asserts that all values between 0 and 1 were equally likely before the sample was taken. Given this prior distribution, the *posterior* probability to be assigned to the hypothesis that $\tilde{p}$ is below any specified value p_b after observing r successes in a sample of n can be shown to be numerically equal to the binomial probability

$$P_b(\tilde{r} \geq r + 1 | n + 1, p_b).$$

This is *not* strictly equal to the probability

$$P_b(\tilde{r} \geq r | n, p_b)$$

which measures the *statistical significance* of the statistic r against the hypothesis that $\tilde{p} < p_b$, but if both r and n are reasonably large the two probabilities will be *nearly* even though not exactly equal. Taking $p_b = .5$, $r = 55$, $n = 100$ as an example, we find that the statistical significance is .18 whereas the posterior probability that $\tilde{p} < p_b$ is .16. If 65 successes had been observed rather than 55, the significance would have been .0018 while the posterior probability would have been .0013.

41.3.3   The Proper Level for a Sequential Test of Significance

When a sample is taken simply in order to obtain background information in some problem area and no specific terminal acts have been defined, an exact or even a rough calculation of the posterior probability that the less likely hypothesis is in fact true is often a very adequate basis for deciding whether or not more sample evidence should be collected. Suppose, for example, that in order to obtain basic information for use in redesigning his package our marketer had conducted a consumer survey in which he showed 100 housewives two packages, one with a red label and one with a green label, and had simply asked each housewife which color she preferred; and suppose that 65 per cent of the respondents had preferred the red label. We have already seen that the statistical significance of this sample result is

$$P_b(\tilde{r} \geq 65 | n = 100, p = .5) = .0018,$$

and we have also seen that unless the marketer had strong convictions before the sample was taken he can immediately conclude that there are roughly only one or two chances in a thousand that an infinitely large sample taken in this same way would show a majority preference for the green label. This probability is so low that it strongly indicates that further sampling on this particular question in this particular way would be a waste of money, and the whole inquiry is so loosely related to the ultimate choice of a specific package and the effect of this specific package on sales that computation of posterior costs or losses would be a waste of time and effort.

Even when terminal acts *are* well defined and conditional costs and losses are known, a simple computation of statistical significance will often indicate very clearly that further sampling is unnecessary. Suppose, for example, that the sample mean in our original packaging example had indicated that the new package would increase sales by

$$\bar{x} = +.500$$

ounce per store per month. The statistical significance of this statistic is

$$P(\tilde{x} > +.5|\mu = +.019) = P_N\left(\tilde{u} > \frac{.500 - .019}{.125}\right) = .00006,$$

and as soon as we see this number we can conclude that no matter what halfway reasonable *prior* distribution the marketer assigns to $\tilde{\mu}$ the *posterior* probability that $\tilde{\mu}$ is less than μ_b will be totally negligible. Given this sample result, the marketer could immediately decide that further sampling was unnecessary without going to the trouble of assigning a specific prior distribution to $\tilde{\mu}$ and then computing the exact posterior distribution of $\tilde{\mu}$ and the posterior expected loss of adopting the new package.

Observe, however, that it is only when the statistical significance of the observed sample is an *extremely* small number that this informal kind of reasoning will suffice if substantial losses may be incurred by choosing the wrong terminal act. If in such a situation there is any real doubt about the true value of $\tilde{\mu}$, we *must* bring costs explicitly into the picture in the way described in Part Four of this course; it is *not* possible to make reasonable decisions by simply comparing the statistical significance of the observed sample with a completely arbitrary traditional number such as .05 or .01.

We have already seen (Chapter 40) how these traditional numbers can lead to a really serious "cost of irrationality" when tests of significance are used as a basis for choice between two terminal acts; to see how far they may be from the correct criterion for a choice between further sampling and immediate terminal action, let us continue our analysis of the packaging example on the assumption that the marketer regards his prior information as negligible in comparison with the sample information and therefore assigns to $\tilde{\mu}$ a Normal posterior distribution with parameters

$$E(\tilde{\mu}) = \bar{x} = +.157,$$
$$\sigma(\tilde{\mu}) = \sigma(\tilde{x}) = .125.$$

If the marketer feels that he must settle his packaging problem reasonably soon and therefore has decided that he will take *at most one* more sample, we can use the method of Chapter 35 to decide whether or not another sample should be taken. Assuming as before that $\sigma(\tilde{\beta}) = 0$ and remembering that the distribution of $\tilde{\mu} = \xi$ posterior to the sample already taken is the prior distribution as regards a *new* sample, we have (Section 35.2)

$$\sigma_\epsilon^* = \sigma(\tilde{\epsilon}) = s = 1.25, \qquad \sigma_\infty(\tilde{E}_1) = \sigma_0(\tilde{\mu}) = .125,$$

$$Z = \frac{.125}{1.25} \sqrt[3]{\frac{\$1,056,000 \times 1.25}{\$30}} = .1 \times 35.3 = 3.53,$$

$$D_\infty = \frac{|.019 - .157|}{.125} = 1.10.$$

Looking at Figure 35.4, we see that when $D_\infty = 1.10$ no sample should be taken unless Z is greater than 3.73; and therefore in our present example *no additional sample should be taken* even though the sample already taken is "not significant" at even the .05 level (cf. Section 41.3.1), let alone the .01 which is supposed to be used for really important decisions.

41.4 Null Hypotheses and Errors of the Third Kind

Someone has remarked that the most serious statistical error of all is neither an error of the second kind nor yet one of the first but the error of the third kind which occurs when the statistician delivers a carefully computed solution of the wrong problem. We shall now examine two different errors of the third kind which are very frequently made in analyzing problems of the sort typified by our packaging example—i.e., *two-action problems with linear costs.*

41.4.1 "Null" Values vs. Break-even Values

In analyzing the packaging example the first step we took was to compute the break-even value μ_b for which the two acts under consideration were *equally* profitable. We then defined the statistical significance of the sample mean $\bar{x}$ as a conditional probability *given this break-even value μ_b,*

$$P_N(\tilde{u} > |u|), \qquad |u| = \frac{|\bar{x} - \mu_b|}{\sigma(\bar{\tilde{x}})},$$

and showed that if prior information was negligible in comparison with the information in the sample, then because the conditional costs of the two terminal acts were linear functions of μ

1. The better terminal act could be chosen by simply comparing $\bar{x}$ with μ_b—no test of significance was needed for this purpose (Section 40.2.2);
2. The statistical significance of the sample measured the probability that the act thus chosen would be proved wrong after the event (Section 41.3.1).

The essence of this example lies in the fact that profit is a *linear* function of the increased *yield* (sales) which will result from a new *treatment* (package design). In other situations a sample will be taken or an experiment conducted to obtain evidence on the effect of a new fertilizer on crop yield, on the effect of a new drug on the fraction of patients cured, or on any of an infinity of formally similar questions; and in very many problems of this sort the conditional profits of the two terminal acts will be at least approximately linear functions of the yield. This is true of the effect of a new fertilizer, where crop yield has an obviously linear relation to monetary profit. It is equally true in the case of the new drug, where "profit" is measured directly by the cure rate and does not have to be translated into monetary units.

In all such problems the better act can be chosen by a direct comparison of $\bar{x}$ with μ_b when prior information is negligible; but in many situations the person who takes the sample or conducts the experiment will not even know the person or persons who will ultimately use his data to choose a package design, fertilizer, or drug; and this means that the person who obtains the data *cannot* compute the break-even value or values for the decision or decisions which may be based on this data.† In such situations it is traditional for the sampler or experimenter to test the null hypothesis that the new treatment *does not increase the "yield" at all*—i.e., to use 0 in place of a break-even value and define the two hypotheses as

Null: $\mu \leq 0$ (new treatment does not increase yield),
Alternate: $\mu > 0$ (new treatment increases yield).

The statistical significance of the observed $\bar{x}$ is accordingly defined as

$$P(\tilde{\bar{x}} > \bar{x}|\mu = 0) = P_N\left[\tilde{u} > \frac{\bar{x} - 0}{\sigma(\tilde{\bar{x}})}\right],$$

and it is often argued that statistical significance computed in this way *is* a legitimate basis for an immediate *choice between terminal acts*. The argument runs that changing over from the old to the new treatment will involve *some* change-over cost (possibly nonmonetary‡) and that testing the null hypothesis $\mu \leq 0$ at some level such as .05 or .01 protects the decision maker against making the change when μ is actually greater than 0 but by an amount too small to pay for the change-over.

Now it is perfectly true that such a test conducted at any level below .5 does afford protection against uneconomic change-overs, but it is equally true that *use of an arbitrarily chosen level such as .05 or .01 is almost certain to result in either too little or too much protection.* To see why

---

† A break-even value will usually exist even in examples where "profit" is not measured in monetary units. If for example a new drug has dangerous side effects, a doctor might prefer not to use it even though it did increase the cure rate by some small amount. A certain definite increase in the cure rate would be needed simply to offset the risk of side effects, and there would be a "net" profit only if the increase in the cure rate exceeded this break-even increase.

‡ See previous footnote.

this is true, we have only to return to our packaging example and see how we would have to compute the *correct* level for a test of significance of this kind. Assuming that prior information is negligible, we already know that a reasonable man will change over to the new package if $\bar{x}$ is greater than $+.019$. If $\bar{x}$ is *equal* to $+.019$, then the statistical significance of $\bar{x}$ against the hypothesis $\mu \leq 0$ is

$$P(\bar{x} > +.019|\mu = 0) = P_N\left[\tilde{u} > \frac{+.019}{\sigma(\bar{x})}\right],$$

so that if $\bar{x}$ is *greater* than $+.019$ the statistical significance will be *less* than

$$\alpha^* = P_N\left[\tilde{u} > \frac{+.019}{\sigma(\bar{x})}\right].$$

In other words, *α^* as given by this last formula is the economically correct level for a test of significance used as the basis for a choice between terminal acts*, and we see at once that the *correct* level for such a test

1. Cannot be determined unless we first determine the break-even value μ_b,
2. Depends not only on μ_b but also on $\sigma(\bar{x}) = \sigma(\bar{\epsilon})/\sqrt{n}$ and thus on the sample size n.

If μ_b has to be computed in order to make a rational choice between acts and if the choice can then be made by simply comparing $\bar{x}$ with μ_b, it is clearly doing things the hard way to compute α^* and then conduct a test of significance at level α^* in order to arrive at the same result. It is out of sheer curiosity that we show in Table 41.1 the value of α^* in our

Table 41.1

n	$\sigma(\bar{x}) = \dfrac{1.25}{\sqrt{n}}$	$u = \dfrac{+.019}{\sigma(\bar{x})}$	$\alpha^* = P_N(\tilde{u} > u)$
25	.2500	.076	.47
100	.1250	.152	.44
400	.0625	.304	.38
1,600	.0312	.608	.27
11,707	.0116	1.645	.05

packaging example for each of several arbitrarily chosen sample sizes and also for the one sample size $n = 11,707$ which justifies a test at the traditional .05 level.

41.4.2 *"Point" Null Hypotheses and "Two-tail" Significance*

The error of the third kind discussed in the previous section consisted essentially in thinking that testing significance at some arbitrarily chosen level can replace calculation of the true economic break-even value.

Another very common error of the third kind consists in confusing the problem of deciding whether some quantity is *greater or less* than a specified value with the problem of deciding whether the quantity *is or is not exactly equal* to the specified value.

As an example of a problem where we really do want to know whether a parameter is or is not exactly equal to some specified value, consider the problem of deciding whether or not an individual is gifted with extra-sensory perception. An experiment might be conducted by tossing a coin repeatedly and on each toss allowing a "sender" to see which face is up and then asking a "receiver" in the next room to say which face is up. In this problem one hypothesis will be that the sender has no effect on the receiver and that the receiver's guesses are right or wrong purely by chance; the other hypothesis will be that the receiver's guesses *are* affected by what the sender sees and therefore that the receiver will do either better than chance or, conceivably, worse than chance if the astral wires are crossed. Before the currently classical theory of testing hypotheses was developed, the former of these two hypotheses would always have been called the *null* hypothesis because it asserts that the person tested has *no* extrasensory perception; and although classical theory says that the hypothesis that the person tested *does* have extrasensory perception should be considered as the null hypothesis if the consequence of rejecting this hypothesis when true is more serious than the consequence of accepting it when false, we shall label the hypotheses in the traditional manner. Letting p denote the long-run fraction of correct guesses, we take as our two statistical hypotheses

Null: $p = \frac{1}{2}$,
Alternate: $p \neq \frac{1}{2}$.

We note in passing that it is this kind of problem which explains the word "null": the null hypothesis asserts that the sender has *no* effect on the receiver.

If the null hypothesis is *true*, the expected number of correct guesses in a sample of n guesses is $\frac{1}{2}n$, and it is clear that we will want to reject the null hypothesis if the actual number r of correct guesses is very far from $\frac{1}{2}n$ *in either direction*. Letting d_c denote the smallest discrepancy between the actual and the expected number of correct guesses which is to be considered "very far," a reasonable decision rule will be of the form

Take a sample of size n and reject the null hypothesis if *either* $r \leq (\frac{1}{2}n - d_c)$ *or* $r \geq (\frac{1}{2}n + d_c)$.

The probability of an error of the first kind under such a rule will be the *sum of two* binomial tail probabilities,

$$P_b(\tilde{r} \leq \tfrac{1}{2}n - d_c | p = .5) + P_b(\tilde{r} \geq \tfrac{1}{2}n + d_c | p = .5),$$

and if the conditional probabilities of errors of the second kind are to be minimized subject to a limitation α on the conditional probability of an error of the first kind, d_c must be made as *small* as it can be made without causing the sum of the two tail probabilities to exceed α. If for example the sample is of size $n = 100$ and α has been set at .05, d_c would be set equal to 11 because

$$P(\tilde{r} \leq 39 | n = 100, p = .5) + P(\tilde{r} \geq 61 | n = 100, p = .5) = .0352$$
$$< .05$$

while

$$P(\tilde{r} \leq 40 | n = 100, p = .5) + P(\tilde{r} \geq 60 | n = 100, p = .5) = .0568$$
$$> .05.$$

The argument is illustrated by the graph of the conditional distribution of $\tilde{r}$ given $n = 100$, $p = \frac{1}{2}$, which is shown as Figure 41.2. The shaded area corresponding to the values of r which will lead to rejection of the null hypothesis is .0352; if one more bar were added to each tail, the area would be .0568 and would exceed the required $\alpha = .05$.

As usual, a test of significance can be used instead of actually determining the critical value d_c which yields the required α, but the significance of the sample must be computed in the same way that the probability that d_c will be equaled or exceeded by pure chance is computed. Since the null hypothesis will be rejected if r is very far from $\frac{1}{2}n$ *in either direction*, the test statistic is really not r but

$$d = |\tfrac{1}{2}n - r|;$$

and looking at Figure 41.2 we see that if the *sum*

$$P_b(\tilde{r} \leq \tfrac{1}{2}n - d | p = .5) + P_b(\tilde{r} \geq \tfrac{1}{2}n + d | p = .5)$$

is *greater* than α, then d itself must be *less* than d_c and the null hypothesis is to be accepted; if this sum is less than or equal to α, then d must be at least as great as d_c and the null hypothesis is to be rejected. This sum is known as the *two-tail significance* of the observed sample to distinguish it from the *one-tail significance* which is appropriate when we wish to know whether a quantity is *above* or *below* some specified value.

The error of the third kind to which we referred at the beginning of this section consists in treating problems like our setup and packaging examples as if they did involve a "point" null hypothesis asserting that $p = .04$ exactly or $\mu = +.019$ exactly. The error is obvious without argument: if we asked the businessman faced with either of these problems how much he would pay to learn for certain whether or not $p = .04$ or $\mu = +.019$ exactly, he would tell us very clearly that this information is totally worthless.

1. It is flatly incredible before any sample is taken that $p = .04$

exactly or that $\mu = +.019$ *exactly.* The prior probability which a reasonable man will attach to such a hypothesis is zero.

2. Even if such an amazing accident were not regarded as virtually impossible, learning that p or μ is *not* equal to the specified value without learning whether it is above or below this value is of no help in choosing the better act, while learning that it *is* equal to the specified value means simply that it makes no difference which act is chosen. The hypotheses

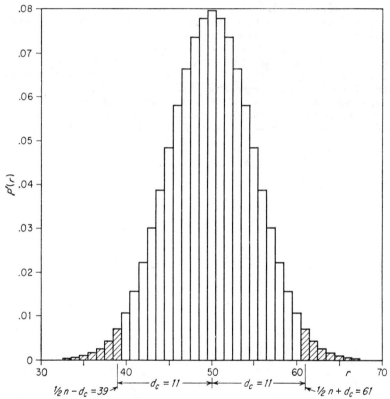

Figure 41.2. Conditional distribution of $\tilde{r}$, given $p = .5$ $(n = 100)$.

in terms of which the problem was stated do not express the true nature of the problem.

Observe that the problem of extrasensory perception differs from the setup and packaging problems in *both* these respects.

1. A reasonable person might well attach a substantial *prior probability* to the proposition that the phenomenon does not exist and therefore to the hypothesis that $p = \frac{1}{2}$ *exactly.*

2. Any difference whatever between $\frac{1}{2}$ and the true value of p implies that extrasensory perception does exist,† and therefore it would

† Unless it implies that the experiment has been poorly designed or conducted.

be extremely interesting and important to learn of the *mere existence of such a difference* regardless of its amount or direction.

PROBLEMS

1. In the situation of Chapter 30, Problem 1*a* to *c*, assuming that management decides that its prior information is negligible in comparison with the information gained from the pilot sample of 100 observations and assuming that further sampling will cost $25 per observation:

   a. Determine by use of Figure 35.4 the proper level at which to test the significance of the pilot sample if the test is to be used as a *sequential* decision procedure. (HINT: Given the value of Z as computed after the pilot sample has been taken, which values of D_∞ would make further sampling desirable and which would not?)

   b. What is the proper level at which to test the significance of the pilot sample if the test is to be used as a *single-sample* decision procedure?

   c. Compute the significance of the mean of the pilot sample actually taken.

2. Same as Problem 1 above for the situation of Chapter 32, Problem 4*a*, with a variable sampling cost of $100 per observation but with *no* fixed sampling cost.

CHAPTER 42

Confidence Intervals

In the last three chapters we have examined the classical approach to the use of sample information in clearly defined two-action problems. In this final chapter we shall examine the classical approach to the problem of reporting sample information on the value of some unknown quantity when the person reporting the information does not know the use to which the information will ultimately be put or when he knows that the same information will be put to many different uses by many different people. It is obvious that merely reporting one specific number as a best estimate of the value of the unknown quantity will not be satisfactory in such a situation, since any such estimate will almost certainly differ by some amount from the true value of the quantity being estimated and the user of the estimate will want some indication of its reliability. The classical solution to this problem is to report a band of possible values of the unknown quantity rather than a single value and in addition to quote a number which purports to measure the "confidence" which the user may place in the proposition that the true value actually lies within the reported band or "interval."

42.1 The Theory of Confidence Intervals

Formally, the classical school regards the problem of "estimating" the value of an unknown quantity as one of *making a statement* about this quantity in such a way that *the "objective" probability that the statement will be correct is known.* To make the discussion concrete, let us assume that the unknown quantity is the parameter p of a Bernoulli process and that a researcher has observed 11 successes in a sample of 20 observations from this process. The statement which the researcher should make according to classical theory is an assertion that p is *greater* than some number p_1 and/or *less* than some number p_2; and in principle the numbers p_1 and/or p_2 should be computed in such a way that if the researcher were to draw a very large number of samples from this same process and make similar statements on the basis of the number of successes observed in each sample, he could be sure that *some specified fraction of all these statements would be right in the long run.*

It turns out that this objective can be *fully* achieved only by introducing a very peculiar step into the computation of p_1 and p_2, a step so peculiar that most practicing statisticians refuse to take it and instead compute the numbers p_1 and p_2 in such a way that all they can be sure of is that *at least* the specified fraction of statements would be right in the long run.   We shall begin our explanation of the classical procedure by showing how this limited objective is accomplished when the statistician wishes to state merely that p is *greater* than some definite number p_1; and to simplify the argument we shall restate the objective as making sure that *not more than* a specified fraction γ_1 of all statements would be *wrong*. What we shall show is that

> If the statistician draws a large number of samples from the *same population*, if on each occasion he determines the value p_1 for which the conditional probability $P_b(\tilde{r} \geq r | p = p_1)$ is just equal to the specified number γ_1, and if on each occasion he then states that p *is greater than* p_1, the fraction of all such statements which will be incorrect *will not exceed* γ_1.

To see why this is true, let us imagine that the statistician sets $\gamma_1 = .05$ and then draws a very large number of samples all of size $n = 20$ from a Bernoulli process, and let us examine the statements he will make when his sample contains 10, 11, or 12 successes.   When he draws 10 successes he will interpolate in the binomial tables to find that

$$P_b(\tilde{r} \geq 10 | n = 20, p = .302) = .05$$

and he will state that p *is greater than* .302.   When he draws 11 successes he will find that

$$P_b(\tilde{r} \geq 11 | n = 20, p = .347) = .05$$

and he will state that p *is greater than* .347.   When he draws 12, he will find that

$$P_b(\tilde{r} \geq 12 | n = 20, p = .393) = .05$$

and he will state that p *is greater than* .393.   Observe that the lower limit above which the statistician asserts that the true value of p actually lies increases as the number of successes in the sample increases.

Now suppose first that the true value of p in this population is in fact .393.   Whenever the statistician draws 11 *or less* successes, he will state that p is greater than .347 or some *lower* number and all these statements will be *right*.   Whenever he draws 12 *or more* successes, he will state that p is greater than .393 or some *higher* number and all these statements will be *wrong*.   He will *actually draw* 12 or more successes in a fraction

$$P_b(\tilde{r} \geq 12 | n = 20, p = .393) = .05$$

of all samples, and therefore exactly .05 of his statements will be wrong.

Suppose next that the true value of p is below .393 but not so low as .347. In this case the statistician will still make erroneous statements when and only when he draws 12 or more successes, but he will actually draw 12 or more successes somewhat *less* than .05 of the time. If, for example, the true value of p is .35, he will draw 12 or more successes and make an erroneous statement on only

$$P_b(\tilde{r} \geq 12 | n = 20, p = .35) = .0196$$

of all occasions.

Finally, suppose that the true value of p is exactly .347. In this case the statistician will make an erroneous statement whenever he draws *eleven* or more successes and the fraction of wrong statements jumps back to .05 exactly.

The *general* way in which the procedure will work should now be clear. If p is below .347 but not so low as .302, errors will occur whenever 11 or more successes are drawn and this will happen on *less* than .05 of all draws. If $p = .302$ exactly, errors will occur whenever *ten* or more successes are drawn and this will happen on *exactly* .05 of all draws; and so forth. We conclude that the method we have described does make it possible for the statistician to make statements in such a way that *not more than* the specified fraction γ_1 of all statements would be wrong in the long run, although it does *not* assure him that *exactly* this fraction of the statements would be wrong in the long run.

Turning next to the second form of statement, the student can easily modify the argument used above to show that

> If the statistician draws a large number of samples from the *same population*, if on each occasion he computes the value p_2 for which the *left-tail* conditional probability $P_b(\tilde{r} \leq r | p = p_2)$ is just equal to some specified number γ_2, and if on each occasion he then states that p *is less than* p_2, the fraction of all such statements which will be incorrect *will not exceed* γ_2.

If a statistician sets $\gamma_2 = .05$ and then observes 11 successes in a sample of 20, he will find that

$$P_b(\tilde{r} \leq 11 | n = 20, p = .741) = .05$$

and he can assert that p *is less than* .741 with the assurance that not more than .05 of all statements computed in this same manner would be wrong in the long run.

Finally, let us consider what will happen if the statistician computes both p_1 and p_2 according to the rules given above and then combines both assertions into a single assertion that p is greater than p_1 *and* less than p_2. If the sum of the specified numbers γ_1 and γ_2 is less than 1—and in practice the sum is always made *much* less than 1—then it is easy to see that p_1 as calculated for any given sample *must* be less than p_2 as calculated for that same sample and the combined statement that p is greater than p_1 and less than p_2 can then be expressed as an assertion that p is *between* p_1 and p_2.   When this is true, the two individual statements cannot *both* be wrong on any one occasion—if $p_1 < p_2$, then p cannot be simultaneously below p_1 and above p_2—and therefore the probability that the combined statement will be wrong is simply the sum of the two probabilities that each of the two separate parts will be wrong.   While these two probabilities are not known exactly, we do know that they do not exceed γ_1 and γ_2 respectively; and therefore we know that the probability that the combined statement will be wrong does not exceed $\gamma = \gamma_1 + \gamma_2$.   The statistician who sets $\gamma_1 = .05$, $\gamma_2 = .05$, observes 11 successes in a sample of 20 and asserts that p *is greater than* .347 *but less than* .741 can be sure that *not more than* .05 + .05 = .1 of all statements computed in this same manner would be wrong in the long run.

Assertions about an unknown parameter made in the way we have just described are known in the classical literature as *confidence intervals*. A statement that $p > p_1$ or a statement that $p < p_2$ is a *one-sided* confidence interval; a statement that $p_1 < p < p_2$ is a *two-sided* confidence interval.   Whenever such a confidence-interval statement is made, it is accompanied by an indication of the limiting conditional probabilities γ_1 and/or γ_2 which were used in its computation, but these numbers are not usually quoted directly.   Instead, they are subtracted from 1 and the statistician will assert that $p > p_1$ *with confidence* $1 - \gamma_1$ or that $p < p_2$ *with confidence* $1 - \gamma_2$ or that $p_1 < p < p_2$ *with confidence* $1 - \gamma_1 - \gamma_2$.   Thus observing 11 successes in a sample of 20 Bernoulli trials would lead to a statement that p *is between* .347 *and* .741 *with confidence* .90.

We have already emphasized that when confidence intervals are computed in the way described above the stated confidence level does *not* actually tell us the relative frequency with which a large number of similar statements would be right in the long run; all that we know is that *at least* the stated fraction of all such statements would be correct.   Not a few statisticians have been so troubled by the problem of deciding what it means to be "at least" 90 per cent confident about anything at all that they have seriously proposed that after the numbers p_1 and/or p_2 have been computed from the sample data in the way described above they should be arbitrarily altered in such a way that the statistician *can* be sure that he would make exactly the specified fraction of errors in the long run and therefore that the long-run fraction of correct statements, would be exactly equal to the stated confidence level.   The amounts by which the two numbers must be altered to achieve this objective can be determined in a most ingenious way by drawing numbers from a table of random numbers, but since a businessman will probably find it very hard to understand how a table of random numbers can possibly tell him anything at all about the number of people who prefer red labels to green, the procedure will not be described in this course.

The fact that it is necessary to make completely arbitrary alterations in the values of p_1 and/or p_2 as determined from the sample evidence in order to be objectively sure that the specified fraction of all statements will be correct in the long run would seem to be a fairly serious objection to this whole approach, but it is by no means the most serious objection. What is much more serious is the fact that it is impossible under this approach to take account of any information about the unknown quantity which comes from any source other than the particular sample which has just been taken, even in situations where this information is of such a nature that it throws very serious doubt on the correctness of a statement which is alleged to be worthy of, say, "at least 90 per cent confidence."

In some situations, in fact, we may *know for certain* that a duly computed confidence-interval statement is false.   Suppose for example that a manufacturer has in storage 1000 units of some part which deteriorates on the shelf, and suppose that a complete count made at some previous time revealed that 500 units were already defective at that time but that the tags labeling these defectives have since been removed through a stock boy's error.   To obtain some information on the total number of parts which are now defective the manufacturer takes a sample of 20 parts and has them inspected; and by the luck of the draw only 5 of the parts in the sample turn out to be defective.   By using the binomial tables to show that

$$P_b(\tilde{r} \leq 5 | n = 20, p = .456) = .05$$

we see that we are entitled in classical theory to assert that we are "at least 95 per cent confident" that there are *less* than 456 defectives among the 1000 pieces on the shelf despite the fact that we know for certain that there are at least 500 defectives among these 1000 pieces.

Some statisticians will defend confidence intervals against counter-examples of this sort by saying that no sensible person would make an interval statement which he actually knew to be false, but this defense violates the most fundamental principle of all classical theory: namely, that *the rule for using sample evidence must be chosen* before *the sample evidence is examined.*   If before taking the sample just discussed the manufacturer's statistician had decided that a 95 per cent one-sided interval was the proper estimate for the manufacturer's purposes, then he *must* proceed to compute and make such a statement. If he does not—if he picks and chooses when he will abide by the classical rules and when he will not—then the confidence levels which he *does* quote will have *no basis in "objective" probability.*

Observe carefully that this does *not* mean that confidence intervals fail to do what they are supposed to do. The theory explicitly assumes that a certain fraction of wrong statements would be made in the long run, and this particular statement simply happens to be one of these wrong statements. The real trouble lies much deeper. *As such, the long-run frequency with which a certain method of making statements would produce incorrect statements is of no real interest to anyone;* this frequency is interesting only as *part* of the information which a reasonable man will wish to consider in deciding what probability he wishes to attach to the truth of a *particular* statement. We *cannot* act sensibly under uncertainty if in order to achieve "objectivity" we deliberately blind ourselves to part of the information bearing on the truth of a particular statement which is before us.

42.2   Confidence Intervals and Posterior Probability

In Section 41.3.2 we saw that if r successes are observed in a sample of n, the *conditional* probability

$$P_b(\tilde{r} \geq r | p = p_b)$$

is a good rough indication of the *posterior* probability

$$P(\tilde{p} < p_b | \tilde{r} = r)$$

which a reasonable person should assign to the proposition that $\tilde{p} < p_b$ after the sample evidence has been reported *provided that before the sample was taken he considered all possible values of $\tilde{p}$ to be about equally likely.* The argument which was used to prove this relation depended in no way on the fact that p_b had been fixed at some particular value by the economics of a particular decision problem; the relation holds for any and all values of $\tilde{p}$ in which a person may be interested.

It follows immediately that the same relation between conditional and posterior probability holds under the same proviso if, instead of taking a predetermined p_b and computing $P(\tilde{r} \geq r)$ *given* p_b, the statistician fixes the value of the conditional probability at some predetermined number γ_1 and reports the value p_1 of $\tilde{p}$ which makes the probability equal to γ_1 or which makes 1 minus the probability equal to $1 - \gamma_1$. If, for example, the statistician observes 65 successes in 100 Bernoulli trials and then reports that p is *greater* than .564 with confidence $1 - \gamma_1 = .95$, we know immediately that

$$P_t(\tilde{r} \geq 65 | p = .564) = \gamma_1 = .05;$$

and a person who felt that all values of $\bar{p}$ were about equally likely *before* this information was reported could conclude that careful computation of the probability which *he* should now assign to the proposition that $\bar{p}$ is *less* than .564 would yield a number fairly close to .05. This means of course that the posterior probability which he should assign to the proposition that $\bar{p}$ is *greater* than .564 is very close to the "confidence" in this proposition quoted by the statistician.

The same relation which holds for confidence-interval statements that p is greater than p_1 will obviously hold for confidence-interval statements that p is *less* than p_2 or that p is *between* p_1 and p_2. In general,

Any person who assigned roughly equal probabilities to all possible values of some quantity before being informed of the evidence on this quantity which has been obtained from a particular sample may interpret confidence-interval statements about this quantity as roughly equivalent to statements of the posterior probabilities which *he* should now assign.

Whether such a person will be satisfied with approximate rather than exact knowledge of the posterior probabilities which logical consistency requires him to assign will of course depend on the value which accurate knowledge of this probability has for him, and this in turn depends on the way in which the consequences of the various acts which he is contemplating depend on the unknown quantity.

PROBLEMS

1. A sample of 20 pieces is drawn from a Bernoulli process and 7 defectives are found. Compute:

a. A 95 per cent one-sided confidence interval setting a *lower* bound on the true value of p.

b. A 95 per cent one-sided confidence interval setting an *upper* bound on the true value of p.

c. A 90 per cent two-sided confidence interval for p.

2. When a sample mean is Normally rather than binomially distributed, confidence intervals are found by determining the value μ_1 for which $P(\bar{x} > \bar{x}|\mu_1) = \gamma_1$ and then stating $\mu > \mu_1$ and/or the value μ_2 for which $P(\bar{x} < \bar{x}|\mu_2) = \gamma_2$ and then stating $\mu < \mu_2$.

a. A sample of size 100 is drawn from a population in which $\sigma(\tilde{\epsilon}) = 1.25$; the mean of the sample is found to be $\bar{x} = +.157$. Compute 99.5 per cent one-sided confidence intervals setting upper and lower bounds on μ and a 99 per cent two-sided interval for μ.

b. Show that if the bars in the histogram of the true distribution of $\bar{x}$ are so narrow that this distribution can be treated as practically continuous, then γ_1 and γ_2 are the *exact* frequencies with which erroneous statements would be made in the long run rather than mere upper bounds on these frequencies.

3. A businessman who must choose between two acts whose costs are linear functions of the value of the mean μ of a population with unknown standard deviation

$\sigma(\bar{\varepsilon})$ is told on the basis of a sample of size 100 drawn from this population that $75 < \mu < 85$ is a 90 per cent confidence interval for μ.   How should he decide what course of action to follow:

    a. If his break-even value $\mu_b = 50$ and a terminal act must be chosen immediately?
    b. If $\mu_b = 50$ and there is time for further sampling?
    c. If $\mu_b = 77$ and a terminal act must be chosen immediately?
    d. If $\mu_b = 77$ and there is time for further sampling?
    e. If $\mu_b = 74$ and a terminal act must be chosen immediately?
    f. If $\mu_b = 74$ and there is time for further sampling?

    4. A businessman must select a stock level in a situation where he will lose \$30 for each unit by which stock per potential customer is *over* demand or will lose \$1000 for each unit by which stock per potential customer is *under* demand.   He is told on the basis of a sample of 100 drawn from his population of 10,000 potential customers that $75 < \mu < 85$ is a 90 per cent confidence interval for demand per potential customer μ.   How many units should he stock per potential customer?   How many units in all?   (HINT: Review Section 37.2.)

Appendix

Continuous Prior Distributions for the
Parameters of Bernoulli and Poisson Processes

When the information provided by a sample can be summarized by a statistic which is Normally distributed with known variance, we have seen that it is very convenient to approximate the prior distribution of the basic random variable by a Normal distribution because the posterior distribution of the basic random variable and the prior distribution of $\tilde{E}_1$ will then be Normal and probabilities and expectations under these distributions will be very easy to compute. In this appendix we shall show that this same convenience can be gained by an appropriate choice of prior distribution when the sample is summarized by a statistic which has either a *binomial* or a *Poisson* distribution. We shall present only results, without proofs, since supplying the proofs will be a good exercise for students who have a reasonable command of simple algebra and calculus while reading the proofs would be useless for those who do not.

A.1 Poisson Sampling Distribution

A.1.1 *Gamma Prior and Posterior Distributions*

If successes are generated by a Poisson process with unknown intensity $\tilde{\kappa}$, then for any *given* κ the *conditional* distribution of the number of successes $\tilde{r}$ observed in time or space t is Poisson:

$$P(r|\kappa) = \frac{e^{-\kappa t}(\kappa t)^r}{r!}. \tag{1}$$

If we take as the *prior* distribution of the basic random variable $\tilde{\kappa}$ a *gamma distribution* with parameters ρ and τ,

$$P_0'(\kappa) = P_\gamma'(\kappa;\rho,\tau) = \tau \frac{e^{-\kappa\tau}(\kappa\tau)^{\rho-1}}{(\rho-1)!}, \tag{2}$$

the *posterior* distribution of $\tilde{\kappa}$ will be of exactly the same form as the prior distribution but the parameter ρ will be replaced by $r + \rho$ and τ by $t + \tau$:

$$P_1'(\kappa) = P_\gamma'(\kappa; r + \rho, t + \tau) = (t + \tau) \frac{e^{-\kappa(t+\tau)}[\kappa(t + \tau)]^{r+\rho-1}}{(r + \rho - 1)!}. \tag{3}$$

The parameter ρ of the gamma distribution defined by (2) determines the shape of the distribution; the parameter τ determines its scale; both parameters must be greater than 0. The mean and variance of the distribution are

$$\mathrm{E}(\tilde{\kappa}) = \frac{\rho}{\tau}; \qquad \sigma^2(\tilde{\kappa}) = \frac{\rho}{\tau^2}. \tag{4}$$

Partial expectations are given by

$$\mathrm{E}_0^\kappa(\tilde{\kappa}) = \frac{\rho}{\tau} \, \mathrm{P}_\gamma(\tilde{\kappa} < \kappa | \rho + 1, \tau). \tag{5}$$

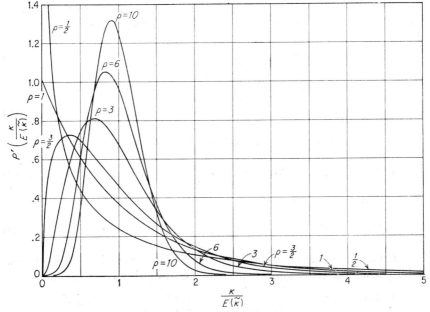

Figure A.1. Gamma distributions.

The shape of the distribution for various values of the parameter ρ is shown in Figure A.1. Notice particularly that:

1. When $\rho \leq 1$ the distribution is J-shaped. When $\rho < 1$, the ordinate is infinite at $\kappa = 0$; when $\rho = 1$ exactly, the ordinate is finite at $\kappa = 0$.
2. When $\rho > 1$, the distribution is single-humped with a peak at $\kappa = (\rho - 1)/\tau$, i.e. at $\kappa/\mathrm{E}(\tilde{\kappa}) = (\rho - 1)/\rho$.

The cumulative gamma distribution has been tabulated by Pearson;[†] in his notation

$$P_\gamma(\tilde{\kappa} < \kappa | \rho, \tau) = I(u,p),$$

$$u = \frac{\kappa\tau}{\sqrt{\rho}}, \qquad p = \rho - 1.$$

Cumulative probabilities can also be obtained from Molina's table of the Poisson distribution[‡] by using the relation

$$P_\gamma(\tilde{\kappa} < \kappa | \rho, \tau) = P(c,a),$$

$$c = \rho, \qquad a = \kappa\tau.$$

A.1.2   The Marginal Distribution of $\tilde{r}$

If the prior distribution of the basic random variable $\tilde{\kappa}$ is gamma with parameters ρ and τ as defined by Equation (2) and the conditional distribution of the statistic $\tilde{r}$ is Poisson with parameters κ and t as defined by Equation (1), the *marginal* distribution of $\tilde{r}$ (cf. Section 34.3.1) is *negative binomial:*

$$P(r) = P_{nb}(r; \rho, \pi) = C_r^{r+\rho-1} \pi^r (1-\pi)^\rho, \tag{6}$$

where

$$\pi = \frac{t}{t+\tau}. \tag{7}$$

The mean and variance of this distribution are

$$E(\tilde{r}) = t\frac{\rho}{\tau}, \qquad \sigma^2(\tilde{r}) = t(t+\tau)\frac{\rho}{\tau^2}. \tag{8}$$

Partial expectations are given by

$$E_0^r(\tilde{r}) = t\frac{\rho}{\tau} P_{nb}(\tilde{r} \le r - 1 | \rho + 1, \pi). \tag{9}$$

Cumulative negative binomial probabilities may be obtained from tables of cumulative binomial probabilities by using the relation[§]

$$P_{nb}(\tilde{r} \ge r | \rho, \pi) = P_b(\tilde{r} \ge r | r + \rho - 1, \pi), \qquad \pi \le .5,$$
$$P_{nb}(\tilde{r} < r | \rho, \pi) = P_b(\tilde{r} \ge \rho | r + \rho - 1, 1 - \pi), \qquad \pi \ge .5.$$

They may also be obtained from Pearson's tables of the incomplete beta function[||] by using the appropriate one of the two relations

† K. Pearson, "Tables of the Incomplete Γ-Function," Biometrika, London, 1934.

‡ E. C. Molina, "Poisson's Exponential Binomial Limit," D. Van Nostrand Company, Inc., Princeton, N.J., 1942.

§ When the parameter ρ is integral, the negative binomial distribution gives the probability that there will be exactly r successes before the ρth failure in sampling from a Bernoulli process in which the probability of a success on any trial is π.

|| K. Pearson, "Tables of the Incomplete Beta-Function," Biometrika, London, 1948.

$$P_{nb}(\tilde{r} \geq r|\rho,\pi) = I_{\pi}(r,\rho), \qquad r \geq \rho,$$
$$P_{nb}(\tilde{r} < r|\rho,\pi) = I_{1-\pi}(\rho,r), \qquad r \leq \rho.$$

A.1.3   The Prior Distribution of $\tilde{E}_1$

By Equations (3) and (4), the mean of the *posterior* distribution of $\tilde{\kappa}$ will be

$$E_1(\tilde{\kappa}) = \frac{r + \rho}{t + \tau} \tag{10}$$

and therefore to any specified value E_1 of the random variable $\tilde{E}_1$ there corresponds a value

$$r_E = (t + \tau)E_1 - \rho.$$

The exact prior probability that $\tilde{E}_1$ will fall short of or exceed any specified value E_1 can be found by finding the negative binomial probability that $\tilde{r}$ will fall short of or exceed the corresponding value r_E. Partial expectations of $\tilde{E}_1$ may be computed by using the relation

$$E_0^{E_1}(\tilde{E}_1) = \frac{1}{t + \tau} [E_0^{r_E}(\tilde{r}) + \rho\, P(\tilde{r} \leq r_E)]. \tag{11}$$

Approximations. From Equations (8) and (10) it follows (cf. Section 16.5.3) that the distribution of $\tilde{E}_1$ has mean and variance

$$E(\tilde{E}_1) = \frac{\rho}{\tau} = E_0(\tilde{\kappa}),$$

$$\sigma^2(\tilde{E}_1) = \frac{t}{t + \tau}\, \frac{\rho}{\tau^2} = \frac{t}{t + \tau}\, \sigma_0^2(\tilde{\kappa}). \tag{12}$$

These results make it easy to use the Normal approximation to the distribution of $\tilde{E}_1$; but because the distribution of $\tilde{E}_1$ approaches the gamma prior distribution of $\tilde{\kappa}$ as t becomes large relative to τ, a gamma approximation will be better than the Normal for large t. A gamma distribution with parameters

$$\tau^* = \frac{t + \tau}{t}\, \tau, \qquad \rho^* = \frac{t + \tau}{t}\, \rho, \tag{13}$$

will have the same mean and variance as the exact distribution of $\tilde{E}_1$, and probabilities and partial expectations may be obtained from the formulas in Section A.1.1 by replacing κ by E_1, τ by τ^*, and ρ by ρ^*.

A.2   Binomial Sampling Distribution

A.2.1   Beta Prior and Posterior Distributions

If successes are generated by a Bernoulli process with unknown process average fraction successful p, then for any *given* p the *conditional* distribution of the number of successes $\tilde{r}$ observed in n trials is binomial:

$$P(r|p) = C_r^n p^r (1 - p)^{n-r}. \tag{14}$$

If we take as the *prior* distribution of the basic random variable $\tilde{p}$ a *beta distribution* with parameters ρ and ν,

$$P_0'(p) = P_\beta(p;\rho,\nu) = \frac{(\nu - 1)!}{(\rho - 1)!(\nu - \rho - 1)!}\, p^{\rho-1}(1 - p)^{\nu-\rho-1}, \tag{15}$$

the *posterior* distribution of $\tilde{p}$ will be of exactly this same form but with ρ replaced by $r + \rho$ and ν replaced by $n + \nu$:

$$P_1'(p) = P_\beta(p; r + \rho, n + \nu). \tag{16}$$

The parameter ρ of the beta distribution as defined by (14) above must be greater than 0 and the parameter ν must be greater than ρ.   The mean and variance of the distribution are

$$E(\tilde{p}) = \frac{\rho}{\nu}; \qquad \sigma^2(\tilde{p}) = \frac{\rho(\nu - \rho)}{\nu^2(\nu + 1)}. \tag{17}$$

Partial expectations are given by

$$E_0^p(\tilde{p}) = \frac{\rho}{\nu}\, P_\beta(\tilde{p} < p|\rho + 1, \nu + 1). \tag{18}$$

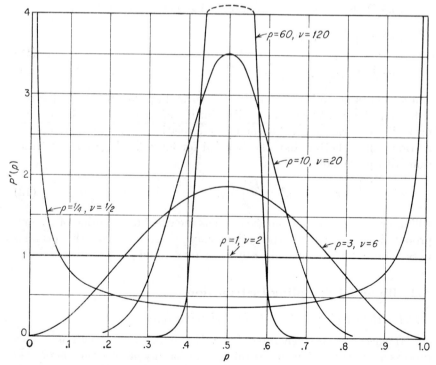

Figure A.2. Beta distributions, $E(\tilde{p}) = .5$.

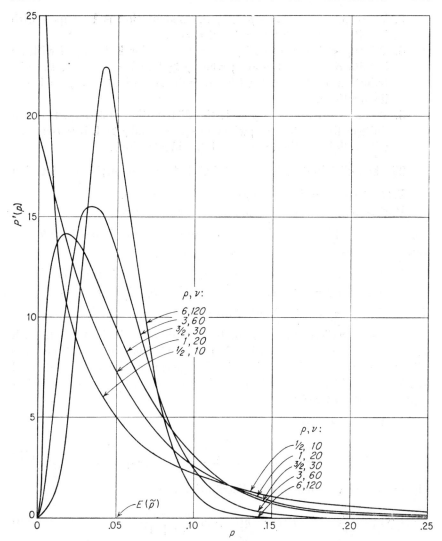

Figure A.3. Beta distributions, $E(\tilde{p}) = .05$.

The shape of the distribution for a number of pairs of values of ρ and ν all of which give $E(\tilde{p}) = .5$ is shown in Figure A.2; the shape for a number of pairs with $E(\tilde{p}) = .05$ is shown in Figure A.3. Notice particularly that:

1. When $\rho > 1$ and $\nu - \rho > 1$, the distribution has a single hump with a peak at $p = (\rho - 1)/(\nu - 2)$.
2. When $\rho = 1$ and $\nu - \rho = 1$, the distribution is "rectangular"— all values of p are equally likely.

3. When $\rho < 1$ and $\nu - \rho < 1$, the distribution is U-shaped with infinite ordinates at $p = 0$ and $p = 1$.
4. When $\rho < 1$ and $\nu - \rho \geq 1$, the distribution is J-shaped with an infinite ordinate at $p = 0$; when $\rho \geq 1$ and $\nu - \rho < 1$, the distribution is J-shaped with an infinite ordinate at $p = 1$ (no illustration).
5. When $\rho = 1$ and $\nu - \rho > 1$, the distribution is J-shaped with a finite ordinate at $p = 0$; when $\nu - \rho = 1$ and $\rho > 1$, it is *J*-shaped with a finite ordinate at $p = 1$ (no illustration).

The beta distribution has been tabulated by Pearson;† in his notation

$$P_\beta(\tilde{p} < p|\rho,\nu) = I_p(\rho, \nu - \rho), \qquad \rho \geq \nu - \rho,$$
$$P_\beta(\tilde{p} > p|\rho,\nu) = I_{1-p}(\nu - \rho, \rho), \qquad \rho \leq \nu - \rho.$$

Cumulative probabilities can also be obtained from binomial tables by use of the appropriate one of the two relations

$$P_\beta(\tilde{p} < p|\rho,\nu) = P_b(\tilde{r} \geq \rho|\nu - 1, p), \qquad p \leq .5,$$
$$P_\beta(\tilde{p} > p|\rho,\nu) = P_b(\tilde{r} \geq \nu - \rho|\nu - 1, 1 - p), \qquad p \geq .5.$$

A.2.2 The Marginal Distribution of $\tilde{r}$

If the prior distribution of the basic random variable $\tilde{p}$ is beta with parameters ρ and ν as defined by Equation (15) and the conditional distribution of the statistic $\tilde{r}$ is binomial with parameters p and n as defined by Equation (14), the *marginal* distribution of $\tilde{r}$ (cf. Section 34.3.1) is *negative hypergeometric:*‡

$$P(r) = P_{nh}(r;\rho,n,\nu)$$
$$= \frac{C_r^{r+\rho-1}C_{n-r}^{(n+\nu-1)-(r+\rho-1)}}{C_n^{n+\nu-1}} \frac{(\nu - 1) - (\rho - 1)}{(n + \nu - 1) - (r + \rho - 1)}. \qquad (19)$$

The mean and variance of this distribution are

$$E(\tilde{r}) = n\frac{\rho}{\nu}, \qquad \sigma^2(\tilde{r}) = n(n + \nu)\frac{\rho(\nu - \rho)}{\nu^2(\nu + 1)}. \qquad (20)$$

Partial expectations are given by

$$E_0^r(\tilde{r}) = n\frac{\rho}{\nu} P_{nh}(\tilde{r} \leq r - 1|\rho + 1, n - 1, \nu + 1). \qquad (21)$$

A.2.3 The Prior Distribution of $\tilde{E}_1$

By Equations (16) and (17), the mean of the *posterior* distribution of

† Pearson, "Tables of the Incomplete Beta-Function."
‡ When the parameters ρ and ν are integral, this formula gives the probability that there will be exactly r successes before the ρth failure in simple sampling without replacement from a finite population containing n successes and $\nu - 1$ failures.

$\tilde{p}$ will be

$$E_1(\tilde{p}) = \frac{r + \rho}{n + \nu}, \tag{22}$$

and therefore to any specified value E_1 of the random variable $\tilde{E}_1$ there corresponds a value

$$r_E = (n + \nu)E_1 - \rho.$$

The exact cumulative distribution of $\tilde{E}_1$ is therefore given by

$$P(\tilde{E}_1 \leq E_1) = P(\tilde{r} \leq r_E)$$

and partial expectations are given by

$$E_0^{E_1}(\tilde{E}_1) = \frac{1}{n + \nu} [E_0^{r_E}(\tilde{r}) + \rho \, P(\tilde{r} \leq r_E)]. \tag{23}$$

Negative-hypergeometric cumulative probabilities can easily be expressed in terms of ordinary hypergeometric probabilities, but since even the ordinary hypergeometric distribution is not tabulated, exact values can actually be found only by term-by-term computation.

Approximations. From Equations (20) and (22) it follows that the distribution of $\tilde{E}_1$ has mean and variance

$$E(\tilde{E}_1) = \frac{\rho}{\nu} = E_0(\tilde{p}),$$

$$\sigma^2(\tilde{E}_1) = \frac{n}{n + \nu} \frac{\rho(\nu - \rho)}{\nu^2(\nu + 1)} = \frac{n}{n + \nu} \sigma_0^2(\tilde{p}). \tag{24}$$

These results make it easy to use the Normal approximation to the distribution of $\tilde{E}_1$; but because the distribution of $\tilde{E}_1$ approaches the beta prior distribution of $\tilde{p}$ as n becomes large relative to ν, a beta approximation will be better than the Normal for large n. A beta distribution with parameters ν^* and ρ^* given by

$$\nu^* + 1 = \frac{n + \nu}{n}(\nu + 1),$$

$$\rho^* = \frac{\nu^*}{\nu}\rho,$$

will have the same mean and variance as the exact distribution of $\tilde{E}_1$, and probabilities and partial expectations may be obtained from the formulas in Section A.2.1 by replacing p by E_1, ν by ν^*, and ρ by ρ^*.

A.3 Two-action Problems with Linear Costs

At the end of Section 30.4.3 we arrived at completely general formulas for the expected value of *perfect* information (or expected loss of immediate terminal action) in any two-action problem with linear costs:

$$\text{Expected VPI} = \begin{cases} k_t[\mathrm{E}^{\infty}_{\mu_b}(\tilde{\mu}) - \mu_b\, \mathrm{P}(\tilde{\mu} \geq \mu_b)] & \textit{if } \mathrm{E}(\tilde{\mu}) < \mu_b, \\ k_t[\mu_b\, \mathrm{P}(\tilde{\mu} \leq \mu_b) - \mathrm{E}^{\mu_b}_{-\infty}(\tilde{\mu})] & \textit{if } \mathrm{E}(\tilde{\mu}) > \mu_b. \end{cases}$$

These formulas hold for *any* random variable whatever; specifically, they hold if the p of a Bernoulli process or the κ of a Poisson process is substituted for μ.

In Section 34.4.2 we pointed out that these same formulas give the expected value of *sample* information when the random variable $\tilde{E}_1$ is substituted for the basic random variable. Continuing to use μ_b to denote the break-even value we have

$$\text{Expected VSI} = \begin{cases} k_t[\mathrm{E}^{\infty}_{\mu_b}(\tilde{E}_1) - \mu_b\, \mathrm{P}(\tilde{E}_1 \geq \mu_b)] & \textit{if } \mathrm{E}_0(\tilde{\mu}) < \mu_b, \\ k_t[\mu_b\, \mathrm{P}(\tilde{E}_1 \leq \mu_b) - \mathrm{E}^{\mu_b}_{-\infty}(\tilde{E}_1)] & \textit{if } \mathrm{E}_0(\tilde{\mu}) > \mu_b. \end{cases}$$

Tables

Table I: Cumulative Binomial Distribution

$$\mathrm{P}_b(\bar{r} \geq r|n,p)$$

$n = 1$

P R	01	02	03	04	05	06	07	08	09	10
1	0100	0200	0300	0400	0500	0600	0700	0800	0900	1000

P R	11	12	13	14	15	16	17	18	19	20
1	1100	1200	1300	1400	1500	1600	1700	1800	1900	2000

P R	21	22	23	24	25	26	27	28	29	30
1	2100	2200	2300	2400	2500	2600	2700	2800	2900	3000

P R	31	32	33	34	35	36	37	38	39	40
1	3100	3200	3300	3400	3500	3600	3700	3800	3900	4000

P R	41	42	43	44	45	46	47	48	49	50
1	4100	4200	4300	4400	4500	4600	4700	4800	4900	5000

$n = 2$

P R	01	02	03	04	05	06	07	08	09	10
1	0199	0396	0591	0784	0975	1164	1351	1536	1719	1900
2	0001	0004	0009	0016	0025	0036	0049	0064	0081	0100

P R	11	12	13	14	15	16	17	18	19	20
1	2079	2256	2431	2604	2775	2944	3111	3276	3439	3600
2	0121	0144	0169	0196	0225	0256	0289	0324	0361	0400

P R	21	22	23	24	25	26	27	28	29	30
1	3759	3916	4071	4224	4375	4524	4671	4816	4959	5100
2	0441	0484	0529	0576	0625	0676	0729	0784	0841	0900

P R	31	32	33	34	35	36	37	38	39	40
1	5239	5376	5511	5644	5775	5904	6031	6156	6279	6400
2	0961	1024	1089	1156	1225	1296	1369	1444	1521	1600

P R	41	42	43	44	45	46	47	48	49	50
1	6519	6636	6751	6864	6975	7084	7191	7296	7399	7500
2	1681	1764	1849	1936	2025	2116	2209	2304	2401	2500

$n = 3$

P R	01	02	03	04	05	06	07	08	09	10
1	0297	0588	0873	1153	1426	1694	1956	2213	2464	2710
2	0003	0012	0026	0047	0073	0104	0140	0182	0228	0280
3				0001	0001	0002	0003	0005	0007	0010

P R	11	12	13	14	15	16	17	18	19	20
1	2950	3185	3415	3639	3859	4073	4282	4486	4686	4880
2	0336	0397	0463	0533	0608	0686	0769	0855	0946	1040
3	0013	0017	0022	0027	0034	0041	0049	0058	0069	0080

P R	21	22	23	24	25	26	27	28	29	30
1	5070	5254	5435	5610	5781	5948	6110	6268	6421	6570
2	1138	1239	1344	1452	1563	1676	1793	1913	2035	2160
3	0093	0106	0122	0138	0156	0176	0197	0220	0244	0270

$n = 3$ *Table I: Cumulative Binomial Distribution*

P	31	32	33	34	35	36	37	38	39	40
R										
1	6715	6856	6992	7125	7254	7379	7500	7617	7730	7840
2	2287	2417	2548	2682	2818	2955	3094	3235	3377	3520
3	0298	0328	0359	0393	0429	0467	0507	0549	0593	0640

P	41	42	43	44	45	46	47	48	49	50
R										
1	7946	8049	8148	8244	8336	8425	8511	8594	8673	8750
2	3665	3810	3957	4104	4253	4401	4551	4700	4850	5000
3	0689	0741	0795	0852	0911	0973	1038	1106	1176	1250

$n = 4$

P	01	02	03	04	05	06	07	08	09	10
R										
1	0394	0776	1147	1507	1855	2193	2519	2836	3143	3439
2	0006	0023	0052	0091	0140	0199	0267	0344	0430	0523
3			0001	0002	0005	0008	0013	0019	0027	0037
4									0001	0001

P	11	12	13	14	15	16	17	18	19	20
R										
1	3726	4003	4271	4530	4780	5021	5254	5479	5695	5904
2	0624	0732	0847	0968	1095	1228	1366	1509	1656	1808
3	0049	0063	0079	0098	0120	0144	0171	0202	0235	0272
4	0001	0002	0003	0004	0005	0007	0008	0010	0013	0016

P	21	22	23	24	25	26	27	28	29	30
R										
1	6105	6298	6485	6664	6836	7001	7160	7313	7459	7599
2	1963	2122	2285	2450	2617	2787	2959	3132	3307	3483
3	0312	0356	0403	0453	0508	0566	0628	0694	0763	0837
4	0019	0023	0028	0033	0039	0046	0053	0061	0071	0081

P	31	32	33	34	35	36	37	38	39	40
R										
1	7733	7862	7985	8103	8215	8322	8425	8522	8615	8704
2	3660	3837	4015	4193	4370	4547	4724	4900	5075	5248
3	0915	0996	1082	1171	1265	1362	1464	1569	1679	1792
4	0092	0105	0119	0134	0150	0168	0187	0209	0231	0256

P	41	42	43	44	45	46	47	48	49	50
R										
1	8788	8868	8944	9017	9085	9150	9211	9269	9323	9375
2	5420	5590	5759	5926	6090	6252	6412	6569	6724	6875
3	1909	2030	2155	2283	2415	2550	2689	2831	2977	3125
4	0283	0311	0342	0375	0410	0448	0488	0531	0576	0625

$n = 5$

P	01	02	03	04	05	06	07	08	09	10
R										
1	0490	0961	1413	1846	2262	2661	3043	3409	3760	4095
2	0010	0038	0085	0148	0226	0319	0425	0544	0674	0815
3		0001	0003	0006	0012	0020	0031	0045	0063	0086
4						0001	0001	0002	0003	0005

P	11	12	13	14	15	16	17	18	19	20
R										
1	4416	4723	5016	5296	5563	5818	6061	6293	6513	6723
2	0965	1125	1292	1467	1648	1835	2027	2224	2424	2627
3	0112	0143	0179	0220	0266	0318	0375	0437	0505	0579
4	0007	0009	0013	0017	0022	0029	0036	0045	0055	0067
5				0001	0001	0001	0001	0002	0002	0003

P	21	22	23	24	25	26	27	28	29	30
R										
1	6923	7113	7293	7464	7627	7781	7927	8065	8196	8319
2	2833	3041	3251	3461	3672	3883	4093	4303	4511	4718
3	0659	0744	0836	0933	1035	1143	1257	1376	1501	1631
4	0081	0097	0114	0134	0156	0181	0208	0238	0272	0308
5	0004	0005	0006	0008	0010	0012	0014	0017	0021	0024

Table I: Cumulative Binomial Distribution   n = 5

P	31	32	33	34	35	36	37	38	39	40
R										
1	8436	8546	8650	8748	8840	8926	9008	9084	9155	9222
2	4923	5125	5325	5522	5716	5906	6093	6276	6455	6630
3	1766	1905	2050	2199	2352	2509	2670	2835	3003	3174
4	0347	0390	0436	0486	0540	0598	0660	0726	0796	0870
5	0029	0034	0039	0045	0053	0060	0069	0079	0090	0102

P	41	42	43	44	45	46	47	48	49	50
R										
1	9285	9344	9398	9449	9497	9541	9582	9620	9655	9688
2	6801	6967	7129	7286	7438	7585	7728	7865	7998	8125
3	3349	3525	3705	3886	4069	4253	4439	4625	4813	5000
4	0949	1033	1121	1214	1312	1415	1522	1635	1753	1875
5	0116	0131	0147	0165	0185	0206	0229	0255	0282	0313

n = 6

P	01	02	03	04	05	06	07	08	09	10
R										
1	0585	1142	1670	2172	2649	3101	3530	3936	4321	4686
2	0015	0057	0125	0216	0328	0459	0608	0773	0952	1143
3		0002	0005	0012	0022	0038	0058	0085	0118	0159
4					0001	0002	0003	0005	0008	0013
5										0001

P	11	12	13	14	15	16	17	18	19	20
R										
1	5030	5356	5664	5954	6229	6487	6731	6960	7176	7379
2	1345	1556	1776	2003	2235	2472	2713	2956	3201	3446
3	0206	0261	0324	0395	0473	0560	0655	0759	0870	0989
4	0018	0025	0034	0045	0059	0075	0094	0116	0141	0170
5	0001	0001	0002	0003	0004	0005	0007	0010	0013	0016
6										0001

P	21	22	23	24	25	26	27	28	29	30
R										
1	7569	7748	7916	8073	8220	8358	8487	8607	8719	8824
2	3692	3937	4180	4422	4661	4896	5128	5356	5580	5798
3	1115	1250	1391	1539	1694	1856	2023	2196	2374	2557
4	0202	0239	0280	0326	0376	0431	0492	0557	0628	0705
5	0020	0025	0031	0038	0046	0056	0067	0079	0093	0109
6	0001	0001	0001	0002	0002	0003	0004	0005	0006	0007

P	31	32	33	34	35	36	37	38	39	40
R										
1	8921	9011	9095	9173	9246	9313	9375	9432	9485	9533
2	6012	6220	6422	6619	6809	6994	7172	7343	7508	7667
3	2744	2936	3130	3328	3529	3732	3937	4143	4350	4557
4	0787	0875	0969	1069	1174	1286	1404	1527	1657	1792
5	0127	0148	0170	0195	0223	0254	0288	0325	0365	0410
6	0009	0011	0013	0015	0018	0022	0026	0030	0035	0041

P	41	42	43	44	45	46	47	48	49	50
R										
1	9578	9619	9657	9692	9723	9752	9778	9802	9824	9844
2	7819	7965	8105	8238	8364	8485	8599	8707	8810	8906
3	4764	4971	5177	5382	5585	5786	5985	6180	6373	6563
4	1933	2080	2232	2390	2553	2721	2893	3070	3252	3438
5	0458	0510	0566	0627	0692	0762	0837	0917	1003	1094
6	0048	0055	0063	0073	0083	0095	0108	0122	0138	0156

n = 7

P	01	02	03	04	05	06	07	08	09	10
R										
1	0679	1319	1920	2486	3017	3515	3983	4422	4832	5217
2	0020	0079	0171	0294	0444	0618	0813	1026	1255	1497
3		0003	0009	0020	0038	0063	0097	0140	0193	0257
4				0001	0002	0004	0007	0012	0018	0027
5								0001	0001	0002

P	11	12	13	14	15	16	17	18	19	20
R										
1	5577	5913	6227	6521	6794	7049	7286	7507	7712	7903
2	1750	2012	2281	2556	2834	3115	3396	3677	3956	4233
3	0331	0416	0513	0620	0738	0866	1005	1154	1313	1480
4	0039	0054	0072	0094	0121	0153	0189	0231	0279	0333
5	0003	0004	0006	0009	0012	0017	0022	0029	0037	0047
6					0001	0001	0001	0002	0003	0004

P	21	22	23	24	25	26	27	28	29	30
R										
1	8080	8243	8395	8535	8665	8785	8895	8997	9090	9176
2	4506	4775	5040	5298	5551	5796	6035	6266	6490	6706
3	1657	1841	2033	2231	2436	2646	2861	3081	3304	3529
4	0394	0461	0536	0617	0706	0802	0905	1016	1134	1260
5	0058	0072	0088	0107	0129	0153	0181	0213	0248	0288
6	0005	0006	0008	0011	0013	0017	0021	0026	0031	0038
7					0001	0001	0001	0001	0002	0002

P	31	32	33	34	35	36	37	38	39	40
R										
1	9255	9328	9394	9454	9510	9560	9606	9648	9686	9720
2	6914	7113	7304	7487	7662	7828	7987	8137	8279	8414
3	3757	3987	4217	4447	4677	4906	5134	5359	5581	5801
4	1394	1534	1682	1837	1998	2167	2341	2521	2707	2898
5	0332	0380	0434	0492	0556	0625	0701	0782	0869	0963
6	0046	0055	0065	0077	0090	0105	0123	0142	0164	0188
7	0003	0003	0004	0005	0006	0008	0009	0011	0014	0016

P	41	42	43	44	45	46	47	48	49	50
R										
1	9751	9779	9805	9827	9848	9866	9883	9897	9910	9922
2	8541	8660	8772	8877	8976	9068	9153	9233	9307	9375
3	6017	6229	6436	6638	6836	7027	7213	7393	7567	7734
4	3094	3294	3498	3706	3917	4131	4346	4563	4781	5000
5	1063	1169	1282	1402	1529	1663	1803	1951	2105	2266
6	0216	0246	0279	0316	0357	0402	0451	0504	0562	0625
7	0019	0023	0027	0032	0037	0044	0051	0059	0068	0078

$n = 8$

P	01	02	03	04	05	06	07	08	09	10
R										
1	0773	1492	2163	2786	3366	3904	4404	4868	5297	5695
2	0027	0103	0223	0381	0572	0792	1035	1298	1577	1869
3	0001	0004	0013	0031	0058	0096	0147	0211	0289	0381
4			0001	0002	0004	0007	0013	0022	0034	0050
5							0001	0001	0003	0004

P	11	12	13	14	15	16	17	18	19	20
R										
1	6063	6404	6718	7008	7275	7521	7748	7956	8147	8322
2	2171	2480	2794	3111	3428	3744	4057	4366	4670	4967
3	0487	0608	0743	0891	1052	1226	1412	1608	1815	2031
4	0071	0097	0129	0168	0214	0267	0328	0397	0476	0563
5	0007	0010	0015	0021	0029	0038	0050	0065	0083	0104
6		0001	0001	0002	0002	0003	0005	0007	0009	0012
7									0001	0001

P	21	22	23	24	25	26	27	28	29	30
R										
1	8483	8630	8764	8887	8999	9101	9194	9278	9354	9424
2	5257	5538	5811	6075	6329	6573	6807	7031	7244	7447
3	2255	2486	2724	2967	3215	3465	3718	3973	4228	4482
4	0659	0765	0880	1004	1138	1281	1433	1594	1763	1941
5	0129	0158	0191	0230	0273	0322	0377	0438	0505	0580
6	0016	0021	0027	0034	0042	0052	0064	0078	0094	0113
7	0001	0002	0002	0003	0004	0005	0006	0008	0010	0013
8									0001	0001

P / R	31	32	33	34	35	36	37	38	39	40
1	9486	9543	9594	9640	9681	9719	9752	9782	9808	9832
2	7640	7822	7994	8156	8309	8452	8586	8711	8828	8936
3	4736	4987	5236	5481	5722	5958	6189	6415	6634	6846
4	2126	2319	2519	2724	2936	3153	3374	3599	3828	4059
5	0661	0750	0846	0949	1061	1180	1307	1443	1586	1737
6	0134	0159	0187	0218	0253	0293	0336	0385	0439	0498
7	0016	0020	0024	0030	0036	0043	0051	0061	0072	0085
8	0001	0001	0001	0002	0002	0003	0004	0004	0005	0007

P / R	41	42	43	44	45	46	47	48	49	50
1	9853	9872	9889	9903	9916	9928	9938	9947	9954	9961
2	9037	9130	9216	9295	9368	9435	9496	9552	9602	9648
3	7052	7250	7440	7624	7799	7966	8125	8276	8419	8555
4	4292	4527	4762	4996	5230	5463	5694	5922	6146	6367
5	1895	2062	2235	2416	2604	2798	2999	3205	3416	3633
6	0563	0634	0711	0794	0885	0982	1086	1198	1318	1445
7	0100	0117	0136	0157	0181	0208	0239	0272	0310	0352
8	0008	0010	0012	0014	0017	0020	0024	0028	0033	0039

$n = 9$

P / R	01	02	03	04	05	06	07	08	09	10
1	0865	1663	2398	3075	3698	4270	4796	5278	5721	6126
2	0034	0131	0282	0478	0712	0978	1271	1583	1912	2252
3	0001	0006	0020	0045	0084	0138	0209	0298	0405	0530
4			0001	0003	0006	0013	0023	0037	0057	0083
5					0001	0002	0003	0005	0009	
6										0001

P / R	11	12	13	14	15	16	17	18	19	20
1	6496	6835	7145	7427	7684	7918	8131	8324	8499	8658
2	2599	2951	3304	3657	4005	4348	4685	5012	5330	5638
3	0672	0833	1009	1209	1409	1629	1861	2105	2357	2618
4	0117	0158	0209	0269	0339	0420	0512	0615	0730	0856
5	0014	0021	0030	0041	0056	0075	0098	0125	0158	0196
6	0001	0002	0003	0004	0006	0009	0013	0017	0023	0031
7						0001	0001	0002	0002	0003

P / R	21	22	23	24	25	26	27	28	29	30
1	8801	8931	9048	9154	9249	9335	9411	9480	9542	9596
2	5934	6218	6491	6750	6997	7230	7452	7660	7856	8040
3	2885	3158	3434	3713	3993	4273	4552	4829	5102	5372
4	0994	1144	1304	1475	1657	1849	2050	2260	2478	2703
5	0240	0291	0350	0416	0489	0571	0662	0762	0870	0988
6	0040	0051	0065	0081	0100	0122	0149	0179	0213	0253
7	0004	0006	0008	0010	0013	0017	0022	0028	0035	0043
8			0001	0001	0001	0001	0002	0003	0003	0004

P / R	31	32	33	34	35	36	37	38	39	40
1	9645	9689	9728	9762	9793	9820	9844	9865	9883	9899
2	8212	8372	8522	8661	8789	8908	9017	9118	9210	9295
3	5636	5894	6146	6390	6627	6856	7076	7287	7489	7682
4	2935	3173	3415	3662	3911	4163	4416	4669	4922	5174
5	1115	1252	1398	1553	1717	1890	2072	2262	2460	2666
6	0298	0348	0404	0467	0536	0612	0696	0787	0886	0994
7	0053	0064	0078	0094	0112	0133	0157	0184	0215	0250
8	0006	0007	0009	0011	0014	0017	0021	0026	0031	0038
9				0001	0001	0001	0001	0002	0002	0003

P / R	41	42	43	44	45	46	47	48	49	50
1	9913	9926	9936	9946	9954	9961	9967	9972	9977	9980
2	9372	9442	9505	9563	9615	9662	9704	9741	9775	9805
3	7866	8039	8204	8359	8505	8642	8769	8889	8999	9102
4	5424	5670	5913	6152	6386	6614	6836	7052	7260	7461
5	2878	3097	3322	3551	3786	4024	4265	4509	4754	5000
6	1109	1233	1366	1508	1658	1817	1985	2161	2346	2539
7	0290	0334	0383	0437	0498	0564	0637	0717	0804	0898
8	0046	0055	0065	0077	0091	0107	0125	0145	0169	0195
9	0003	0004	0005	0006	0008	0009	0011	0014	0016	0020

Table I: Cumulative Binomial Distribution

$n = 10$

P	01	02	03	04	05	06	07	08	09	10
R										
1	0956	1829	2626	3352	4013	4614	5160	5656	6106	6513
2	0043	0162	0345	0582	0861	1176	1517	1879	2254	2639
3	0001	0009	0028	0062	0115	0188	0283	0401	0540	0702
4			0001	0004	0010	0020	0036	0058	0088	0128
5					0001	0002	0003	0006	0010	0016
6									0001	0001

P	11	12	13	14	15	16	17	18	19	20
R										
1	6882	7215	7516	7787	8031	8251	8448	8626	8784	8926
2	3028	3417	3804	4184	4557	4920	5270	5608	5932	6242
3	0884	1087	1308	1545	1798	2064	2341	2628	2922	3222
4	0178	0239	0313	0400	0500	0614	0741	0883	1039	1209
5	0025	0037	0053	0073	0099	0130	0168	0213	0266	0328
6	0003	0004	0006	0010	0014	0020	0027	0037	0049	0064
7			0001	0001	0001	0002	0003	0004	0006	0009
8									0001	0001

P	21	22	23	24	25	26	27	28	29	30
R										
1	9053	9166	9267	9357	9437	9508	9570	9626	9674	9718
2	6536	6815	7079	7327	7560	7778	7981	8170	8345	8507
3	3526	3831	4137	4442	4744	5042	5335	5622	5901	6172
4	1391	1587	1794	2012	2241	2479	2726	2979	3239	3504
5	0399	0479	0569	0670	0781	0904	1037	1181	1337	1503
6	0082	0104	0130	0161	0197	0239	0287	0342	0404	0473
7	0012	0016	0021	0027	0035	0045	0056	0070	0087	0106
8	0001	0002	0002	0003	0004	0006	0007	0010	0012	0016
9							0001	0001	0001	0001

P	31	32	33	34	35	36	37	38	39	40
R										
1	9755	9789	9818	9843	9865	9885	9902	9916	9929	9940
2	8656	8794	8920	9035	9140	9236	9323	9402	9473	9536
3	6434	6687	6930	7162	7384	7595	7794	7983	8160	8327
4	3772	4044	4316	4589	4862	5132	5400	5664	5923	6177
5	1679	1867	2064	2270	2485	2708	2939	3177	3420	3669
6	0551	0637	0732	0836	0949	1072	1205	1348	1500	1662
7	0129	0155	0185	0220	0260	0305	0356	0413	0477	0548
8	0020	0025	0032	0039	0048	0059	0071	0086	0103	0123
9	0002	0003	0003	0004	0005	0007	0009	0011	0014	0017
10								0001	0001	0001

P	41	42	43	44	45	46	47	48	49	50
R										
1	9949	9957	9964	9970	9975	9979	9983	9986	9988	9990
2	9594	9645	9691	9731	9767	9799	9827	9852	9874	9893
3	8483	8628	8764	8889	9004	9111	9209	9298	9379	9453
4	6425	6665	6898	7123	7340	7547	7745	7933	8112	8281
5	3922	4178	4436	4696	4956	5216	5474	5730	5982	6230
6	1834	2016	2207	2407	2616	2832	3057	3288	3526	3770
7	0626	0712	0806	0908	1020	1141	1271	1410	1560	1719
8	0146	0172	0202	0236	0274	0317	0366	0420	0480	0547
9	0021	0025	0031	0037	0045	0054	0065	0077	0091	0107
10	0001	0002	0002	0003	0003	0004	0005	0006	0008	0010

$n = 11$

P	01	02	03	04	05	06	07	08	09	10
R										
1	1047	1993	2847	3618	4312	4937	5499	6004	6456	6862
2	0052	0195	0413	0692	1019	1382	1772	2181	2601	3026
3	0002	0012	0037	0083	0152	0248	0370	0519	0695	0896
4			0002	0007	0016	0030	0053	0085	0129	0185
5					0001	0003	0005	0010	0017	0028
6								0001	0002	0003

P	11	12	13	14	15	16	17	18	19	20
R										
1	7225	7549	7839	8097	8327	8531	8712	8873	9015	9141
2	3452	3873	4286	4689	5078	5453	5811	6151	6474	6779
3	1120	1366	1632	1915	2212	2521	2839	3164	3494	3826
4	0256	0341	0442	0560	0694	0846	1013	1197	1397	1611
5	0042	0061	0087	0119	0159	0207	0266	0334	0413	0504
6	0005	0008	0012	0018	0027	0037	0051	0068	0090	0117
7		0001	0001	0002	0003	0005	0007	0010	0014	0020
8							0001	0001	0002	0002

P	21	22	23	24	25	26	27	28	29	30
R										
1	9252	9350	9436	9511	9578	9636	9686	9730	9769	9802
2	7065	7333	7582	7814	8029	8227	8410	8577	8730	8870
3	4158	4488	4814	5134	5448	5753	6049	6335	6610	6873
4	1840	2081	2333	2596	2867	3146	3430	3719	4011	4304
5	0607	0723	0851	0992	1146	1313	1493	1685	1888	2103
6	0148	0186	0231	0283	0343	0412	0490	0577	0674	0782
7	0027	0035	0046	0059	0076	0095	0119	0146	0179	0216
8	0003	0005	0007	0009	0012	0016	0021	0027	0034	0043
9			0001	0001	0001	0002	0002	0003	0004	0006

P	31	32	33	34	35	36	37	38	39	40
R										
1	9831	9856	9878	9896	9912	9926	9938	9948	9956	9964
2	8997	9112	9216	9310	9394	9470	9537	9597	9650	9698
3	7123	7361	7587	7799	7999	8186	8360	8522	8672	8811
4	4598	4890	5179	5464	5744	6019	6286	6545	6796	7037
5	2328	2563	2807	3059	3317	3581	3850	4122	4397	4672
6	0901	1031	1171	1324	1487	1661	1847	2043	2249	2465
7	0260	0309	0366	0430	0501	0581	0670	0768	0876	0994
8	0054	0067	0082	0101	0122	0148	0177	0210	0249	0293
9	0008	0010	0013	0016	0020	0026	0032	0039	0048	0059
10	0001	0001	0001	0002	0002	0003	0004	0005	0006	0007

P	41	42	43	44	45	46	47	48	49	50
R										
1	9970	9975	9979	9983	9986	9989	9991	9992	9994	9995
2	9739	9776	9808	9836	9861	9882	9900	9916	9930	9941
3	8938	9055	9162	9260	9348	9428	9499	9564	9622	9673
4	7269	7490	7700	7900	8089	8266	8433	8588	8733	8867
5	4948	5223	5495	5764	6029	6288	6541	6787	7026	7256
6	2690	2924	3166	3414	3669	3929	4193	4460	4729	5000
7	1121	1260	1408	1568	1738	1919	2110	2312	2523	2744
8	0343	0399	0461	0532	0610	0696	0791	0895	1009	1133
9	0072	0087	0104	0125	0148	0175	0206	0241	0282	0327
10	0009	0012	0014	0018	0022	0027	0033	0040	0049	0059
11	0001	0001	0001	0001	0002	0002	0002	0003	0004	0005

$$n = 12$$

P	01	02	03	04	05	06	07	08	09	10
R										
1	1136	2153	3062	3873	4596	5241	5814	6323	6775	7176
2	0062	0231	0486	0809	1184	1595	2033	2487	2948	3410
3	0002	0015	0048	0107	0196	0316	0468	0652	0866	1109
4		0001	0003	0010	0022	0043	0075	0120	0180	0256
5				0001	0002	0004	0009	0016	0027	0043
6							0001	0002	0003	0005
7										0001

P	11	12	13	14	15	16	17	18	19	20
R										
1	7530	7843	8120	8363	8578	8766	8931	9076	9202	9313
2	3867	4314	4748	5166	5565	5945	6304	6641	6957	7251
3	1377	1667	1977	2303	2642	2990	3344	3702	4060	4417
4	0351	0464	0597	0750	0922	1114	1324	1552	1795	2054
5	0065	0095	0133	0181	0239	0310	0393	0489	0600	0726
6	0009	0014	0022	0033	0046	0065	0088	0116	0151	0194
7	0001	0002	0003	0004	0007	0010	0015	0021	0029	0039
8					0001	0001	0002	0003	0004	0006
9										0001

P	21	22	23	24	25	26	27	28	29	30
R										
1	9409	9493	9566	9629	9683	9730	9771	9806	9836	9862
2	7524	7776	8009	8222	8416	8594	8755	8900	9032	9150
3	4768	5114	5450	5778	6093	6397	6687	6963	7225	7472
4	2326	2610	2904	3205	3512	3824	4137	4452	4765	5075
5	0866	1021	1192	1377	1576	1790	2016	2254	2504	2763
6	0245	0304	0374	0453	0544	0646	0760	0887	1026	1178
7	0052	0068	0089	0113	0143	0178	0219	0267	0322	0386
8	0008	0011	0016	0021	0028	0036	0047	0060	0076	0095
9	0001	0001	0002	0003	0004	0005	0007	0010	0013	0017
10						0001	0001	0001	0002	0002

P	31	32	33	34	35	36	37	38	39	40
R										
1	9884	9902	9918	9932	9943	9953	9961	9968	9973	9978
2	9256	9350	9435	9509	9576	9634	9685	9730	9770	9804
3	7704	7922	8124	8313	8487	8648	8795	8931	9054	9166
4	5381	5681	5973	6258	6533	6799	7053	7296	7528	7747
5	3032	3308	3590	3876	4167	4459	4751	5043	5332	5618
6	1343	1521	1711	1913	2127	2352	2588	2833	3087	3348
7	0458	0540	0632	0734	0846	0970	1106	1253	1411	1582
8	0118	0144	0176	0213	0255	0304	0359	0422	0493	0573
9	0022	0028	0036	0045	0056	0070	0086	0104	0127	0153
10	0003	0004	0005	0007	0008	0011	0014	0018	0022	0028
11				0001	0001	0001	0001	0002	0002	0003

P	41	42	43	44	45	46	47	48	49	50
R										
1	9982	9986	9988	9990	9992	9994	9995	9996	9997	9998
2	9834	9860	9882	9901	9917	9931	9943	9953	9961	9968
3	9267	9358	9440	9513	9579	9637	9688	9733	9773	9807
4	7953	8147	8329	8498	8655	8801	8934	9057	9168	9270
5	5899	6175	6443	6704	6956	7198	7430	7652	7862	8062
6	3616	3889	4167	4448	4731	5014	5297	5577	5855	6128
7	1765	1959	2164	2380	2607	2843	3089	3343	3604	3872
8	0662	0760	0869	0988	1117	1258	1411	1575	1751	1938
9	0183	0218	0258	0304	0356	0415	0481	0555	0638	0730
10	0035	0043	0053	0065	0079	0095	0114	0137	0163	0193
11	0004	0005	0007	0009	0011	0014	0017	0021	0026	0032
12				0001	0001	0001	0001	0001	0002	0002

$$n = 13$$

P	01	02	03	04	05	06	07	08	09	10
R										
1	1225	2310	3270	4118	4867	5526	6107	6617	7065	7458
2	0072	0270	0564	0932	1354	1814	2298	2794	3293	3787
3	0003	0020	0062	0135	0245	0392	0578	0799	1054	1339
4		0001	0005	0014	0031	0060	0103	0163	0242	0342
5				0001	0003	0007	0013	0024	0041	0065
6						0001	0001	0003	0005	0009
7									0001	0001

P	11	12	13	14	15	16	17	18	19	20
R										
1	7802	8102	8364	8592	8791	8963	9113	9242	9354	9450
2	4270	4738	5186	5614	6017	6396	6751	7080	7384	7664
3	1651	1985	2337	2704	3080	3463	3848	4231	4611	4983
4	0464	0609	0776	0967	1180	1414	1667	1939	2226	2527
5	0097	0139	0193	0260	0342	0438	0551	0681	0827	0991
6	0015	0024	0036	0053	0075	0104	0139	0183	0237	0300
7	0002	0003	0005	0008	0013	0019	0027	0038	0052	0070
8			0001	0001	0002	0003	0004	0006	0009	0012
9								0001	0001	0002

Table I: Cumulative Binomial Distribution $n = 13$

P R	21	22	23	24	25	26	27	28	29	30
1	9533	9604	9666	9718	9762	9800	9833	9860	9883	9903
2	7920	8154	8367	8559	8733	8889	9029	9154	9265	9363
3	5347	5699	6039	6364	6674	6968	7245	7505	7749	7975
4	2839	3161	3489	3822	4157	4493	4826	5155	5478	5794
5	1173	1371	1585	1816	2060	2319	2589	2870	3160	3457
6	0375	0462	0562	0675	0802	0944	1099	1270	1455	1654
7	0093	0120	0154	0195	0243	0299	0365	0440	0527	0624
8	0017	0024	0032	0043	0056	0073	0093	0118	0147	0182
9	0002	0004	0005	0007	0010	0013	0018	0024	0031	0040
10			0001	0001	0001	0002	0003	0004	0005	0007
11									0001	0001

P R	31	32	33	34	35	36	37	38	39	40
1	9920	9934	9945	9955	9963	9970	9975	9980	9984	9987
2	9450	9527	9594	9653	9704	9749	9787	9821	9849	9874
3	8185	8379	8557	8720	8868	9003	9125	9235	9333	9421
4	6101	6398	6683	6957	7217	7464	7698	7917	8123	8314
5	3760	4067	4376	4686	4995	5301	5603	5899	6188	6470
6	1867	2093	2331	2581	2841	3111	3388	3673	3962	4256
7	0733	0854	0988	1135	1295	1468	1654	1853	2065	2288
8	0223	0271	0326	0390	0462	0544	0635	0738	0851	0977
9	0052	0065	0082	0102	0126	0154	0187	0225	0270	0321
10	0009	0012	0015	0020	0025	0032	0040	0051	0063	0078
11	0001	0001	0002	0003	0003	0005	0006	0008	0010	0013
12							0001	0001	0001	0001

P R	41	42	43	44	45	46	47	48	49	50
1	9990	9992	9993	9995	9996	9997	9997	9998	9998	9999
2	9895	9912	9928	9940	9951	9960	9967	9974	9979	9983
3	9499	9569	9630	9684	9731	9772	9808	9838	9865	9888
4	8492	8656	8807	8945	9071	9185	9288	9381	9464	9539
5	6742	7003	7254	7493	7721	7935	8137	8326	8502	8666
6	4552	4849	5146	5441	5732	6019	6299	6573	6838	7095
7	2524	2770	3025	3290	3563	3842	4127	4415	4707	5000
8	1114	1264	1426	1600	1788	1988	2200	2424	2659	2905
9	0379	0446	0520	0605	0698	0803	0918	1045	1183	1334
10	0096	0117	0141	0170	0203	0242	0287	0338	0396	0461
11	0017	0021	0027	0033	0041	0051	0063	0077	0093	0112
12	0002	0002	0003	0004	0005	0007	0009	0011	0014	0017
13							0001	0001	0001	0001

$n = 14$

P R	01	02	03	04	05	06	07	08	09	10
1	1313	2464	3472	4353	5123	5795	6380	6888	7330	7712
2	0084	0310	0645	1059	1530	2037	2564	3100	3632	4154
3	0003	0025	0077	0167	0301	0478	0698	0958	1255	1584
4		0001	0006	0019	0042	0080	0136	0214	0315	0441
5				0002	0004	0010	0020	0035	0059	0092
6						0001	0002	0004	0008	0015
7									0001	0002

P R	11	12	13	14	15	16	17	18	19	20
1	8044	8330	8577	8789	8972	9129	9264	9379	9477	9560
2	4658	5141	5599	6031	6433	6807	7152	7469	7758	8021
3	1939	2315	2708	3111	3521	3932	4341	4744	5138	5519
4	0594	0774	0979	1210	1465	1742	2038	2351	2679	3018
5	0137	0196	0269	0359	0467	0594	0741	0907	1093	1298
6	0024	0038	0057	0082	0115	0157	0209	0273	0349	0439
7	0003	0006	0009	0015	0022	0032	0046	0064	0087	0116
8		0001	0001	0002	0003	0005	0008	0012	0017	0024
9						0001	0001	0002	0003	0004

$n = 14$ — Table I: Cumulative Binomial Distribution

P R	21	22	23	24	25	26	27	28	29	30
1	9631	9691	9742	9786	9822	9852	9878	9899	9917	9932
2	8259	8473	8665	8837	8990	9126	9246	9352	9444	9525
3	5887	6239	6574	6891	7189	7467	7727	7967	8188	8392
4	3366	3719	4076	4432	4787	5136	5479	5813	6137	6448
5	1523	1765	2023	2297	2585	2884	3193	3509	3832	4158
6	0543	0662	0797	0949	1117	1301	1502	1718	1949	2195
7	0152	0196	0248	0310	0383	0467	0563	0673	0796	0933
8	0033	0045	0060	0079	0103	0132	0167	0208	0257	0315
9	0006	0008	0011	0016	0022	0029	0038	0050	0065	0083
10	0001	0001	0002	0002	0003	0005	0007	0009	0012	0017
11						0001	0001	0001	0002	0002

P R	31	32	33	34	35	36	37	38	39	40
1	9945	9955	9963	9970	9976	9981	9984	9988	9990	9992
2	9596	9657	9710	9756	9795	9828	9857	9881	9902	9919
3	8577	8746	8899	9037	9161	9271	9370	9457	9534	9602
4	6747	7032	7301	7556	7795	8018	8226	8418	8595	8757
5	4486	4813	5138	5458	5773	6080	6378	6666	6943	7207
6	2454	2724	3006	3297	3595	3899	4208	4519	4831	5141
7	1084	1250	1431	1626	1836	2059	2296	2545	2805	3075
8	0381	0458	0545	0643	0753	0876	1012	1162	1325	1501
9	0105	0131	0163	0200	0243	0294	0353	0420	0497	0583
10	0022	0029	0037	0048	0060	0076	0095	0117	0144	0175
11	0003	0005	0006	0008	0011	0014	0019	0024	0031	0039
12		0001	0001	0001	0001	0002	0003	0003	0005	0006
13										0001

P R	41	42	43	44	45	46	47	48	49	50
1	9994	9995	9996	9997	9998	9998	9999	9999	9999	9999
2	9934	9946	9956	9964	9971	9977	9981	9985	9988	9991
3	9661	9713	9758	9797	9830	9858	9883	9903	9921	9935
4	8905	9039	9161	9270	9368	9455	9532	9601	9661	9713
5	7459	7697	7922	8132	8328	8510	8678	8833	8974	9102
6	5450	5754	6052	6344	6627	6900	7163	7415	7654	7880
7	3355	3643	3937	4236	4539	4843	5148	5451	5751	6047
8	1692	1896	2113	2344	2586	2840	3105	3380	3663	3953
9	0680	0789	0910	1043	1189	1348	1520	1707	1906	2120
10	0212	0255	0304	0361	0426	0500	0583	0677	0782	0898
11	0049	0061	0076	0093	0114	0139	0168	0202	0241	0287
12	0008	0010	0013	0017	0022	0027	0034	0042	0053	0065
13	0001	0001	0001	0002	0003	0003	0004	0006	0007	0009
14										0001

$n = 15$

P R	01	02	03	04	05	06	07	08	09	10
1	1399	2614	3667	4579	5367	6047	6633	7137	7570	7941
2	0096	0353	0730	1191	1710	2262	2832	3403	3965	4510
3	0004	0030	0094	0203	0362	0571	0829	1130	1469	1841
4		0002	0008	0024	0055	0104	0175	0273	0399	0556
5			0001	0002	0006	0014	0028	0050	0082	0127
6					0001	0001	0003	0007	0013	0022
7							0001	0002	0003	

P R	11	12	13	14	15	16	17	18	19	20
1	8259	8530	8762	8959	9126	9269	9389	9490	9576	9648
2	5031	5524	5987	6417	6814	7179	7511	7813	8085	8329
3	2238	2654	3084	3520	3958	4392	4819	5234	5635	6020
4	0742	0959	1204	1476	1773	2092	2429	2782	3146	3518
5	0187	0265	0361	0478	0617	0778	0961	1167	1394	1642
6	0037	0057	0084	0121	0168	0227	0300	0387	0490	0611
7	0006	0010	0015	0024	0036	0052	0074	0102	0137	0181
8	0001	0001	0002	0004	0006	0010	0014	0021	0030	0042
9					0001	0001	0002	0003	0005	0008
10									0001	0001

P	21	22	23	24	25	26	27	28	29	30
R										
1	9709	9759	9802	9837	9866	9891	9911	9928	9941	9953
2	8547	8741	8913	9065	9198	9315	9417	9505	9581	9647
3	6385	6731	7055	7358	7639	7899	8137	8355	8553	8732
4	3895	4274	4650	5022	5387	5742	6086	6416	6732	7031
5	1910	2195	2495	2810	3135	3469	3810	4154	4500	4845
6	0748	0905	1079	1272	1484	1713	1958	2220	2495	2784
7	0234	0298	0374	0463	0566	0684	0817	0965	1130	1311
8	0058	0078	0104	0135	0173	0219	0274	0338	0413	0500
9	0011	0016	0023	0031	0042	0056	0073	0094	0121	0152
10	0002	0003	0004	0006	0008	0011	0015	0021	0028	0037
11			0001	0001	0001	0002	0002	0003	0005	0007
12									0001	0001

P	31	32	33	34	35	36	37	38	39	40
R										
1	9962	9969	9975	9980	9984	9988	9990	9992	9994	9995
2	9704	9752	9794	9829	9858	9883	9904	9922	9936	9948
3	8893	9038	9167	9281	9383	9472	9550	9618	9678	9729
4	7314	7580	7829	8060	8273	8469	8649	8813	8961	9095
5	5187	5523	5852	6171	6481	6778	7062	7332	7587	7827
6	3084	3393	3709	4032	4357	4684	5011	5335	5654	5968
7	1509	1722	1951	2194	2452	2722	3003	3295	3595	3902
8	0599	0711	0837	0977	1132	1302	1487	1687	1902	2131
9	0190	0236	0289	0351	0422	0504	0597	0702	0820	0950
10	0048	0062	0079	0099	0124	0154	0190	0232	0281	0338
11	0009	0012	0016	0022	0028	0037	0047	0059	0075	0093
12	0001	0002	0003	0004	0005	0006	0009	0011	0015	0019
13					0001	0001	0001	0002	0002	0003

P	41	42	43	44	45	46	47	48	49	50
R										
1	9996	9997	9998	9998	9999	9999	9999	9999	10000	10000
2	9958	9966	9973	9979	9983	9987	9990	9992	9994	9995
3	9773	9811	9843	9870	9893	9913	9929	9943	9954	9963
4	9215	9322	9417	9502	9576	9641	9697	9746	9788	9824
5	8052	8261	8454	8633	8796	8945	9080	9201	9310	9408
6	6274	6570	6856	7131	7392	7641	7875	8095	8301	8491
7	4214	4530	4847	5164	5478	5789	6095	6394	6684	6964
8	2374	2630	2898	3176	3465	3762	4065	4374	4686	5000
9	1095	1254	1427	1615	1818	2034	2265	2510	2767	3036
10	0404	0479	0565	0661	0769	0890	1024	1171	1333	1509
11	0116	0143	0174	0211	0255	0305	0363	0430	0506	0592
12	0025	0032	0040	0051	0063	0079	0097	0119	0145	0176
13	0004	0005	0007	0009	0011	0014	0018	0023	0029	0037
14			0001	0001	0001	0002	0002	0003	0004	0005

$n = 16$

P	01	02	03	04	05	06	07	08	09	10
R										
1	1485	2762	3857	4796	5599	6284	6869	7366	7789	8147
2	0109	0399	0818	1327	1892	2489	3098	3701	4289	4853
3	0005	0037	0113	0242	0429	0673	0969	1311	1694	2108
4		0002	0011	0032	0070	0132	0221	0342	0496	0684
5			0001	0003	0009	0019	0038	0068	0111	0170
6					0001	0002	0005	0010	0019	0033
7							0001	0001	0003	0005
8										0001

P	11	12	13	14	15	16	17	18	19	20
R										
1	8450	8707	8923	9105	9257	9386	9493	9582	9657	9719
2	5386	5885	6347	6773	7161	7513	7830	8115	8368	8593
3	2545	2999	3461	3926	4386	4838	5277	5698	6101	6482
4	0907	1162	1448	1763	2101	2460	2836	3223	3619	4019
5	0248	0348	0471	0618	0791	0988	1211	1458	1727	2018
6	0053	0082	0120	0171	0235	0315	0412	0527	0662	0817
7	0009	0015	0024	0038	0056	0080	0112	0153	0204	0267
8	0001	0002	0004	0007	0011	0016	0024	0036	0051	0070
9			0001	0001	0002	0003	0004	0007	0010	0015
10							0001	0001	0002	0002

P R	21	22	23	24	25	26	27	28	29	30
1	9770	9812	9847	9876	9900	9919	9935	9948	9958	9967
2	8791	8965	9117	9250	9365	9465	9550	9623	9686	9739
3	6839	7173	7483	7768	8029	8267	8482	8677	8851	9006
4	4418	4814	5203	5583	5950	6303	6640	6959	7260	7541
5	2327	2652	2991	3341	3698	4060	4425	4788	5147	5501
6	0992	1188	1405	1641	1897	2169	2458	2761	3077	3402
7	0342	0432	0536	0657	0796	0951	1125	1317	1526	1753
8	0095	0127	0166	0214	0271	0340	0420	0514	0621	0744
9	0021	0030	0041	0056	0075	0098	0127	0163	0206	0257
10	0004	0006	0008	0012	0016	0023	0031	0041	0055	0071
11	0001	0001	0001	0002	0003	0004	0006	0008	0011	0016
12						0001	0001	0001	0002	0003

P R	31	32	33	34	35	36	37	38	39	40
1	9974	9979	9984	9987	9990	9992	9994	9995	9996	9997
2	9784	9822	9854	9880	9902	9921	9936	9948	9959	9967
3	9144	9266	9374	9467	9549	9620	9681	9734	9778	9817
4	7804	8047	8270	8475	8661	8830	8982	9119	9241	9349
5	5846	6181	6504	6813	7108	7387	7649	7895	8123	8334
6	3736	4074	4416	4759	5100	5438	5770	6094	6408	6712
7	1997	2257	2531	2819	3119	3428	3746	4070	4398	4728
8	0881	1035	1205	1391	1594	1813	2048	2298	2562	2839
9	0317	0388	0470	0564	0671	0791	0926	1076	1242	1423
10	0092	0117	0148	0185	0229	0280	0341	0411	0491	0583
11	0021	0028	0037	0048	0062	0079	0100	0125	0155	0191
12	0004	0005	0007	0010	0013	0017	0023	0030	0038	0049
13		0001	0001	0001	0002	0003	0004	0005	0007	0009
14								0001	0001	0001

P R	41	42	43	44	45	46	47	48	49	50
1	9998	9998	9999	9999	9999	9999	10000	10000	10000	10000
2	9974	9979	9984	9987	9990	9992	9994	9995	9997	9997
3	9849	9876	9899	9918	9934	9947	9958	9966	9973	9979
4	9444	9527	9600	9664	9719	9766	9806	9840	9869	9894
5	8529	8707	8869	9015	9147	9265	9370	9463	9544	9616
6	7003	7280	7543	7792	8024	8241	8441	8626	8795	8949
7	5058	5387	5711	6029	6340	6641	6932	7210	7476	7728
8	3128	3428	3736	4051	4371	4694	5019	5343	5665	5982
9	1619	1832	2060	2302	2559	2829	3111	3405	3707	4018
10	0687	0805	0936	1081	1241	1416	1607	1814	2036	2272
11	0234	0284	0342	0409	0486	0574	0674	0786	0911	1051
12	0062	0078	0098	0121	0149	0183	0222	0268	0322	0384
13	0012	0016	0021	0027	0035	0044	0055	0069	0086	0106
14	0002	0002	0003	0004	0006	0007	0010	0013	0016	0021
15					0001	0001	0001	0001	0002	0003

$n = 17$

P R	01	02	03	04	05	06	07	08	09	10
1	1571	2907	4042	5004	5819	6507	7088	7577	7988	8332
2	0123	0446	0909	1465	2078	2717	3362	3995	4604	5182
3	0006	0044	0134	0286	0503	0782	1118	1503	1927	2382
4		0003	0014	0040	0088	0164	0273	0419	0603	0826
5			0001	0004	0012	0026	0051	0089	0145	0221
6					0001	0003	0007	0015	0027	0047
7							0001	0002	0004	0008
8										0001

P R	11	12	13	14	15	16	17	18	19	20
1	8621	8862	9063	9230	9369	9484	9579	9657	9722	9775
2	5723	6223	6682	7099	7475	7813	8113	8379	8613	8818
3	2858	3345	3836	4324	4802	5266	5711	6133	6532	6904
4	1087	1383	1710	2065	2444	2841	3251	3669	4091	4511
5	0321	0446	0598	0778	0987	1224	1487	1775	2087	2418
6	0075	0114	0166	0234	0319	0423	0548	0695	0864	1057
7	0014	0023	0037	0056	0083	0118	0163	0220	0291	0377
8	0002	0004	0007	0011	0017	0027	0039	0057	0080	0109
9		0001	0001	0002	0003	0005	0008	0012	0018	0026
10						0001	0001	0002	0003	0005
11										0001

P	21	22	23	24	25	26	27	28	29	30
R										
1	9818	9854	9882	9906	9925	9940	9953	9962	9970	9977
2	8996	9152	9285	9400	9499	9583	9654	9714	9765	9807
3	7249	7567	7859	8123	8363	8578	8771	8942	9093	9226
4	4927	5333	5728	6107	6470	6814	7137	7440	7721	7981
5	2766	3128	3500	3879	4261	4643	5023	5396	5760	6113
6	1273	1510	1770	2049	2347	2661	2989	3329	3677	4032
7	0479	0598	0736	0894	1071	1268	1485	1721	1976	2248
8	0147	0194	0251	0320	0402	0499	0611	0739	0884	1046
9	0037	0051	0070	0094	0124	0161	0206	0261	0326	0403
10	0007	0011	0016	0022	0031	0042	0057	0075	0098	0127
11	0001	0002	0003	0004	0006	0009	0013	0018	0024	0032
12				0001	0001	0002	0002	0003	0005	0007
13									0001	0001

P	31	32	33	34	35	36	37	38	39	40
R										
1	9982	9986	9989	9991	9993	9995	9996	9997	9998	9998
2	9843	9872	9896	9917	9933	9946	9957	9966	9973	9979
3	9343	9444	9532	9608	9673	9728	9775	9815	9849	9877
4	8219	8437	8634	8812	8972	9115	9241	9353	9450	9536
5	6453	6778	7087	7378	7652	7906	8142	8360	8559	8740
6	4390	4749	5105	5458	5803	6139	6465	6778	7077	7361
7	2536	2838	3153	3479	3812	4152	4495	4839	5182	5522
8	1227	1426	1642	1877	2128	2395	2676	2971	3278	3595
9	0492	0595	0712	0845	0994	1159	1341	1541	1757	1989
10	0162	0204	0254	0314	0383	0464	0557	0664	0784	0919
11	0043	0057	0074	0095	0120	0151	0189	0234	0286	0348
12	0009	0013	0017	0023	0030	0040	0051	0066	0084	0106
13	0002	0002	0003	0004	0006	0008	0011	0015	0019	0025
14				0001	0001	0001	0002	0002	0003	0005
15										0001

P	41	42	43	44	45	46	47	48	49	50
R										
1	9999	9999	9999	9999	10000	10000	10000	10000	10000	10000
2	9984	9987	9990	9992	9994	9996	9997	9998	9998	9999
3	9900	9920	9935	9948	9959	9968	9975	9980	9985	9988
4	9610	9674	9729	9776	9816	9849	9877	9901	9920	9936
5	8904	9051	9183	9301	9404	9495	9575	9644	9704	9755
6	7628	7879	8113	8330	8529	8712	8878	9028	9162	9283
7	5856	6182	6499	6805	7098	7377	7641	7890	8122	8338
8	3920	4250	4585	4921	5257	5590	5918	6239	6552	6855
9	2238	2502	2780	3072	3374	3687	4008	4335	4667	5000
10	1070	1236	1419	1618	1834	2066	2314	2577	2855	3145
11	0420	0503	0597	0705	0826	0962	1112	1279	1462	1662
12	0133	0165	0203	0248	0301	0363	0434	0517	0611	0717
13	0033	0042	0054	0069	0086	0108	0134	0165	0202	0245
14	0006	0008	0011	0014	0019	0024	0031	0040	0050	0064
15	0001	0001	0002	0002	0003	0004	0005	0007	0009	0012
16							0001	0001	0001	0001

$n = 18$

P	01	02	03	04	05	06	07	08	09	10
R										
1	1655	3049	4220	5204	6028	6717	7292	7771	8169	8499
2	0138	0495	1003	1607	2265	2945	3622	4281	4909	5497
3	0007	0052	0157	0333	0581	0898	1275	1702	2168	2662
4		0004	0018	0050	0109	0201	0333	0506	0723	0982
5			0002	0006	0015	0034	0067	0116	0186	0282
6				0001	0002	0005	0010	0021	0038	0064
7							0001	0003	0006	0012
8									0001	0002

P	11	12	13	14	15	16	17	18	19	20
R										
1	8773	8998	9185	9338	9464	9566	9651	9719	9775	9820
2	6042	6540	6992	7398	7759	8080	8362	8609	8824	9009
3	3173	3690	4206	4713	5203	5673	6119	6538	6927	7287
4	1282	1618	1986	2382	2798	3229	3669	4112	4554	4990
5	0405	0558	0743	0959	1206	1482	1787	2116	2467	2836

$n = 18$

Table I: Cumulative Binomial Distribution

P → R	11	12	13	14	15	16	17	18	19	20
6	0102	0154	0222	0310	0419	0551	0708	0889	1097	1329
7	0021	0034	0054	0081	0118	0167	0229	0306	0400	0513
8	0003	0006	0011	0017	0027	0041	0060	0086	0120	0163
9		0001	0002	0003	0005	0008	0013	0020	0029	0043
10					0001	0001	0002	0004	0006	0009
11								0001	0001	0002

P → R	21	22	23	24	25	26	27	28	29	30
1	9856	9886	9909	9928	9944	9956	9965	9973	9979	9984
2	9169	9306	9423	9522	9605	9676	9735	9784	9824	9858
3	7616	7916	8187	8430	8647	8839	9009	9158	9288	9400
4	5414	5825	6218	6591	6943	7272	7578	7860	8119	8354
5	3220	3613	4012	4414	4813	5208	5594	5968	6329	6673
6	1586	1866	2168	2488	2825	3176	3538	3907	4281	4656
7	0645	0799	0974	1171	1390	1630	1891	2171	2469	2783
8	0217	0283	0363	0458	0569	0699	0847	1014	1200	1407
9	0060	0083	0112	0148	0193	0249	0316	0395	0488	0596
10	0014	0020	0028	0039	0054	0073	0097	0127	0164	0210
11	0003	0004	0006	0009	0012	0018	0025	0034	0046	0061
12		0001	0001	0002	0002	0003	0005	0007	0010	0014
13						0001	0001	0001	0002	0003

P → R	31	32	33	34	35	36	37	38	39	40
1	9987	9990	9993	9994	9996	9997	9998	9998	9999	9999
2	9886	9908	9927	9942	9954	9964	9972	9978	9983	9987
3	9498	9581	9652	9713	9764	9807	9843	9873	9897	9918
4	8568	8759	8931	9083	9217	9335	9439	9528	9606	9672
5	7001	7309	7598	7866	8114	8341	8549	8737	8907	9058
6	5029	5398	5759	6111	6450	6776	7086	7379	7655	7912
7	3111	3450	3797	4151	4509	4867	5224	5576	5921	6257
8	1633	1878	2141	2421	2717	3027	3349	3681	4021	4366
9	0720	0861	1019	1196	1391	1604	1835	2084	2350	2632
10	0264	0329	0405	0494	0597	0714	0847	0997	1163	1347
11	0080	0104	0133	0169	0212	0264	0325	0397	0480	0576
12	0020	0027	0036	0047	0062	0080	0102	0130	0163	0203
13	0004	0005	0008	0011	0014	0019	0026	0034	0044	0058
14	0001	0001	0001	0002	0003	0004	0005	0007	0010	0013
15						0001	0001	0001	0002	0002

P → R	41	42	43	44	45	46	47	48	49	50
1	9999	9999	10000	10000	10000	10000	10000	10000	10000	10000
2	9990	9992	9994	9996	9997	9998	9998	9999	9999	9999
3	9934	9948	9968	9975	9981	9985	9989	9991	9993	
4	9729	9777	9818	9852	9880	9904	9923	9939	9952	9962
5	9193	9313	9418	9510	9589	9658	9717	9767	9810	9846
6	8151	8372	8573	8757	8923	9072	9205	9324	9428	9519
7	6582	6895	7193	7476	7742	7991	8222	8436	8632	8811
8	4713	5062	5408	5750	6085	6412	6728	7032	7322	7597
9	2928	3236	3556	3885	4222	4562	4906	5249	5591	5927
10	1549	1768	2004	2258	2527	2812	3110	3421	3742	4073
11	0686	0811	0951	1107	1280	1470	1677	1902	2144	2403
12	0250	0307	0372	0449	0537	0638	0753	0883	1028	1189
13	0074	0094	0118	0147	0183	0225	0275	0334	0402	0481
14	0017	0022	0029	0038	0049	0063	0079	0100	0125	0154
15	0003	0004	0006	0007	0010	0013	0017	0023	0029	0038
16		0001	0001	0001	0001	0002	0003	0004	0005	0007
17									0001	0001

$n = 19$

P → R	01	02	03	04	05	06	07	08	09	10
1	1738	3188	4394	5396	6226	6914	7481	7949	8334	8649
2	0153	0546	1100	1751	2453	3171	3879	4560	5202	5797
3	0009	0061	0183	0384	0665	1021	1439	1908	2415	2946
4		0005	0022	0061	0132	0243	0398	0602	0853	1150
5			0002	0007	0020	0044	0085	0147	0235	0352
6				0001	0002	0006	0014	0029	0051	0086
7						0001	0002	0004	0009	0017
8								0001	0001	0003

Table I: Cumulative Binomial Distribution $n = 19$

P / R	11	12	13	14	15	16	17	18	19	20
1	8908	9119	9291	9431	9544	9636	9710	9770	9818	9856
2	6342	6835	7277	7669	8015	8318	8581	8809	9004	9171
3	3488	4032	4568	5089	5587	6059	6500	6910	7287	7631
4	1490	1867	2275	2708	3159	3620	4085	4549	5005	5449
5	0502	0685	0904	1158	1444	1762	2107	2476	2864	3267
6	0135	0202	0290	0401	0537	0700	0891	1110	1357	1631
7	0030	0048	0076	0113	0163	0228	0310	0411	0532	0676
8	0005	0009	0016	0026	0041	0061	0089	0126	0173	0233
9	0001	0002	0003	0005	0008	0014	0021	0032	0047	0067
10				0001	0001	0002	0004	0007	0010	0016
11							0001	0001	0002	0003

P / R	21	22	23	24	25	26	27	28	29	30
1	9887	9911	9930	9946	9958	9967	9975	9981	9985	9989
2	9313	9434	9535	9619	9690	9749	9797	9837	9869	9896
3	7942	8222	8471	8692	8887	9057	9205	9333	9443	9538
4	5877	6285	6671	7032	7369	7680	7965	8224	8458	8668
5	3681	4100	4520	4936	5346	5744	6129	6498	6848	7178
6	1929	2251	2592	2950	3322	3705	4093	4484	4875	5261
7	0843	1034	1248	1487	1749	2032	2336	2657	2995	3345
8	0307	0396	0503	0629	0775	0941	1129	1338	1568	1820
9	0093	0127	0169	0222	0287	0366	0459	0568	0694	0839
10	0023	0034	0047	0066	0089	0119	0156	0202	0258	0326
11	0005	0007	0011	0016	0023	0032	0044	0060	0080	0105
12	0001	0001	0002	0003	0005	0007	0010	0015	0021	0028
13				0001	0001	0001	0002	0003	0004	0006
14									0001	0001

P / R	31	32	33	34	35	36	37	38	39	40
1	9991	9993	9995	9996	9997	9998	9998	9999	9999	9999
2	9917	9935	9949	9960	9969	9976	9981	9986	9989	9992
3	9618	9686	9743	9791	9830	9863	9890	9913	9931	9945
4	8856	9022	9169	9297	9409	9505	9588	9659	9719	9770
5	7486	7773	8037	8280	8500	8699	8878	9038	9179	9304
6	5641	6010	6366	6707	7032	7339	7627	7895	8143	8371
7	3705	4073	4445	4818	5188	5554	5913	6261	6597	6919
8	2091	2381	2688	3010	3344	3690	4043	4401	4762	5122
9	1003	1186	1389	1612	1855	2116	2395	2691	3002	3325
10	0405	0499	0608	0733	0875	1035	1213	1410	1626	1861
11	0137	0176	0223	0280	0347	0426	0518	0625	0747	0885
12	0038	0051	0068	0089	0114	0146	0185	0231	0287	0352
13	0009	0012	0017	0023	0031	0041	0054	0070	0091	0116
14	0002	0002	0003	0005	0007	0009	0013	0017	0023	0031
15			0001	0001	0001	0002	0002	0003	0005	0006
16									0001	0001

P / R	41	42	43	44	45	46	47	48	49	50
1	10000	10000	10000	10000	10000	10000	10000	10000	10000	10000
2	9994	9995	9996	9997	9998	9999	9999	9999	9999	10000
3	9957	9967	9974	9980	9985	9988	9991	9993	9995	10000
4	9813	9849	9878	9903	9923	9939	9952	9963	9971	9996
5	9413	9508	9590	9660	9720	9771	9814	9850	9879	9904
6	8579	8767	8937	9088	9223	9342	9446	9537	9615	9682
7	7226	7515	7787	8039	8273	8488	8684	8862	9022	9165
8	5480	5832	6176	6509	6831	7138	7430	7706	7964	8204
9	3660	4003	4353	4706	5060	5413	5762	6105	6439	6762
10	2114	2385	2672	2974	3290	3617	3954	4299	4648	5000
11	1040	1213	1404	1613	1841	2087	2351	2631	2928	3238
12	0429	0518	0621	0738	0871	1021	1187	1372	1575	1796
13	0146	0183	0227	0280	0342	0415	0500	0597	0709	0835
14	0040	0052	0067	0086	0109	0137	0171	0212	0261	0318
15	0009	0012	0016	0021	0028	0036	0046	0060	0076	0096
16	0001	0002	0003	0004	0005	0007	0010	0013	0017	0022
17				0001	0001	0001	0001	0002	0003	0004

Table I: Cumulative Binomial Distribution

n = 20

P	01	02	03	04	05	06	07	08	09	10
R										
1	1821	3324	4562	5580	6415	7099	7658	8113	8484	8784
2	0169	0599	1198	1897	2642	3395	4131	4831	5484	6083
3	0010	0071	0210	0439	0755	1150	1610	2121	2666	3231
4		0006	0027	0074	0159	0290	0471	0706	0993	1330
5			0003	0010	0026	0056	0107	0183	0290	0432
6				0001	0003	0009	0019	0038	0068	0113
7						0001	0003	0006	0013	0024
8								0001	0002	0004
9										0001

P	11	12	13	14	15	16	17	18	19	20
R										
1	9028	9224	9383	9510	9612	9694	9759	9811	9852	9885
2	6624	7109	7539	7916	8244	8529	8773	8982	9159	9308
3	3802	4369	4920	5450	5951	6420	6854	7252	7614	7939
4	1710	2127	2573	3041	3523	4010	4496	4974	5439	5886
5	0610	0827	1083	1375	1702	2059	2443	2849	3271	3704
6	0175	0260	0370	0507	0673	0870	1098	1356	1643	1958
7	0041	0067	0103	0153	0219	0304	0409	0537	0689	0867
8	0008	0014	0024	0038	0059	0088	0127	0177	0241	0321
9	0001	0002	0005	0008	0013	0021	0033	0049	0071	0100
10			0001	0001	0002	0004	0007	0011	0017	0026
11						0001	0001	0002	0004	0006
12									0001	0001

P	21	22	23	24	25	26	27	28	29	30
R										
1	9910	9931	9946	9959	9968	9976	9982	9986	9989	9992
2	9434	9539	9626	9698	9757	9805	9845	9877	9903	9924
3	8230	8488	8716	8915	9087	9237	9365	9474	9567	9645
4	6310	6711	7085	7431	7748	8038	8300	8534	8744	8929
5	4142	4580	5014	5439	5852	6248	6625	6981	7315	7625
6	2297	2657	3035	3427	3828	4235	4643	5048	5447	5836
7	1071	1301	1557	1838	2142	2467	2810	3169	3540	3920
8	0419	0536	0675	0835	1018	1225	1455	1707	1982	2277
9	0138	0186	0246	0320	0409	0515	0640	0784	0948	1133
10	0038	0054	0075	0103	0139	0183	0238	0305	0385	0480
11	0009	0013	0019	0028	0039	0055	0074	0100	0132	0171
12	0002	0003	0004	0006	0009	0014	0019	0027	0038	0051
13			0001	0001	0002	0003	0004	0006	0009	0013
14							0001	0001	0002	0003

P	31	32	33	34	35	36	37	38	39	40
R										
1	9994	9996	9997	9998	9998	9999	9999	9999	9999	10000
2	9940	9953	9964	9972	9979	9984	9988	9991	9993	9995
3	9711	9765	9811	9848	9879	9904	9924	9940	9953	9964
4	9092	9235	9358	9465	9556	9634	9700	9755	9802	9840
5	7911	8173	8411	8626	8818	8989	9141	9274	9390	9490
6	6213	6574	6917	7242	7546	7829	8090	8329	8547	8744
7	4305	4693	5079	5460	5834	6197	6547	6882	7200	7500
8	2591	2922	3268	3624	3990	4361	4735	5108	5478	5841
9	1340	1568	1818	2087	2376	2683	3005	3341	3688	4044
10	0591	0719	0866	1032	1218	1424	1650	1897	2163	2447
11	0220	0279	0350	0434	0532	0645	0775	0923	1090	1275
12	0069	0091	0119	0154	0196	0247	0308	0381	0466	0565
13	0018	0025	0034	0045	0060	0079	0102	0132	0167	0210
14	0004	0006	0008	0011	0015	0021	0028	0037	0049	0065
15	0001	0001	0001	0002	0003	0004	0006	0009	0012	0016
16						0001	0001	0002	0002	0003

P	41	42	43	44	45	46	47	48	49	50
R										
1	10000	10000	10000	10000	10000	10000	10000	10000	10000	10000
2	9996	9997	9998	9998	9999	9999	9999	10000	10000	10000
3	9972	9979	9984	9988	9991	9993	9995	9996	9997	9998
4	9872	9898	9920	9937	9951	9962	9971	9977	9983	9987
5	9577	9651	9714	9767	9811	9848	9879	9904	9924	9941

Table I: Cumulative Binomial Distribution   n = 20

R \ P	41	42	43	44	45	46	47	48	49	50
6	8921	9078	9217	9340	9447	9539	9619	9687	9745	9793
7	7780	8041	8281	8501	8701	8881	9042	9186	9312	9423
8	6196	6539	6868	7183	7480	7759	8020	8261	8482	8684
9	4406	4771	5136	5499	5857	6207	6546	6873	7186	7483
10	2748	3064	3394	3736	4086	4443	4804	5166	5525	5881
11	1480	1705	1949	2212	2493	2791	3104	3432	3771	4119
12	0679	0810	0958	1123	1308	1511	1734	1977	2238	2517
13	0262	0324	0397	0482	0580	0694	0823	0969	1133	1316
14	0084	0107	0136	0172	0214	0265	0326	0397	0480	0577
15	0022	0029	0038	0050	0064	0083	0105	0133	0166	0207
16	0004	0006	0008	0011	0015	0020	0027	0035	0046	0059
17	0001	0001	0001	0002	0003	0004	0005	0007	0010	0013
18						0001	0001	0001	0001	0002

n = 50

R \ P	01	02	03	04	05	06	07	08	09	10
1	3950	6358	7819	8701	9231	9547	9734	9845	9910	9948
2	0894	2642	4447	5995	7206	8100	8735	9173	9468	9662
3	0138	0784	1892	3233	4595	5838	6892	7740	8395	8883
4	0016	0178	0628	1391	2396	3527	4673	5747	6697	7497
5	0001	0032	0168	0490	1036	1794	2710	3710	4723	5688
6		0005	0037	0144	0378	0776	1350	2081	2928	3839
7		0001	0007	0036	0118	0289	0583	1019	1596	2298
8			0001	0008	0032	0094	0220	0438	0768	1221
9				0001	0008	0027	0073	0167	0328	0579
10					0002	0007	0022	0056	0125	0245
11						0002	0006	0017	0043	0094
12							0001	0005	0013	0032
13								0001	0004	0010
14									0001	0003
15										0001

R \ P	11	12	13	14	15	16	17	18	19	20
1	9971	9983	9991	9995	9997	9998	9999	10000	10000	10000
2	9788	9869	9920	9951	9971	9983	9990	9994	9997	9998
3	9237	9487	9661	9779	9858	9910	9944	9965	9979	9987
4	8146	8655	9042	9330	9540	9688	9792	9863	9912	9943
5	6562	7320	7956	8472	8879	9192	9428	9601	9726	9815
6	4760	5647	6463	7186	7806	8323	8741	9071	9327	9520
7	3091	3935	4789	5616	6387	7081	7686	8199	8624	8966
8	1793	2467	3217	4010	4812	5594	6328	6996	7587	8096
9	0932	1392	1955	2605	3319	4071	4832	5576	6280	6927
10	0435	0708	1074	1537	2089	2718	3403	4122	4849	5563
11	0183	0325	0535	0824	1199	1661	2203	2813	3473	4164
12	0069	0135	0242	0402	0628	0929	1309	1768	2300	2893
13	0024	0051	0100	0179	0301	0475	0714	1022	1405	1861
14	0008	0018	0037	0073	0132	0223	0357	0544	0791	1106
15	0002	0006	0013	0027	0053	0096	0164	0266	0411	0607
16	0001	0002	0004	0009	0019	0038	0070	0120	0197	0308
17			0001	0003	0007	0014	0027	0050	0087	0144
18				0001	0002	0005	0010	0019	0036	0063
19						0001	0003	0007	0013	0025
20							0001	0002	0005	0009
21								0001	0002	0003
22										0001

R \ P	21	22	23	24	25	26	27	28	29	30
1	10000	10000	10000	10000	10000	10000	10000	10000	10000	10000
2	9999	9999	10000	10000	10000	10000	10000	10000	10000	10000
3	9992	9995	9997	9998	9999	10000	10000	10000	10000	10000
4	9964	9978	9986	9992	9995	9997	9998	9999	9999	10000
5	9877	9919	9948	9967	9979	9987	9992	9995	9997	9998
6	9663	9767	9841	9893	9930	9954	9970	9981	9988	9993
7	9236	9445	9603	9720	9806	9868	9911	9941	9961	9975
8	8523	8874	9156	9377	9547	9676	9772	9842	9892	9927
9	7505	8009	8437	8794	9084	9316	9497	9635	9740	9817
10	6241	6870	7436	7934	8363	8724	9021	9260	9450	9598

P\R	21	22	23	24	25	26	27	28	29	30
11	4864	5552	6210	6822	7378	7871	8299	8663	8965	9211
12	3533	4201	4878	5544	6184	6782	7329	7817	8244	8610
13	2383	2963	3585	4233	4890	5539	6163	6749	7287	7771
14	1490	1942	2456	3023	3630	4261	4901	5534	6145	6721
15	0862	1181	1565	2013	2519	3075	3669	4286	4912	5532
16	0462	0665	0926	1247	1631	2075	2575	3121	3703	4308
17	0229	0347	0508	0718	0983	1306	1689	2130	2623	3161
18	0105	0168	0259	0384	0551	0766	1034	1359	1741	2178
19	0045	0075	0122	0191	0287	0418	0590	0809	1080	1406
20	0018	0031	0054	0088	0139	0212	0314	0449	0626	0848
21	0006	0012	0022	0038	0063	0100	0155	0232	0338	0478
22	0002	0004	0008	0015	0026	0044	0071	0112	0170	0251
23	0001	0001	0003	0006	0010	0018	0031	0050	0080	0123
24			0001	0002	0004	0007	0012	0021	0035	0056
25				0001	0001	0002	0004	0008	0014	0024
26						0001	0002	0003	0005	0009
27								0001	0002	0003
28									0001	0001

P\R	31	32	33	34	35	36	37	38	39	40
1	10000	10000	10000	10000	10000	10000	10000	10000	10000	10000
2	10000	10000	10000	10000	10000	10000	10000	10000	10000	10000
3	10000	10000	10000	10000	10000	10000	10000	10000	10000	10000
4	10000	10000	10000	10000	10000	10000	10000	10000	10000	10000
5	9999	9999	10000	10000	10000	10000	10000	10000	10000	10000
6	9996	9997	9998	9999	9999	10000	10000	10000	10000	10000
7	9984	9990	9994	9996	9998	9999	9999	10000	10000	10000
8	9952	9969	9980	9987	9992	9995	9997	9998	9999	9999
9	9874	9914	9942	9962	9975	9984	9990	9994	9996	9998
10	9710	9794	9856	9901	9933	9955	9971	9981	9988	9992
11	9409	9563	9683	9773	9840	9889	9924	9949	9966	9978
12	8916	9168	9371	9533	9658	9753	9825	9878	9916	9943
13	8197	8564	8873	9130	9339	9505	9635	9736	9811	9867
14	7253	7732	8157	8524	8837	9097	9310	9481	9616	9720
15	6131	6698	7223	7699	8122	8491	8805	9069	9286	9460
16	4922	5530	6120	6679	7199	7672	8094	8462	8779	9045
17	3734	4328	4931	5530	6111	6664	7179	7649	8070	8439
18	2666	3197	3760	4346	4940	5531	6105	6653	7164	7631
19	1786	2220	2703	3227	3784	4362	4949	5533	6101	6644
20	1121	1447	1826	2257	2736	3255	3805	4376	4957	5535
21	0657	0882	1156	1482	1861	2289	2764	3278	3824	4390
22	0360	0503	0685	0912	1187	1513	1890	2317	2788	3299
23	0184	0267	0379	0525	0710	0938	1214	1540	1916	2340
24	0087	0133	0196	0282	0396	0544	0730	0960	1236	1562
25	0039	0061	0094	0141	0207	0295	0411	0560	0748	0978
26	0016	0026	0042	0066	0100	0149	0216	0305	0423	0573
27	0006	0011	0018	0029	0045	0070	0106	0155	0223	0314
28	0002	0004	0007	0012	0019	0031	0048	0074	0110	0160
29	0001	0001	0002	0004	0007	0012	0020	0032	0050	0076
30			0001	0002	0003	0005	0008	0013	0021	0034
31					0001	0002	0003	0005	0008	0014
32						0001	0001	0002	0003	0005
33								0001	0001	0002
34										0001

P\R	41	42	43	44	45	46	47	48	49	50
1	10000	10000	10000	10000	10000	10000	10000	10000	10000	10000
2	10000	10000	10000	10000	10000	10000	10000	10000	10000	10000
3	10000	10000	10000	10000	10000	10000	10000	10000	10000	10000
4	10000	10000	10000	10000	10000	10000	10000	10000	10000	10000
5	10000	10000	10000	10000	10000	10000	10000	10000	10000	10000
6	10000	10000	10000	10000	10000	10000	10000	10000	10000	10000
7	10000	10000	10000	10000	10000	10000	10000	10000	10000	10000
8	10000	10000	10000	10000	10000	10000	10000	10000	10000	10000
9	9999	9999	9999	10000	10000	10000	10000	10000	10000	10000
10	9995	9997	9998	9999	9999	9999	10000	10000	10000	10000
11	9986	9991	9994	9997	9998	9999	9999	10000	10000	10000
12	9962	9975	9984	9990	9994	9996	9998	9999	9999	10000
13	9908	9938	9958	9973	9982	9989	9993	9996	9997	9998
14	9799	9858	9902	9933	9955	9970	9981	9988	9992	9995
15	9599	9707	9789	9851	9896	9929	9952	9968	9980	9987

P\R	41	42	43	44	45	46	47	48	49	50
16	9265	9443	9585	9696	9780	9844	9892	9926	9950	9967
17	8757	9025	9248	9429	9573	9687	9774	9839	9888	9923
18	8051	8421	8740	9010	9235	9418	9565	9680	9769	9836
19	7152	7617	8037	8406	8727	8998	9225	9410	9559	9675
20	6099	6638	7143	7608	8026	8396	8718	8991	9219	9405
21	4965	5539	6099	6635	7138	7602	8020	8391	8713	8987
22	3840	4402	4973	5543	6100	6634	7137	7599	8018	8389
23	2809	3316	3854	4412	4981	5548	6104	6636	7138	7601
24	1936	2359	2826	3331	3866	4422	4989	5554	6109	6641
25	1255	1580	1953	2375	2840	3343	3876	4431	4996	5561
26	0762	0992	1269	1593	1966	2386	2850	3352	3885	4439
27	0432	0584	0772	1003	1279	1603	1975	2395	2858	3359
28	0229	0320	0439	0591	0780	1010	1286	1609	1981	2399
29	0113	0164	0233	0325	0444	0595	0784	1013	1289	1611
30	0052	0078	0115	0166	0235	0327	0446	0596	0784	1013
31	0022	0034	0053	0079	0116	0167	0236	0327	0445	0595
32	0009	0014	0022	0035	0053	0079	0116	0166	0234	0325
33	0003	0005	0009	0014	0022	0035	0053	0078	0114	0164
34	0001	0002	0003	0005	0009	0014	0022	0034	0052	0077
35		0001	0001	0002	0003	0005	0008	0014	0021	0033
36				0001	0001	0002	0003	0005	0008	0013
37						0001	0001	0002	0003	0005
38								0001	0001	0002

$n = 100$

P\R	01	02	03	04	05	06	07	08	09	10
1	6340	8674	9524	9831	9941	9979	9993	9998	9999	10000
2	2642	5967	8054	9128	9629	9848	9940	9977	9991	9997
3	0794	3233	5802	7679	8817	9434	9742	9887	9952	9981
4	0184	1410	3528	5705	7422	8570	9256	9633	9827	9922
5	0034	0508	1821	3711	5640	7232	8368	9097	9526	9763
6	0005	0155	0808	2116	3840	5593	7086	8201	8955	9424
7	0001	0041	0312	1064	2340	3936	5557	6968	8060	8828
8		0009	0106	0475	1280	2517	4012	5529	6872	7939
9		0002	0032	0190	0631	1463	2660	4074	5506	6791
10			0009	0068	0282	0775	1620	2780	4125	5487
11			0002	0022	0115	0376	0908	1757	2882	4168
12				0007	0043	0168	0469	1028	1876	2970
13				0002	0015	0069	0224	0559	1138	1982
14					0005	0026	0099	0282	0645	1239
15					0001	0009	0041	0133	0341	0726
16						0003	0016	0058	0169	0399
17						0001	0006	0024	0078	0206
18							0002	0009	0034	0100
19							0001	0003	0014	0046
20								0001	0005	0020
21									0002	0008
22									0001	0003
23										0001

P\R	11	12	13	14	15	16	17	18	19	20
1	10000	10000	10000	10000	10000	10000	10000	10000	10000	10000
2	9999	10000	10000	10000	10000	10000	10000	10000	10000	10000
3	9992	9997	9999	10000	10000	10000	10000	10000	10000	10000
4	9966	9985	9994	9998	9999	10000	10000	10000	10000	10000
5	9886	9947	9977	9990	9996	9998	9999	10000	10000	10000
6	9698	9848	9926	9966	9984	9993	9997	9999	10000	10000
7	9328	9633	9808	9903	9953	9978	9990	9996	9998	9999
8	8715	9239	9569	9766	9878	9939	9970	9986	9994	9997
9	7835	8614	9155	9508	9725	9853	9924	9962	9982	9991
10	6722	7743	8523	9078	9449	9684	9826	9908	9953	9977
11	5471	6663	7663	8440	9006	9393	9644	9800	9891	9943
12	4206	5458	6611	7591	8365	8939	9340	9605	9773	9874
13	3046	4239	5446	6566	7527	8297	8876	9289	9567	9747
14	2076	3114	4268	5436	6526	7469	8234	8819	9241	9531
15	1330	2160	3173	4294	5428	6490	7417	8177	8765	9196
16	0802	1414	2236	3227	4317	5420	6458	7370	8125	8715
17	0456	0874	1492	2305	3275	4338	5414	6429	7327	8077
18	0244	0511	0942	1563	2367	3319	4357	5408	6403	7288
19	0123	0282	0564	1006	1628	2424	3359	4374	5403	6379
20	0059	0147	0319	0614	1065	1689	2477	3395	4391	5398

R \ P	11	12	13	14	15	16	17	18	19	20
21	0026	0073	0172	0356	0663	1121	1745	2525	3429	4405
22	0011	0034	0088	0196	0393	0710	1174	1797	2570	3460
23	0005	0015	0042	0103	0221	0428	0754	1223	1846	2611
24	0002	0006	0020	0051	0119	0246	0462	0796	1270	1891
25	0001	0003	0009	0024	0061	0135	0271	0496	0837	1314
26		0001	0004	0011	0030	0071	0151	0295	0528	0875
27			0001	0005	0014	0035	0081	0168	0318	0558
28			0001	0002	0006	0017	0041	0091	0184	0342
29				0001	0003	0008	0020	0048	0102	0200
30					0001	0003	0009	0024	0054	0112
31						0001	0004	0011	0027	0061
32						0001	0002	0005	0013	0031
33							0001	0002	0006	0016
34								0001	0003	0007
35									0001	0003
36										0001
37										0001

R \ P	21	22	23	24	25	26	27	28	29	30
1	10000	10000	10000	10000	10000	10000	10000	10000	10000	10000
2	10000	10000	10000	10000	10000	10000	10000	10000	10000	10000
3	10000	10000	10000	10000	10000	10000	10000	10000	10000	10000
4	10000	10000	10000	10000	10000	10000	10000	10000	10000	10000
5	10000	10000	10000	10000	10000	10000	10000	10000	10000	10000
6	10000	10000	10000	10000	10000	10000	10000	10000	10000	10000
7	10000	10000	10000	10000	10000	10000	10000	10000	10000	10000
8	9999	10000	10000	10000	10000	10000	10000	10000	10000	10000
9	9996	9998	9999	10000	10000	10000	10000	10000	10000	10000
10	9989	9995	9998	10000	10000	10000	10000	10000	10000	10000
11	9971	9986	9993	9997	9999	9999	10000	10000	10000	10000
12	9933	9965	9983	9992	9996	9998	9999	10000	10000	10000
13	9857	9922	9959	9979	9990	9995	9998	9999	10000	10000
14	9721	9840	9911	9953	9975	9988	9994	9997	9999	9999
15	9496	9695	9823	9900	9946	9972	9986	9993	9997	9998
16	9153	9462	9671	9806	9889	9939	9967	9983	9992	9996
17	8668	9112	9430	9647	9789	9878	9932	9963	9981	9990
18	8032	8625	9074	9399	9624	9773	9867	9925	9959	9978
19	7252	7991	8585	9038	9370	9601	9757	9856	9918	9955
20	6358	7220	7953	8547	9005	9342	9580	9741	9846	9911
21	5394	6338	7189	7918	8512	8973	9316	9560	9726	9835
22	4419	5391	6320	7162	7886	8479	8943	9291	9540	9712
23	3488	4432	5388	6304	7136	7856	8448	8915	9267	9521
24	2649	3514	4444	5386	6289	7113	7828	8420	8889	9245
25	1933	2684	3539	4455	5383	6276	7091	7802	8393	8864
26	1355	1972	2717	3561	4465	5381	6263	7071	7778	8369
27	0911	1393	2009	2748	3583	4475	5380	6252	7053	7756
28	0588	0945	1429	2043	2776	3602	4484	5378	6242	7036
29	0364	0616	0978	1463	2075	2803	3621	4493	5377	6232
30	0216	0386	0643	1009	1495	2105	2828	3638	4501	5377
31	0123	0232	0406	0669	1038	1526	2134	2851	3654	4509
32	0067	0134	0247	0427	0693	1065	1554	2160	2873	3669
33	0035	0074	0144	0262	0446	0717	1091	1580	2184	2893
34	0018	0039	0081	0154	0276	0465	0739	1116	1605	2207
35	0009	0020	0044	0087	0164	0290	0482	0760	1139	1629
36	0004	0010	0023	0048	0094	0174	0303	0499	0780	1161
37	0002	0005	0011	0025	0052	0101	0183	0316	0515	0799
38	0001	0002	0005	0013	0027	0056	0107	0193	0328	0530
39		0001	0002	0006	0014	0030	0060	0113	0201	0340
40			0001	0003	0007	0015	0032	0064	0119	0210
41				0001	0003	0008	0017	0035	0068	0125
42				0001	0001	0004	0008	0018	0037	0072
43					0001	0002	0004	0009	0020	0040
44						0001	0002	0005	0010	0021
45							0001	0002	0005	0011
46								0001	0002	0005
47									0001	0003
48										0001
49										0001

Table I: Cumulative Binomial Distribution $n = 100$

P / R	31	32	33	34	35	36	37	38	39	40
1	10000	10000	10000	10000	10000	10000	10000	10000	10000	10000
2	10000	10000	10000	10000	10000	10000	10000	10000	10000	10000
3	10000	10000	10000	10000	10000	10000	10000	10000	10000	10000
4	10000	10000	10000	10000	10000	10000	10000	10000	10000	10000
5	10000	10000	10000	10000	10000	10000	10000	10000	10000	10000
6	10000	10000	10000	10000	10000	10000	10000	10000	10000	10000
7	10000	10000	10000	10000	10000	10000	10000	10000	10000	10000
8	10000	10000	10000	10000	10000	10000	10000	10000	10000	10000
9	10000	10000	10000	10000	10000	10000	10000	10000	10000	10000
10	10000	10000	10000	10000	10000	10000	10000	10000	10000	10000
11	10000	10000	10000	10000	10000	10000	10000	10000	10000	10000
12	10000	10000	10000	10000	10000	10000	10000	10000	10000	10000
13	10000	10000	10000	10000	10000	10000	10000	10000	10000	10000
14	10000	10000	10000	10000	10000	10000	10000	10000	10000	10000
15	9999	10000	10000	10000	10000	10000	10000	10000	10000	10000
16	9998	9999	10000	10000	10000	10000	10000	10000	10000	10000
17	9995	9998	9999	10000	10000	10000	10000	10000	10000	10000
18	9989	9995	9997	9999	9999	10000	10000	10000	10000	10000
19	9976	9988	9994	9997	9999	9999	10000	10000	10000	10000
20	9950	9973	9986	9993	9997	9998	9999	10000	10000	10000
21	9904	9946	9971	9985	9992	9996	9998	9999	10000	10000
22	9825	9898	9942	9968	9983	9991	9996	9998	9999	10000
23	9698	9816	9891	9938	9966	9982	9991	9995	9998	9999
24	9504	9685	9806	9885	9934	9963	9980	9990	9995	9997
25	9224	9487	9672	9797	9879	9930	9961	9979	9989	9994
26	8841	9204	9471	9660	9789	9873	9926	9958	9977	9988
27	8346	8820	9185	9456	9649	9780	9867	9922	9956	9976
28	7736	8325	8800	9168	9442	9638	9773	9862	9919	9954
29	7021	7717	8305	8781	9152	9429	9628	9765	9857	9916
30	6224	7007	7699	8287	8764	9137	9417	9618	9759	9852
31	5376	6216	6994	7684	8270	8748	9123	9405	9610	9752
32	4516	5376	6209	6982	7669	8254	8733	9110	9395	9602
33	3683	4523	5375	6203	6971	7656	8240	8720	9098	9385
34	2912	3696	4530	5375	6197	6961	7643	8227	8708	9087
35	2229	2929	3708	4536	5376	6192	6953	7632	8216	8697
36	1650	2249	2946	3720	4542	5376	6188	6945	7623	8205
37	1181	1671	2268	2961	3731	4547	5377	6184	6938	7614
38	0816	1200	1690	2285	2976	3741	4553	5377	6181	6932
39	0545	0833	1218	1708	2301	2989	3750	4558	5378	6178
40	0351	0558	0849	1235	1724	2316	3001	3759	4562	5379
41	0218	0361	0571	0863	1250	1739	2330	3012	3767	4567
42	0131	0226	0371	0583	0877	1265	1753	2343	3023	3775
43	0075	0136	0233	0380	0594	0889	1278	1766	2355	3033
44	0042	0079	0141	0240	0389	0605	0901	1290	1778	2365
45	0023	0044	0082	0146	0246	0397	0614	0911	1301	1789
46	0012	0024	0046	0085	0150	0252	0405	0623	0921	1311
47	0006	0012	0025	0048	0088	0154	0257	0411	0631	0930
48	0003	0006	0013	0026	0050	0091	0158	0262	0417	0638
49	0001	0003	0007	0014	0027	0052	0094	0162	0267	0423
50	0001	0001	0003	0007	0015	0029	0054	0096	0165	0271
51		0001	0002	0003	0007	0015	0030	0055	0098	0168
52			0001	0002	0004	0008	0016	0030	0056	0100
53				0001	0002	0004	0008	0016	0031	0058
54					0001	0002	0004	0008	0017	0032
55						0001	0002	0004	0009	0017
56							0001	0002	0004	0009
57								0001	0002	0004
58									0001	0002
59										0001

P / R	41	42	43	44	45	46	47	48	49	50
1	10000	10000	10000	10000	10000	10000	10000	10000	10000	10000
2	10000	10000	10000	10000	10000	10000	10000	10000	10000	10000
3	10000	10000	10000	10000	10000	10000	10000	10000	10000	10000
4	10000	10000	10000	10000	10000	10000	10000	10000	10000	10000
5	10000	10000	10000	10000	10000	10000	10000	10000	10000	10000
6	10000	10000	10000	10000	10000	10000	10000	10000	10000	10000
7	10000	10000	10000	10000	10000	10000	10000	10000	10000	10000
8	10000	10000	10000	10000	10000	10000	10000	10000	10000	10000
9	10000	10000	10000	10000	10000	10000	10000	10000	10000	10000
10	10000	10000	10000	10000	10000	10000	10000	10000	10000	10000
11	10000	10000	10000	10000	10000	10000	10000	10000	10000	10000
12	10000	10000	10000	10000	10000	10000	10000	10000	10000	10000
13	10000	10000	10000	10000	10000	10000	10000	10000	10000	10000
14	10000	10000	10000	10000	10000	10000	10000	10000	10000	10000
15	10000	10000	10000	10000	10000	10000	10000	10000	10000	10000
16	10000	10000	10000	10000	10000	10000	10000	10000	10000	10000
17	10000	10000	10000	10000	10000	10000	10000	10000	10000	10000
18	10000	10000	10000	10000	10000	10000	10000	10000	10000	10000
19	10000	10000	10000	10000	10000	10000	10000	10000	10000	10000
20	10000	10000	10000	10000	10000	10000	10000	10000	10000	10000
21	10000	10000	10000	10000	10000	10000	10000	10000	10000	10000
22	10000	10000	10000	10000	10000	10000	10000	10000	10000	10000
23	10000	10000	10000	10000	10000	10000	10000	10000	10000	10000
24	9999	9999	10000	10000	10000	10000	10000	10000	10000	10000
25	9997	9999	9999	10000	10000	10000	10000	10000	10000	10000
26	9994	9997	9999	9999	10000	10000	10000	10000	10000	10000
27	9987	9994	9997	9998	9999	10000	10000	10000	10000	10000
28	9975	9987	9993	9997	9998	9999	10000	10000	10000	10000
29	9952	9974	9986	9993	9996	9998	9999	10000	10000	10000
30	9913	9950	9972	9985	9992	9996	9998	9999	10000	10000
31	9848	9910	9948	9971	9985	9992	9996	9998	9999	10000
32	9746	9844	9907	9947	9970	9984	9992	9996	9998	9999
33	9594	9741	9840	9905	9945	9969	9984	9991	9996	9998
34	9376	9587	9736	9837	9902	9944	9969	9983	9991	9996
35	9078	9368	9581	9732	9834	9900	9942	9968	9983	9991
36	8687	9069	9361	9576	9728	9831	9899	9941	9967	9982
37	8196	8678	9061	9355	9571	9724	9829	9897	9941	9967
38	7606	8188	8670	9054	9349	9567	9721	9827	9896	9940
39	6927	7599	8181	8663	9049	9345	9563	9719	9825	9895
40	6176	6922	7594	8174	8657	9044	9341	9561	9717	9824
41	5380	6174	6919	7589	8169	8653	9040	9338	9558	9716
42	4571	5382	6173	6916	7585	8165	8649	9037	9335	9557
43	3782	4576	5383	6173	6913	7582	8162	8646	9035	9334
44	3041	3788	4580	5385	6172	6912	7580	8160	8645	9033
45	2375	3049	3794	4583	5387	6173	6911	7579	8159	8644
46	1799	2384	3057	3799	4587	5389	6173	6911	7579	8159
47	1320	1807	2391	3063	3804	4590	5391	6174	6912	7579
48	0938	1328	1815	2398	3069	3809	4593	5393	6176	6914
49	0644	0944	1335	1822	2404	3074	3813	4596	5395	6178
50	0428	0650	0950	1341	1827	2409	3078	3816	4599	5398
51	0275	0432	0655	0955	1346	1832	2413	3082	3819	4602
52	0170	0278	0436	0659	0960	1350	1836	2417	3084	3822
53	0102	0172	0280	0439	0662	0963	1353	1838	2419	3086
54	0059	0103	0174	0282	0441	0664	0965	1355	1840	2421
55	0033	0059	0104	0175	0284	0443	0666	0967	1356	1841
56	0017	0033	0060	0105	0176	0285	0444	0667	0967	1356
57	0009	0018	0034	0061	0106	0177	0286	0444	0667	0967
58	0004	0009	0018	0034	0061	0106	0177	0286	0444	0666
59	0002	0005	0009	0018	0034	0061	0106	0177	0285	0443
60	0001	0002	0005	0009	0018	0034	0061	0106	0177	0284
61		0001	0002	0005	0009	0018	0034	0061	0106	0176
62			0001	0002	0005	0009	0018	0034	0061	0105
63				0001	0002	0005	0009	0018	0034	0060
64					0001	0002	0005	0009	0018	0033
65						0001	0002	0005	0009	0018
66							0001	0002	0004	0009
67								0001	0002	0004
68									0001	0002
69										0001

Table II
Unit Normal Probability Distribution
$P'_N(u)$

u	.00	.01	.02	.03	.04	.05	.06	.07	.08	.09
.0	.3989	.3989	.3989	.3988	.3986	.3984	.3982	.3980	.3977	.3973
.1	.3970	.3965	.3961	.3956	.3951	.3945	.3939	.3932	.3925	.3918
.2	.3910	.3902	.3894	.3885	.3876	.3867	.3857	.3847	.3836	.3825
.3	.3814	.3802	.3790	.3778	.3765	.3752	.3739	.3725	.3712	.3697
.4	.3683	.3668	.3653	.3637	.3621	.3605	.3589	.3572	.3555	.3538
.5	.3521	.3503	.3485	.3467	.3448	.3429	.3410	.3391	.3372	.3352
.6	.3332	.3312	.3292	.3271	.3251	.3230	.3209	.3187	.3166	.3144
.7	.3123	.3101	.3079	.3056	.3034	.3011	.2989	.2966	.2943	.2920
.8	.2897	.2874	.2850	.2827	.2803	.2780	.2756	.2732	.2709	.2685
.9	.2661	.2637	.2613	.2589	.2565	.2541	.2516	.2492	.2468	.2444
1.0	.2420	.2396	.2371	.2347	.2323	.2299	.2275	.2251	.2227	.2203
1.1	.2179	.2155	.2131	.2107	.2083	.2059	.2036	.2012	.1989	.1965
1.2	.1942	.1919	.1895	.1872	.1849	.1826	.1804	.1781	.1758	.1736
1.3	.1714	.1691	.1669	.1647	.1626	.1604	.1582	.1561	.1539	.1518
1.4	.1497	.1476	.1456	.1435	.1415	.1394	.1374	.1354	.1334	.1315
1.5	.1295	.1276	.1257	.1238	.1219	.1200	.1182	.1163	.1145	.1127
1.6	.1109	.1092	.1074	.1057	.1040	.1023	.1006	.09893	.09728	.09566
1.7	.09405	.09246	.09089	.08933	.08780	.08628	.08478	.08329	.08183	.08038
1.8	.07895	.07754	.07614	.07477	.07341	.07206	.07074	.06943	.06814	.06687
1.9	.06562	.06438	.06316	.06195	.06077	.05959	.05844	.05730	.05618	.05508
2.0	.05399	.05292	.05186	.05082	.04980	.04879	.04780	.04682	.04586	.04491
2.1	.04398	.04307	.04217	.04128	.04041	.03955	.03871	.03788	.03706	.03626
2.2	.03547	.03470	.03394	.03319	.03246	.03174	.03103	.03034	.02965	.02898
2.3	.02833	.02768	.02705	.02643	.02582	.02522	.02463	.02406	.02349	.02294
2.4	.02239	.02186	.02134	.02083	.02033	.01984	.01936	.01888	.01842	.01797

x										
2.5	.01394	.01431	.01468	.01506	.01545	.01585	.01625	.01667	.01709	.01753
2.6	.01071	.01100	.01130	.01160	.01191	.01223	.01256	.01289	.01323	.01358
2.7	$.0^28140$	$.0^28370$	$.0^28605$	$.0^28846$	$.0^29094$	$.0^29347$	$.0^29606$	$.0^29871$	.01014	.01042
2.8	$.0^26127$	$.0^26307$	$.0^26491$	$.0^26679$	$.0^26873$	$.0^27071$	$.0^27274$	$.0^27483$	$.0^27697$	$.0^27915$
2.9	$.0^24567$	$.0^24705$	$.0^24847$	$.0^24993$	$.0^25143$	$.0^25296$	$.0^25454$	$.0^25616$	$.0^25782$	$.0^25953$
3.0	$.0^23370$	$.0^23475$	$.0^23584$	$.0^23695$	$.0^23810$	$.0^23928$	$.0^24049$	$.0^24173$	$.0^24301$	$.0^24432$
3.1	$.0^22461$	$.0^22541$	$.0^22623$	$.0^22707$	$.0^22794$	$.0^22884$	$.0^22975$	$.0^23070$	$.0^23167$	$.0^23267$
3.2	$.0^21780$	$.0^21840$	$.0^21901$	$.0^21964$	$.0^22029$	$.0^22096$	$.0^22165$	$.0^22236$	$.0^22309$	$.0^22384$
3.3	$.0^21275$	$.0^21319$	$.0^21364$	$.0^21411$	$.0^21459$	$.0^21508$	$.0^21560$	$.0^21612$	$.0^21667$	$.0^21723$
3.4	$.0^39037$	$.0^39358$	$.0^39689$	$.0^21003$	$.0^21038$	$.0^21075$	$.0^21112$	$.0^21151$	$.0^21191$	$.0^21232$
3.5	$.0^36343$	$.0^36575$	$.0^36814$	$.0^37061$	$.0^37317$	$.0^37581$	$.0^37853$	$.0^38135$	$.0^38426$	$.0^38727$
3.6	$.0^34408$	$.0^34573$	$.0^34744$	$.0^34921$	$.0^35105$	$.0^35294$	$.0^35490$	$.0^35693$	$.0^35902$	$.0^36119$
3.7	$.0^33032$	$.0^33149$	$.0^33271$	$.0^33396$	$.0^33526$	$.0^33661$	$.0^33800$	$.0^33944$	$.0^34093$	$.0^34248$
3.8	$.0^32065$	$.0^32147$	$.0^32232$	$.0^32320$	$.0^32411$	$.0^32506$	$.0^32604$	$.0^32705$	$.0^32810$	$.0^32919$
3.9	$.0^31393$	$.0^31449$	$.0^31508$	$.0^31569$	$.0^31633$	$.0^31698$	$.0^31766$	$.0^31837$	$.0^31910$	$.0^31987$
4.0	$.0^49299$	$.0^49687$	$.0^31009$	$.0^31051$	$.0^31094$	$.0^31140$	$.0^31186$	$.0^31235$	$.0^31286$	$.0^31338$
4.1	$.0^46147$	$.0^46410$	$.0^46683$	$.0^46967$	$.0^47263$	$.0^47570$	$.0^47890$	$.0^48222$	$.0^48567$	$.0^48926$
4.2	$.0^44023$	$.0^44199$	$.0^44382$	$.0^44573$	$.0^44772$	$.0^44979$	$.0^45194$	$.0^45418$	$.0^45652$	$.0^45894$
4.3	$.0^42606$	$.0^42723$	$.0^42845$	$.0^42972$	$.0^43104$	$.0^43242$	$.0^43386$	$.0^43535$	$.0^43691$	$.0^43854$
4.4	$.0^41672$	$.0^41749$	$.0^41829$	$.0^41912$	$.0^41999$	$.0^42090$	$.0^42185$	$.0^42284$	$.0^42387$	$.0^42494$
4.5	$.0^41062$	$.0^41112$	$.0^41164$	$.0^41218$	$.0^41275$	$.0^41334$	$.0^41396$	$.0^41461$	$.0^41528$	$.0^41598$
4.6	$.0^56676$	$.0^56996$	$.0^57331$	$.0^57681$	$.0^58047$	$.0^58430$	$.0^58830$	$.0^59248$	$.0^59684$	$.0^41014$
4.7	$.0^54156$	$.0^54360$	$.0^54573$	$.0^54796$	$.0^55030$	$.0^55274$	$.0^55530$	$.0^55797$	$.0^56077$	$.0^56370$
4.8	$.0^52561$	$.0^52690$	$.0^52824$	$.0^52965$	$.0^53112$	$.0^53267$	$.0^53428$	$.0^53598$	$.0^53775$	$.0^53961$
4.9	$.0^51563$	$.0^51643$	$.0^51727$	$.0^51814$	$.0^51907$	$.0^52003$	$.0^52105$	$.0^52211$	$.0^52322$	$.0^52439$

Example: $P'_N(3.57) = P'_N(-3.57) = .0^36814 = .0006814$

Reproduced by permission from A. Hald, "Statistical Tables and Formulas," John Wiley & Sons, Inc., New York, 1952.

Table III
Cumulative Unit Normal Distribution
$$P_N(\tilde{u} > u)$$

u	.00	.01	.02	.03	.04	.05	.06	.07	.08	.09
0	.5000	.4960	.4920	.4880	.4840	.4801	.4761	.4721	.4681	.4641
.1	.4602	.4562	.4522	.4483	.4443	.4404	.4364	.4325	.4286	.4247
.2	.4207	.4168	.4129	.4090	.4052	.4013	.3974	.3936	.3897	.3859
.3	.3821	.3783	.3745	.3707	.3669	.3632	.3594	.3557	.3520	.3483
.4	.3446	.3409	.3372	.3336	.3300	.3264	.3228	.3192	.3156	.3121
.5	.3085	.3050	.3015	.2981	.2946	.2912	.2877	.2843	.2810	.2776
.6	.2743	.2709	.2676	.2643	.2611	.2578	.2546	.2514	.2483	.2451
.7	.2420	.2389	.2358	.2327	.2297	.2266	.2236	.2206	.2177	.2148
.8	.2119	.2090	.2061	.2033	.2005	.1977	.1949	.1922	.1894	.1867
.9	.1841	.1814	.1788	.1762	.1736	.1711	.1685	.1660	.1635	.1611
1.0	.1587	.1562	.1539	.1515	.1492	.1469	.1446	.1423	.1401	.1379
1.1	.1357	.1335	.1314	.1292	.1271	.1251	.1230	.1210	.1190	.1170
1.2	.1151	.1131	.1112	.1093	.1075	.1056	.1038	.1020	.1003	.09853
1.3	.09680	.09510	.09342	.09176	.09012	.08851	.08691	.08534	.08379	.08226
1.4	.08076	.07927	.07780	.07636	.07493	.07353	.07215	.07078	.06944	.06811
1.5	.06681	.06552	.06426	.06301	.06178	.06057	.05938	.05821	.05705	.05592
1.6	.05480	.05370	.05262	.05155	.05050	.04947	.04846	.04746	.04648	.04551
1.7	.04457	.04363	.04272	.04182	.04093	.04006	.03920	.03836	.03754	.03673
1.8	.03593	.03515	.03438	.03362	.03288	.03216	.03144	.03074	.03005	.02938
1.9	.02872	.02807	.02743	.02680	.02619	.02559	.02500	.02442	.02385	.02330
2.0	.02275	.02222	.02169	.02118	.02068	.02018	.01970	.01923	.01876	.01831
2.1	.01786	.01743	.01700	.01659	.01618	.01578	.01539	.01500	.01463	.01426
2.2	.01390	.01355	.01321	.01287	.01255	.01222	.01191	.01160	.01130	.01101
2.3	.01072	.01044	.01017	$.0^{2}9903$	$.0^{2}9642$	$.0^{2}9387$	$.0^{2}9137$	$.0^{2}8894$	$.0^{2}8656$	$.0^{2}8424$
2.4	$.0^{2}8198$	$.0^{2}7976$	$.0^{2}7760$	$.0^{2}7549$	$.0^{2}7344$	$.0^{2}7143$	$.0^{2}6947$	$.0^{2}6756$	$.0^{2}6569$	$.0^{2}6387$

$\bar{u}$	0	1	2	3	4	5	6	7	8	9
2.5	$.0^26210$	$.0^26037$	$.0^25868$	$.0^25703$	$.0^25543$	$.0^25386$	$.0^25234$	$.0^25085$	$.0^24940$	$.0^24799$
2.6	$.0^24661$	$.0^24527$	$.0^24396$	$.0^24269$	$.0^24145$	$.0^24025$	$.0^23907$	$.0^23793$	$.0^23681$	$.0^23573$
2.7	$.0^23467$	$.0^23364$	$.0^23264$	$.0^23167$	$.0^23072$	$.0^22980$	$.0^22890$	$.0^22803$	$.0^22718$	$.0^22635$
2.8	$.0^22555$	$.0^22477$	$.0^22401$	$.0^22327$	$.0^22256$	$.0^22186$	$.0^22118$	$.0^22052$	$.0^21988$	$.0^21926$
2.9	$.0^21866$	$.0^21807$	$.0^21750$	$.0^21695$	$.0^21641$	$.0^21589$	$.0^21538$	$.0^21489$	$.0^21441$	$.0^21395$
3.0	$.0^21350$	$.0^21306$	$.0^21264$	$.0^21223$	$.0^21183$	$.0^21144$	$.0^21107$	$.0^21070$	$.0^21035$	$.0^21001$
3.1	$.0^39676$	$.0^39354$	$.0^39043$	$.0^38740$	$.0^38447$	$.0^38164$	$.0^37888$	$.0^37622$	$.0^37364$	$.0^37114$
3.2	$.0^36871$	$.0^36637$	$.0^36410$	$.0^36190$	$.0^35976$	$.0^35770$	$.0^35571$	$.0^35377$	$.0^35190$	$.0^35009$
3.3	$.0^34834$	$.0^34665$	$.0^34501$	$.0^34342$	$.0^34189$	$.0^34041$	$.0^33897$	$.0^33758$	$.0^33624$	$.0^33495$
3.4	$.0^33369$	$.0^33248$	$.0^33131$	$.0^33018$	$.0^32909$	$.0^32803$	$.0^32701$	$.0^32602$	$.0^32507$	$.0^32415$
3.5	$.0^32326$	$.0^32241$	$.0^32158$	$.0^32078$	$.0^32001$	$.0^31926$	$.0^31854$	$.0^31785$	$.0^31718$	$.0^31653$
3.6	$.0^31591$	$.0^31531$	$.0^31473$	$.0^31417$	$.0^31363$	$.0^31311$	$.0^31261$	$.0^31213$	$.0^31166$	$.0^31121$
3.7	$.0^31078$	$.0^31036$	$.0^49961$	$.0^49574$	$.0^49201$	$.0^48842$	$.0^48496$	$.0^48162$	$.0^47841$	$.0^47532$
3.8	$.0^47235$	$.0^46948$	$.0^46673$	$.0^46407$	$.0^46152$	$.0^45906$	$.0^45669$	$.0^45442$	$.0^45223$	$.0^45012$
3.9	$.0^44810$	$.0^44615$	$.0^44427$	$.0^44247$	$.0^44074$	$.0^43908$	$.0^43747$	$.0^43594$	$.0^43446$	$.0^43304$
4.0	$.0^43167$	$.0^43036$	$.0^42910$	$.0^42789$	$.0^42673$	$.0^42561$	$.0^42454$	$.0^42351$	$.0^42252$	$.0^42157$
4.1	$.0^42066$	$.0^41978$	$.0^41894$	$.0^41814$	$.0^41737$	$.0^41662$	$.0^41591$	$.0^41523$	$.0^41458$	$.0^41395$
4.2	$.0^41335$	$.0^41277$	$.0^41222$	$.0^41168$	$.0^41118$	$.0^41069$	$.0^41022$	$.0^59774$	$.0^59345$	$.0^58934$
4.3	$.0^58540$	$.0^58163$	$.0^57801$	$.0^57455$	$.0^57124$	$.0^56807$	$.0^56503$	$.0^56212$	$.0^55934$	$.0^55668$
4.4	$.0^55413$	$.0^55169$	$.0^54935$	$.0^54712$	$.0^54498$	$.0^54294$	$.0^54098$	$.0^53911$	$.0^53732$	$.0^53561$
4.5	$.0^53398$	$.0^53241$	$.0^53092$	$.0^52949$	$.0^52813$	$.0^52682$	$.0^52558$	$.0^52439$	$.0^52325$	$.0^52216$
4.6	$.0^52112$	$.0^52013$	$.0^51919$	$.0^51828$	$.0^51742$	$.0^51660$	$.0^51581$	$.0^51506$	$.0^51434$	$.0^51366$
4.7	$.0^51301$	$.0^51239$	$.0^51179$	$.0^51123$	$.0^51069$	$.0^51017$	$.0^69680$	$.0^69211$	$.0^68765$	$.0^68339$
4.8	$.0^67933$	$.0^67547$	$.0^67178$	$.0^66827$	$.0^66492$	$.0^66173$	$.0^65869$	$.0^65580$	$.0^65304$	$.0^65042$
4.9	$.0^64792$	$.0^64554$	$.0^64327$	$.0^64111$	$.0^63906$	$.0^63711$	$.0^63525$	$.0^63348$	$.0^63179$	$.0^63019$

Examples: $P_N(\bar{u} > 3.57) = P_N(\bar{u} < -3.57) = .0^31785 = .0001785$

$P_N(\bar{u} < 3.57) = P_N(\bar{u} > -3.57) = 1 - .0^31785 = .9998215$

Reproduced by permission from A. Hald, "Statistical Tables and Formulas," John Wiley & Sons, Inc., New York, 1952.

Table IV
Unit Normal Loss Integral
$$G(u) = P'_N(u) - u\, P_N(\tilde{u} > u)$$

u	.00	.01	.02	.03	.04	.05	.06	.07	.08	.09
.0	.3989	.3940	.3890	.3841	.3793	.3744	.3697	.3649	.3602	.3556
.1	.3509	.3464	.3418	.3373	.3328	.3284	.3240	.3197	.3154	.3111
.2	.3069	.3027	.2986	.2944	.2904	.2863	.2824	.2784	.2745	.2706
.3	.2668	.2630	.2592	.2555	.2518	.2481	.2445	.2409	.2374	.2339
.4	.2304	.2270	.2236	.2203	.2169	.2137	.2104	.2072	.2040	.2009
.5	.1978	.1947	.1917	.1887	.1857	.1828	.1799	.1771	.1742	.1714
.6	.1687	.1659	.1633	.1606	.1580	.1554	.1528	.1503	.1478	.1453
.7	.1429	.1405	.1381	.1358	.1334	.1312	.1289	.1267	.1245	.1223
.8	.1202	.1181	.1160	.1140	.1120	.1100	.1080	.1061	.1042	.1023
.9	.1004	.09860	.09680	.09503	.09328	.09156	.08986	.08819	.08654	.08491
1.0	.08332	.08174	.08019	.07866	.07716	.07568	.07422	.07279	.07138	.06999
1.1	.06862	.06727	.06595	.06465	.06336	.06210	.06086	.05964	.05844	.05726
1.2	.05610	.05496	.05384	.05274	.05165	.05059	.04954	.04851	.04750	.04650
1.3	.04553	.04457	.04363	.04270	.04179	.04090	.04002	.03916	.03831	.03748
1.4	.03667	.03587	.03508	.03431	.03356	.03281	.03208	.03137	.03067	.02998
1.5	.02931	.02865	.02800	.02736	.02674	.02612	.02552	.02494	.02436	.02380
1.6	.02324	.02270	.02217	.02165	.02114	.02064	.02015	.01967	.01920	.01874
1.7	.01829	.01785	.01742	.01699	.01658	.01617	.01578	.01539	.01501	.01464
1.8	.01428	.01392	.01357	.01323	.01290	.01257	.01226	.01195	.01164	.01134
1.9	.01105	.01077	.01049	.01022	$.0^{2}9957$	$.0^{2}9698$	$.0^{2}9445$	$.0^{2}9198$	$.0^{2}8957$	$.0^{2}8721$
2.0	$.0^{2}8491$	$.0^{2}8266$	$.0^{2}8046$	$.0^{2}7832$	$.0^{2}7623$	$.0^{2}7418$	$.0^{2}7219$	$.0^{2}7024$	$.0^{2}6835$	$.0^{2}6649$
2.1	$.0^{2}6468$	$.0^{2}6292$	$.0^{2}6120$	$.0^{2}5952$	$.0^{2}5788$	$.0^{2}5628$	$.0^{2}5472$	$.0^{2}5320$	$.0^{2}5172$	$.0^{2}5028$
2.2	$.0^{2}4887$	$.0^{2}4750$	$.0^{2}4616$	$.0^{2}4486$	$.0^{2}4358$	$.0^{2}4235$	$.0^{2}4114$	$.0^{2}3996$	$.0^{2}3882$	$.0^{2}3770$
2.3	$.0^{2}3662$	$.0^{2}3556$	$.0^{2}3453$	$.0^{2}3352$	$.0^{2}3255$	$.0^{2}3159$	$.0^{2}3067$	$.0^{2}2977$	$.0^{2}2889$	$.0^{2}2804$
2.4	$.0^{2}2720$	$.0^{2}2640$	$.0^{2}2561$	$.0^{2}2484$	$.0^{2}2410$	$.0^{2}2337$	$.0^{2}2267$	$.0^{2}2199$	$.0^{2}2132$	$.0^{2}2067$

u	.00	.01	.02	.03	.04	.05	.06	.07	.08	.09
2.5	$.0^2 2004$	$.0^2 1943$	$.0^2 1883$	$.0^2 1826$	$.0^2 1769$	$.0^2 1715$	$.0^2 1662$	$.0^2 1610$	$.0^2 1560$	$.0^2 1511$
2.6	$.0^2 1464$	$.0^2 1418$	$.0^2 1373$	$.0^2 1330$	$.0^2 1288$	$.0^2 1247$	$.0^2 1207$	$.0^2 1169$	$.0^2 1132$	$.0^2 1095$
2.7	$.0^2 1060$	$.0^2 1026$	$.0^3 9928$	$.0^3 9607$	$.0^3 9295$	$.0^3 8992$	$.0^3 8699$	$.0^3 8414$	$.0^3 8138$	$.0^3 7870$
2.8	$.0^3 7611$	$.0^3 7359$	$.0^3 7115$	$.0^3 6879$	$.0^3 6650$	$.0^3 6428$	$.0^3 6213$	$.0^3 6004$	$.0^3 5802$	$.0^3 5606$
2.9	$.0^3 5417$	$.0^3 5233$	$.0^3 5055$	$.0^3 4883$	$.0^3 4716$	$.0^3 4555$	$.0^3 4398$	$.0^3 4247$	$.0^3 4101$	$.0^3 3959$
3.0	$.0^3 3822$	$.0^3 3689$	$.0^3 3560$	$.0^3 3436$	$.0^3 3316$	$.0^3 3199$	$.0^3 3087$	$.0^3 2978$	$.0^3 2873$	$.0^3 2771$
3.1	$.0^3 2673$	$.0^3 2577$	$.0^3 2485$	$.0^3 2396$	$.0^3 2311$	$.0^3 2227$	$.0^3 2147$	$.0^3 2070$	$.0^3 1995$	$.0^3 1922$
3.2	$.0^3 1852$	$.0^3 1785$	$.0^3 1720$	$.0^3 1657$	$.0^3 1596$	$.0^3 1537$	$.0^3 1480$	$.0^3 1426$	$.0^3 1373$	$.0^3 1322$
3.3	$.0^3 1273$	$.0^3 1225$	$.0^3 1179$	$.0^3 1135$	$.0^3 1093$	$.0^3 1051$	$.0^3 1012$	$.0^4 9734$	$.0^4 9365$	$.0^4 9009$
3.4	$.0^4 8666$	$.0^4 8335$	$.0^4 8016$	$.0^4 7709$	$.0^4 7413$	$.0^4 7127$	$.0^4 6852$	$.0^4 6587$	$.0^4 6331$	$.0^4 6085$
3.5	$.0^4 5848$	$.0^4 5620$	$.0^4 5400$	$.0^4 5188$	$.0^4 4984$	$.0^4 4788$	$.0^4 4599$	$.0^4 4417$	$.0^4 4242$	$.0^4 4073$
3.6	$.0^4 3911$	$.0^4 3755$	$.0^4 3605$	$.0^4 3460$	$.0^4 3321$	$.0^4 3188$	$.0^4 3059$	$.0^4 2935$	$.0^4 2816$	$.0^4 2702$
3.7	$.0^4 2592$	$.0^4 2486$	$.0^4 2385$	$.0^4 2287$	$.0^4 2193$	$.0^4 2103$	$.0^4 2016$	$.0^4 1933$	$.0^4 1853$	$.0^4 1776$
3.8	$.0^4 1702$	$.0^4 1632$	$.0^4 1563$	$.0^4 1498$	$.0^4 1435$	$.0^4 1375$	$.0^4 1317$	$.0^4 1262$	$.0^4 1208$	$.0^4 1157$
3.9	$.0^4 1108$	$.0^4 1061$	$.0^4 1016$	$.0^5 9723$	$.0^5 9307$	$.0^5 8908$	$.0^5 8525$	$.0^5 8158$	$.0^5 7806$	$.0^5 7469$
4.0	$.0^5 7145$	$.0^5 6835$	$.0^5 6538$	$.0^5 6253$	$.0^5 5980$	$.0^5 5718$	$.0^5 5468$	$.0^5 5227$	$.0^5 4997$	$.0^5 4777$
4.1	$.0^5 4566$	$.0^5 4364$	$.0^5 4170$	$.0^5 3985$	$.0^5 3807$	$.0^5 3637$	$.0^5 3475$	$.0^5 3319$	$.0^5 3170$	$.0^5 3027$
4.2	$.0^5 2891$	$.0^5 2760$	$.0^5 2635$	$.0^5 2516$	$.0^5 2402$	$.0^5 2292$	$.0^5 2188$	$.0^5 2088$	$.0^5 1992$	$.0^5 1901$
4.3	$.0^5 1814$	$.0^5 1730$	$.0^5 1650$	$.0^5 1574$	$.0^5 1501$	$.0^5 1431$	$.0^5 1365$	$.0^5 1301$	$.0^5 1241$	$.0^5 1183$
4.4	$.0^5 1127$	$.0^5 1074$	$.0^5 1024$	$.0^6 9756$	$.0^6 9296$	$.0^6 8857$	$.0^6 8437$	$.0^6 8037$	$.0^6 7655$	$.0^6 7290$
4.5	$.0^6 6942$	$.0^6 6610$	$.0^6 6294$	$.0^6 5992$	$.0^6 5704$	$.0^6 5429$	$.0^6 5167$	$.0^6 4917$	$.0^6 4679$	$.0^6 4452$
4.6	$.0^6 4236$	$.0^6 4029$	$.0^6 3833$	$.0^6 3645$	$.0^6 3467$	$.0^6 3297$	$.0^6 3135$	$.0^6 2981$	$.0^6 2834$	$.0^6 2694$
4.7	$.0^6 2560$	$.0^6 2433$	$.0^6 2313$	$.0^6 2197$	$.0^6 2088$	$.0^6 1984$	$.0^6 1884$	$.0^6 1790$	$.0^6 1700$	$.0^6 1615$
4.8	$.0^6 1533$	$.0^6 1456$	$.0^6 1382$	$.0^6 1312$	$.0^6 1246$	$.0^6 1182$	$.0^6 1122$	$.0^6 1065$	$.0^6 1011$	$.0^7 9588$
4.9	$.0^7 9096$	$.0^7 8629$	$.0^7 8185$	$.0^7 7763$	$.0^7 7362$	$.0^7 6982$	$.0^7 6620$	$.0^7 6276$	$.0^7 5950$	$.0^7 5640$

$$G(-u) = u + G(u)$$

Examples: $G(3.57) = .0^4 4417 = .00004417$

$$G(-3.57) = 3.57004417$$

708   *Tables*

Table V
Random Digits

10	09	73	25	33	76	52	01	35	86	34	67	35	48	76	80	95	90	91	17	39	29	27	49	45
37	54	20	48	05	64	89	47	42	96	24	80	52	40	37	20	63	61	04	02	00	82	29	16	65
08	42	26	89	53	19	64	50	93	03	23	20	90	25	60	15	95	33	47	64	35	08	03	36	06
99	01	90	25	29	09	37	67	07	15	38	31	13	11	65	88	67	67	43	97	04	43	62	76	59
12	80	79	99	70	80	15	73	61	47	64	03	23	66	⌐⌐	98	95	11	68	77	12	17	17	68	33
66	06	57	47	17	34	07	27	68	50	36	69	73	61	70	65	81	33	98	85	11	19	92	91	70
31	06	01	08	05	45	57	18	24	06	35	30	34	26	14	86	79	90	74	39	23	40	30	97	32
85	26	97	76	02	02	05	16	56	92	68	66	57	48	18	73	05	38	52	47	18	62	38	85	79
63	57	33	21	35	05	32	54	70	48	90	55	35	75	48	28	46	82	87	09	83	49	12	56	24
73	79	64	57	53	03	52	96	47	78	35	80	83	42	82	60	93	52	03	44	35	27	38	84	35
98	52	01	77	67	14	90	56	86	07	22	10	94	05	58	60	97	09	34	33	50	50	07	39	98
11	80	50	54	31	39	80	82	77	32	50	72	56	82	48	29	40	52	42	01	52	77	56	78	51
83	45	29	96	34	06	28	89	80	83	13	7⌐	67	00	78	18	47	54	06	10	68	71	17	78	17
88	68	54	02	00	86	50	75	84	01	36	76	66	79	51	90	36	47	64	93	29	60	91	10	62
99	59	46	73	48	87	51	76	49	69	91	82	60	89	28	93	78	56	13	68	23	47	83	41	13
65	48	11	76	74	17	46	85	09	50	58	04	77	69	74	73	03	95	71	86	40	21	81	65	44
80	12	43	56	35	17	72	70	80	15	45	31	82	23	74	21	11	57	82	53	14	38	55	37	63
74	35	09	98	17	77	40	27	72	14	43	23	60	02	10	45	52	16	42	37	96	28	60	26	55
69	91	62	68	03	66	25	22	91	48	36	93	68	72	03	76	62	11	39	90	94	40	05	64	18
09	89	32	05	05	14	22	56	85	14	46	42	75	67	88	96	29	77	88	22	54	38	21	45	98
91	49	91	45	23	68	47	92	76	86	46	16	28	35	54	94	75	08	99	23	37	08	92	00	48
80	33	69	45	98	26	94	03	68	58	70	29	73	41	35	53	14	03	33	40	42	05	08	23	41
44	10	48	19	49	85	15	74	79	54	32	97	92	65	75	57	60	04	08	81	22	22	20	64	13
12	55	07	37	42	11	10	00	20	40	12	86	07	46	97	96	64	48	94	39	28	70	72	58	15
63	60	64	93	29	16	50	53	44	84	40	21	95	25	63	43	65	17	70	82	07	20	73	17	90
61	19	69	04	46	26	45	74	77	74	51	92	43	37	29	65	39	45	95	93	42	58	26	05	27
15	47	44	52	66	95	27	07	99	53	59	36	78	38	48	82	39	61	01	18	33	21	15	94	66
94	55	72	85	73	67	89	75	43	87	54	62	24	44	31	91	19	04	25	92	92	92	74	59	73
42	48	11	62	13	97	34	40	87	21	16	86	84	87	67	03	07	11	20	59	25	70	14	66	70
23	52	37	83	17	73	20	88	98	37	68	93	59	14	16	26	25	22	96	63	05	52	28	25	62
04	49	35	24	94	75	24	63	38	24	45	86	25	10	25	61	96	27	93	35	65	33	71	24	72
00	54	99	76	54	64	05	18	81	59	96	11	96	38	96	54	69	28	23	91	23	28	72	95	29
35	96	31	53	07	26	89	80	93	54	33	35	13	54	62	77	97	45	00	24	90	10	33	93	33
59	80	80	83	91	45	42	72	68	42	83	60	94	97	00	13	02	12	48	92	78	56	52	01	06
46	05	88	52	36	01	39	09	22	86	77	28	14	40	77	93	91	08	36	47	70	61	74	29	41
32	17	90	05	97	87	37	92	52	41	05	56	70	70	07	86	74	31	71	57	85	39	41	18	38
69	23	46	14	06	20	11	74	52	04	15	95	66	00	00	18	74	39	24	23	97	11	89	63	38
19	56	54	14	30	01	75	87	53	79	40	41	92	15	85	66	67	43	68	06	84	96	28	52	07
45	15	51	49	38	19	47	60	72	46	43	66	79	45	43	59	04	79	00	33	20	82	66	95	41
94	86	43	19	94	36	16	81	08	51	34	88	88	15	53	01	54	03	54	56	05	01	45	11	76
98	08	62	48	26	45	24	02	84	04	44	99	90	88	96	39	09	47	34	07	35	44	13	18	80
33	18	51	62	32	41	94	15	09	49	89	43	54	85	81	88	69	54	19	94	37	54	87	30	43
80	95	10	04	06	96	38	27	07	74	20	15	12	33	87	25	01	62	52	98	94	62	46	11	71
79	75	24	91	40	71	96	12	82	96	69	86	10	25	91	74	85	22	05	39	00	38	75	95	79
18	63	33	25	37	98	14	50	65	71	31	01	02	46	74	05	45	56	14	27	77	93	89	19	36
74	02	94	39	02	77	55	73	22	70	97	79	01	71	19	52	52	75	80	21	80	81	45	17	48
54	17	84	56	11	80	99	33	71	43	05	33	51	29	69	56	12	71	92	55	36	04	09	03	24
11	66	44	98	83	52	07	98	48	27	59	38	17	15	39	09	97	33	34	40	88	46	12	33	56
48	32	47	79	28	31	24	96	47	10	02	29	53	68	70	32	30	75	75	46	15	02	00	99	94
69	07	49	41	38	87	63	79	19	76	35	58	40	44	01	10	51	82	16	15	01	84	87	69	38

Reproduced by permission from The RAND Corporation, "A Million Random Digits," Free Press, Glencoe, Ill., 1955.

Table VI
Square Roots

n	0	1	2	3	4	5	6	7	8	9	10	Tenths of the tabular difference 1	2	3	4	5
.1	.316	.332	.346	.361	.374	.387						1	3	4	6	7
						.387	.400	.412	.424	.436	.447	1	2	4	5	6
.2	.447	.458	.469	.480	.490	.500	.510	.520	.529	.539	.548	1	2	3	4	5
.3	.548	.557	.566	.574	.583	.592	.600	.608	.616	.624	.632	1	2	3	3	4
.4	.632	.640	.648	.656	.663	.671	.678	.686	.693	.700	.707	1	1	2	3	4
.5	.707	.714	.721	.728	.735	.742	.748	.755	.762	.768	.775	1	1	2	3	3
.6	.775	.781	.787	.794	.800	.806	.812	.819	.825	.831	.837	1	1	2	2	3
.7	.837	.843	.849	.854	.860	.866	.872	.877	.883	.889	.894	1	1	2	2	3
.8	.894	.900	.906	.911	.917	.922	.927	.933	.938	.943	.949	1	1	2	2	3
.9	.949	.954	.959	.964	.970	.975	.980	.985	.990	.995	1.000	1	1	2	2	3
1.0	1.000	1.005	1.010	1.015	1.020	1.025	1.030	1.034	1.039	1.044	1.049	0	1	1	2	2
1.1	1.049	1.054	1.058	1.063	1.068	1.072	1.077	1.082	1.086	1.091	1.095	0	1	1	2	2
1.2	1.095	1.100	1.105	1.109	1.114	1.118	1.122	1.127	1.131	1.136	1.140	0	1	1	2	2
1.3	1.140	1.145	1.149	1.153	1.158	1.162	1.166	1.170	1.175	1.179	1.183	0	1	1	2	2
1.4	1.183	1.187	1.192	1.196	1.200	1.204	1.208	1.212	1.217	1.221	1.225	0	1	1	2	2
1.5	1.225	1.229	1.233	1.237	1.241	1.245	1.249	1.253	1.257	1.261	1.265	0	1	1	2	2
1.6	1.265	1.269	1.273	1.277	1.281	1.285	1.288	1.292	1.296	1.300	1.304	0	1	1	2	2
1.7	1.304	1.308	1.311	1.315	1.319	1.323	1.327	1.330	1.334	1.338	1.342	0	1	1	2	2
1.8	1.342	1.345	1.349	1.353	1.356	1.360	1.364	1.367	1.371	1.375	1.378	0	1	1	1	2
1.9	1.378	1.382	1.386	1.389	1.393	1.396	1.400	1.404	1.407	1.411	1.414	0	1	1	1	2
2.0	1.414	1.418	1.421	1.425	1.428	1.432	1.435	1.439	1.442	1.446	1.449	0	1	1	1	2
2.1	1.449	1.453	1.456	1.459	1.463	1.466	1.470	1.473	1.476	1.480	1.483	0	1	1	1	2
2.2	1.483	1.487	1.490	1.493	1.497	1.500	1.503	1.507	1.510	1.513	1.517	0	1	1	1	2
2.3	1.517	1.520	1.523	1.526	1.530	1.533	1.536	1.539	1.543	1.546	1.549	0	1	1	1	2
2.4	1.549	1.552	1.556	1.559	1.562	1.565	1.568	1.572	1.575	1.578	1.581	0	1	1	1	2
2.5	1.581	1.584	1.587	1.591	1.594	1.597	1.600	1.603	1.606	1.609	1.612	0	1	1	1	2
2.6	1.612	1.616	1.619	1.622	1.625	1.628	1.631	1.634	1.637	1.640	1.643	0	1	1	1	2
2.7	1.643	1.646	1.649	1.652	1.655	1.658	1.661	1.664	1.667	1.670	1.673	0	1	1	1	2
2.8	1.673	1.676	1.679	1.682	1.685	1.688	1.691	1.694	1.697	1.700	1.703	0	1	1	1	1
2.9	1.703	1.706	1.709	1.712	1.715	1.718	1.720	1.723	1.726	1.729	1.732	0	1	1	1	1
3.0	1.732	1.735	1.738	1.741	1.744	1.746	1.749	1.752	1.755	1.758	1.761	0	1	1	1	1
3.1	1.761	1.764	1.766	1.769	1.772	1.775	1.778	1.780	1.783	1.786	1.789	0	1	1	1	1
3.2	1.789	1.792	1.794	1.797	1.800	1.803	1.806	1.808	1.811	1.814	1.817	0	1	1	1	1
3.3	1.817	1.819	1.822	1.825	1.828	1.830	1.833	1.836	1.838	1.841	1.844	0	1	1	1	1
3.4	1.844	1.847	1.849	1.852	1.855	1.857	1.860	1.863	1.865	1.868	1.871	0	1	1	1	1
3.5	1.871	1.873	1.876	1.879	1.881	1.884	1.887	1.889	1.892	1.895	1.897	0	1	1	1	1
3.6	1.897	1.900	1.903	1.905	1.908	1.910	1.913	1.916	1.918	1.921	1.924	0	1	1	1	1
3.7	1.924	1.926	1.929	1.931	1.934	1.936	1.939	1.942	1.944	1.947	1.949	0	1	1	1	1
3.8	1.949	1.952	1.954	1.957	1.960	1.962	1.965	1.967	1.970	1.972	1.975	0	1	1	1	1
3.9	1.975	1.977	1.980	1.982	1.985	1.987	1.990	1.992	1.995	1.997	2.000	0	1	1	1	1
4.0	2.000	2.002	2.005	2.007	2.010	2.012	2.015	2.017	2.020	2.022	2.025	0	0	1	1	1
4.1	2.025	2.027	2.030	2.032	2.035	2.037	2.040	2.042	2.045	2.047	2.049	0	0	1	1	1
4.2	2.049	2.052	2.054	2.057	2.059	2.062	2.064	2.066	2.069	2.071	2.074	0	0	1	1	1
4.3	2.074	2.076	2.078	2.081	2.083	2.086	2.088	2.090	2.093	2.095	2.098	0	0	1	1	1
4.4	2.098	2.100	2.102	2.105	2.107	2.110	2.112	2.114	2.117	2.119	2.121	0	0	1	1	1
4.5	2.121	2.124	2.126	2.128	2.131	2.133	2.135	2.138	2.140	2.142	2.145	0	0	1	1	1
4.6	2.145	2.147	2.149	2.152	2.154	2.156	2.159	2.161	2.163	2.166	2.168	0	0	1	1	1
4.7	2.168	2.170	2.173	2.175	2.177	2.179	2.182	2.184	2.186	2.189	2.191	0	0	1	1	1
4.8	2.191	2.193	2.195	2.198	2.200	2.202	2.205	2.207	2.209	2.211	2.214	0	0	1	1	1
4.9	2.214	2.216	2.218	2.220	2.223	2.225	2.227	2.229	2.232	2.234	2.236	0	0	1	1	1
5.	2.236	2.258	2.280	2.302	2.324	2.345	2.366	2.387	2.408	2.429	2.449	2	4	6	9	11
6.	2.449	2.470	2.490	2.510	2.530	2.550	2.569	2.588	2.608	2.627	2.646	2	4	6	8	10
7.	2.646	2.665	2.683	2.702	2.720	2.739	2.757	2.775	2.793	2.811	2.828	2	4	5	7	9
8.	2.828	2.846	2.864	2.881	2.898	2.915	2.933	2.950	2.966	2.983	3.000	2	3	5	7	9
9.	3.000	3.017	3.033	3.050	3.066	3.082	3.098	3.114	3.130	3.146	3.162	2	3	5	6	8

Reproduced by permission from E. V. Huntington, "Four-place Tables," Houghton Mifflin Company, Boston, 1931.

Table VII
Cube Roots

n	0	1	2	3	4	5	6	7	8	9	10	Tenths of the tabular difference 1	2	3	4	5
.010	.2154	.2162	.2169	.2176	.2183	.2190	.2197	.2204	.2210	.2217|	.2224	1	1	2	3	3
.011	.2224	.2231	.2237	.2244	.2251	.2257	.2264	.2270	.2277	.2283	.2289	1	1	2	3	3
.012	.2289	.2296	.2302	.2308	.2315	.2321	.2327	.2333	.2339	.2345	.2351	1	1	2	2	3
.013	.2351	.2357	.2363	.2369	.2375	.2381	.2387	.2393	.2399	.2404	.2410	1	1	2	2	3
.014	.2410	.2416	.2422	.2427	.2433	.2438	.2444	.2450	.2455	.2461	.2466	1	1	2	2	3
.015	.2466	.2472	.2477	.2483	.2488	.2493	.2499	.2504	.2509	.2515	.2520	1	1	2	2	3
.016	.2520	.2525	.2530	.2535	.2541	.2546	.2551	.2556	.2561	.2566	.2571	1	1	2	2	3
.017	.2571	.2576	.2581	.2586	.2591	.2596	.2601	.2606	.2611	.2616	.2621	0	1	1	2	2
.018	.2621	.2626	.2630	.2635	.2640	.2645	.2650	.2654	.2659	.2664	.2668	0	1	1	2	2
.019	.2668	.2673	.2678	.2682	.2687	.2692	.2696	.2701	.2705	.2710	.2714	0	1	1	2	2
.020	.2714	.2719	.2723	.2728	.2732	.2737	.2741	.2746	.2750	.2755	.2759	0	1	1	2	2
.021	.2759	.2763	.2768	.2772	.2776	.2781	.2785	.2789	.2794	.2798	.2802	0	1	1	2	2
.022	.2802	.2806	.2811	.2815	.2819	.2823	.2827	.2831	.2836	.2840	.2844	0	1	1	2	2
.023	.2844	.2848	.2852	.2856	.2860	.2864	.2868	.2872	.2876	.2880	.2884	0	1	1	2	2
.024	.2884	.2888	.2892	.2896	.2900	.2904	.2908	.2912	.2916	.2920	.2924	0	1	1	2	2
.025	.2924	.2928	.2932	.2936	.2940	.2943	.2947	.2951	.2955	.2959	.2962	0	1	1	2	2
.026	.2962	.2966	.2970	.2974	.2978	.2981	.2985	.2989	.2993	.2996	.3000	0	1	1	2	2
.027	.3000	.3004	.3007	.3011	.3015	.3018	.3022	.3026	.3029	.3033	.3037	0	1	1	1	2
.028	.3037	.3040	.3044	.3047	.3051	.3055	.3058	.3062	.3065	.3069	.3072	0	1	1	1	2
.029	.3072	.3076	.3079	.3083	.3086	.3090	.3093	.3097	.3100	.3104	.3107	0	1	1	1	2
.03	.311	.314	.317	.321	.324	.327	.330	.333	.336	.339	.342	0	1	1	1	2
.04	.342	.345	.348	.350	.353	.356	.358	.361	.363	.366	.368	0	1	1	1	1
.05	.368	.371	.373	.376	.378	.380	.383	.385	.387	.389	.391	0	0	1	1	1
.06	.391	.394	.396	.398	.400	.402	.404	.406	.408	.410	.412	0	0	1	1	1
.07	.412	.414	.416	.418	.420	.422	.424	.425	.427	.429	.431	0	0	1	1	1
.08	.431	.433	.434	.436	.438	.440	.441	.443	.445	.446	.448	0	0	1	1	1
.09	.448	.450	.451	.453	.455	.456	.458	.459	.461	.463	.464	0	0	0	1	1
.1	.464	.479	.493	.507	.519	.531						1	3	4	5	7
						.531	.543	.554	.565	.575	.585	1	2	3	4	5
.2	.585	.594	.604	.613	.621	.630	.638	.646	.654	.662	.669	1	2	3	3	4
.3	.669	.677	.684	.691	.698	.705	.711	.718	.724	.731	.737	1	1	2	3	3
.4	.737	.743	.749	.755	.761	.766	.772	.777	.783	.788	.794	1	1	2	2	3
.5	.794	.799	.804	.809	.814	.819	.824	.829	.834	.839	.843	0	1	1	2	2
.6	.843	.848	.853	.857	.862	.866	.871	.875	.879	.884	.888	0	1	1	2	2
.7	.888	.892	.896	.900	.905	.909	.913	.917	.921	.924	.928	0	1	1	2	2
.8	.928	.932	.936	.940	.944	.947	.951	.955	.958	.962	.965	0	1	1	1	2
.9	.965	.969	.973	.976	.980	.983	.986	.990	.993	.997	1.000	0	1	1	1	2
1.0	1.000	1.003	1.007	1.010	1.013	1.016	1.020	1.023	1.026	1.029	1.032	0	1	1	1	2
1.1	1.032	1.035	1.038	1.042	1.045	1.048	1.051	1.054	1.057	1.060	1.063	0	1	1	1	2
1.2	1.063	1.066	1.069	1.071	1.074	1.077	1.080	1.083	1.086	1.089	1.091	0	1	1	1	1
1.3	1.091	1.094	1.097	1.100	1.102	1.105	1.108	1.111	1.113	1.116	1.119	0	1	1	1	1
1.4	1.119	1.121	1.124	1.127	1.129	1.132	1.134	1.137	1.140	1.142	1.145	0	1	1	1	1
1.5	1.145	1.147	1.150	1.152	1.155	1.157	1.160	1.162	1.165	1.167	1.170	0	0	1	1	1
1.6	1.170	1.172	1.174	1.177	1.179	1.182	1.184	1.186	1.189	1.191	1.193	0	0	1	1	1
1.7	1.193	1.196	1.198	1.200	1.203	1.205	1.207	1.210	1.212	1.214	1.216	0	0	1	1	1
1.8	1.216	1.219	1.221	1.223	1.225	1.228	1.230	1.232	1.234	1.236	1.239	0	0	1	1	1
1.9	1.239	1.241	1.243	1.245	1.247	1.249	1.251	1.254	1.256	1.258	1.260	0	0	1	1	1
2.	1.260	1.281	1.301	1.320	1.339	1.357						2	4	6	8	10
						1.357	1.375	1.392	1.409	1.426	1.442	2	3	5	7	9
3.	1.442	1.458	1.474	1.489	1.504	1.518	1.533	1.547	1.560	1.574	1.587	1	3	4	6	7
4.	1.587	1.601	1.613	1.626	1.639	1.651	1.663	1.675	1.687	1.698	1.710	1	2	4	5	6
5.	1.710	1.721	1.732	1.744	1.754	1.765	1.776	1.786	1.797	1.807	1.817	1	2	3	4	5
6.	1.817	1.827	1.837	1.847	1.857	1.866	1.876	1.885	1.895	1.904	1.913	1	2	3	4	5
7.	1.913	1.922	1.931	1.940	1.949	1.957	1.966	1.975	1.983	1.992	2.000	1	2	3	3	4
8.	2.000	2.008	2.017	2.025	2.033	2.041	2.049	2.057	2.065	2.072	2.080	1	2	2	3	4
9.	2.080	2.088	2.095	2.103	2.110	2.118	2.125	2.133	2.140	2.147	2.154	1	1	2	3	4

Reproduced by permission from E. V. Huntington, "Four-place Tables," Houghton Mifflin Company, Boston, 1931.

Charts

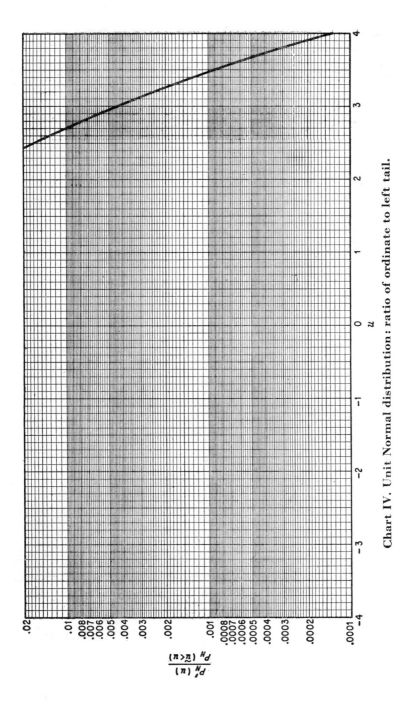

Chart IV. Unit Normal distribution: ratio of ordinate to left tail.

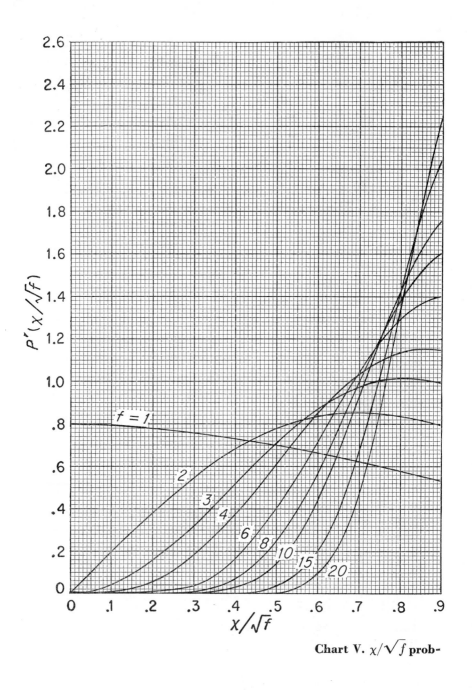

Chart V. $\chi/\sqrt{f}$ prob-

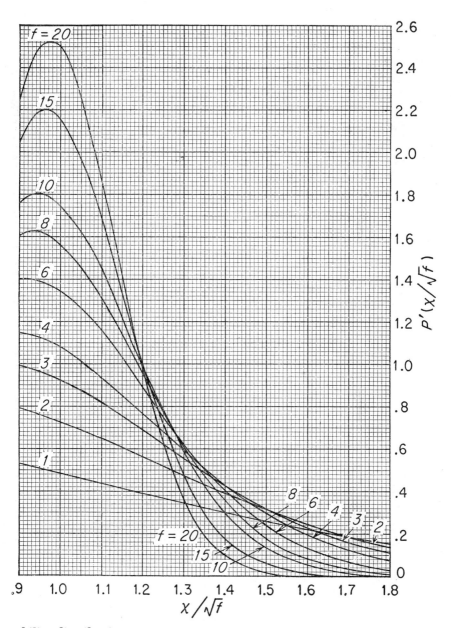

ability distribution.

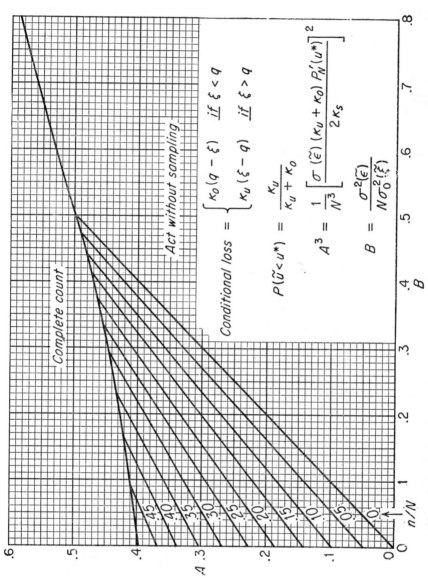

$$\text{Conditional loss} = \begin{cases} \kappa_0 (q - \xi) & \underline{\text{if }} \xi < q \\ \kappa_u (\xi - q) & \underline{\text{if }} \xi > q \end{cases}$$

$$P(\tilde{u} < u^*) = \frac{\kappa_u}{\kappa_u + \kappa_0}$$

$$A^3 = \frac{1}{N^3} \left[\frac{\sigma(\tilde{\epsilon}) (\kappa_u + \kappa_0) P_N'(u^*)}{2\kappa_s} \right]^2$$

$$B = \frac{\sigma^{-2}(\epsilon)}{N\sigma_0^2(\tilde{\xi})}$$

Chart VI. Optimal sample size: many-action problems with proportional losses.

Index of Symbols

Index includes those symbols which are used in more than one chapter. **Boldface** numbers shown in parentheses refer to problems on the pages indicated.

0 as subscript, denotes *prior* value, 337

00 as subscript, denotes *original* value, 529

1 as subscript, denotes *posterior* value, 337

α = maximum conditional probability of error of first kind, 614

β = bias of measuring or sampling process, 459
> distribution of, 468–469
>> after a sample has been taken, 473–474

C_r^n = number of possible orders in which r successes can occur in a sequence of n trials, 176

$$D = \frac{|\mu_b - \mathrm{E}(\tilde{\mu})|}{\sigma(\tilde{\mu})}, \text{ where } \mu \text{ stands for } any \text{ random variable, 455}$$

$$D_E = \frac{|\xi_b - \mathrm{E}_0(\tilde{\xi})|}{\sigma(\tilde{E}_1)}, \text{ 532}$$

$$D_\infty = \frac{|\xi_b - \mathrm{E}_0(\tilde{\xi})|}{\sigma_\infty(\tilde{E}_1)}, \text{ 537}$$

E = expectation, 87

$\tilde{E}_1$ = mean of posterior distribution considered as random variable before sample outcome is known, 522
> distribution of, 522
>> when $\tilde{r}$ is binomial and $\tilde{p}$ is beta, 676–677
>> when $\tilde{x}$ is Normal with known variance and $\tilde{\xi}$ is Normal, 525–531
>> when $\tilde{r}$ is Poisson and $\tilde{\kappa}$ is gamma, 673
> use of, to compute cost, 522–524
> value of sample information, 524–525

$\mathrm{E}_a^b(\tilde{z})$ = partial expectation of $\tilde{z}$ over interval a to b inclusive, 88

ϵ = pure sampling error of single observation, 459
> distribution of, 463–465

$\bar{\epsilon}$ = mean sampling error or pure sampling error of sample mean, 460
> distribution of, 465–467

f = number of degrees of freedom, 418, 432

$F_{.f}$ = point-f fractile, 81

G = required number of good pieces in production run, 135

$g(R) = m\,\mathrm{P}_{Po}(\tilde{r} \geq R) - R\,\mathrm{P}_{Po}(\tilde{r} > R)$, 245
> approximated by Normal loss integral $G(u)$, 293

$G(u) = \mathrm{P}'_N(u) - u\,\mathrm{P}_N(\tilde{u} > u)$, unit Normal loss integral, 293

I = quantity of information, 443

k_n = negative profit per unit stocked but not sold, 74

k_o = loss per unit of overage, 128, 134

k_p = profit per unit stocked and sold, 74

k_s = variable sampling cost, per item in sample, 536–537

K_s = fixed element in sampling cost, independent of sample size, 536

k_t = terminal loss constant in two-action problems with linear costs or profits, 451

k_u = loss per unit of underage, 128

K_u = lump-sum loss of underage, 134

    second-order components of, in scrap-allowance problems, 135, 154–156

κ = intensity of Poisson process, 212

    gamma distribution of, 670–672

$m = \kappa t$, expected number of Poisson successes in space t, 212

μ = mean, of many-valued population, 392

    of potential measurements, as distinguished from true value of quantity measured, 401, 458–459

$\mu = 1/\kappa$, mean interval between Poisson successes, 223–224

    as parameter of gamma distribution, 229

n = number of Bernoulli trials, 176–179

    as random variable, 135, 183–184

        distribution of, when Bernoulli variation is negligible, 142–149, 207

        when p is known (*see* Pascal distribution in Subject Index)

        when p is unknown (**2**), 208

n = number of items in sample, 392

p = long-run fraction successful in Bernoulli process, 176–179

    beta distribution of, 673–676

p = mean of two-valued population, 392

$\mathrm{P}(A)$ = probability of A, 60–61, 167

$\mathrm{P}(A,B)$ = joint probability of A and B, 167

$\mathrm{P}(A|B)$ = conditional probability of A given B, 167

$\mathrm{P}'(z)$ = probability per unit width at value z of $\tilde{z}$, 61

$\mathrm{P}_b(\tilde{r} \geq r|n,p)$ = binomial probability, 179

$\mathrm{P}_g(\tilde{v} < v|r)$ = standardized gamma probability, 231

$\mathrm{P}_N(\tilde{u} > u)$ = standardized Normal probability, 278

$\mathrm{P}_{Pa}(\tilde{n} \geq n|r,p)$ = Pascal probability, 184

$\mathrm{P}_{Po}(\tilde{r} \geq r|m)$ = Poisson probability, 213

P_r = long-run fraction reported as successes, 475

Q = number of units stocked, 67

    produced, 136

r = number of Bernoulli successes, 177–178

    distribution of, when Bernoulli variation is negligible, 207

        when p is known (*see* Binomial distribution in Subject Index)

        when p is unknown, 198–203, 676

    as parameter of Pascal distribution, 184

r = number of Poisson successes, 212

    distribution of, when κ is known (*see* Poisson distribution in Subject Index)

    when κ is unknown (**11**), 220, 672–673

    as parameter of gamma distribution, 229

r = total value of sample from two-valued population, 392

$$s = \sqrt{\frac{1}{f}\,\Sigma(x - \bar{x})^2},\ 418$$

Subject Index

Boldface numbers shown in parentheses refer to problems on the pages indicated

Acceptance lot as finite or infinite population, 377–380
Acceptance sampling, 371–374
  (*See also* Interdependent decision problems; Two-action problems)
Accidents, in mines, 227
  as Poisson process, 215
  (*See also* Horse kicks)
Acme Automatic Machine Company
  (**2, 3**), 304
Acts, 3
  comparison of, under uncertainty, 4–5, 24
  in terms of loss, 123–124, 351
Additivity of means, variances, and standard deviations, 263–264
Allied Electromechanical Corporation, 570–572
American Rubber Products Company
  (**1**), 303
Art-Craft Company (**4**), 302
ASN (average sample number), 191
Assignable causes, of irregularities in historical frequency distributions, 97, 100
  of run-to-run variation in process average, 144, 156
Average, weighted, 8–9, 86
  (*See also* Location, measures of)
Average sample number, 191

Ball bearings, sorting of, 172, 427
Bayes' postulate, 445n.
Bayes' theorem, 333, 338
  when prior distribution is continuous, 338–339
  when prior distribution is discrete, 338
Beacon Catering Corporation, 77

Bernoulli process, 174–175, 194–208
  conditions defining, 174–175, 194–196
    (*See also* Independence; Stability)
  control of output of, by sampling, 380–381
  parameter of, 174
    assessment of distribution of, 199–200, 207–208, 380
    beta distributed, 673–676
    known versus unknown, 196–198, 205–207
    uncertainty about, neglect of, 207
    (*See also* Binomial distribution; Pascal distribution)
Bernoulli trial, 174
  unconditional probability of success on single, 201
  (*See also* Independence)
Bernoulli uncertainty or variance, 198
  neglect of, 207–208; (**10**), 273
Beta distribution, 673–676
Bias, 458–483
  in classical statistics, 610
  effect of sample size on, 473–474, 478–479
  measurement, 458–475
    distribution of, 468–469
    in samples from two-valued populations, 474–475
    variation of, 465
  selection, 475–483
    avoidance of, 479–480
    total, 477–478
    of $\tilde{d} = \tilde{x}_2 - \tilde{x}_1$, 492–494
Binomial distribution, 176–179
  approximated, by Normal distribution, 274–285
    by Poisson distribution, 217–218, 281–285

723